c Barber Mueller

EVARTS A. GRAHAM

The Life, Lives, and Times of the
Surgical Spirit of St. Louis

C. Barber Mueller, MD, FACS

2002

BC Decker Inc

Hamilton • London

BC Decker Inc
P.O. Box 620, L.C.D. 1
Hamilton, Ontario L8N 3K7
Tel: 800-568-7281
Fax: 888-311-4987
E-mail: info@bcdecker.com
www.bcdecker.com

Sales and Distribution

Bryan Prince Booksellers
1060 King Street West
Hamilton, ON L8S 1L7
Canada
Tel: 905-528-4508; 1-800-867-0090
Fax: 905-528-1877
E-mail: orders@princebooks.net
Web site: www.princebooks.net

02 03 04 /UTP/ 5 4 3 2 1
ISBN 1-55009-222-7
Printed in Canada

Oil portrait by Robert Brachman, 1952

To the Memory of
Peter D. Olch
(1930–1991)

The physiological frontier is capable of indefinite expansion if we think of a surgeon as one who is interested in something more than cutting and sewing.

—E.A. GRAHAM, 1956

FOREWORD

Biographies of great surgeons written by idolizing ex-residents are usually of limited interest, except to the few students who knew the Great Man and who use the text to recall the good old days of youth. This biography by a distinguished academic surgeon, Dr. C.B. Mueller of McMaster University's Medical School in Hamilton, Ontario, is an exception. It is the result of more than 8 years of meticulous scholarly research, based on primary sources and numerous interviews that describe the life and times of Dr. Evarts Graham of Washington University in St. Louis.

Graham dominated almost every facet of American surgery during the middle third of the twentieth century. As a clinical scientist, his innovations altered the management of gallbladder disease by his invention of a radiologic method to visualize the gallbladder; his laboratory and clinical studies altered the management of the empyema that was a major source of mortality during the influenza epidemic; his physiologic studies set the stage for the emergence of thoracic surgery. Graham performed the first one-stage pneumonectomy for lung cancer, and he was a major force in establishing the relationship between cigarette smoking and lung cancer. As chairman of the board of regents of the American College of Surgeons in its early years, he guided this fledgling organization into the position of prestige and power that is now its accepted role in organized medicine. When he saw a need to establish criteria for the training of young physicians to practice safe surgery, he became the key figure in creating the American Board of Surgery, now the recognized qualifying body. When he found that many hospitals were inadequate for the performance of major surgery, he created the Joint Commission on the Accreditation of Hospitals.

This partial list of his achievements indicates the quality of the man. When he was convinced something needed to be done to improve the quality of surgery at a national level, he simply found those who agreed with him and created the organization that would get the job done. When others were unsure, they habitually turned to Graham, who became their spokesman. He had what is known in the military as a "command presence."

The life of such a man is worth serious study, and there is no better person to write his biography than C.B. Mueller who, for so many years, was intimately acquainted with Graham, his idol and role model.

Graham was a big, tall, portly, dignified man who stood straight, dressed conservatively, and spoke sparingly until the thunder was aroused. He gave the appearance of looking down a bit as an Olympian on those with whom he spoke. To his residents he seemed to be approximately 8 feet in height. We pictured him as standing only a few inches behind God, on his right, as a senior advisor or perhaps a latter-day vice-president on judgment day. Graham seldom used body language or showed much emotion when he talked. Only when one came to know him could one detect what he was thinking, or what emotions were being aroused. Graham did not wear his personality on his sleeve.

Graham was born in Chicago, the son of a well-known, community surgeon. He was raised to accept his outstanding intellect as a birthright, similar to the affluence of his parents. In the strict Victorian tradition of his time, he accepted such inherited benefits as a binding clause in a stern societal bargain: From whom much is given, much is expected.

Following a private high-school education in Chicago, Graham entered Princeton, where he, of course, graduated first in his class. His lifelong friend and classmate Allen Whipple—who subsequently became chairman of the Department of Surgery at Columbia—tells the story that as a sophomore Graham defined his objective in life: to perform meaningful surgical research, to become a surgical leader, and to train young surgeons. Although the story smacks of the apocryphal, knowing the two men, it probably is accurate. It certainly characterized both men. One of my fondest memories as a young chief resident was witnessing these two old tigers quietly needling each other and reliving some of their mutual professional conquests in surgical academia and medical politics. In awe, I pictured the bony carcasses of those who dared to oppose them.

Following graduation from medical school, and an internship, Graham took the unorthodox step of dropping out of clinical surgery and working in a basic science research laboratory, where he developed skills that subsequently made possible the development of cholecystography. Interrupting a surgical training program to learn techniques of research is now an accepted pattern, but it was unknown in the early years of the twentieth century, and Graham set the pattern for those who thereafter aspired to advance in academic surgery.

Following his subsequent training in surgery, Graham left what would have been a guaranteed successful career in clinical surgery in Chicago. For reasons that remain unclear, he chose to enter solo practice as a community surgeon in Mason City, Iowa. The result was a disaster. Graham had many talents, but he was not designed to fit comfortably into the competitive role of a small town surgeon. He ran head-on into the accepted pattern of fee splitting, whereby a surgeon returned part of his professional fee to the referring primary care or family physician. Graham was outraged by the practice, which compromised the best interests of the patient. With characteristic vigor he took up the challenge in Mason City to prohibit surgeons from such behavior. Predictably, it brought down the wrath of his colleague surgeons and referring family physicians. Without doubt, this experience in Mason City was the genesis of Graham's lifelong fight against fee splitting. In subsequent years when Graham was chairman of the board of regents of the

American College of Surgeons, he continued this battle at a national level, and created one of the underlying objectives of the college that would guarantee the best interests of the patient, even when such a course conflicted with the economic best interests of the surgeon. It is our priceless and persistent legacy.

Raised at home to be a gentleman, Graham's manners were exquisite. He was reserved, quiet, polite, and undemonstrative with strangers. One had to earn his confidence before Graham permitted himself to engage in more than superficial topics of formal conversation. Only when he detected a spark of imagination or intellectual challenge, did his true personality reveal it to others who then could, if they had the spirit, engage him in a meaningful conversation. He delighted in crossing intellectual swords with those who had opinions, whether they matched or were at odds with his own. Inevitably it was a grueling, no-holds-barred battle if one disagreed. Once the intellectual challenge had been defined, the subsequent conversation was a matter of thrust and parry, and the loser—who seldom was Graham—ended up pleading for mercy. As a master of the technique, Graham reveled in such an exchange if his antagonist was prepared and showed sufficient fight to take on the Master. This was Graham's way, for his own edification, and for sizing up his opponent. Those who survived, though pricked and bleeding, earned Graham's respect and confidence.

Graham seldom engaged in small talk. He and his wife Helen were close friends of my parents. My mother always said that Helen was a delightful dinner partner, but it was difficult to find someone up to engaging Evarts in a light dinner table conversation. The only way to stimulate Graham's interest was to identify a substantive societal, political, educational, or scientific problem, analyze it, and then ask Graham's opinion. Inevitably he would rise to the occasion, defend his stand, and delight in opposition.

While Graham was in practice in Mason City, America entered World War I, and Graham felt it his duty to enlist. Graham, the brilliant intellectual individualist, predictably took poorly to the military hierarchy. When the sole water source in the small French village where his unit was posted was found to be contaminated with typhoid, and Graham found that his colonel had been indolent in making the changes he knew were indicated, Graham went straight to the commanding general of the European theater.

Before being sent overseas, Graham, because of his prior training in basic science, was asked to investigate methods for improved management of empyema (infection in the chest cavity), which was the source of mortality in so many patients infected by influenza. Graham obtained the use of a research laboratory at the Johns Hopkins Hospital and, while in uniform, evaluated the clinical problem, proposed a better method for draining the infection, tested his hypothesis on animals in a marvelously simple series of animal studies, and, thus, ultimately saved many lives during the epidemic. In so doing, he defined principals of pulmonary physiology that were important in the subsequent development of thoracic surgery—a field in which Graham subsequently became pre-eminent.

While still in uniform, following World War I, Graham was recruited to the chair as professor of surgery at Washington University in St. Louis. At the time, this fledgling medical school was emerging in the pattern of the Johns Hopkins Medical School, and Graham quickly led his department to the forefront of medical and surgical education.

True to his earlier vision, Graham established a residency training program to which other medical schools looked when seeking chairmen. His brilliant studies in devising methods for visualizing the gallbladder altered the management of biliary tract disease. Not long thereafter, his performance of a one-stage technique for removing an entire lung opened up new vistas in management of pulmonary disease. Subsequently, his studies with a sophomore medical student were instrumental in relating cigarette smoking with lung cancer. All of these events provided the intellectual background of his training program that provided professors and chairmen throughout the world.

Graham's office wall was decorated, not by some of the numerous diplomas and other evidence of national and international honors conferred upon him, but by a long row of photographs of his trainees who subsequently became department chairmen. As residents reporting to our chief in his office, we faced the stare of a long row of our predecessors who had achieved fame following their training. It was a powerful unspoken message as to what was expected of us.

Mueller's biographic style in this book is worthy of careful study. With remarkable restraint, he avoids the blind hero worship that characteristically flaws so many biographies written by amateurs. As a scientist accustomed to rely on facts, not on emotions or subjective impressions, Mueller gives the facts in exquisite detail. This story is based on hundreds of hours of reviewing Graham's profuse correspondence and published papers now preserved in the Washington University Library. Mueller was a student, an intern, a resident, and ultimately, a full-time faculty member under Graham. He was personally and intimately acquainted with almost all of the personalities that make up the cast of characters in this story. He interviewed many in preparation of the manuscript, yet rarely does he interpose his own evaluation of either Graham or those with whom he dealt. Strictly speaking, Mueller acts as a reporter, not an interpreter of events. At times, the story literally pleads for comment, but the biography remains restrained. He lets events and quotations from carefully selected letters speak for themselves. This is a dangerous literary gamble that, if inappropriately designed, could make for a long, boring litany. In Mueller's hands the result is the opposite. The facts are so dramatic, and the pattern of Graham's remarkable life so repetitively successful, that the reader quickly comes to his own assessment of Graham's style and performance. The result is even more positive than if the biographer had inserted his subjective assessment of the story.

This book meets all the criteria of good biography. Its subject was an influential leader of his time whose privileged background and subsequent work ethic typified his era. His colorful personality, hidden behind a Victorian reserve, provides continued interest. Because he felt strongly about important subjects, he engendered violent likes and dislikes in those with whom he dealt. His unique personal style and direct methods for attacking a well-identified objective provide a consistent theme that provides continued interest throughout the book.

Mueller knew Graham intimately and spent years in preparation of this fact-filled volume that meticulously documents the life and times of one of the leading figures in twentieth century medicine. This book will become the definitive volume on Graham's life and a valuable source for historians seeking to understand the genesis of the organizations of American medicine that arose during Graham's time, and in which he played such a consistent leadership role.

BEN EISEMAN, MD, FACS

PREFACE

Evarts Graham was American surgery's "Man for All Seasons," and his accomplishments are of such importance that he deserves more than a cluster of obituaries as a final record. His high ideals and many achievements placed him alongside Halsted and Cushing as one of the three most eminent American surgeons of the day. He was so highly regarded that, without an interview, the governing bodies of Johns Hopkins and Harvard agreed to appoint him to the vacant chairs of Halsted and Cushing before they asked if he were willing to consider the positions. Graham was sufficiently astute to refuse both offers, for Washington University had given him all he needed, permitting him to be a leader in the development of clinical research, clinical surgical techniques, and residency surgical education. A half century later, abandoned by the historians of our day, he has become a forgotten hero.

This book documents Graham's life within the setting of hospitals and operative surgery from 1910 to 1960; it shows Graham, the times in which he lived, and his interplay with the medical greats of those years. Graham has received neither the publicity nor the accolades given to Halsted and Cushing, for, although his scientific and political contributions were as great as were theirs, his personal and social lives were far less dramatic and less scrutinized.

Graham was a large presence—an overpowering man who commanded respect, demanded decency, and decried hypocrisy. He was a patrician with admirers and connections with many surgeons of his day, yet he had few close friends among his staff, particularly during his latter years. Always conservatively groomed, he strode the hall ahead of his entourage in a long, neatly-starched white coat, with a freshly lit cigarette in the corner of his mouth. Although the eyes behind rimmed spectacles seemed cold and gray, his mind was engrossed in contemporary issues, not in unfriendly thoughts. He possessed an awesome dignity that was not accustomed to shared responsibility.

Beneath an abrupt exterior, Graham was shy and lonely, a man who had difficulty in making warm personal contact with the many committee and board members with whom he shared the business of the day. On occasion he would be excluded when committee members chose dinner companions but, if approached by a rescuer, he was a charming guest who could discuss many topics. George Stephenson, assistant director of the American College of Surgeons, invited Graham to his home for dinner on the occasion of Graham's final meeting as chairman of the board of regents. Graham never forgot the courtesy, and he penned a postscript of thanks to every letter he subsequently wrote to Stephenson.

A cult of Evarts Graham residents never developed, and, although camaraderie among Barnes Hospital residents was strong, they were more Barnes residents than they were Graham residents. An attempt by Gordon Moore to form a "Graham Club" that would meet once a year to honor him and maintain contacts among his ex-residents came to naught.

Peter D. Olch, whose father I.Y. Olch (see chapter 8) had been a member of Graham's staff during the 1920s, began this biography. As a medical historian, he published three short historic articles about Graham, and in 1983 Eugene Bricker and I encouraged him to abandon his proposed biography of William Halsted in favor of one about Evarts Graham. Olch was the ideal biographer, for not only did he live in Washington, DC, he was affiliated with the National Library of Medicine, which contains microfilm copies of almost all of the material housed in St. Louis. Olch began the task and distilled a large amount of the source material, even as he battled with lymphoma. In 1991 he succumbed to an aggressive carcinoma, an event that cut short his effort. The task then fell to either Gene Bricker or to me; Gene prevailed, and I was transformed into an amateur biographer.

The Graham source material, containing 1568 files and covering 78 linear feet of shelving, is housed in the Washington University Medical Library Archives, and three or four visits to St. Louis per year for 8 years were required. The files are a record of his activities outside clinics and operating rooms, and they do not contain any patient or hospital records. In the early years I made an attempt to speak to almost everyone who was still alive who might have had significant contacts with Evarts Graham, including his two sons, one granddaughter, and medical school associates Oliver Lowry, Ed Hunter, Doug Eastwood, Henry Schwartz, and Harry Reidel. The unpublished *History of Barnes Hospital* by Frank Bradley was particularly helpful.

I have attempted to give Evarts Graham to the reader through his own words, relying heavily on quotation from his writings, sometimes verbatim, sometimes paraphrased. I wish to show his vision of greatness and purpose, as well as his pettiness, suspicions, anger, and sense of injury. Flashes of imprudent arrogance that he acquired after years in which there were few who challenged him are visible. There seem to be no moments of frailty, rather a consummate sense of authority. Graham wished to have his voice heard in many features of national policy, and he was unable to refuse membership on committees, commissions, or other bodies that dealt with great issues. He was a political committee junkie.

I also have attempted to show the status of surgery, anesthesia, and pathology during these years, and how Graham related to and influenced them. There are short biographical sketches of some of the many individuals with whom Graham had contact. The selection was arbitrary, and many sketches have been omitted due to lack of space, or because I felt the individual was so well known, a sketch would not be needed.

Writing this book has been a labor of love and a time of discovery—to see how the man I knew as a medical student, intern, resident, and junior faculty member moved in a world of which I was unaware. It has been an enriching experience that I wish to pass on to my readers. The selection of topics, items, or actions of course demonstrates personal biases, and any significant portions of the source material that are omitted are done so by oversight, not by design. In writing a biography, one has the liberty of personal interpretation, something not permitted in scientific writing; insofar as is possible, I have attempted to present Graham as he wrote and spoke about his surgical world. I hope it transports the caring reader into his life and thoughts, with only a few of my personal views.

Evarts Graham was my mentor, caretaker, and surgical surrogate father. Upon entering medical school in 1938 with National Youth Administration support, I was assigned to a faculty member with whom I worked 8 hours per week. George Bishop, James O'Leary, and Nathan Womack inspired me; Philip Shaffer supported me; Glover Copher taught me surgery; and Graham oversaw all. After I served with the Fleet Marine Forces, Pacific, during 1943 to 1946, Dr. Graham provided me a Rockefeller Fellowship, a residency opportunity, a research laboratory, a Markle Scholarship, and a full-time position on the Washington University faculty. I openly acknowledge the huge debt I feel for the opportunities he and others afforded me, and I hope this outline of Graham's career will serve as partial payment.

Evarts Graham: The Life, Lives, and Times of the Surgical Spirit of St. Louis explores events in the American surgical scene of the first half of the twentieth century that created my world of surgery in the second half of the century. I hope it conveys to every reader my admiration of Evarts Graham, his victories, and his defeats.

C. Barber Mueller, MD, FACS
March 2002

ACKNOWLEDGMENTS

The writing of this book would have been impossible without the help of many others. Foremost is Peter D. Olch (see appendix F), to whom the book is dedicated, for he provided its basic outline and organized a fair amount of the source material. My dependable and ever-cheerful secretarial assistant, Sandra Carpenter, was indispensable; without her there would be no book. Soraya Erian graciously acted as editorial reviewer. The generous support of Paul Anderson and Jim Curley, his faithful assistant, of the Becker Library Archives was invaluable, and Tom Ferguson, Bill Landau, Josh Jurkiewiecz, Roy Peterson, and Doug Eastwood deserve a special mention for their willingness to review and correct many pages. I received constant support and encouragement from Ben Eiseman and others whose names appear in the text. Susan Cooper, Jill Toffoli, Susan Harrison, and Paula Presutti of BC Decker, Inc, transformed my thoughts and words into a beautiful book.

Last, but not least, I thank my wife, Jean, for her patience, endurance, and tolerance. She not only permitted, but seemed to understand, my lapses into silence, moodiness, and distraction from issues of the moment.

CONTENTS

Chapter 1

PROLOGUE:
THE LIFE AS LIVED

This is the life story of Evarts Ambrose Graham, whose major accomplishments influenced the surgical world of his day; insofar as is possible, this book attempts to capture his essence through his own words. Graham's triumphs, tribulations, and sensitivities are placed against the backdrop of contemporaries and of surgery as practiced in the first half of the twentieth century. Evarts Graham's accomplishments and the practice of surgery are intertwined—as the times shaped him, so did he shape the times—more so than any surgeon of his day.

Graham was born into a family of financial and intellectual means and, with a prominent surgeon for a father and a socially conscious woman for a mother, he was reared as a child of privilege. He was a Midwesterner—from Chicago and St. Louis—and he held the typically Midwestern belief that truth, faith, work, integrity, and responsibility are essential values in the social order. Although he came from a line that harked back to thieves and robbers, he belonged to a culture that built churches, libraries, universities, and hospitals with the high-minded convictions of Scotch-Irish Presbyterianism. Possessed of lofty ideals and dedicated to the technical and ethical luster of his profession, he was endowed with purpose in life, not a desire to become a celebrity. An overpowering figure with a commanding presence and uncompromising demeanor, he pioneered changes in the political, financial, educational, and ethical aspects of surgery; he considered the operation, the hospital in which it occurred, and all of its social and ethical features to be within his domain. He was aware of his position of authority, accepted its obligations, and was certain that he possessed only the highest aspirations for everything he touched.

After completing his education in avant-garde schools of Chicago and Princeton University, he received a doctor of medicine degree from Rush Medical College in 1907. His next 8 years were spent in training and postgraduate study as an intern at the Presbyterian Hospital, a fellow in pathology, a student in biochemistry at the University of Chicago for 2 years, an instructor in surgery at Rush, and an associate in the Otho S.A. Sprague Research Institute.

His professional career began with 2 uncomfortable years (1915 to 1917) in private practice in Mason City, Iowa, before active duty with the United States Army (1917 to 1919). As a major figure in the Empyema Commission, he outlined a treatment for streptococcal empyema that radically changed its mortality rates, and he investigated pulmonary dynamics at Johns Hopkins before going to France as the commanding officer of an evacuation hospital. His years in Mason City and the army introduced him to a world he had never known and left him antagonistic and angry, determined to make improvements.

In 1919 he became chairman of the Department of Surgery at the rejuvenated Washington University School of Medicine, and 5 years later he reported laboratory experiments that led to cholecystography, an x-ray test that refined the diagnosis of gallbladder disease and began a new era of radiology. In 1933 his successful removal of a lung compromised by bronchogenic carcinoma began a new era in thoracic surgery. These research and clinical successes resulted in two major buildings being erected at the Barnes Hospital complex.

Graham was a major figure in the up-and-down relationship between Washington University and Barnes Hospital, consistently defending a university-appointed closed hospital staff; these years saw the expansion of his department to include all of the newly developing subspecialties of surgery.

Graham moved in a circle of municipal leaders in St. Louis and became an intimate of the Rockefeller Foundation through Abraham Flexner and other members of the General Education Board. His larger social circle of elite and powerful figures included surgeons general, cabinet secretaries, congressmen, industrialists, and intellectuals. As chairman of the board of regents of the American College of Surgeons, he led its effort to condemn fee splitting and ghost surgery and was the central figure in the creation of the American Board of Surgery and the Joint Commission on Accreditation of Hospitals. His surgical residency program became a prototype for many American training programs.

As chairman of the Committee on Surgery of the National Research Council during World War II, Graham supervised features of military medical research, even as he publicly criticized the army and the selective service system for policies that wasted medical personnel, devastating medical education and resident training. Membership on presidential commissions foreshadowed public statements that espoused health as a basic right of every citizen and denounced nuclear weapons testing. His 1950 study that showed an epidemiologic relationship between smoking and lung cancer was followed by laboratory experiments demonstrating that cigarette tars could cause cancer.

Fourteen honorary degrees and 21 prizes and awards were bestowed upon Evarts Graham before he died of cancer of the lung, his bête noire for 25 years. His position as doyen of American surgery was visible in the roster of speakers assembled to eulogize and praise him 3 weeks later. He had many colleagues, a few close friends, and an even smaller elite inner circle.

Evarts Ambrose Graham was a persuasive speaker, a voluminous correspondent, and a pervasive influence on the American surgical scene for 35 years.

Chapter 2

BACKGROUND
AND BEGINNINGS

LINEAGE

The Grahams

Evarts Graham was born into the line of Scotch Presbyterians who arrived in the New World after a 100-year sojourn in Ireland. The surname Graham, or Graeme, appeared in Scottish history in the twelfth century when an Anglo-Norman ancestor from *Grey Home* arrived. A northern arm held territories in the Highlands, and in 1445 Patrick, one of its chiefs, became a peer as Lord Graham. Three hundred years later, Mary Cathcart, wife of Thomas Graham of Bolgowan, was painted by Gainsborough as "The Beautiful Mrs. Graham"—in elegant costume, it was a regal portrait.[1] In 1945 the chief was lord, the earl of Montrose of Scotland; the clan had entered the mainstream of English nobility.[2]

A less tractable clan of Grahams lived as reivers[a] on the western end of the Scottish-English border. As "the biggest family on the western border they also had a fair claim to being the worst. In murder, blackmail, theft, extortion and intrigue they were second to none."[4] Border reivers were aggressive, ruthless, violent people who created a society in which deadly family feud was common. These were Evarts's forebears. King James I initially tried to move them to the lowlands, but when this proved unsuccessful, he banished the clan to Roscommon County in

---

a. "Reiver, reaver *n.* (arch) a robber, plunderer, pirate or sea robber."[3]

central Ireland, and "Thomas, eldest son of Killerby…fourteenth Lord of the Manor of Cliborn…was assessed for the transportation of the Graemes or Grahams, who were shipped at Workington for Ireland. The whole of the Graemes or Grahams (under their Chief Walter, the 'gude' man of Neatherby) being troublesome on the Scottish border, were transplanted from Cumberland to Roscommon."[4] In the schedule of articles affecting the transfer, it appears that it consisted of 124 persons, nearly all bearing the surname of Graeme or Graham. Quiet was restored to the borders, and Thomas could then live a gentleman's life in Cliborn.

Around 1720 to 1750 there was a daily litany by the family of Mungo Maxton, the tenth earl of Cultoquhey:

> From the greed of the Campbells
> From the ire of the Drummonds
> From the pride of the Grahams
> From the winds of the Murrays
> Good Lord, deliver us.

The whole gallant history of this clan shows that, to those who did not follow what the Grahams believed to be right and true, the pride of the Grahams was more dangerous than a pride of lions.[5]

James I encouraged Scottish highlanders to cross from Scotland to Northern Ireland in the expectation that this would prevent the use of Catholic Ireland as a springboard for the invasion of Protestant England (Anglican, not Presbyterian), and by 1640 there were approximately 100,000 Presbyterian Scotsmen settled in Ulster. Becoming impatient with the intolerance of their religion, many Ulster Presbyterians left for the New World in a migration that began around 1718 and continued for the rest of the eighteenth century. During their stay in Northern Ireland, these Scotch Presbyterians remained Scotsmen who were living on Irish soil. They neither intermarried with the Irish nor embraced its Catholicism, and, almost entirely of Saxon blood and Presbyterian in religion, they retained their individuality for centuries. The term "Scotch-Irish" was applied after their arrival in the New World to distinguish them from the Catholic "Irish Irish" who were also among the flood of immigrants. Six of these Scotch-Irish became presidents of the United States[b].

Among those thousands was David Graham of Belfast, Donegal County, Ulster, who reached Chester County, South Carolina, in 1772 after passage aboard the *Pennsylvania Farmer*. A ship of 350 tons, she arrived in Charleston, South Carolina, on December 19, 1772, as one of five chartered by the Reverend William

---

b. Andrew Jackson, James Polk, James Buchanan, Ulysses S. Grant, William McKinley, Woodrow Wilson.

Martin to transport his flock of 1100 parishioners to the New World. David Graham later moved to Augusta County, Virginia, with his son Andrew, Evarts's great-great-grandfather. David and Andrew, both blacksmiths and farmers, supported the Revolutionaries; David provided food and blacksmith service for the patriots, while Andrew fought in the militia. Andrew later migrated to Todd County, Kentucky, where he produced a son, Matthew. In 1807 Matthew's son, Andrew Graham Jr., was born. This Graham married Rachel Davis, and sometime around 1830 moved to Biggsville, Henderson County, Illinois.

Biggsville lies 10 to 12 miles east of the Mississippi River and 15 to 20 miles west of Monmouth in northwest Illinois. In this small farming community in 1843, David Wilson Graham, Evarts's father, was born and raised.[6] In 1861 David formally joined the South Henderson Presbyterian Church, and in 1862, at 19 years old, he enlisted as a private in Captain Cutler's Company C of the 83rd Regiment Illinois Infantry. Mustered in at Monmouth, Illinois, David served 3 years of the Civil War in a regiment assigned garrison duty in northwest Tennessee and southwest Kentucky. He saw action against Confederate troops at Fort Donelson, Tennessee, and against guerilla forces in both states. David Graham was mustered out at Nashville, Tennessee, in January 1865 and discharged in Chicago, Illinois, in July 1865 with the rank of corporal. The regiment had lost four officers and 34 enlisted men—killed and mortally wounded; one officer and 82 enlisted men died of disease.[7]

Upon returning from the war, David Wilson Graham entered Monmouth College[c], graduating in 1870 with a bachelor's degree. He immediately gained entrance to Bellevue Hospital Medical School[d], from which he acquired a doctor of medicine degree in 1872. Monmouth College awarded him an honorary degree in 1910.

---

c. The town of Monmouth, Illinois, was settled in 1824. Four years later Associate Reformed Presbyterians who arrived in Warren and Henderson Counties desired an educational institution. By 1853 the Monmouth Academy was created, and a college charter was obtained in 1857. A.Y. Graham Jr. and David Graham, uncles of David Wilson Graham and members of the board of trustees, donated 35 acres of land, 10 for the college campus and 25 more to be sold in support of a Presbyterian school of higher learning.

d. In 1847 the Bellevue Hospital Medical School began to give instruction to students from several New York medical colleges that had no clinical facilities. Formal schooling at Bellevue began in 1860, when the city of New York authorized the hospital to erect a college building on hospital grounds, thus providing opportunity for preclinical instruction; it was the first laboratory in the United States to give instruction in pathology and bacteriology.

Bellevue Hospital Medical School was one of the first, if not the earliest, American medical schools to integrate formal clinical teaching as the core of its curriculum, with a lecture hall on hospital grounds. Ten of the original 13 professors held appointments on the medical staff of Bellevue Hospital, and the faculty was allowed to take students onto hospital wards for clinical instruction. The daily ward visits gave the Bellevue Hospital Medical School an advantage over other medical institutions, and it shortly became acknowledged as one of the most advanced schools of instruction in the United States. It was this institution that David Wilson Graham attended. By March of 1866,

Despite Lister's publications on antisepsis in 1871, it was not practiced at Belle-vue during David Graham's student years. Dr. James R. Wood, who gave the principal surgical clinic, would "enter the surgical amphitheatre wearing a black silk gown buttoned tightly about the neck and wrists, with a boutonniere of bright flowers. His house surgeon wore an old coat with waxed silk ligatures hanging from a buttonhole and highly-polished unsterile instruments awaited on the table. The operation proceeded with no special preparation of surgeon, assistants, patient, instruments, or dressings."[8]

In 1874, following the completion of 2 more years of study in New York, David Graham moved to Chicago to become a demonstrator of anatomy at the Womens' Medical College; in 1877 he became a professor of surgery. One of his female students, Mary Bates, wrote of him: "Dr. Graham 'crammed' me almost daily—I took the oral competitive examination for interns in the Cook County Hospital—the only woman to take it. Dr. Frank Billings[e] took first place, and I the second. We were the only two intern physicians to be competed for." Dr. Mary Bates became the first woman intern in Cook County Hospital.[10]

---

a regular admission policy to the Bellevue Hospital Medical School had been designed, along with a formal summer session and a winter session. Attendance at both sessions was considered to constitute 1 year of instruction, and 2 years were required to complete the degree.

Organized in 1841, the Medical School of New York University functioned without close hospital affiliation for many years and, like others, sent its students to hospital schools for clinical experience. An 1898 consolidation of the Medical School of New York University and the Bellevue Hospital Medical College created the current New York University School of Medicine.

e. Frank Billings (1854 to 1932) of Mineral Point, Wisconsin, was the nephew of Albert Merritt Billings, owner of the Chicago Peoples' Gas Light and Coke Company, after whom the hospital of the University of Chicago is named. After teaching 2 years in public schools, Frank received his doctor of medicine degree from the Chicago Medical School in 1881. After an internship at Cook County Hospital, he entered the private practice of medicine and taught anatomy at the Chicago Medical School. He spent 2 years in Vienna, Paris, and London, where he studied bacteriology and clinical care. Returning to private practice in Chicago, he became a professor of medicine at Rush in 1889 and served as dean from 1900 to 1920.

In 1905 William Rainey Harper appointed Billings professor of medicine at the University of Chicago in order to further plans for a medical school on the South Side. In 1917, at 63, Billings entered the US Army. Abraham Flexner wrote of him: "Plans for medicine at the University of Chicago depend very largely upon the influence of one man—Dr. Frank Billings—a wise, clear-headed and absolutely unselfish leader."[9] Billings was a member of the educational reform movement and helped to place academic medicine as a distinct area within the medical profession. He was a partner in this effort with William Welch, Franklin Mall, Harry Bowditch, Simon Flexner, and many others. The Otho S.A. Sprague Memorial Institute and McCormick Institute for Infectious Diseases were results of his efforts. He served as president of both the American Medical Association and the Association of American Physicians, and he headed the board of charities for the state of Illinois. He had an unswerving devotion to the idea of a medical school on the Chicago campus, and he personally gave $100,000 to the University of Chicago. His uncle's family matched it 10 times to construct the Albert Merritt Billings Hospital on the Midway Campus.

David Graham held surgical appointments at the Rush Medical College, the Central Free Dispensary, and the Cook County Hospital. With the 1883 opening of the Presbyterian Hospital of Chicago, he held a surgical appointment and, ultimately, became its chief of medical staff and a member of its board of managers. The Presbyterian Hospital boasted several other outstanding surgeons: Fenger, Murphy, Ochsner, Andrews, Harris, Dean Lewis, and Arthur Dean Bevan[f]. James B. Herrick[g], who knew David Graham intimately, wrote of him:

> The Scotch in his ancestry may explain a streak of canniness in his makeup, the Irish his pugnaciousness. His friends spoke of him as a persistent man, his critics called him stubborn. He was certainly hard to drive. He was an individualist, had his own way of doing things and clung to beliefs and techniques that seemed old fashioned.... He was repeatedly in disagreement with his colleagues, yet his interns liked him, said they learned much from him and warmly defended him against his highbrow, over-scientific critics. Dr. Graham had many little tiffs with colleagues, the function of which at times generated heat, though it rarely caused explosions.[11]

Although David Graham had contact with Christian Fenger, the Danish physician who first brought to Chicago the current knowledge of cellular pathology, bacteria, and infectious disease, he remained sceptical and paid scant attention to

---

f. Arthur Dean Bevan (1861 to 1943) of Chicago was educated at the Yale Scientific School and Rush Medical College, where he obtained his degree in 1883. After 5 years in the US Marine Hospital Services, he served as chairman of anatomy at Rush until 1902, when he resigned to become head of the surgical service until 1934. He was surgeon to the Presbyterian Hospital, president of the Chicago Medical Society in 1899 and the Chicago Surgical Society in 1910, and in 1907 he became chairman of the surgical section of the American Medical Association (AMA). With creation of the AMA Council on Medical Education and Hospitals in 1904, he was chosen to be its first chairman, a position that he occupied for 24 years (with the exception of 1919 in which he was president of the AMA). Besides surgery, he had deeply held interests in medical education and the prohibition of alcoholic beverages. With a driving personality and compelling character, his decisions as a leader in the advancement of medical education were both strong and forceful. His disdain of personal criticism was notorious, and he was fearless when attacked. For a quarter of a century, he set the tone for the AMA Council on Medical Education and Hospitals, whose far-reaching influences were so great that he remains an icon in Chicago surgical circles and highly revered both locally and nationally.

g. James B. Herrick (1861 to 1954) obtained his doctor of medicine degree at Rush Medical College (University of Chicago). In 1888 he became professor of medicine at Rush and he was attending physician at the Presbyterian Hospital from 1895 to 1945. He was a cultured physician, remarkable teacher, medical philosopher, and historian. He held the presidency of every important organization in internal medicine and will be forever remembered as the man who first described coronary infarction as a distinct disease. Awarded the American Medical Association Distinguished Service Medal in 1939, he was also an honorary member of the New York Academy of Medicine.

aseptic techniques in his surgical work. A beginning medical student in 1911, Lester Dragstedt[h] recalled

> seeing "Daddy" Graham, as we students called him, perform an operation for the removal of tuberculous lymph glands in the neck of a child. Evarts Graham was his assistant and did all that he could to persuade his father to observe the principles of aseptic surgery. However, when Daddy Graham had finished scrubbing his hands and rinsing them in an antiseptic solution, as a final measure he washed his beard in the solution to the dismay of his son Evarts.... The students were delighted because they had been taught something of bacteriology and were persuaded about the aseptic method of surgery.[12]

Evarts Graham was later to write about his father:

> He was not by any means a polished or trained surgeon in the modern sense. He received his M.D. from Bellevue, supposedly the best medical school in the U.S. at the time, but actually the course of instruction was very inferior and aseptic surgery at that time was nonexistent. I shall always be grateful to him however for his sympathetic understanding of my desire to get the sort of educational experience and training which would enable me to stick my head up above the crowd. He supported me yearly, both financially and by sympathetic understanding.[13]

---

h. Lester Dragstedt (1893 to 1975) was born in Anaconda, Michigan, and as a youth came under the influence of A.J. Carlson, who attracted him to the University of Chicago for collegiate and professional education. There Dragstedt obtained his bachelor's degree in 1915, his master's degree in 1916, and his doctor of philosophy degree in 1920; he received a doctor of medicine degree from Rush Medical School in 1921. A physiologist by temperament, he spent 1 year at the University of Iowa as physiologist before becoming chairman of pharmacology and physiology at Northwestern University. In 1925, as the University of Chicago was building a university hospital on its campus, Dallas Phemister, the chairman of surgery, asked Dragstedt to design the research facilities for his department, with the premise that he could teach surgery to physiologists but was interested in teaching physiology to surgeons. Dragstedt remained a member of the surgical faculty at the University of Chicago, and in 1947 he succeeded Phemister as chairman. After his retirement in 1959, he moved to the University of Florida in Gainesville, whose chairman, Dr. Edward Woodward, was one of his students.

Ever interested in the physiology of the stomach and the pathophysiology of peptic ulcer, he introduced the concept of truncal vagotomy and, after studying it from 1917 to 1943, performed the first human transthoracic vagotomy. A brilliant scientific thinker, he was elected to the National Academy of Sciences to follow Halsted, Cushing, Graham, and Blalock. A kind, gentle man who always had a smile, he was ever concerned for his students and their creativity. He inspired a large number of surgeons to be interested in the pathophysiology of gastric illness.

A Chicago surgeon, Gustav Blech, wrote to Evarts about his father: "He reject-ed a statement made to the effect that if you will turn out to be as good a surgeon as he, it will be more than satisfactory.... He foresaw that you would become not only an operator, but a great surgical scientist and that is what he stressed."[14]

David Graham became president of the Illinois State Medical Society in 1894, the Chicago Medical Society in 1895, and the Chicago Surgical Society in 1906 to 1907. He was a member of the Chicago Pathological Society, president of the medical staff of the Presbyterian Hospital (1898 to 1901), a member of its board of managers (1900 to 1904), and continued to operate until his colleagues became concerned about his capability. Charles Johnson was a beloved friend and Civil War comrade of D.W. Gra-ham, and on December 3, 1924, while they were discussing several medical friends who had died, Graham told him, "I will be the next one, [because] I have carcinoma of the esophagus."[15] During this illness, Evarts wrote to a noted endoscopist, Cheva-lier Jackson of Philadelphia, to determine if any special therapy could be given to his father, and he was not surprised to receive a negative answer. David Wilson Graham died of carcinoma of the esophagus in Chicago, Illinois, February 9, 1925.

Ida Anspach Barned Graham

Ida Barned was born in Philadelphia on January 17, 1850. Her mother died in Ida's childhood, and, at the age of 7, she and her father, a merchant coal dealer, moved to central Chicago. There is little documentation of Ida's schooling and early years. In July 1877, at age 27, she married David Wilson Graham, and they established themselves as active members of the Third Presbyterian Church of Chicago locat-ed at Ashland Boulevard and Ogden Avenue. They lived at 101 Warren Avenue until a move in 1890 to 672 West Monroe. Two children were born to this union—David Barned in April 1879 and Evarts Ambrose in March 1883.

When the Presbyterian Hospital of the city of Chicago was opened, Ida Graham organized and established the Women's Board. She was a member of the board for more than 50 years, its president from 1909 until 1921, and then honorary presi-dent until her death. She was active in the Ladies Aid Society as well as the Nursing School of the Presbyterian Hospital, organizing a loan and scholarship program for student nurses. She became chairman of the Central Council for Nursing Educa-tion, and her greatest hobby was to educate the public as well as doctors to proper-ly understand the role of the private duty nurse. She was active on the boards of the Art Institute and the Chicago Symphony Orchestra. Under her executive direction, the Presbyterian Hospital Women's Board was organized sufficiently well that when World War I broke out and Hospital Unit No. 13 was activated, the Women's Board was ready; it organized and completely equipped a Red Cross unit from its mem-bers.[16] A member of the Presbyterian Hospital Board wrote: "Her vital personali-ty, wise judgement and alert interest in all matters pertaining to the missionary cause were a constant stimulus to the Presbyterian Womens' Board of Missions of

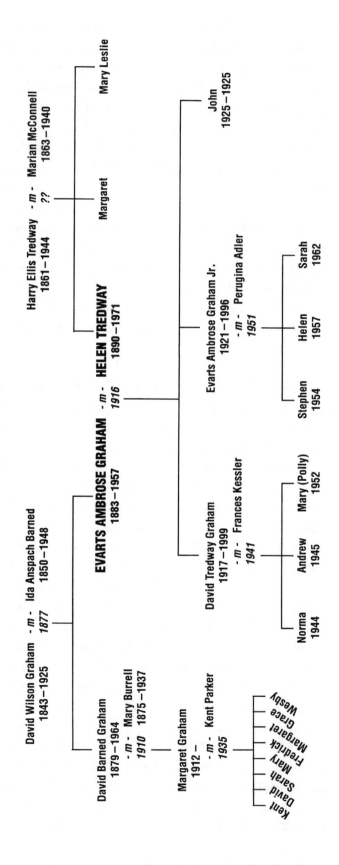

the North West. She secured the consent of the president of the board of managers and established a Child's Free Bed Fund, which endowed free beds for the care of children. She was an active participant in all features of board activity, loyal to established methods but ever ready to back the introduction and foster the best in every new idea."[17] A memorial fund was established to further the education and welfare of nurses. In Mrs. David Wilson's later years she became homebound and lived with son David until her death on May 8, 1948, at the age of 98.[18]

A resolution from the board of the Presbyterian Hospital of Chicago noted of Ida Barned Graham:

> She had a capacity for warm and affectionate friendships and many intimate associations were the result of companionship in the work of the Board.... Her genius as a presiding officer was augmented by her fine carriage and her alert and energetic manner. Her clear and animated voice conveyed such definite conclusions showing so much thoughtful consideration that she commanded everyone's attention. Her opinions and decisions represented wise judgement and were unanimously accepted. Her tact in dealing with administrators and executives was ever apparent and her deference and consideration of the opinion of others proved her capable of handling any problem. Her Christian steadfastness never wavered and her stand on matters of principle was always definite.[17]

EARLY YEARS

Home and Lewis Institute

Two sons were born to David Wilson and Ida Barned Graham. The Graham's first child, David Barned, born April 9, 1879, received his primary and secondary education in the public schools of the city of Chicago before enrolling in 1896 in the new Lewis Institute at the corner of Madison and Robey, approximately 10 blocks west of home. David spent 1 preparatory and 2 junior college years at the institute; then he transferred to Princeton to graduate in 1902. His was the world of business, the publication and distribution of greeting cards. Mary Burrell, his wife, was a Chicago kindergarten teacher, a playground director, and a pottery instructor at the Art Institute of Chicago. For most of their lives they lived in Joliet, Illinois, with a summer home in Michillinda, Michigan, north of Muskegon—a house that was used for family celebrations and reunions. There was one child, Margaret. David died in Summit, New Jersey, on July 15, 1964.

The second son, Evarts Ambrose, was born March 19, 1883. *Evarts* and *Ambrose* were names that came from family friends.[19] *Evarts* came from a woman named Ella Evarts, a member of a relatively large and well-established Boston family that included novelists, writers of scientific books for children, and a secretary of state in Garfield's cabinet of 1881. *Ambrose* came from Chicago friends, a family of no particular social or historic distinction. Throughout his life, Evarts Graham never used the name Ambrose, preferring the initial *A*, and he stuffily defended the pronunciation of Evarts as *Ev´ərts*, becoming upset and somewhat angry when referred to as *Ēv arts*. Years later, realizing that he could anger Graham by calling him *Ēv arts*, one of his staff at Barnes Hospital occasionally did so. Graham attached no special significance to the name Evarts other than the inability of most people to either pronounce it or spell it correctly, unless they came from New England. Years later his two children, David and Evarts Jr., agreed between themselves that they would join his crusade and find names for their Grahams other than David (too frequent in the Graham lineage) or Evarts or Ambrose (not in the lineage). It was Evarts Jr. who broke the compact and decided reluctantly to name his middle daughter Helen Evarts.[19]

In the footsteps of his elder brother, Evarts attended public schools in the Chicago system for his first 8 years, entering at age 5 from their home on Warren Avenue, then later from the new home on West Monroe Avenue, approximately three blocks away. At this time, the office from which his father conducted his practice was at 133 Clark Street, approximately 10 blocks east of the Monroe Avenue house.

In 1896 Evarts followed David by going to the Lewis Institute[i] for his 4 high school years, spending the first in the preparatory, and the last three in the academic division, before graduating in 1900 with a high school diploma, ready for admission to Princeton University. The Lewis faculty that had been collected by its

---

i. The Lewis Institute was created with a bequest from Allan C. Lewis, who wished to found a school of science, literature, and technology. William Rainey Harper, the president of the University of Chicago, was instrumental in organizing its academic program and selecting his protégé, George Noble Carman, as its first president, a position Carman held for 40 years. The school was composed of three divisions: an academic program offering conventional 4-year high school courses in science and liberal arts; a technical 4-year study program in mechanical, civil, and electrical engineering; and an associate in arts degree 2-year junior college that offered courses in arts and engineering. It was the first junior college in the United States. The Lewis Institute was considered the epitome of modern education, and the economic background of those who attended the institute in its early years led it to gain the reputation of a fashionable preparatory school. Its first faculty meeting was held on March 6, 1896, in a building at 1951 West Madison, at the corner of Madison and Robey, and its first students were enrolled that autumn. The next two decades produced several graduates who became well known: among them were Arthur Krock, head of the Washington Bureau of the *New York Times*; Benny Goodman, a clarinetist and band leader; Luther Adler, a distinguished actor; and Dorothy Thompson (Mrs. Sinclair Lewis), a newspaper writer and internationally known journalist. Dr. James Herrick, the renowned internist from Rush Medical School, served on its board for more than 30 years. On June 18, 1940, the Armour Institute of Technology and the Lewis Institute were merged to create the Illinois Institute of Technology, located at 3300 South Federal Street in South Chicago.

President, George N. Carman, consisted of Lewis (no relation to the founder) in English, Mann in history, Durham and Shipley in Greek and Latin, Rogers in physics, and Delango in French. From among this superb faculty, Evarts Graham, Arthur Krock, and Dorothy Thompson selected Edwin Herbert Lewis, head of the English department, as the one who had had a major influence on their lives. Krock and Thompson became writers, and Graham was forever-after preoccupied with grammar, spelling, and the precise use of words and phrases. Not infrequently he would interrupt speakers at conferences to offer suggestions as to the correctness of grammar, spelling, or the proper use of English. In 1945 he took issue with the editors of the *St. Louis Post-Dispatch* regarding their use of *wait on* instead of *await* or *wait for* after the paper had published a headline stating "Big Three Meeting Waits on Stalin." Graham wrote: "Perhaps the writer was a joker and used a double-entendre in order to confuse people." He concluded: "Many people fear that the Big Three meeting will wait on Stalin but I don't believe it will."[20]

Recalling those Lewis Institute years 50 years later, Graham wrote: "I was greatly inspired by each one of the faculty members with whom I came in contact.... learning became fun for all of us. I think intellectual accomplishment was the most important goal to all of the students, certain remarkable members of that faculty come to mind from whom I derived very great inspiration.... The Lewis Institute ...perhaps...might be called one of the pioneers of progressive education. It had sound concepts."[21] Additionally, "I think that one of the strongest influences which I have had in my life I received while a student at the Lewis Institute."[22]

Princeton

Evarts entered Princeton University[j] in the fall of 1900 with a career choice already shaped—he desired to become a physician or, more appropriately, a surgeon, and to follow in the footsteps of his father by beginning at Princeton (a proper Presbyterian university) and then attending Rush Medical College (home). By the turn of

j. Princeton University is a privately endowed, nonsectarian institution of higher learning that owes its 1739 origin to a movement within the Presbyterian Synod of Philadelphia that wished to establish a college in the middle colonies to rank with Harvard and Yale in New England and with William and Mary in Virginia. Officially opened in 1747, it was called the College of New Jersey; 5 years later it moved to Princeton, the city from which it now derives its name.

Upon assuming the name of Princeton University in 1896, its board stated that Princeton's future did not lie in developing professional schools for utilitarian ends but in upholding pure learning and devoting itself to the liberal aspects of studies that underlie and broaden professional and technical education. A feature of its instruction was the preceptorial method, introduced in 1905, in which large classes were broken into small groups or informal conferences. A quadrangle dormitory system was devised in lieu of the eating clubs so prominent at Yale and Harvard. Woodrow Wilson, a member of the class of 1879, was elected president in 1902 and held the position until 1910. During his administration the undergraduate curriculum was revised, a departmental system was organized, and an extensive building program was completed.

the twentieth century, eastern American Universities were beginning to move from a strict instruction in the classics to more vocationally oriented topics. Woodrow Wilson became president of Princeton in 1902, succeeding theologian Francis L. Patton, who had succumbed to pressures from the anticleric alumni and allowed the last 2 years of the Princeton curriculum to become entirely elective; even worse, he was in favor of vocational training. Mental discipline and education in the classics at Princeton were ebbing, and it was a conservative revolution that placed Wilson as president; he felt that Princeton should be a place of general, not special, education—an institution where a student found himself, rather than a profession. Refusing to support a preprofessional curriculum with electives, he moved the school in the direction of a more prescribed curriculum that emphasized the humanities, especially literature, history, and political science.[23]

During Graham's preparation for his bachelor of arts degree, he studied the usual premedical prerequisites. His courses included general physics, qualitative analysis, quantitative analysis, inorganic chemistry, and an introduction to organic chemistry. Biology included two introductory courses in zoology and botany that were followed by invertebrate and vertebrate anatomy, embryology, and neurology. The 1904 Princeton yearbook noted his favorite study as biology.

Mr. Oliver Reynolds[k] reported that sometime during his second year, "Evarts explained his plan for a career. Following medical school and internship he had three objectives—to do major surgery, to engage in research work, and to have a clinic of younger men who would be interested in studying and developing ideas."[24] This is an extraordinary statement of purpose by a college sophomore, reflecting not what he would like to become but what he would like to do.

Evarts and a few classmates who planned to study medicine found a German professor who was willing to give a special course in scientific German, one not included in the university curriculum. In his third year, Evarts approached President Wilson with the request that such a course be given for credit. Wilson refused on the grounds that it was not properly a subject of undergraduate study, but Graham argued that if a group of students wished a course that would be of help in their professional careers, the college was under an obligation to include it, regardless of its cultural value. Wilson was adamant, claiming there was no more reason why he should permit a course in scientific German than a course in stenography, which might well be of value to someone going into journalism or other fields where the

---

k. Oliver Charlick Reynolds was a classmate and close friend of Evarts Graham at Princeton, graduating with him in 1904. After attending law school in New York, Reynolds was admitted to the New York Bar Association and became a partner in a major New York firm—Reynolds, Richard and McCutcheon. He concurrently maintained wide-ranging interests in the Young Women's Christian Association (YWCA), American Schools for Oriental Research, and New York City Presbyterian Clubs. He contributed information about Graham's Princeton years to Dr. Edward Churchill for the 1951 retirement dinner.

skill of shorthand would be useful.[24] Undeterred, the group arranged for the sessions, and the educational benefit to Graham was later visible in articles published throughout his career with many references to the German scientific literature.

Graham's contacts with Wilson must have been close and friendly, reflecting a mutual respect by both in the life of the campus. Dissatisfaction with a grade Graham received from a Mr. Elliott in one of his courses led him to ask President Wilson to review his paper and its grade. The president responded: "Dear Mr. Graham: Mr. Elliott brought me your paper. I have read it and am sorry to say that I see no reason to revise his decision in the manner of your grade. While the paper is quite correct enough to pass you easily the mistakes, which are very numerous, are such as to show that you did not stop really to *comprehend* what you were studying. I hope that at the next examination you will take time enough to *think* the matter out. Very truly yours, Woodrow Wilson."[25]

The Princeton years also provided Graham with a journalistic outlet by membership on the editorial board of the college newspaper, *The Daily Princetonian*; it was an effort that he shared with classmate Allen O. Whipple, initiating a friendship that lasted throughout their parallel careers in surgery.

During the summer months between his sophomore/junior and junior/senior years, Graham took courses at Rush Medical College in preparation for admission in 1904 to 2 years at the University of Chicago, followed by 2 years at Rush Medical College. During these years Graham began to reflect on the essential elements of the education he desired to become the type of surgeon he wished. It was becoming obvious to him that work in the operating room was not the only way to achieve his three stated goals.

Rush Medical School

Founded in 1837, Rush Medical College[l] is the oldest medical college in Chicago. A proprietary school, as were the others, it was located in west Chicago, adjacent to the Presbyterian and Cook County Hospitals, and it was comprised of physicians who provided lectures, demonstrations, and clinics. The Presbyterian Hospital of Chicago was founded in 1883, and the Rush faculty became its staff. Immediately north of the hospital, the medical college owned two buildings that provided lecture halls and laboratory space for students.[26,27]

---

l. Rush Medical College was chartered by the state of Illinois in 1837, a few days prior to the city of Chicago's charter. Before an 1898 affiliation with the University of Chicago, its professors constituted its board of trustees; the Presbyterian and Cook County Hospitals and the Central Free Dispensary were used as clinical facilities. At the affiliation Rush boasted of two buildings in west Chicago, one devoted to classrooms and the other to the laboratories that supported clinical activities in the Presbyterian Hospital and the Central Free Dispensary. President Harper of the University of Chicago and the leaders of Rush desired an organic union whereby Rush would become the Medical School of the University of Chicago. Frederick Gates of the Rockefeller Foundation, as well as Mr. David Rockefeller

As medical knowledge was expanding, it was becoming apparent by the turn of the century that basic science instruction would be important to clinical practice, and the proprietary schools of Chicago looked to merge with a university. In 1891 the Chicago Medical College became an integral part of Northwestern University, with the Women's Medical College following the next year, and in 1913 the College of Physicians and Surgeons of Chicago became the Medical School of the University of Illinois. The arrangement between Rush Medical College and the University of Chicago was loosely knit. In 1898 Rush affiliated with, but did not join, the University of Chicago, which by then had buildings in south Chicago to house its biology and chemistry departments. In 1901 the first 2 years of medical study that had been in Rush faculty buildings were transferred to the University of Chicago campus, and anatomy, physiology, chemistry, pharmacology, and bacteriology were taught to freshmen. Sophomores took courses in pathology, materia medica, and medicine. The third and fourth year clinical courses and electives were held at the Rush campus at the Presbyterian Hospital or the adjacent Central Free Dispensary under the tutelage of Rush faculty. Rush Medical College graduated the student and endowed the degree.[28]

With courses taken at Rush during his two Princeton summers, Evarts Graham was able to complete the University of Chicago requirements of the preclinical years in 1 year, during which time he joined the Nu Sigma Nu medical fraternity and was elected a class councilor. In 1905, his junior year on the Rush Campus, he was made class president;[29] then, during his senior year, he was elected to the honorary medical society, Alpha Omega Alpha, received a fellowship in pathology, performed approximately 50 autopsies, and assisted in pathology departmental teaching. With his father a member of both the Rush faculty and the Presbyterian Hospital staff,

himself, opposed such a union, and, because the 1898 affiliation had happened without his approval, Gates became upset. At this time the Rockefeller Foundation was deeply involved in the financing and the academic aspirations of the University of Chicago. In 1902, 1 year after the first 2 years of the medical curriculum had been transferred to the university quadrangles, Harper again tried to unite the two institutions. With the support of the university trustees, he proposed to Frederick Gates that Rush would raise $1 million in the ensuing year if the Rockefeller Foundation would provide $5 million over the subsequent 5 years, to assist in union of the two institutions (with preclinical and clinical education divided between the two campuses). The latter sum was never forthcoming. By 1924 the University of Chicago had begun to develop its own 4-year medical curriculum on the south Chicago campus, planning that Rush and the Presbyterian Hospital on the west side of the city would become the nucleus of a postgraduate department. Three years later clinical departments of medicine and surgery were established on the University of Chicago campus. Rush continued its participation in University of Chicago medical education until 1942, when the university and Billings Hospital were able to provide instruction for all University of Chicago students, and a formal separation of the two institutions occurred. Differences in educational philosophy between Rush and the university were always visible. Rush was interested in training good practitioners of medicine, whereas the university's concern was the advancement of science in medicine. The Rush charter was never revoked, and it continues as one of the six medical schools of Chicago.

Evarts was well known to many members of the faculty, and among his favorite teachers he listed Anton J. (Ajax) Carlson, Jacques Loeb, and Ludvig Hektoen. Carlson considered Evarts Graham his greatest student.[30] Nicholas Senn, Arthur Dean Bevan, and his father were Presbyterian Hospital's leaders in surgery; Frank Billings, James B. Herrick, and Bertram W. Sippy were its leading internists. Among the younger internists was Rollin T. Woodyatt, a man who would have a major influence on Graham's education and his Washington University appointment.

Evarts Graham's scientific interests surfaced while in medical school; his initial scientific publication, made during his first year at Rush, was a case report on a 47-year-old lumberman with a rare fungal infection (blastomycosis). The patient was admitted to the Presbyterian Hospital in September 1905 from David Graham's clinic, and he died in January 1906. During this time he was shown to the students and interns on several occasions. With Graham as assistant, Dr. E. LeCount, pathologist, performed the patient's autopsy. With E.E. Irons, Graham coauthored the case report, which was published in the *Journal of Infectious Diseases*. Five such cases had been reported from Chicago, but many were inclined to doubt that *Blastomyces* was the sole factor (syphilis and tuberculosis were ever-present considerations), and the case was reported with Graham's hope to add to the knowledge of the clinical course and pathology of this disease.[31]

A second manuscript, prepared while a medical student, was a case report and literature review on the 6-year survival of a woman with carcinoma of the breast. Graham obtained 15 such cases, mostly from European sources, and followed with a pathologic description of the tumor in a woman whose survival seemed unusual because of the prevailing idea that a 3-year limit without recurrence was equal to cure. Graham concluded: "Carcinoma cells frequently are rendered inert in the body....it is not likely that every carcinoma cell is removed, and the remaining ones must subsequently be overcome by a natural protective process of the body."[32] It was a thoughtful prescient conclusion that antedated the finding of tumor cell antigens and host immunity.

Postgraduate Years

Following receipt of his medical school degree, Graham began an internship at the Presbyterian Hospital. At that time post–medical school education was not required for licensure, and most graduates left school to become general practitioners. Hospitals had no organized arrangement or specially designed programs to enroll interns and oversee their activities; many hospitals denied that this was their responsibility.[33] It was a time of apprenticeships, and Graham planned to spend 2 years, 1 in medicine and 1 in surgery, at the Presbyterian Hospital. It appears that even then he was concerned about the basic and essential nature of such an education. He spent his first year on the medical service with Bertram W. Sippy, a physician with interests in gastrointestinal diseases who designed what came to be known as the "Sippy diet" for the treatment of duodenal ulcer. During this year Graham continued his contacts with pathologists Ludvig Hektoen, who was studying and writing about allergy and immunity (see Graham's papers on phagocytosis[34–36]), and Edwin LeCount, who was undertaking investigations on the genesis of fatty liver (see Graham's papers on chloroform-induced hepatic injury[37,38]). In addition, Graham maintained an interest in the nondidactic teaching of pathology to small student groups. He had several contacts with H. Gideon Wells, a pathologist with interests in the chemistry and specificity of anaphylaxis, who later became director of the Otho S.A. Sprague Institute.

Work at his father's office and an assignment at the Central Free Dispensary provided opportunities for Evarts to obtain clinical experience. Starting his second post–medical school year as a surgical intern, Graham spent 5 months on the surgical service of his father, assisting and occasionally performing operations under supervision, and then spent an unspecified number of months on the service of Arthur Dean Bevan, chief of surgery. Before the year was complete, he left the clinical activity of Bevan to become a Nicholas Senn Fellow in Surgery.[39] Remembering these years, Graham later wrote to E.D. Churchill: "I am sorry that I cannot say that I derived any particular inspiration from Bevan. He had many qualities which I did not admire at all and I have never felt any sense of loyalty to him. I am sure that he never understood my general philosophy and his ideas and mine about training in surgery were fundamentally opposed."[40] Bevan, an influential member of the Council on Medical Education of the American Medical Association, was convinced that the surgeon's role was to perform operations and that surgery was learned in the operating theater; its underpinnings were anatomy and pathology. The concept that chemistry and physiology, rather than morphology, had a bearing on the specialty of surgery was foreign to Bevan, and he discouraged Graham's efforts in this direction.[40]

During 15 months as a Nicholas Senn Fellow, Graham studied the effect of anesthetic drugs on various immune processes; tissue asphyxia; the effect of chloroform and ether on the liver; the effect of ether on the phenomena of bacteriolysis, agglutination, and phagocytosis; and the use of olive oil in restoring the capability of phagocytosis after ether anesthesia.[34–37] His contacts with the pathologists who were integrating physiology and chemistry with morbid anatomy stimulated and inspired him. He was appreciative that his father was sympathetic and supportive of his extended postgraduate training in nonoperative fields and his desire to get the sort of educational experience and training that would enable him to stick his head up a little above the crowd. Graham stated: "He supported me very eagerly, both financially and by sympathetic understanding, during the time that I stretched out my period of graduate training."[40]

Two years after graduation from medical school, Graham, Dallas Phemister, and Vernon David organized the first surgical-pathologic conferences held in the Department of Surgery. They reorganized the teaching schedule, developed the conference idea of presenting topics to the medical students that the three considered of importance, and gave a daily course called "Principles of Surgery" from 5:00 to 6:00 pm. Discussions of current medical problems were almost always on the docket.[41] In 1910, now 3 years out of medical school and at the completion of his Senn Fellowship, Graham was appointed assistant surgeon on the active staff of the Presbyterian Hospital. He held the title of instructor in surgery at Rush Medical College and was surgical instructor at the Central Free Dispensary.

Just as he was being introduced to private practice research and medical student education, Graham became deeply involved with Rollin T. Woodyatt[m]. The two first met in a corridor of the Presbyterian Hospital shortly after Woodyatt's return from a stimulating experience with Frederick Müller in Munich. Graham, being an intern on Sippy's medical service and 5 years Woodyatt's junior, became impressed with the man, whom he decided he would like to know. The opportunity presented itself in 1909 when the Otho S.A. Sprague Memorial Institute[n] was established, with Woodyatt in charge of its laboratories. This association continued until Graham's departure from Chicago, and it was significant in his subsequent invitation

---

m. Rollin Woodyatt (1878 to 1953) was born in Chicago, educated in the Chicago Manual Training School, and in 1902, after 2 years at Cornell University, obtained a doctor of medicine degree from Rush Medical College. He was an intern at the Presbyterian Hospital for 2 years, then practiced internal medicine for 2 years prior to a trip to Europe in 1906 to 1908. During this time he studied with Dr. Frederick Müller in Munich, a first rank clinician who worked in his own chemistry laboratory, attached to both his office and a ward in the hospital. This experience forever changed Woodyatt and was a singular event in the establishment of the Otho S.A. Sprague Institute. Upon his return to the United States, Woodyatt looked for a position similar to that of the salaried assistants in German clinics; he found none. There were positions in nonclinical departments where one could do research, and positions in a clinical department where one could do research on borrowed time. Before Woodyatt left Munich, Müller told him that nothing would be of greater service to American medicine than the creation of similar positions in American clinics; from this suggestion came the Otho S.A. Sprague Memorial Institute, developed by Woodyatt with the understanding support of Frank Billings.

Woodyatt spent 1908 to 1909 in the University of Chicago chemistry department, studying basic chemistry rather than biochemistry. He became an associate professor of medicine at Rush Medical College, then professor of medicine at the University of Chicago in 1924 when clinical departments were established on the south Chicago campus. He held a similar appointment at Rush Medical College. In 1915 Philip Shaffer approached him to offer a position in the Department of Medicine. Woodyatt refused the offer because of the "full-time" requirement that Shaffer and the Rockefeller Foundation felt was important in the development of new schools—a concept that subsequently was to dominate the direction of the University of Chicago development. Medical politics did not interest Woodyatt, although he did become a member of several biologic/chemistry societies and president of the Association of American Physicians. He was a perfectionist and was not interested in becoming prominent in medical circles. Well versed in art history, he enjoyed the give and take of table conversation with the brilliant intellectuals who surrounded him.

n. The Otho S.A. Sprague Institute was organized in 1911 following a bequest made 2 years earlier by Mr. Otho S.A. Sprague, a wholesale grocer, who requested that it be for the relief of human suffering. Organized by his brother, Albert A. Sprague, its board decided to use the bequest for medical research

to Washington University. Woodyatt's primary scientific interest was in carbohy-drate metabolism, and he discontinued his practice of medicine to study organic chemistry under J.V. Nef, analytic chemistry under Julius Steiglitz, and physical and theoretic chemistry under William Draper Harkins at the University of Chicago. Woodyatt felt that basic chemistry would serve him better than would biochem-istry. It was Woodyatt that led Graham to the University of Chicago for his 2 years (1913 to 1915) of study with Steiglitz and Nef, and, in his tribute to Woodyatt (as the first Woodyatt lecturer), Graham acknowledged, "I have always felt greatly indebted to him for the inspiration I received from him. To a considerable degree he changed my life."[42]

In 1911 Graham became an active member of the Otho S.A. Sprague Institute, and, with Woodyatt's support, he studied anesthesia and its effects on both the immune sys-tem and the alimentary tract. He became interested in hypoxia, and, after studying the effects of asphyxia or hypoxia on fetal movements, ascribed the effects to temporary fetal asphyxia. After examining the effects of anesthesia on the unborn fetus, he relat-ed his observations to hemorrhagic diseases of the newborn, concluding that chloro-form and asphyxia in many instances were the determining causes.[43] In further work with chloroform, he showed that it converts to hydrochloric acid, and he postulated that the acid was responsible for the edema, multiple hemorrhages, fat infiltration, and necrosis of the liver. He concluded that all the late features of chloroform poisoning were produced by the hydrochloric acid derived from its metabolism.[44]

In another study, which used fox terrier pups, Graham measured the glycogen in the liver and concluded that protection against chloroform-induced liver necro-sis was in some way referable to a high glycogen content. He attempted to explain the protective action of glycogen against liver necrosis by posing the question of whether the part played by glycogen could be of a physical nature; in his reading he had found that glucose, alcohol, and glycerin retarded the diffusion of some sub-stances into gels[o]. This became his major research topic during his 2 years with Steiglitz at the University of Chicago.

---

to secure the greatest possible return. The board adopted a policy that the funds would not be used for the erection of buildings, but that the institute would cooperate with existing institutions when and where medical research could be furthered. Administrative officers supported projects in several local-ities, wherever appropriate. For several years assistance was provided to Frank Billings of the Presby-terian Hospital for studies on focal infections, and to Dr. Maude Slye for her studies on the influence of heredity on cancer. The major thrust of the institute's efforts had a clinical/chemical background, and for several years the institute financed the research of R.T. Woodyatt on diabetes and its related problems, work that included the efforts of Drs. Russell Wilder and Evarts Graham. Later most of the institute's support went to the new laboratories of pathology at the University of Chicago clinics, where its department chairman, H. Gideon Wells, also held the position of director of the institute.

o. *Author's note*: Graham's facility with scientific German is apparent in the reference list to this article. Of 64 references, only 15 are written in English, a smattering are in French, and all the rest are in German.

The project had a secondary outcome: it led to a romance that lasted throughout his life. Steiglitz's chemistry department housed a petite, vivacious graduate student named Helen Tredway. She was a woman holding her own in a man's world; he was a handsome, slightly older, mature special student, and the two were immediately attracted to each other. The attraction must have been strong and immediate, for she became a partner in his research and then in his life. It was Graham's first and only serious relationship, and their collaboration was to be permanent. There were never any others.

Ending the Age of Innocence

By the end of 1914, well into his second year of chemistry at the University of Chicago, Graham began to realize that his time of training should come to an end. He was completing his studies, he had produced a dozen manuscripts worthy of publication, he had met Helen Tredway, and it was time to consider the options available to him to move into the productive professional life that should follow student days.

He was licensed to practice medicine in Illinois, and he could do so from the office of his father in central Chicago, just four blocks from the Art Institute and the cultural center of Chicago. However, the opportunity to practice with his father was unattractive for several reasons. His father was of a different generation, and Graham felt that the course of instruction his father had received at Bellevue was inferior; he did not practice aseptic surgery and failed to appreciate that basic science innovations were occurring in medicine. There was always the opportunity to move to another medical school or hospital in Chicago, but this presented nothing more attractive than did his Presbyterian Hospital appointment. It would require his entrance to an entirely new medical and social environment, without the support afforded by the many contacts in the Rush-Presbyterian system that would give him an expanding practice and allow him to maintain his contacts with Woodyatt and the Otho S.A. Sprague Institute.

In the spring of 1916, recruiters from Mason City, Iowa, arrived to offer him the chiefship of surgery in a hospital with a closed staff and the certainty of patient referrals from within this group, if not from other practitioners in Mason City.

Before his second year with Steiglitz and Nef was completed, he decided that Mason City was for him, and he embarked upon his new adventure—2 years that would be a surprise and forever leave their imprint.[45]

Chapter 3
_____

THE MASON CITY YEARS

At the turn of the century, Mason City, Iowa, was a bustling, ambitious community of approximately 22,000 people, situated 16 miles from the Minnesota State
Line, 90 miles south of the Mayo Clinic. Its industrial bases were a brick and tile
company, a cement company, and a meat packing plant. Five railroads passed
through the city, and there were two newspapers. Mason City contained a collection of Frank Lloyd Wright homes and was to become River City in Meredith Will-
son's 1957 Broadway hit *The Music Man*. When Graham arrived in 1915, there
were three hospitals: a large frame residence that was a boarding, self-care hospital
run by two sister nurses—the Storeys; a relatively new St. Joseph's Hospital run by
a Catholic Order—The Sisters of Mercy; and the City Park Hospital, operated as
the Park Clinic by a group of physicians within a gentlemen's agreement.

THE PARK HOSPITAL BUILDING COMPANY

In 1906 Drs. C.F. Starr and Fred Albert became partners who invited C.M. Swale (a
surgeon), W.E. Long, and C.L. Marsten into their group. The practice flourished, and
facilities greater than those provided by the City Park Hospital were needed. City
Park Hospital was located in a building owned by an industrial group and shared
with the Times Printing Company. It was a noisy unsatisfactory arrangement. Fred
Albert died of typhoid fever, and C.F. Marsten left after becoming dissatisfied with
the loosely knit type of practice. In 1909 the remaining associates, together with
some younger men—Drs. L.E. Newcomber, A.E. Echternacht, M.J. Fitzpatrick, and

F.G. Murphy — organized the Park Hospital Building Company, which would build a hospital with 56 beds and was to be completed in the latter part of 1911. In 1913 the surgeon, C.M. Swale, died; the group, realizing a need for someone other than a self-trained general practitioner, initiated a search for his replacement. The surgeons of the town were deemed inadequate for the demands of this group; an itinerant surgeon from Rochester, Minnesota, made an occasional appearance.[1]

One of the men with contacts in Chicago learned that a young surgeon, Evarts Graham, had a lot of experience, was the son of a surgeon, and was interested in leaving Chicago. Graham was invited to Mason City and, after being given every consideration to encourage him to come, accepted the offer and left the Presbyterian Hospital of Chicago to become a member of the Park Clinic in Mason City, with offices in Park Hospital. The group practice had grown slowly, and, in order to pay building costs, space in the basement of the northeast portion of the building was rented out to Long for use as a Turkish Bath; in the southeast corner, there was a dental office for a short period of time that was later replaced by Mrs. Meyer's Beauty Salon. Dr. Echternacht owned and operated a private diagnostic laboratory in the building, and Graham was given a laboratory in the basement where he could research "strawberry gallbladder" disease[a]. Starr later reported that he "never got to see the inside of the research laboratory, he kept it locked up tighter than a drum."[1]

On April 30, 1915, the Park Hospital Staff announced the addition of Dr. E.A. Graham of Chicago, who would confine himself exclusively to surgery and consultation. The *Mason City Morning Times* called Graham "a man with a vision" and stated, "He feels that there is a great field here and an opportunity to carry out his idea of building up a great institution—an opportunity to give the patients the very best up-to-date service in every detail."[2] The Park Hospital staff also made a public statement concerning "new management and necessary changes in the hospital": "The staff consider themselves well prepared to take care of all surgical cases, a Department for Medical Diagnosis and Treatment will be further developed."[2] At the time of his arrival, Graham envisioned the development of a group practice of specialties that would emulate the nearby Mayo Clinic. Soon the group recruited an internist, Dr. Robert S. McCaughey, to head a medical department that would complement the surgical section. McCaughey's tenure was short; he left for military service in mid-1917.

There is no record of meetings of the hospital staff for medical purposes during the 2 years of Graham's stay in Mason City; such activity was carried out by the Cerro Gordo County Medical Society. Minutes of the board of directors of the Park Hospital Building Company display financial concerns of the seven physicians

---

a. "Strawberry gallbladder" disease was first described by Lord Moynihan: yellow specks (cholesterol) are present on the red lining mucosa, giving it the surface appearance of a strawberry. It is currently known as cholesterosis of the gallbladder.

and Mrs. Swale, who continued to hold the stock formerly owned by her deceased husband—stock that was transferred to Graham on September 16, 1915, for an undisclosed amount. Mrs. Swale remained on the board of directors for several years, serving for a time as its vice-president. On January 15, 1917, Graham was elected the board's secretary. Minutes of these meetings indicate concern for the operation of the building but rarely for items related to quality or quantity of patient care; they do, however, record the appointment in early 1916 of a dietitian at $60 per month and a surgical nurse at $90. Ownership of the building was the cohesive force for the group.

Graham's attempts to establish a multispecialty group are recorded in the actions of the board. On March 19, 1917, a special meeting of the stockholders amended the Articles of Incorporation to establish the capital stock of the corporation at $30,000, divided into 3000 shares with a value of $10 each. A second amendment omitted the line "with five members" and inserted "all of the stockholders." This change reflected Graham's effort to permit expansion of the group.[3] In September 1917 the stockholders passed a motion to buy the laboratory from Echternacht and the Turkish Bath from Long.[4]

Although the group owned and operated its own clinic and hospital with a closed staff, and only members of the group could admit patients to Park Hospital, each member also had privileges on the open staff at St. Joseph's Mercy Hospital; however, surgery was not always performed within the confines of the hospitals. About 20 years later, W.E. Long wrote to Graham inviting him to visit Mason City. In that letter he reminisced about the events of years ago. He asked:

> Why not come back to the haunts of the days of your youth in surgical experience—the days of pioneering on improvised kitchen tables in farm houses if need be? I shall never forget the day you removed a 500 carat, solitaire gallstone from a little old lady who lived near Fertile. This was done under local anesthetic—a most unheard of venture in those days. The little pink skinned Jersey Red piglets in the front yard grunted approval as you triumphantly emerged from the house. All in all, just another day—yet we had in that operation a preview of oncoming advancements which eventually became regular routine and accepted practice in surgery.[5]

FEE SPLITTING

Shortly after Graham arrived in Mason City, he was approached as to how he would split fees[b], something for which his experiences in Chicago had left him unprepared.

---

b. *Fee splitting* is the practice in which a physician approaches one or more surgeons to determine what percentage of the surgical fee for an operation will be rebated to him. As a result of this prac-

His Presbyterian sense of propriety led him to the conclusion that surgery was not being done by the best but by those who most often gave back some of their pay. This was not a problem within the Park Clinic group, since members shared their incomes, but it was a factor in his relations with other general practitioners. Graham was perplexed and distressed by the lack of referrals or consultations from St. Joseph's Mercy; he operated in that hospital only four or five times during his 2 years in Mason City. Concluding that cases were being bought through the widespread practice of fee splitting, he began to create a stir within the community by encouraging public disdain of the practice and by denouncing surgery done by incompetent physicians. He made it known that he felt quackery in Mason City was rampant.

Graham took his case to the public and waged a campaign against fee splitting by speaking in the churches, before women's clubs or organizations such as the Rotary Club, and even getting the local newspapers to print some editorials about it.[6] Though fee splitting did exist, some of his failure to establish a large practice may well have stemmed from his candid remarks about fee splitting and what he felt was a generally inferior level of existing surgical care.[7] This was an unfortunate political stance so early in the evolution of specialty medicine, but his thrust was clear—specialty medicine required care based on skill and knowledge and not on monetary inter-relationships. His crusade reached its peak in a two-page article published as a supplement in the *Mason City Daily Globe Gazette* of May 24, 1916, that was devoted to medical care in Mason City. The article promoted the more frequent use of specialists and castigated quackery and fee splitting. There was one paragraph that especially supported his feelings. Authorship of the article is unrecorded, but this portion of the text is typical Graham:

> The bane of the medical profession among its surgical specialists is usually the fee splitting proposition. By this is meant the division of the surgical fees unknown to the patient. The practice is a pernicious one and invariably results in the patient being referred to the surgeon who divides the fee most liberally regardless of his surgical ability. The members of the [Cerro Gordo County Medical] Society are proud of their reputation in this respect, and so far as the society knows none of its members are guilty in this respect. Certainly, the practice would not be carried on anywhere should patients inform themselves in regard to this questionable practice before submitting to an operation.[8]

---

tice, patients in need of surgical procedures are sold to the highest bidder and sent to the surgeon who offers the greatest percentage of fee to the referring physician, regardless of ability as a surgeon or knowledge of the problem at hand.

If the referring physician accompanies his patient to the hospital, perhaps even administers the anesthetic, he is entitled to a professional fee from the patient but not from the operating surgeon.

The article also described the Cerro Gordo County Medical Society (organized in 1903 with a membership of five, which grew to 42 by 1916) as "one of the most active in the state," and stated: "Some of its members have more than a statewide reputation. This Society has contributed more to medical science than has [sic] the members of any other county in the state." It went on proudly to describe Park Hospital, which was of fireproof construction and was owned and managed by a group of physicians; and Mercy Hospital, also of fireproof construction, which was owned and managed by the Sisters of Mercy. It stated that the society boasted a high standard of ethics and that its best surgeons were known all over the state for their conscientious work. The article claimed: "Mason City has no quack doctors... and as honesty in business has become a necessary qualification for continued success, so it has become in all other alliances of endeavor. Mason City has a strong specialist in many lines and no city can become a Medical Center that does not have those who devote all of their time to the various branches of medicine and surgery." It ended with the statement "Mason City as a Medical Center is not surpassed by any city in the whole state."[8]

Graham was thought of by many as a young upstart—a fairly thorny character whose ideas, as with those expressed in the editorial, were not entirely generous; he became the victim of personal attacks that charged that he spent too much time in research, public speaking, and publishing[c] and not enough time with patients or referring physicians. Raymond Weston, a surgeon who began his practice in Mason City shortly after Graham's departure, described some of Graham's initial clinical problems and wrote that Graham managed to have a series of rather unfortunate complications and a couple of surgical deaths very early in his career. However, Graham's efforts did lead to an official ban of fee splitting by the Cerro Gordo County Medical Society, even though the practice continued sub rosa.[7]

THE CERRO GORDO COUNTY MEDICAL SOCIETY

On Tuesday, January 25, 1916, the County Medical Society meeting was held in the assembly room of the courthouse, and attorney Clair Smith discussed the law pertaining to quack doctors. He described some of the practices of fake doctors, and outlined the course that needed to be taken by physicians to eliminate quack doctors from the profession.[13] On Tuesday evening, November 28, 1916, the County Medical Society met again in the courthouse, prior to its scheduled formal

c. *Author's note*: Graham published four articles during his Mason City period. Two were case reports of patients he cared for in Mason City[9,10] and two were reports of his Chicago studies.[11,12] No publications resulted from any research in Mason City. His manuscript about strawberry gallbladder disease resulted from work done years later in St. Louis.

meeting to debate the question of fee splitting and the cutting of fees. President C.L. Marsten presided at the meeting; no minutes were kept.[14] Fee splitting was discussed as being unethical, grafting, and dangerous since patients were often taken to the surgeon offering the greatest percentage of fee, regardless of the surgeon's ability or knowledge. At the meeting the society formally placed a ban on fee splitting. The secretary, Dr. W.J. Egloff, introduced the resolution: "Resolved: That any member of the Cerro Gordo County Medical Society found guilty of fee splitting or fee division or any secret or implied understanding between two or more physicians or surgeons whereby any fee is divided between them shall be expelled from the Society and thereby automatically causing expulsion [sic] from the State and the AMA Society." Evarts Graham proposed an amendment that expanded it to all individuals, not just physicians: "Resolved: That any member of the Cerro Gordo Medical Society found guilty of fee splitting or fee division or any secretly implied understanding between any members and any other persons whereby any fees are secretly divided shall be. ..." The society passed both the resolution and the amendment. The *Mason City Morning Times* of December 2, 1916, devoted two columns to praising the actions of the society, stating: "*The Times* congratulates the physicians of the county upon the bold stand taken in announcing to the world that they propose to clean their own stables. The Cerro Gordo County Medical Society has taken the first important stand towards re-establishing the honor system.... The work should not stop with this one resolution."[15] It was the first time a county medical society had taken such a stand.

One month later, on December 28, 1916, the annual meeting of the County Medical Society adopted the motto "All's well that ends well," and, in reviewing the year's activities, Dr. Marsten's presidential address incorporated the fee splitting problem and the November resolution. Following the address, Graham proposed the establishment of a medical library for the benefit of the physicians and surgeons. The proposal was approved, and a committee composed of Drs. Graham, W.J. Egloff, and S. O'Brien was to proceed with the project and to make plans to provide a central reading place where all physicians of the city might find current magazines and journals. The meeting also acknowledged that the "publicity given to our fine hospitals has been of much benefit to Mason City and the people of this part of the state and ... has stimulated us to greater cooperative efforts and also to renew our vigilance in ridding our community of the fee splitting practice."[16]

WEDDING AND WAR

For Graham the Mason City years consisted of more than work and public controversy over fee splitting. At 9:00 pm on January 29, 1916, Evarts Graham married Helen Tredway at the Tredway home on Fenlon Place in Dubuque, Iowa. This culminated a 2-year courtship that began in a Chicago chemistry laboratory and was subsequently conducted by mail and through occasional visits between Mason City and Dubuque during a 9-month separation. The ceremony was simple, with 60 guests that included Evarts's parents, Dr. and Mrs. David Graham, his brother and Mrs. David Graham from Chicago, and two women who had been classmates of Helen at Bryn Mawr. The Reverend John Dysartodd of St. John's Episcopal Church conducted the service, and there were no attendants for either bride or groom. The couple then spent a 6-week honeymoon in Chicago and several places in the eastern United States, and in mid-February Evarts and Helen returned to Mason City to make their home in the Crane Apartments on 7th Street, Northwest. On June 20, 1917, in the Park Hospital, H.L. Brenton supervised the successful birth of their first child, David Tredway Graham.

Four months after the County Medical Society action on fee splitting, the United States entered the European War, and mobilization was the order of the day. In addition to a draft board, the Draft Exemption Board for the Northern District of Iowa was formed to review requests for the medical exemption of potential draftees. Dr. W.J. Egloff of Mason City was its medical representative until July 30, when Governor Harding announced the appointment of Evarts Graham as the medical officer of the exemption board, replacing Egloff.[17] Graham's appointment was brief, for Graham had applied for a captaincy in the Army Medical Corps Reserve, and on August 30 he submitted his resignation. Neither the date of his relief nor the time of his call to active army service were known, but his resignation was accepted on October 30 in anticipation of his call to active duty; Dr. William Bowen of Fort Dodge, Iowa, became his successor.[18] At his first physical examination in September, Graham was rejected because of poor vision, but a second examination in December found him fit for special duty, and he made plans to leave Mason City. Christmas was spent with his family in Chicago, and when his Army Commission arrived on January 5, 1918, he, Helen, and David, left Mason City for induction at Fort Sheridan, Illinois, and an assignment to the Brain Surgery Unit based in Chicago, under the directorship of Dean Lewis, his colleague from Presbyterian Hospital days.

GOODBYE TO MASON CITY

It was immediately apparent that this departure was to be permanent. Graham gave the voting proxy for his stock to Dr. Long and authorized its sale. In mid-December the Park Hospital stockholders authorized the secretary to borrow $675 from the Security National Bank in order to purchase Dr. Graham's operating stock; 1 year later on December, 1919, after his arrival in St. Louis, Graham received his money.[19]

Graham received an invitation to return to Mason City to renew old acquaintances and present some scientific material on three occasions. Two invitations came in 1934, the first from Morgan of St. Joseph's Mercy Hospital[20] and the second from Long of Park Hospital.[21] Graham refused both. Four years later he was approached by Dr. Houlahan on behalf of the Cerro Gordo County Medical Society who requested that he address the society on September 20, 1938.[22] The date conflicted with the opening of the Medical School, at which Graham was to give the welcoming address to the entering class. He wrote: "I am still hoping that sometime during the Fall I may be able to come to Mason City to renew some of my old friendships."[23] In May 1917, Graham had presented a paper at the Iowa State Medical Society annual meeting in which he discussed acidosis in surgery, material derived from his Chicago years;[24] between 1927 and 1957, in addition to the offers from Mason City, there were 10 invitations from the Iowa State Medical Society for him to speak at one of their meetings—Graham refused all. His 2 years had made him one of Iowa's own, even as he felt alienated and was always suspicious of their financial arrangements.

Nathan Womack later reminisced about one of his early encounters with Iowa surgeons after he had become professor of surgery at the University of Iowa, replacing a dearly loved Frank Peterson. He visited a small town in rural Iowa, and his host, after introducing himself, continued: "I think it is only fair to say to you as you start out here in Iowa City that we are prejudiced against you on two accounts. One is you are taking the job of one of our very good friends. . . . the next is that you had your surgical training with a man we consider the world's biggest son-of-a-bitch."[25] Womack responded with a humorous rejoinder, and, although the two became friends, their dissimilar feelings regarding Graham and fee splitting were never resolved. Womack left for North Carolina after 2 stormy years in Iowa City, not all of his own making.[25] Graham never returned to Mason City.

Graham expressed his views on Mason City and the state of surgery in Iowa in a letter to Alan Kanavel, who had written to Graham in 1919 as to the possibilities that might exist for a young man from Chicago to go to Mason City and establish a surgical practice. Graham wrote: "The greatest difficulties [sic] in all that part of the country is the question of fee splitting. . . . I carried on a vigorous fight against it. . . . this materially diminished the amount of work which I otherwise could have done. I was also instrumental in putting over a rule in the local Medical Society that any member who is found guilty of fee splitting will be automatically expelled from membership. . . . whether or not this rule still holds good I do not know." Graham was still concerned about incompetence and closed his letter by stating: "I do not know of anyone at the present time who is really sufficiently well trained to carry on important surgical work. Of course there are many who attempt it, but there ought to be no difficulty in showing up these various tyros."[26] His concern for fee splitting in the state of Iowa was seemingly never ending, and, as late as 1954, he wrote to Nathan Womack asking him to arrange a meeting "to discuss the whole question of what the American College of Surgeons should do about the state of Iowa and its applications for Fellowship."[27] A meeting at the Drake Hotel in Chicago on the evening of Sunday, March 21, 1954, was attended by Paul Hawley (director of the American College of Surgeons), Isadore Ravdin (chairman of a special committee of the regents to make recommendations about what to do concerning the state of Iowa), Frank Peterson (emeritus professor of surgery and past chairman of the University of Iowa), Womack, and Graham. No changes came as a result of the meeting.

SPECULATIONS AS TO WHY GRAHAM INITIALLY CHOSE MASON CITY

Several authors have speculated as to the reasons for Graham's move to Mason City. There is no information on how the war on Europe affected his decision, and in none of his correspondence does he give a clear explanation for this move. Several possible factors should be entertained:

1. Chicago and Presbyterian Hospital held Murphy, Bevan, Lewis, and Graham Sr., all towering figures who dominated the surgical scene. It seems likely that Graham's desire to move west may have been influenced by the fact that the possibility of being "chief" at Presbyterian Hospital seemed a long way in the future, and that a Presbyterian setting in which he could develop a multidisciplinary group was prohibitive.
2. There is no record as to the magnitude of Graham's personal surgical practice at Presbyterian Hospital, and it is possible that a desire to establish a more active and engaging surgical experience was an incentive.
3. It may be that Graham desired to experience the real world of surgery as it was practiced in the less rarefied atmosphere of smaller communities; he may have chosen Iowa because it was Helen's home state.
4. It is possible that Graham entertained a humanitarian desire to provide facilities and services for areas less well served than metropolitan Chicago.
5. The Mayo Clinic had been established as a group practice, an arrangement that was very attractive to Evarts Graham throughout his life. It is almost certain that he envisioned a smaller version of the Mayo Clinic in Mason City.

Regardless of the reason, it is difficult to see the move to Mason City as a forward move to achieve the objectives that he had defined for himself at Princeton— to do major surgery, to engage in research, and to have a clinic of younger men. But Graham did go to Mason City, and he was forever colored by this experience. In subsequent years he brought his attitudes regarding incompetent surgeons, the measurement of competence, fee splitting, and the field of surgical ethics to the American College of Surgeons. Throughout his life, he remained bitter about many features of his Mason City experience, yet his exposure to group practice and a closed hospital staff were positive events that influenced some of his later decisions. He became aware of the role of a university in a community, and several times he commented to his son, Evarts Jr., about the value of a university to its community and to its students.

Mason City had left a mark on Evarts Graham, and he had left his mark on Mason City. With the help of newspaper publicity, Graham used the medical establishment to accomplish one of his goals: the Cerro Gordo County Medical Society became the first medical society in the United States to publicly disown fee splitting. Although of uncertain permanence, it was a "first." Graham was to have several more. Graham's 2 years in Mason City were significant years for Graham. He always looked back, but he never returned.

Chapter 4

WORLD WAR I

IN THE ARMY: CHICAGO DUTY

Sometime during the summer of 1917, Graham decided to enter the army; however, after physical examination in September, he was declared unfit for duty due to defective vision. Continuing to press for a commission, he requested Maj. Frank Billings to write on his behalf to Captain Badgley of the Army Medical Corps. Billings recommended Graham and described him as being "thoroughly qualified by education and experience to enter the brain surgery division of the Medical Reserve Corps U. S. Army. [He] is a man of unusual ability and skill and I know of few men as qualified as he for a commission in the brain surgery division."[1] Shortly thereafter a reapplication and re-examination resulted in Graham being declared fit for this special duty, and on January 5, 1918, he received his commission as captain in the Medical Section, Officers Reserve Corps of the Army of the United States. Four months later, on May 4, in anticipation of appointment to the Empyema Commission, Graham was promoted to the rank of major, a rank he held for the duration of his military service.

In mid-1917 the Subcommittee on Brain Surgery of the General Medical Board of the Council of National Defense had been transferred to the surgeon general's office, where it was placed within the Division of Head Surgery,[2] and an advisory committee composed of leading neurosurgeons of the country was created. Due to the limited number of qualified neurosurgeons, schools of neurosurgical instruction were planned for Philadelphia, New York, Chicago, and St. Louis, with a mandate to give 10-week courses of lectures and demonstrations in the anatomy, physiology, and pathology of the central nervous system, supplemented by surgical and neuro-logic clinics. Thirty students were assigned to each course, and approximately 250 officers graduated from these programs. Dean Lewis[a] directed the Chicago unit at Presbyterian Hospital, and Graham became a member of the teaching faculty. One such course lasted from early January through mid-March;[2] during these 2½ months, Graham lived at his parents' home in Chicago. At the completion of this course, Col. Allen Kanavel[b] of Chicago, now in the surgeon general's office, arranged Graham's appointment to the newly authorized Empyema Commission that was to be based at Camp Lee, 20 miles south of Richmond, Virginia.

THE EMPYEMA COMMISSION

During 1917 and 1918, the most widespread and fatal epidemic of modern times ravaged the world; an estimated 500 million people contracted and 40 million

---

a. Dean Lewis (1874 to 1941) was born in Kewanee, Illinois. He obtained a bachelor of arts degree at Lake Forest College in 1895 and doctor of medicine degree from Rush in 1899. During these years he came under the influence of Billings, Herrick, Senn, and Bevan, and, after an internship at Cook County Hospital, he became instructor of anatomy at the University of Chicago. There, he was influenced by Bensley, who at that time was introducing the vital staining of tissues. After spending 6 months with Spalteholz in Leipzig, Lewis returned to the Department of Surgery at Rush, where he remained from 1903 to 1924. During World War I, he was one of the chief organizers of Presbyterian Hospital's Base Hospital No. 13, and he went with it to Limoges, France, before being transferred successively to Evacuation Hospitals No. 7, 6, and 5. At the conclusion of the war, Lewis held the rank of a lieutenant colonel. He returned to General Hospital No. 28 at Fort Sheridan to handle nerve injury problems, and he was discharged in August 1919 with the United States Distinguished Service Medal.

In 1920 Lewis became editor of the *Archives of Surgery*; he remained for 10 years, until he became too ill to continue. In 1924 he accepted the chairmanship of surgery at Johns Hopkins, succeeding William S. Halsted; his *Lewis Practice of Surgery* was the first loose-leaf textbook of surgery. Lewis held the chairmanship until 1939, when he retired. Throughout his career he made a host of friends, and maintained loyalty to his ideals and his mastery of the principles of surgery. He died in October 1941 after a lengthy illness.

b. Allen B. Kanavel (1874 to 1938) was a plain-faced boy from Sedgewick, Kansas—a minister's son who worked his way through Northwestern University and its medical school, receiving his doctor of medicine degree cum laude in 1899. After graduate study in Vienna, he returned to Chicago to become an intern at Cook County Hospital; he then rose through the ranks of the surgical depart-ment at Northwestern University. He was particularly stimulated by Franklin Martin, founder of the American College of Surgeons. His experiences with problems of hand injuries at Cook County Hospital became a dominant feature of his professional life, as he explored the anatomic relation-ships of tendons and tendon sheaths in the hand and published a classic text on hand infections. He served in the surgeon general's office during World War I, from 1917 until the end of the war, and was responsible for the assignment of specialists within the military medical corps. He returned to Chicago and Northwestern University as its department chairman, a position he retained until he died in an unfortunate automobile accident in 1938.

people died of swine-type influenza. It was more deadly than the bubonic plague (Black Death) of 1347 to 1351, in which 25 million people perished. All armies of Europe and every camp in the United States felt the toll exacted by the initial upper respiratory viral infection and the subsequent bacterial pneumonia. Medical personnel were among those that sickened and died from the pneumonia that followed epidemics of measles and influenza; during 1917 pneumonia caused 65 percent of all deaths in the US Army. By the time the war ended, 50,510 US soldiers had died from disease, and 50,501 had died as a result of injuries in action.[3]

In February 1918 Surgeon General William Gorgas established the Pneumonia Commission to study the pathology, bacteriology, and clinical course of pneumonia. This commission consisted of Rufus Cole, William MacCallum[c], Alphonse Dochez, Oswald Avery, Thomas Rivers, Francis Blake, and Franklin Stevens. Its important finding was that the pneumonia that occurred following either measles or influenza was caused by *Streptococcus hemolyticus*. The Pneumonia Commission also found hemolytic streptococcus pneumonia to be a distinct pathologic entity, pathologically different from the lobar pneumonia caused by pneumococcus. The commission labeled the condition interstitial bronchopneumonia. The pathologic features were described in detail by MacCallum,[4,5] and an alarming number of these cases were complicated by the development of empyema[d].

At about this time, an inspection of many of the camps alerted Col. William H. Moncrief, chief of the Division of General Surgery in the surgeon general's office, and Col. Allen Kanavel to the severity of the problems posed by the empyema. Because it constituted such a significant and frequently fatal complication, the surgeon general created a second commission to continue the Pneumonia Commission's studies and to investigate empyema and its management. In the early spring of 1918, an Empyema Commission was formed at Camp Lee, Virginia, and its first

---

c. William George MacCallum (1874 to 1944) was born in Dunnville, Ontario; he obtained a bachelor's degree from the University of Toronto in 1894 and a medical degree from Johns Hopkins 3 years later. MacCallum started his career as associate professor of pathology at Johns Hopkins Hospital, and later became professor of pathology and physiology at Columbia University from 1909 to 1917. He was recalled to Johns Hopkins as chairman of the Department of Pathology and Bacteriology in 1917. He served as civilian consultant on the Pneumonia Commission during World War I and was host to Graham and Bell during their 2 months of experimental work in the summer of 1918. In addition to being an influential member of the Johns Hopkins faculty, he published a textbook of pathology and a biography of William Stewart Halsted. As a father figure, he had a major influence on many who passed through his department. Never married, he retained his Johns Hopkins appointment until he died in 1944.

d. *Empyema* is a collection of pus in the cavity between the lung and chest wall (the pleural space). In the vast majority of instances, it develops as a complication of an initial infection by measles, influenza, tonsillitis, or laryngitis that is followed by pneumonia, which leads to a pleural effusion and frank pus.

two appointees were Edward K. Dunham[e], bacteriologist, as its chairman, and Evarts A. Graham, surgeon. The two reported to Camp Lee on April 1, 1918, and were soon joined by surgeons James Mitchell and Alexis Moschcowitz; internists Thomas Rivers, Clifford Hartman, and Franklin Stevens (from the Pneumonia Commission); and bacteriologist W.L. Tower. Eventually the commission also included internists Ralph Kinsella, Richard Bell, Frederick Zeman, and Milton Cohen, dietitian Maude Hayes, artist Bessie Stocking, and secretary Pauline Jacobs. Their diverse qualifications enabled the commission to study bacteriologic, surgical, and nutritional features of empyema.

Moncrief and Kanavel's observations, as well as reports derived from other sources, documented a marked increase in the numbers and severity of postpneumonic empyema in all base hospitals; this prompted Moncrief to design a 22-item questionnaire[f]. On February 21, 1918, the surgeon general issued the questionnaire to 32 major encampments, hoping to determine several particular aspects of the disease and the measures being taken to limit its occurrence. The questionnaire was completed and returned by 27 camps. Immediately upon his arrival at Camp Lee, Graham was given the task of reviewing these responses; 12 days later, on April 13, he sent his typewritten summary[g] to the surgeon general, who acknowledged its receipt and within 10 days forwarded mimeographed copies to the commanding officers of all army hospitals.[7] In an accompanying memorandum, the surgeon general urged any camp with a sufficient number of cases of empyema to form a local team of surgeons, internists, and bacteriologists to study the disease. At least 10 such empyema teams were ultimately formed. Graham's "Report on Replies to Questionnaire on Empyema" was published in the surgeon general's report of 1918.[6] Although it contained no specific recommendations, the report strongly

---

e. Lt. Col. Edward K. Dunham of the medical corps directed the efforts of the Empyema Commission for its duration, and after the war he spent 3 years compiling the data that had been collected. The writing of the final manuscript, with considerable help from Graham and Stevens, was almost complete when, on April 15, 1922, Dunham became suddenly ill and died. In a July 1, 1924, letter to Mrs. Dunham, Graham wrote: "This report is unquestionably the most exhaustive and the finest thing on empyema ... ever written. It will constitute a medical classic for generations and in that sense will be a splendid monument to Dr. Dunham.... One of the most pleasant experiences of my life was the association which I had with him in connection with the empyema problem."

f. The 22 items of the questionnaire by Colonel Moncrief are contained in volume XI of *The Medical Department of the United States Army in the World War*.[5]

g. Graham's report on the responses to the Moncrief questionnaire was submitted to the surgeon general as a 24-page, double-spaced, typewritten manuscript; copies were sent to all camps. It was subsequently reproduced verbatim without attribution to Graham in the report of the surgeon general to the secretary of the army in 1918.[6] A copy of the typescript exists in the archives of the Becker Medical Library (Washington University School of Medicine).

suggested that a delay in operative drainage in patients with pleural effusion due to streptococcal empyema was the course to follow.

In his introductory paragraph, Graham described the magnitude of the problem:

> During January and February 1918 pneumonia was reported from army camps in the south and accompanying the epidemic a large number of empyemas began to be reported. Throughout the different camps it became recognized that this epidemic of pneumonia with accompanying empyema constituted a general septicemia with a tendency to localize in the lungs and pleura.... the invading organism was in a greater proportion of cases a streptococcus and... the mortality varied from 40–70% in those cases in which a large amount of fluid developed in the pleural cavity. As Spring advanced the epidemic spread to the North and invaded army camps there.
>
> The numerous cases of empyema which have occurred in many of the camps during the past winter have presented features so unusual and oft times so puzzling that it is the almost unanimous opinion of those who have seen many of them that the particular complex of symptoms and pathologic findings presented by them is new. Medical officers of wide experience, both in civilian and military life, state unreservedly that they have never before met with anything which corresponds with the recent type of empyema or compares with it in severity.... It is practically the universal opinion that those cases of empyema associated with the prevailing strain of hemolytic streptococcus have had a much higher mortality than those associated with the pneumococcus.... The Commission at Camp Lee soon established the wiser procedure in streptococcus infections and insisted on conservative treatment until the acute pneumonic process had subsided. Aspiration was to be undertaken as long as respirations were embarrassed.... Another factor of great importance has been the occurrence of many cases of empyema secondary to a pneumonic process associated with measles and in one camp the empyema following pneumonia after measles had a mortality rate of 71.4%.[6]

The principle of conservative treatment of pleural effusion and empyema in its early stages became well established early in 1918. The exudate most commonly found had a slightly turbid serofibrinous fluid, with pus demonstrable only microscopically, whereas, in some of the camps, only those cases were considered as empyema that yielded frank macroscopic pus. In general, those camps that reported the lowest mortality rate were those that regarded the cases of empyema as those in which the exudate was frank pus; conversely, the highest mortality rates came from camps in which all cases showing microscopic pus had been considered as cases of empyema[h].

The section on treatment in Graham's report continues:

> The high mortality rate in all the camps bears evidence of the gener- ally unsatisfactory results of the treatment of this condition. On the basis of usual experience... it apparently seems rational... to institute free drainage by opening the chest... but considerable doubt was cast upon the efficiency of instituting drainage through a permanent opening... particularly when the patients seem to be overwhelmed with toxemia.... Some of the camps found by experience that early repeated aspirations were safer than immediate operation and con- cluded that early operation is inadvisable.[6]

In summarizing the mortality rates, Graham found that the average mortality for the 27 camps was 30.2 percent, although mortalities of 84 percent, 65 percent, 57 percent, and 53 percent were reported. The review also revealed that at Camp Sheridan, where there was a pneumococcus rather than a streptococcus epidemic, the mortality rate with empyema was 13 percent. Camps in which the pneumonia and empyema followed measles reported mortality rates of 71 percent.[7]

The commission at Camp Lee also took the opportunity to observe its own 140 cases of empyema that were caused by the hemolytic streptococcus. Ninety-three patients had undergone an operation and were in various stages of convalescence, while the remaining 47 were acute cases that the commission could study during pre- and postoperative periods. Twenty-three patients were studied during the entire course of their disease, before and after the operation, and, of that group, only 1 patient died—a mortality rate of 4.3 percent. Nine patients were apparent- ly out of danger, and 13 had healed entirely at the time of the preliminary report.[8] The commission concluded that the chief factor in reducing mortality had been the method of treatment: late operation, painstaking attention to postoperative care, and maintenance of nutrition. Patients with streptococcal pneumonia had marked shortness of breath (dyspnea) and bluish skin (cyanosis), with respiratory rates from 50 to 70 per minute; it was unwise to perform an open pneumothorax, which

---

h. Classically, pus is a thick, creamy, yellowish material composed of necrotic tissue, a coagulum, liv- ing or dead white blood cells, and bacterial organisms. By the turn of the century, the increasing use of the microscope made it possible to identify white blood cells in the thin, watery material of a streptococcal pleural effusion. Surgeons and internists were prone to call this *pus* and they treated it as though it came from an established thick pus cavity with adhesions that walled it off and pre- vented collapse of the lung when exposed to atmospheric pressure. However, the water-thin strepto- coccal pleural effusion surrounded the entire lung, and there were no adhesions to keep the lung from collapsing if the fluid was removed by an open pneumothorax.

would further compromise respiratory ability. Considerable emphasis was placed on the danger of collapse of the lungs from the pneumothorax that resulted from open drainage[i]. The commission recognized that the pleural effusion was of less importance in producing the high mortality than was the pneumonia; it concluded that there was "no occasion to resort immediately to operative interference on a lesion which is perhaps a relatively insignificant aspect of the condition during the stage of acute illness."[8]

The preliminary report on the empyema cases at Camp Lee was ready for publication by mid-June. Less than 6 weeks later, it appeared in the *Journal of the American Medical Association*, and reprints were sent to all military hospitals. Graham and Dunham prepared the report and, due to demands on editorial space, they divided the article into two parts. The first focused on methods of treatment, with particular reference to the timing of the procedure, emphasizing the respiratory embarrassment occasioned by the pneumonia and the consequences of adding an open pneumothorax, which would further compromise the respiratory effort. It contained descriptions of wound management and the positioning of Carrel tubes, as well as various methods for instilling hypochlorite solution to sterilize the cavity and to flush out much of the fibrinous material from the pleural space. The second part of the report was concerned with the bacteriology of streptococcal empyema and the nutritional requirements that accompanied this illness. One of the "most profitable undertakings of the Commission was the study of the nitrogen output of patients in the early stages of empyema associated with hemolytic streptococcus [for] these patients become emaciated, lose strength with great rapidity and generous feedings should be a part of their treatment."[8] Dr. R.D. Bell directed nitrogen-balance studies of three soldiers in May and early June, during which time food intake, urine output, and pleural exudates were analyzed for nitrogen. Weight loss of 17 lb in a 14-day period was recorded on one patient who went from 128 to 111 lb. The report closed with 21 observations and recommendations made during the first 6 weeks of the commission's existence. There were three main thrusts: (1) delayed operation, (2) sterilization of the cavity, and (3) attention to the nutrient requirements.[8]

Alexis Carrel's studies in Army Auxiliary Laboratory No. 1, located at the Rockefeller Institute, had suggested that sterilization of the empyema cavity might be

---

i. The classic method used to drain an empyema cavity is to perform a rib resection: making a small incision over one of the lower ribs, usually toward the back; removing about two inches of rib; entering the pleural cavity; and leaving a tube to permit drainage of the material contained in the pleural cavity. If the abscess is contained, that is, walled off, air enters the space once filled by pus—that is the extent of the pneumothorax. With thin, watery material and no walling off or containment of the empyema, air freely enters the thoracic cavity, normally below atmospheric pressure. As a consequence, both lungs collapse, respiratory activity is impaired, and sometimes death ensues.

possible with the instillation of sodium hypochlorite (Dakin's solution[j]); he designed systems to provide for instillation of Dakin's solution into the chest through special tubes, giving up to 100 cc of 0.5 percent sodium hypochlorite every hour. This became known as the Carrel-Dakin treatment. Studies at the institute showed that by using Dakin's solution, the pleural space could be rendered sterile within 7 to 10 days in 80 percent of cases, and the wound could then be closed surgically.[9]

By mid-June the surgeon general decided that all empyema cases should be concentrated in six designated hospitals, and on June 22 the empyema cases at Camp Lee, along with Drs. Dunham, Graham, Mitchell, Moskowitz, and Rivers, were moved to General Hospital No. 12[k] at Biltmore, North Carolina.[10] Feeling that the treatment of acute empyema had been satisfactorily defined, the commission planned to study only chronic cases.

Although it was based on a modest number of empyema cases treated at Camp Lee, this preliminary report of the commission was supported by results from a number of other military hospitals, and the surgeon general's annual report of 1919 stated, "It is very gratifying to note that concomitantly or subsequent to the publication of this report, many of the surgeons attached to the hospitals arrived at the conclusion which were very much in accord with those advocated by the Commission."[10]

However, many doubted that an open pneumothorax was a potentially hazardous or lethal situation and felt that improvements in the mortality statistics seen in the commission's report were due to a change in the virulence of the organism,

---

j. Dakin's solution contains 0.5 percent sodium hypochlorite, a crystalline compound that, when put into water, releases free chlorine in amounts sufficient to kill bacteria. It is used as a purifying agent in city water plants and is commercially available for use in swimming pools or as a home laundry bleach. The army prepared paper packages for use in the canvas bags (Lister bags) with four spigots hung on tripods from which soldiers usually obtained their drinking water.

At the Rockefeller Institute, Alexis Carrel designed small tubes that could be introduced into wounds of any type. In the treatment of empyema, they were introduced beside the empyema drainage tube, and, through them, Dakin's solution could be introduced into the chest. The use of hypochlorite in the treatment and expected sterilization of almost all war wounds came to be known as the Carrel-Dakin method of wound management. In the wounds acquired in World War II, sulfanilamide powder was used with the same intent.

k. Leased in January 1918 from the Kenilworth Corporation of Asheville, North Carolina, General Hospital No. 12 in Biltmore occupied a modern, high-class resort hotel located on a plateau with rolling hills and wide valleys, about 2 miles from the business center of Asheville. Its main building was a five-story structure, roughly T-shaped, strictly modern, with an adequate water supply, a sewage system, and several useful smaller outbuildings. Designated a general hospital in March 1918, it was opened in May with a capacity of 450 beds and surgical facilities devoted almost entirely to the treatment of empyema. The building was transferred to the United States Public Health Service as a hospital on March 3, 1919; soon after, it reverted back to the Kenilworth Corporation and became the Grove Park Inn and Country Club of Asheville, North Carolina.[10]

something that the commission attempted to study but was unable to confirm. Among the doubters were two prominent surgeons, Berkley Moynihan of Great Britain and Pierre Duval of France, who felt that early operation and open pneumothorax did not constitute a hazard. Moynihan traveled to the United States in 1917 to address various issues associated with war surgery and wrote: "[when] the pleura [is] incised along the line of the rib … air enters freely … into the pleural cavity. As a rule, this causes no disturbance and does not alter the rate of respiration or of the pulse."[11] Duval participated in a symposium on gunshot wounds of the chest given by the American College of Surgeons; he spoke of trauma occurring in normal young men, not those with lungs compromised by pneumonia. Subsequently he wrote: "Complete pneumothorax is not associated with any particular danger and indeed it is necessary for manipulation of the lung. … it does not cause any respiratory trouble or increase of arterial pressure and causes less shock than a laparotomy. All our observations proved this."[12] Before the Great War, chest wounds were generally caused either by a knife or by low-velocity bullets, and the Allies were unprepared for the wounds caused by the extravagant use of high-explosive artillery and high-velocity rifle bullets. British surgeons initially practiced a policy of nonintervention in chest wounds—a policy stemming from the Boer War. The 660,000 chest wounds that occurred during World War I carried a 56 percent fatality rate.

On June 12, 1919, Major Dunham wrote to Colonel Kanavel stating that he and Mitchell were preparing to leave for Biltmore to survey the equipment at General Hospital No. 12 and to prepare for the transfer of the Camp Lee empyema patients to Biltmore. He wrote that Major Graham was preparing a preliminary report that hopefully would be finished by June 15, and he indicated that there were questions that should be studied experimentally, questions for which there were no facilities either at Camp Lee or at General Hospital No. 12. He said that Graham would write to Colonel Kanavel concerning the matter, and that the surgeon general's office should explore the possibility of Graham's spending some time in a research laboratory, probably at Johns Hopkins in Baltimore, Maryland.[13]

On June 29 Lieutenant Colonel Sullivan of the surgeon general's office wrote to William Halsted of Johns Hopkins to inform him that an extensive study of empyema was being carried out with numerous cases under the "surgical care of Major James F. Mitchell, one of your former house officers. The Division of Surgery of the Surgeon General's Office would be pleased to have you call on him and spend as much time as you can with those cases in order to observe the type of work and to offer any suggestions you may see fit."[14] Halsted always spent summers at High Hampton, Cashiers, Jackson County, North Carolina, 50 miles southwest of Asheville, and, in a remarkable coincidence, Majors Dunham and Mitchell were on the same train as was Halsted, as he journeyed to High Hampton. After discussing the empyema project with them, Halsted stopped at Asheville to spend several hours with members of the commission. In a seven-page hand-written note to Sullivan, he reported on his experience and summarized almost exactly what Mitchell, Dunham, Graham, and others had observed. Halsted acknowledged at the end of his letter: "What I have said is based entirely upon the data given me by Mitchell and Dunham. They seemed to observe their cases very carefully and had given much thought to the many problems. They are working most happily together and I am sorry to hear that they are soon to be separated."[15]

Shortly after the move to Biltmore, the commission was given permission to take the question regarding open pneumothorax to the experimental laboratory. On July 1 Evarts Graham and Richard Bell were detailed to the Johns Hopkins School of Medicine where pathologist William MacCallum (ex-member of the Pneumonia Commission) provided space for them in the Hunterian Laboratory. During the months of July and August, Graham and Bell addressed three of the problems that had arisen from the Camp Lee observations:

1. A study of mediastinum mobility and the intrapleural pressures in both pleural spaces with an open pneumothorax on one side
2. An experimental production of streptococcal pneumonia and empyema in dogs that would be an animal model for the illness seen in human beings
3. A study of the effect of early operation for experimentally produced streptococcal empyema

Graham and Bell's studies on open pneumothorax were by far the most productive and long lasting. During these 2 months, they used 43 dogs, three cats, two rabbits[m], and five human cadavers to study the specific density of each lung after the production of a unilateral pneumothorax. They found that in dogs and humans with a normal mediastinum, if pressure was altered in one pleural space, an almost identical change occurred in the pressure of the opposite pleural space; thus, an open pneumothorax on one side affected both lungs. They also found that unilateral open pneumothorax was fatal if the opening was large, and they calculated that the maximum size of an opening that could be tolerated was largely dependent on

l. Richard Dana Bell (1887 to 1925) was born in Somerville, Massachusetts, which remained his home throughout his life. After graduating from Harvard College in 1908, he received a doctor of medicine degree from Harvard Medical School in 1913 and elected to specialize in chemistry, rather than medicine. Captain, and later major, in the medical corps, he was appointed to the Empyema Commission almost immediately upon receiving his officer's commission. Following the war, he returned to Boston as an assistant professor of biological chemistry at Harvard Medical School. Never married, Bell died at the age of 38 following a long, undiagnosed illness.

m. In 1918 the price of purchase and maintenance of dogs was 50¢ each. Cats were 75¢ cents and rabbits were $3.

the vital capacity[n]. If the vital capacity were to be greatly reduced and its value approximated the amount inhaled and exhaled during normal respiration, an individual would succumb to a very small opening in one pleural cavity. Graham and Bell's attempts to create a rigid mediastinum were not successful.

Graham and Bell examined the relative size of the opening of a chest wound compared to the size of the trachea, and they attempted to quantitate the effect of chest wall expansion as it moved air through the trachea, through the wound, or both. They observed that with inspiration, air rushed down through the trachea as well as in through the wound, and, if the wound was sufficiently large, the tracheal component was too small to sustain life, particularly if the vital capacity was reduced due to pneumonia. This conclusion was quantitated in their report.[16]

The attempts of Graham and Bell to produce streptococcal pneumonia and streptococcal empyema in dogs, in order to evaluate whether early versus later operation made any difference, were not successful. The use of streptococcal organisms cultured in the laboratory failed to produce either pneumonia or empyema, but when chest fluid taken from a soldier with empyema was used, it was possible to produce both pneumonia and empyema in some of the animals. The comparison between effects of early and late operation in dogs was unconvincing. All of the 20 dogs used in this experiment died, but those with a delayed operation lived 2 or 3 days longer than did those with an early operation, an observation that seemed to support the concept that pleural adhesions were necessary before an open chest wall wound could be tolerated[o]. Graham and Bell concluded that the principal factors to be considered in deciding upon time of operative drainage were the relative immobility of the mediastinum, the reduction in vital capacity, and the degree of asphyxia due to the pneumonia.

During these Baltimore days, Helen Graham and their son David also moved to Baltimore, where they obtained an apartment and a temporary housekeeper/nanny named Maria. Mrs. Graham was able to secure a special research fellowship in the laboratories of J.J. Abel, the chairman of pharmacology at Johns Hopkins, where she remained until Christmas of 1918.

---

n. Vital capacity is the volume of air that can be expelled by the most forceful exhalation possible, following the deepest inhalation.

o. The empyema that follows pneumococcal pneumonia is a collection of thick, purulent material (pus) accompanied by fibrinous adhesions between the lung and chest wall. It is recognized late in the disease, after the pneumonia has subsided. Open drainage is in order. The empyema accompanying streptococcal pneumonia is thin and watery, and the organism produces an enzyme (hyaluronidase) that delays or inhibits the production of adhesions. The empyema occurs early, while pneumonia is still present. Open drainage results in the collapse of a compromised lung, frequently with a fatal outcome.

On August 20 Graham received word from the surgeon general's office that he should terminate his studies, write a report on the results, and be prepared for a possible assignment overseas. The experimental work and its application to the clinical problems seen at Camp Lee were completed, and the written report was substantially finished by mid-September when Graham left for Camp Sheridan. Bell was to review and correct the report for spelling, syntax, and style, something that Graham would complain was inadequately done when it was published in December 1918.[16]

The two accomplishments made by Graham during this tour of duty—his report on the management of empyema and the results of his research on the dynamics of open pneumothorax—gave the remainder of Graham's career purpose and direction. He was now on his way to becoming a thoracic surgeon.

EVACUATION HOSPITAL NUMBER 34

Camp Sheridan

During his 2 months in Baltimore, Graham visited the surgeon general's office to inquire whether he could be placed in France before the war was over. One morning Colonels Kanavel and Moncrief informed him that two hospitals were being readied for an overseas assignment. Graham could choose either a large base hospital or a smaller evacuation hospital that was being formed at Camp Sheridan, Montgomery, Alabama. Graham chose the latter and was told that his orders to proceed to Montgomery would soon be ready. He would probably be on his way to France within a week of their receipt. Graham was told that his job certainly would not be that of commanding officer (CO) since Camp Sheridan already had a CO, but that a chief of surgery was needed before they went overseas. Graham wrote letters[p] to his parents expressing his elation at the thought that "he would finally get out of a side show and into the main tent."[17] General Pershing in France sent a cable to the United States requesting more hospital units, and Graham's assignment

---

p. Beginning in August 1918 Graham wrote to his wife Helen every second day, and in a demonstration of filial devotion, he wrote to his mother and father every week, sending an additional postcard almost as often. His mother kept his 39 letters and 42 postcards, and all are available in the archives of the Becker Medical Library (Washington University School of Medicine). Since all overseas correspondence passed through military censorship, Graham reports on living conditions, mud, incessant rain, lack of medical activity, his thoughts, his despondency, and to some extent his travels and location, but he is circumspect regarding relations with superiors in Joinville and Curel. Three other documents (a handwritten history of Evacuation Hospital No. 34, written in Carignan; a 1920 letter to Dr. Haven Emerson; and a 1920 letter to officers and men of Evacuation Hospital No. 34) contain uncensored details of Graham's overseas activities. This correspondence provides a fascinating insight into his activities, confrontations, frustrations, and accomplishments.

to the evacuation hospital was confirmed. Graham's assignment was chief of the surgical service, and he expected there would be a regular army man as CO to care for the administrative paperwork and the drills and training of enlisted personnel.

Evacuation Hospital No. 34 was mobilized at Camp Sheridan. Maj. B.R. Corbus, MD, was its commanding officer; 1st Lts. J.A. McCaffrey, J. Weigen, and F.C. Payne reported for duty on August 22, 1918; and the first detachment of 100 men arrived from Camp Greenleaf, Georgia, on September 10.[18] After arriving at Camp Sheridan on the morning of September 18, Graham reported to the camp surgeon, a 30-year-old regular army Lieutenant Colonel named Smart, who had been in the army slightly more than a year. When Graham showed Smart his orders to become chief surgeon of Evacuation Hospital No. 34, Smart informed him that he was to be its CO and immediately wrote an order to that effect and told Graham to give it to Major Corbus. Graham's protests that his orders from Washington were to be the chief of surgery not the CO were of no avail, for Smart replied that he "didn't give a damn about these orders Graham brought: that Washington was more than a thousand miles away and that he had the power to displace the present commanding officer, with whom he had had some disagreements."[17] Smart also informed Graham that he would have a good chance to learn the duties of being CO before the outfit left for France, to which Graham expressed astonishment, for he had understood the hospital was practically ready to leave.[17]

Lieutenant Colonel Smart then directed Graham to the camp by pointing down the road and telling him to go about a mile then turn right for another quarter of a mile until he reached some vacated artillery barracks, where he would probably find a sign designating his hospital. Graham was surprised that his hospital was not located at the Camp Sheridan hospital since he knew from experiences gained during his time with the Empyema Commission that it was customary to use the large hospital in a permanent camp as the place in which to train transient overseas hospital personnel. When he asked why his hospital was not located within the Camp Sheridan hospital, Smart replied that Col. Lee Fuller, the camp hospital commanding officer (not a medical doctor), had flatly refused to have anything to do with Evacuation Hospital No. 34. He acknowledged that Fuller was an exceedingly difficult man who had been in the regular army for many years, and that because of the difference in age and rank, Smart was unable to insist that Colonel Fuller take Graham's outfit into his hospital for training. Smart also told Graham that his new hospital was a collection of 27 officers but only 100 men, and when questioned as to why all the men were not there, Smart explained that it was the duty of the current CO to take steps to have the enlisted personnel on hand, and that this was one of his objections to Major Corbus, who had done nothing about getting all the men to the camp or about training those who were there.

Camp Sheridan, at that time, was under the command of a young West Point graduate, a lieutenant colonel of infantry who had become its CO following the departure of the 37th National Guard Division only a few days previously. Graham made his acquaintance and found him to be apprehensive about his new job and terrified of Colonel Fuller. Graham verified these impressions by conversing with the camp adjutant, an old-time regular army sergeant who had been pushed to the rank of captain, a man who had no respect at all for the young lieutenant colonel and the greatest contempt for Fuller.[17]

At this time Graham presented his new orders to Major Corbus, who was understandingly upset at being relieved of his command in this fashion. The episode made Graham feel uncomfortable "because Corbus had things running smoothly and it seemed unwise to change," and because Graham "did not wish to get entangled in an administrative job which meant that he would have no opportunity of seeing a patient."[17] After a rather heated conversation, the two men finally smoothed things over, and they became good friends before they left for France. The change of command made it Graham's responsibility to obtain the enlisted personnel and arrange for their training. Graham thought his command would be temporary, and each day he hoped a regular army CO would arrive.[17] He was now concerned with the problems of "suddenly being put into a job of running a hospital two or three times as large as the Presbyterian [in Chicago] with the added responsibilities of training 237 farmers into proficient nurses, ... to provide military, litter and ambulance drill, ... be sufficiently mobile to be able to move forward within a few hours ... and able to get rid of several hundred to a thousand patients to make room for others."[17] He recognized the need to prepare for a gas attack; the minimum requirement for all officers with overseas assignment was the ability to put on a gas mask in 6 seconds. A daily gas mask drill occasionally included a 2-hour hike with masks in place.[17] He noted that 98 percent of his enlisted men were farmers before entering the service; many had been away from their farms no more than 8 weeks; many could not read or write; and it was now his duty to train this "material" to do aseptic dressings, assist in the operating room, give anesthetics, take care of sterile supplies, give first aid, do general ward work, handle the litters and ambulances, and be soldiers, clerks, cooks. As to his recent assignment, he wrote home that he would "be very much disappointed if he should be stuck in the job of CO," adding: "It is hardly correct to say that the one reason for which I went into the War was to get surgical experience. I should feel very much ashamed of myself if I thought that were true. ... I went in to do my share towards helping to win the War."[17]

The day after his arrival at Camp Sheridan, Graham went to meet Colonel Fuller, who received him harshly. Before any meaningful conversation began, the colonel impressed upon Graham that he had been in the army for 28 years, that Graham had been in it for only a little more than 1 year, and that he, Fuller, had the rank of full colonel, whereas Graham was only a "fly-by-night" major. He told Graham that if and when enlisted personnel for the evacuation hospital arrived, he would have no part in their training, and under no circumstances would Graham's men be assigned to his hospital. When asked for his reasoning, Fuller let Graham know that it was none of his business to enquire, and that Fuller did not feel called upon to state any reasons to Graham, a subordinate officer. Graham wrote: "I was somewhat nonplussed but his attitude filled me with determination to see the whole thing through. Anyone who enjoys a good fight as much as I do could not help being somewhat happy that circumstances had presented such a wonderful opportunity."[19]

Upon returning to the barracks, Graham decided that his next step was to get his enlisted personnel on hand. By now he knew that most of the medical corpsmen were being trained at Camp Greenleaf, Oglethorpe, Georgia, and he sent out two telegrams. The first was sent to the surgeon general's office, stating that he did not have a full complement of enlisted personnel and that it would be necessary to have the men at Camp Sheridan for a matter of at least 2 to 3 weeks to train them. He asked for instructions since it was his understanding that the outfit was to leave soon. The other telegram went to the commanding officer of Camp Greenleaf, asking him to let Graham know when to expect the arrival of enlisted personnel. Two days later replies to both telegrams informed him that his enlisted men would arrive by train on October 24. Since there was no place for them in the barracks, it became necessary to obtain tents from the camp quartermaster; one of his officers with previous military training in a national guard regiment who knew something about making company streets, got the tents set up before the men arrived. To Graham's surprise, the new personnel's last names all began with A, B, C, or D; none had had the slightest training or experience in litter bearing, hospital work, or any occupation related to patient care, and Graham concluded that they had been chosen by no qualifications other than the initial of their family name. He also discovered that most were farmers and were not very intelligent. There were no noncommissioned officers (NCOs), no cooks, no clerks, and no well-qualified soldiers. Fuller refused again to have anything to do with their training, telling Graham that it was his responsibility. That evening Graham decided it would be necessary to have a showdown with "the old martinet," and he took Major Runyan with him to visit Fuller the following morning, determined to have a confrontation. When the adjutant refused to admit them, Graham stated that he was there for business, and that if the colonel did not invite him in, he would go in anyway, whereupon the adjutant stated that the colonel would see them. Graham recorded the episode:

> Major Runyan of course went in the office with me and I introduced him to the Colonel. The Colonel wanted to know why I had brought Runyan and I told him I had brought him along as a witness because I was going to have a showdown. With that the Colonel called in his Adjutant and told him there was probably going to be trouble and he

would like to have him remain in the room.... I closed the door and stood in front of it. The Colonel became infuriated and started to push me away but when cautioned there had better not be any physical violence and that anyone who had been in the Army for 28 years ought to know that, he calmed down a bit.... he paced up and down and shouted at the top of his voice that never before in his experience as a Colonel had a Major conducted himself as I was doing.[19]

Graham finally sat on the corner of the desk and said: "Colonel Fuller, I am going to ask you a question to which I expect a yes or no answer. However I am only giving you two minutes to answer this question. The question is, are you sympathetic to the United States or with Germany in this War? The Colonel shouted it was outrageous that anyone, particularly a subordinate officer, should ask him such a question like that."[19] Graham replied that Fuller didn't have very much time left, and that he had better make his answer. When asked what Graham would do if Fuller didn't answer the question, Graham said he would take the 5:00 pm train to Washington and tell the surgeon general that Colonel Fuller at Camp Sheridan refused to state where his sympathies were in this war. After this exchange Graham looked at his watch, found there were only 15 seconds left, and so told Fuller. The colonel replied: "Well Major, what do you want anyway? There is no use of us becoming angry at each other.... Of course my sympathies are with the U.S. Government."[19] Graham again asked if Fuller would take Evacuation Hospital No. 34 for training. Fuller replied he had no room, and Graham told him he would have to make room and get tents for them. When Fuller refused, Graham replied it was Fuller's responsibility, that he would have his men there by 8:30 the next morning, and that if there were no arrangements for the care and training of his men, he would proceed to Washington to report Fuller's conduct. As Graham prepared to leave after stating his ultimatum, he was called back and informed that he had not saluted properly. Fuller then proceeded to instruct him how to salute. Graham "appreciated the humor of the situation and the next morning marched the men to Fuller's hospital, where tents had been arranged for them."[19] Fuller, who was sure that Graham could not arrange a company street as beautifully as had been done, greeted Graham cordially.[19]

Two days later, Graham went to the Camp Sheridan Hospital to see what his men were doing and, much to his disappointment, found that they were not receiving training but were spending time picking up cigarette butts and generally policing the hospital grounds. He appealed again to Fuller and again threatened him by stating that he would report the matter to the surgeon general. Fuller did not take Graham seriously. Later that morning Graham sent a long telegram to the surgeon general stating it was imperative that he receive an order that he could give to Colonel Fuller telling him to take the men for training. He also stated that since there were no noncommissioned officers, no cooks, no typists, and no specialists of any kind it was necessary either to make provision for the deficiencies or to give up the idea of sending the unit overseas. Within a few hours he heard from the adjutant that a telegraphic order had arrived from the surgeon general, and that it not only ordered Fuller to take the men for training, but it also ordered him to let Graham pick 20 of his own personnel. Graham and the adjutant took the order to Fuller, who read it three times without changing expression before he spoke: "Major Graham, I shall follow out this order." "The sooner the better," said Graham, who also told Fuller he would like a conference with his top sergeant, for Graham had learned that Fuller possessed a good group of NCOs, particularly an Irishman named Fealy (Fuller's top sergeant), an old regular army NCO.[19] Graham conferred with Fealy, who was not only delighted at the opportunity to leave Fuller but pleased at the chance to go to France. Graham picked 19 other NCOs, the best of the group, and, in exchange, Graham left Fuller 20 of his worst. From then on, things proceeded fairly well, although relations between Fuller and Graham were always strained[q,r].[19]

On October 15 Graham wrote home about his thoughts regarding the German request for an armistice: "I do not think there is more than one chance in a million of the War ending this year.... this peace offer is nothing but the expected peace offensive designed to kill the Liberty Loan. The absence of troop trains are to be explained by the epidemic of influenza.... practically all movements of troops have been stopped temporarily."[17] As departure time grew nearer, Graham was still the CO of Evacuation Hospital No. 34 and with no permanent CO in sight, he realized that his position would likely be permanent. He knew that the influenza epidemic was abating and that although there were over 3000 cases of influenza at the camp hospital, there were fewer admissions the last 2 days than there were previously.[17]

On October 24 Graham received the order to move his men and officers from the camp hospital and to put them into quarantine 3½ miles away. This action

---

q. In an 11-page, double-spaced typescript entitled "L'Affaire Fuller,"[19] Graham documented some of his experiences during the days and weeks following his arrival at Camp Sheridan. The reason for this documentation is uncertain; there is no addressee, and it is undated. It is possible that it was prepared in St. Louis, probably in the early or mid-1950s, for it contains a reference to Moncrief's sons as interns. There are discrepancies between this typescript and a five-page handwritten document in which Graham had earlier detailed the origins and travels of Evacuation Hospital No. 34. The handwritten document contains a notation that suggests it was prepared on April 1, 1919, when the hospital was in Carignan. Dates in the handwritten document of the formation of the evacuation hospital and the arrival of personnel are somewhat different from those contained in "L'Affaire Fuller." This author considers the handwritten version to be the more precise document. Copies of both exist in the archives at the Becker Medical Library (Washington University School of Medicine).

r. Graham later learned that Col. Lee Fuller had general paresis of the insane (cerebral syphilis) and had been sent to St. Elizabeth Hospital, where he died a few years after the war.

required that he arrange to have weeds cut, ditches dug, company streets made, tents requisitioned, a field kitchen installed, and emergency rations for 242 men acquired. In addition, electric lights had to be wired to the kitchen and company streets; emergency cooks from a school of bakers and cooks had to be secured; motor trucks had to be obtained to haul equipment; the men had to be accounted for and marched from the camp hospital; all service records, transfer slips, and qualification cards had to be verified; a guard house with a quarantine guard had to be established; and quarters and a mess for 26 officers had to be provided. All this was done before his men arrived in the quarantine area, and Graham determined that his men were comfortable. Sure that they would be leaving in a few days,[17] he became resigned to the role of CO.

On November 1, 1918, Evacuation Hospital No. 34 left Camp Sheridan and traveled for 2 days and 3 nights on a troop train that brought them to Jersey City at midnight. After a ferry ride across the Hudson River at 9:30 am on Monday, November 4, the troops boarded a train and traveled for 3½ hours until they reached Camp Upton[s], which was 65 miles away. At the camp, 15 to 20 hospital units of various kinds were billeted in preparation for overseas assignment. Germany had requested an armistice on October 4, and rumors that all sailing orders might be indefinitely cancelled depressed Graham, who feared that perhaps he would not be sent overseas after all, even though the unit was still officially under orders to be ready for momentary embarkation.[17]

On the afternoon of Thursday, November 5, Graham left Camp Upton to have supper with his wife, Helen, in New York City. She had come from Baltimore for an overnight stay at the Knickerbocker Hotel, and the two found New York City excited over the rumor that Germany had requested an armistice. People refused to believe it was not true, and newsstands that carried papers denying an armistice were raided, and the papers were destroyed. Dining rooms were crowded, and signs everywhere announced that Germany had surrendered. Shortly after breakfast Graham returned to Camp Upton and Helen to Baltimore.[17]

On Saturday, November 9, orders came to pack and be ready to move at midnight, and, after 2 sleepless nights, Evacuation Hospital No. 34 boarded the US Army transport *Northern Pacific*, which departed from New York on November 12 carrying more than a thousand troops.[17]

It was a long, tiresome, and tumultuous passage with rough, stormy weather, and practically everyone, even many of the naval officers and men, became seasick. Sailors on watch were tied to the deck, numerous wireless messages warned of submarine activity, abandon-ship drills were held several times a day, and the ship was

---

s. Camp Upton was situated near Yaphank, New York, a small village in the middle of Long Island, about 65 miles from New York City. It is now the site of the Brookhaven National Laboratory.

not lit at night. The captain felt that this was the roughest crossing he had ever experienced. Graham shared a stateroom with Corbus. He discovered that the ship's naval surgeon, Dr. Robert David, had been an intern with him at Chicago Presbyterian Hospital. The small, poorly lit room reserved as a lounge for officers was usually full, and decks were always crowded with troops, sailors, life rafts, and lifeboats. During the voyage Graham gave a talk on empyema to the medical officers of all the organizations on board. In a long letter written to his parents during the crossing, he expressed hope that his next letter would be from France and that he might possibly be home by Christmas.[17]

Curel and Carignan

The *Northern Pacific* made landfall at Brest, France, on November 22, and Evacuation Hospital No. 34 debarked. Not supposed to see the port, officers and men were marched around it through back roads and alleys to a plain about 4 miles from the dock, where they encamped in ankle deep mud. As CO, Graham was given a tent with a floor, whereas his officers and men were forced to lie in the mud and get through the night as best they could. Bed rolls arrived the next day, and everyone, if not very comfortable, was at least warm. Graham described it as being wet, cold, muddy, and never so dirty in his life with no prospect of getting clean. Scarce water was used only for drinking. The men marched in a column of fours with Graham at the head to a mess hall about 1 mile away, where 8000 officers and men were fed creamless coffee, poorly cooked beans, and one piece of butterless bread. After passing through the main tent where food was placed in their mess kits, the men proceeded to an adjacent room where they stood to eat before washing mess kits in dirty water contained in four galvanized iron cans. Chocolate could be purchased, but crackers were nowhere to be found. Many German prisoners, a "husky and contented lot," kept the camp as clean as possible and performed all the manual labor.[17]

On the evening of November 26, Evacuation Hospital No. 34 began a 3-day journey to Joinville, Haute Marne province. Graham felt that his officers would probably fare pretty well, but he sympathized with all his men who had been working 12 to 15 hours each day unloading the ship and preparing hospital gear for their next move. Brest had been a wet, muddy, cold experience, and all were glad to be leaving; however, Graham dreaded the trip—first, because of his responsibility and, second, because of the discomfort his men would endure in the freight cars. In a letter home, he described the many details to which he must attend—ensuring that the train was properly guarded at all times, that the men were fed and given water, and that they would not have contact with any unauthorized person through the car windows or otherwise. He felt these responsibilities were entirely on his shoulders.[17]

The men were marched from the camp ground in Brest to a railroad station in the dead of night, and Graham, fortunately, found a guide who showed them their train. It was not a long march—"only about five miles." At 4:00 am they were loaded on a French troop train of 50 cars, mostly freight, into which the men were packed 40 to a car. Daylight extended from 8:00 am until 4:00 pm. The men slept by curling up on seats or lying on the floor, and they traveled at about 20 miles/h, with occasional stops for exercise at coffee stations. In contrast, "German prisoners in evidence everywhere were warmly clothed, looked husky, well-fed and returned at night to brilliantly illuminated stockades under the guard of big burly American soldiers."[17]

The trip to Joinville took almost 4 days, and the hospital arrived at 4:00 am on Sunday, December 1. After unloading baggage and supplies, the men were sent to an enclosure behind the railroad station to wait until 9:00 am to receive billeting orders. Graham found a mess hall about ½ mile away, and top sergeant Fealy marched the men for food while the officers found a small French café and had coffee that was undrinkable and wine that was drinkable but not appetizing for breakfast. The billeting officer informed them that Joinville was now too crowded but that Curel, a small village on the Marne about 4½ miles to the north, had space. Curel was a quaint little hamlet with centuries-old stone houses and red tiled roofs, situated about 25 miles south of Verdun; Metz was 50 miles northeast, Reims was 50 miles northwest, and Paris was 130 miles west. Using an ambulance, Graham preceded his men and found accommodations in "a lovely little hamlet tucked away in a valley in the Vosges mountains with a normal peace time population of 430 poverty stricken peasants who suddenly must open their doors to receive 28 officers and 234 men."[17] Graham would change his mind about the loveliness of Curel before he departed. Every house had been posted with a placard by French military authorities listing the number of officers, men, and horses that could be accommodated. Graham checked off some houses to ensure quarters were ready when the men arrived, providing them the first opportunity in 9 days to take off their clothes. Restricted to one canteen of water per day, all had done very little or no washing. The placard on the property occupied by "Monsieur Le Commandant" (Graham) read "Officier 1, homme 15, cheveaux 10."[17] All of his officers were housed, and the men, after being placed in haylofts, were surprisingly comfortable. Graham anticipated that they would be sent into Germany or possibly Russia with the American Army of Occupation.[17]

Within 10 days, five evacuation hospitals, eight ambulance companies, and several sanitary trains totalling over 1600 troops were quartered in Curel. There was no patient within 40 miles, and boredom set in. The brightest spot for Graham was the arrival of Maj. James Mitchell[t], a comember of the Empyema Commission and

---

t. James Farnandis Mitchell (1871 to 1960) was born in Baltimore and attended the Bel Air Academy before entering Johns Hopkins University in 1889. He was a good student, played lacrosse, and was captain of the football team. Due to financial difficulties, the Johns Hopkins Medical School was a year late in opening, and Mitchell entered the University of Maryland Medical School before trans-now the CO of Evacuation Hospital No.32, who shared his quarters. On December 7 the two hitch-hiked to Chaumont, general headquarters of the sector, about 40 miles south of Curel, looking for nothing in particular but hoping to run into some acquaintances from the surgeon general's office. The men Graham had hoped to see at Chaumont were not available, but he described it as "a small Washington. I have never seen so many Colonels and Generals anywhere except in Washington."[17] Learning that many of those on the medical and surgical consulting staff were at Neuf Chateau, he and Mitchell went there a few days later and "found Finney, Cushing, Hugh Young, Kanavel and others mostly from Hopkins. They gave us a most cordial welcome and insisted on our spending the night. Incidentally I was put up in Thayer's room and slept in his bed because he was away. Thayer has the position in Medicine corresponding to that of Finney in Surgery and is likewise a General."[17] Finney told the pair that he wished they had come to France during the past summer when there had been a shortage of medical officers, particularly surgeons, and said that his attempts to get them had failed; now, when the need had passed, they were arriving by the hundreds. However, the French artillery still moving to the front gave an impression that hostilities were by no means over.

In early December, Mitchell, Graham, and Fletcher (of Evacuation Hospital No. 31) were ordered to Toul to see some of the surgery at Evacuation Hospital No. 1, which was set up and finally operating as a hospital. It contained about 500 patients, most with acute influenza; surgical cases had been sent to nearby base hospitals. The three arrived on Saturday evening, December 17, and, with little happening for the next 2 days, they decided to commandeer an ambulance and see the front. A trip to the devastation of Verdun on Sunday was followed by a Monday visit to Nancy, where some shops were already reopening. In discussion with officers who had ventured into Germany, Graham concluded that "the German people do not feel as if they have been beaten. They are even insolent. They are already starting propaganda among the American soldiers in an attempt to curry favour for Germany to the disfavour of France." He wrote, "I hope the peace commissioners will not be too

---

ferring in 1893 to Hopkins with its first class of 18 students. In his first year at medical school, a surgical opportunity appeared when Dr. Halsted discharged the nurse in charge of the operating rooms. After her departure Mitchell obtained her position, which he held during his first 2 years in medical school; upon graduation in 1897 he followed Cushing into Halsted's residency system. Upon completion of his residency, he was advised by Halsted to locate in Washington, DC, where he developed a large surgical practice, becoming a clinical professor of surgery at George Washington University. He had a particular interest in the use of local anesthesia and was one of the pioneers in its development. As a loyal member, he always attended the meetings of the Hopkins Medical and Surgical Association. Mitchell owned a summer home in Bar Harbor, Maine, where he was an honorary deputy chief of the fire department. He was also an honorary inspector of the Metropolitan Police of Washington for 45 years. The James F. Mitchell Institute for Medical Research in Washington, DC, was formally opened several weeks after Mitchell's death, which occurred following an illness that lasted almost a decade. Mitchell was a superb surgeon, a fine gentleman, and a warm friend to many.

lenient."[17] A French captain of artillery had told him "that although he admired Wilson very much as an idealist he was afraid that perhaps he would be a dangerous character at the Peace Conference because of his leniency."[17]

As Christmas 1918 approached, Helen Graham was still in Baltimore with son David and housekeeper Maria. Deciding to spend Christmas in Dubuque with her family, Helen planned to stop in Chicago and visit Evarts's family on her way west. Suddenly Maria decided to leave, a circumstance that led Helen to give up her work at Johns Hopkins and to decide to remain in Dubuque. Upon hearing of this Graham wrote to his mother: "I wanted Helen to keep up her work in Baltimore and hang onto Maria.... As soon as I heard of her decision to stay indefinitely with her mother I sent her a cable to continue at Baltimore if possible."[17]

Graham spent Christmas of 1918 with Mitchell in Curel. The two hung stockings in front of the fireplace and gave each other little gifts. A package from Helen that had arrived 2 days earlier contained David's baby mittens and two pictures of him. Cigarettes, candy, chocolate, toothpaste, and handkerchiefs were articles that Graham had wanted, the book *Letters to His Son* by Lord Chesterfield was welcome, and, in addition to the usual menu, sweet chocolate and olives were extras for the Christmas dinner.[17]

In the early winter of 1918, Curel was under the command of Lieutenant Colonel Hibbett, the CO of a sanitary train that by chance, was the first unit to arrive, preceding Evacuation Hospital No. 34 by a few hours. In civilian life Hibbett had been a country doctor who "never had any experience in executive work of a big kind and....[it was] most unfortunate to place Col Hibbett in command of [Curel]," which was within the military district of Joinville and whose CO was Lt. Col. E.C. Jones. Shortly after Graham and his hospital arrived in Curel, Evacuation Hospitals No. 32, No. 33, and No. 35, as well as five mobile hospitals, appeared, placing 1800 officers and men into a town of 430. Just across the Marne lay a small town, Chaton Ruft, and Graham made a journey to Joinville to suggest to Lieutenant Colonel Jones that some of the outfits should move there. His visit resulted in an order from Jones instructing all commanders in the Curel area not to have any interviews with him regarding Curel, for all Curel affairs were to be taken to Colonel Hibbett.[17]

Shortly after the troops appeared it was realized that there were a limited number of tubes for chlorinating drinking water and that there would not be enough if more troops arrived. Curel's only water source was an old well located in the center of the village, and Hibbett had not ordered a bacteriologic analysis. Some time later the mayor of the town told Graham that in May, when a French outfit had passed through, the well water was tested, and, after finding that it contained a large number of colon bacilli, it was regarded as dangerous. All water for the troops was pumped from the central well and hung in Lister bags, from which the men filled their canteens. A few days following his return from the visit to Toul, Graham discovered that the drinking water was no longer being chlorinated and that there was insufficient fuel to boil water for drinking nor, on some days, to cook three meals.

No provisions had been made for a shelter during mealtimes, and Graham's men were compelled to eat while standing in the middle of the street, even during heavy rainfalls. Graham and 80 officers ate in a café that Colonel Hibbett had assigned for them; all officers were instructed not to eat in any mess other than the one to which they had been allocated. In Graham's café the kitchen and the privy were together, the privy was full, and the owner refused permission for the officers to empty it; during heavy downpours it overflowed into the kitchen. The commanding officers of the evacuation hospitals banded together for a mid-December confrontation with Colonel Hibbett, at which time they insisted there be more chlorinating tubes, more fuel, and that a YMCA (Young Men's Christian Association) hut be obtained.

By the end of December, 775 of the 1800 troops in Curel had dysentery, and many cases were suspected to be typhoid, but since none of the medical organizations in Curel had been set up as a hospital, there were no means to confirm a typhoid diagnosis, and soldiers needing hospitalization were sent to a base hospital in Rouen Court about 25 miles away. Mitchell and Graham decided to go "over the heads" of Hibbett in Curel and Jones in Joinville, and they returned to Chaumont on a rainy day hoping to see the inspector general. After listening to their story, Brigadier General Spinks promptly called Colonel Wadhams,[20] who ordered an immediate investigation. The following day Mitchell and Graham were summoned to Joinville by a furious Jones, who declared he was preparing to institute court martial proceedings for their visit to Chaumont without his permission. This pleased the two men since a court martial and its accompanying publicity was just what they desired. At that precise moment, the telephone rang; Colonel Keller in Chaumont was calling to invite Mitchell and Graham to a New Year's dinner with Colonel Wadhams, Colonel Tudhill, and General Finney. Jones immediately cancelled his plans for a court martial, and on New Year's Eve he sent Mitchell and Graham to Chaumont in his own automobile.

The inspectors who came to Curel confirmed the unfavourable situation described by Graham and Mitchell; 2 or 3 days later General Finney made a visit in person, after which he stated that although he thought he had seen all of the dirty holes in France, Curel was the dirtiest.[18] Mobile labs found typhoid bacilli everywhere, even in the mud on the street. Chlorinating tubes arrived immediately; stoves, fuel, and shelter were forthcoming; and on January 15 Evacuation Hospital No. 34 was moved across the Marne to Chaton Ruft. Morale improved after a few days since most of the illness disappeared[u]. Between Christmas and the New Year's

---

u. On December 16, 1919, during a meeting of the St. Louis Medical Society, Dr. Haven Emerson, a bacteriologist, public health officer from New York, and coauthor of one volume of the medical history of WWI presented a 15-minute talk on typhoid fever as seen in the American Expeditionary

Eve dinner, General Finney came again from Neuf Chateau (a distance of 50 miles) to bring chocolate, cigarettes, and bathrobes to Mitchell and Graham.[17]

On January 7, 1919, Evacuation Hospital No. 34 was alerted to leave for Toul to replace Base Hospital No. 45, which was going home. Orders came the same day for Mitchell and Graham to go to Paris for 10 days to attend surgical clinics. Graham's only opportunity to see Paris coincided with the opening of the Peace Conference;[17] he and Mitchell arrived on the evening of January 10. Graham wrote that just a few hours in Paris was enough to cheer him up and help make him forget about the "mud, filth and ennui of Curel." Paris was filled with soldiers, and "many different kinds of uniforms—East Indians, Belgians, Norwegians, British outfits, Italians, etc.—made a picturesque motley of color on the street [and] everywhere captured German war trophies were to be seen."[17] The two stayed at the Hotel d'Louvre, which had been taken over by the American Red Cross for the exclusive use of American officers. It served American meals, "for example—oatmeal for breakfast with sugar and butter." Graham and Mitchell visited a number of clinics and on January 18 visited Chatros Clinic to see Pierre Duval operate; they subsequently visited with Duval at his home. Graham felt that most of the surgery he had seen was "really awful," and that the only surgeons who came up to American surgical standards were Tuffier and Duval. He commented: "I have seen some horrible results of German surgery on captured Americans and French. But of course I don't know how much the bad result may have been due to maliciousness and how

---

Forces. In June 1920 the *Journal of the Missouri State Medical Association* published Emerson's highly critical remarks about medical officers in France. He wrote:

> An ... important group of typhoid infections occurred ... in Joinville where thirty or forty field, mobile and camp hospitals were waiting.... in the "cream" of the medical profession there was such neglect of the elementary precautions with regard to the drinking of known, obviously polluted water, that twenty of those organizations had to be held for various periods of time.... it was evidently in the consciousness of the medical officers that ... they did not need to bother about ... the water supply ... that they were immune and did not need to fear typhoid fever ... and when they had their own opportunity to be careful or neglectful they were neglectful.[21]

Graham immediately wrote a single-spaced, four-page, typewritten letter to Emerson about the implication of gross negligence. He detailed the actions of Hibbett and Jones, as well as his and Mitchell's activities regarding the lack of chlorinating tubes and unsatisfactory sanitary conditions. After describing the actions taken as a result of the trip to Chaumont, he closed: "Through the energy and activity of those very medical officers whom you accuse of laxity, the regular army officers in command were made to take such measures as would ensure the safety of the men billeted there. I feel no hesitation whatsoever in putting most of the blame for that epidemic right up to Colonel Jones who was in command of the Joinville district."[22] This letter, written without censorship, contains a vivid description of the situation in Curel and, when accompanied by the letters to his parents, is the basis for the material relative to the typhoid epidemic.

much to bad judgement or simple carelessness."[17] At the Pasteur Institute, they were instructed on a serum to be used against gas bacillus infections, and an officer from Base Hospital No. 45 at Toul told Graham there were 1400 patients in the hospital that Graham was about to run.[17]

It was in the Paris Red Cross Medical Library that Graham found a copy of his pneumothorax article,[16] which was full of typographic errors; Graham complained that apparently Bell did not read the proof.[17] He later learned that the surgeon general had ordered 1500 reprints.

The move to Toul never occurred for, upon Graham's return to Curel, Major Corbus informed him that the typhoid among the outfits at Curel was sufficiently troublesome that all those in Curel or Chaton Ruft were to remain in quarantine. It was now apparent to Graham that he would never have an opportunity to do any surgery during his time in France, adding only more misery to his past 5 months of medical inactivity. Mitchell took Evacuation Hospital No. 32 home on January 21, and, although Graham corresponded with him several times after the war, he never saw him again.

Among an estimated 150,000 cases of dysentery in the American Expeditionary Forces, there were approximately 1400 cases of typhoid fever, with a mortality rate of 11 percent. Despite universal immunization, typhoid fever could still develop upon exposure to massive doses of the organism. A major outbreak occurred in the area surrounding Joinville, and 51 cases of positively diagnosed typhoid resulted in the death of 13 people, 2 of whom came from Evacuation Hospital No. 34. The final total of 100 or more cases occurred almost exclusively among members of the 30 or 40 medical units in the Joinville district, and 20 of these organizations were held for varying periods of time before being allowed to embark for home.[21,22]

By January 20 the epidemic was under control, and, during this trying period, Graham's letters home contained frequent comments about mud, rain, bad food, and lack of any medical activity. His mother replied, sympathizing because he had been unable to make any surgical contribution to the war effort, whereupon he cautioned her:

> Mother, your statement in one of your letters that I have been in the service a year without doing any surgery or anything that I was most capable of doing surprises me and certainly does not flatter me.... I feel that I accomplished a great deal in the empyema work, that I saved many lives and that my work in Baltimore gave results which are of great fundamental importance. In fact, if I have to blow my own horn in order to make an impression, I will say without any false modesty, it is true that because of my Army experience I feel I know as much about empyema as anybody. I do feel however that I have wasted the last five months and I shall never become reconciled to the personal

disappointment of not being allowed the privilege of being over here working when activities were at a high pitch. I envy the men who had the experience, not that they learned much but because of the experience of being in the big show. I am disappointed that I couldn't have been under fire, or in a barrage or have seen the big guns in action. ... instead I have had much of the "hell" without any of the thrill and emotions of war. I have wallowed in the mud like a pig and have been for days wet and chilled through to say nothing of the fact that I have been so hungry at times that even hard tack seemed delicious. I have had to drink foul-smelling, typhoid-infected water without any means of either boiling it because of having no fuel, or of chlorinating it because of no chlorine tubes. ... You can talk about the last five months as much as you please, but don't minimize any more than necessary my real worthwhile experiences and work. When I leave the Army I shall be out of a job and I don't care to have people get the impression which would be a false one that I have not done any surgery for a year—the one argument that has been used against me before when I have been under consideration for appointment to a professorship in surgery is that I haven't had enough experience. Please don't encourage that idea.[17]

Graham began to plan for his return home and wrote to MacCallum regarding the possibility of an appointment at Johns Hopkins. MacCallum, after discussing the problems of teaching medical students with a reduced staff, then wrote: "Your paper in the *American Journal of Medical Sciences* has stirred up quite a lot of discussion. They all go back to the old established idea that the mediastinum doesn't give much—especially such fellows as Heuer and the rest who have opened a lot of chests—they can take off the whole chest wall and require no artificial respiration. I don't know—you will have to take up the fight when you get back."[23]

By January 27 Graham found himself in command of the only hospital unit left in Curel, and he knew it would never function as a hospital. Orders to take over Base Hospital No. 45 at Toul had been cancelled. Improvements that had been made increased the comfort of everyone in Curel and Chaton Ruft, and Graham felt it would be preferable to stay in Curel than to return to Brest in midwinter; he concluded, "Over here one gets into such a state of mind that he is happy if he has the bare physical comforts of plenty of food, a place to sleep and an opportunity to get warm." There was no intellectual activity and no hospital to run—only waiting. Amusements or recreation areas for the men were located in the larger towns, but there was nothing available in Curel. Since the units were expected to be temporary, the YMCA apparently felt it was impractical to erect a hut since an organization might be gone by the time it was completed. However, Graham did praise the

YMCA for extending its activities outside of Paris, and he cited the instance in which it came to Curel, cleaned out an old barn, produced a stove and some wood, and was able to provide a place wherein the men could get their feet dry. He thought it was run in a more efficient fashion than the army.[17] Some relief from the boredom occurred when Captain Jacobs, the hospital's ophthalmologist, became acquainted with an elderly lady school teacher in Chaton Ruft, who agreed to spend every evening in French conversation. She was well-educated, lived with her elderly mother, and knew no English, so all conversations were entirely in French. Graham attended regularly.[17]

On February 3 Graham wrote that Dean Lewis, Phemister, and the others are certainly lucky. "They get the cream of the service and in addition the opportunity to go home early. The last five months have been a total loss to me."[18] On February 4 Graham received a telegram from general headquarters ordering him to prepare for transportation to a base post for embarkation to the United States. Major Corbus, the entire medical staff, and two line lieutenants were detached to Base Hospital No. 32 near Neuf Chateau, leaving Graham with six line officers and 165 enlisted men, but no medical work.[17] February 5 saw a trip to Donjeux, about 10 miles from Curel, to see Lieutenant Brosnan, then critically ill with typhoid fever and not likely to recover.[17] On February 9 the order to transfer 50 men out of his dwindling organization gave Graham the opportunity to be rid of some undesirables, and he deported a small clique of "toughs and roughnecks" who had caused him trouble.

Another responsibility during these winter days was the requirement that Graham investigate French claims for damage and theft of property by American soldiers who had been stationed in Curel. Claims of many descriptions convinced him that the local people were taking the opportunity to make "Uncle Sam" pay for long-needed repairs to their houses and barns. The claims filed by the French seemed to be excessive, and Graham thought they expected to be beaten down in price.

On February 13 one officer and three men were sent to Bordeaux to arrange billets for the remainder of Graham's organization, but, even now, 3 months after the armistice, there was sufficient uncertainty that the French army had stopped demobilizing, and some American units ready to be sent home were being sent into Germany.[17] The remnant of Graham's officers and men moved to the village of Carignan about 10 miles from Bordeaux during the week of February 16. Although the trip took 5 days and was considered worse than that from Brest to Curel, Carignan provided the most comfortable accommodations the outfit had seen. (Graham's hospital later donated Fr 200 for a monument to be erected in memory of French soldiers from Carignan killed in the war.[17]) The seven officers plus two cooks and three orderlies lived in an old white stone chateau. They were the only unit quartered in Carignan, and, as commander of the troops, Graham was also commander of the town. Spring was on its way, the air was mild, the winds were soft, and leaves on the trees were beginning to appear. It was initially planned that they would stay 3 to 6 weeks and then move to an embarkation area for another week or 10 days before boarding ship.[17] Although sailing priorities depended mainly on the date at which units arrived within the embarkation district surrounding Bordeaux, other factors were considered: the state of discipline, freedom from communicable diseases, condition of records, and property and condition of the village. Since his unit was inspected almost daily, Graham kept a group of men busy most of the time cleaning the town and guaranteeing the safety of his equipment.

On February 28 Graham received a letter from the surgeon general's office in Washington indicating that he had been selected to prepare for publication a section on the treatment of streptococcal empyema, which would be duly credited to his name. He should aim to make his narratives as accurate, concise, and interesting as possible, for the object of the work was not only to preserve an important record of achievement but to assist the medical department in future wars. The letter read: "This assignment may be regarded as part of your regular military duties. If it is not possible for you to accomplish it or complete it, you will report the fact at once."[24] Graham was immensely pleased and answered it immediately; he wrote home: "The work ought to give me a good deal of prestige. One of the best things about it however seems to me to be in the sentence: 'This assignment may be regarded as part of your regular military duty.'" He thought that he would not be kept in France doing nothing for an indefinite time and stated: "I shall probably be allowed to go to Chicago to write this article if I wish and in the meantime draw my salary from the Army. If that is the case it will be a godsend: for it will mean an income while I am getting settled and perhaps waiting for the medical atmosphere to clear up enough to give me a chance at some good university position somewhere in the Fall."[17] This assignment would become his definitive publication on empyema.

Graham's Carignan headquarters were on the second floor of an old stone building whose first floor was a picturesque French café that served a great variety of Bordeaux wines. Enlisted men were allowed to drink light wines and beer but not strong beverages such as cognac, and Graham was obligated to see that the proprietors of the various cafés did not sell prohibited drinks to his men. He noted all the difference in the world between the people around Carignan and those at Curel: "Everybody here is cordial and is anxious to do things to help out. There is none of the avarice among the people here which is very striking in those around Curel."[17] His "slough of intellectual despond" was partially alleviated by a friendship with the mayor's secretary (who was also the village schoolmaster), with whom Graham held a 1-hour conversation in French nearly every day. He was a better conversationalist than was the old mademoiselle in Chaton Ruft.

During the weeks at Carignan, three of Graham's men came up for a general court martial that was held in Bordeaux: two for theft and a third for attempted rape and a knife attack on the sergeant who pulled him out of the house during the arrest. The third, a New York gangster, had already served several sentences in civilian life, and Graham anticipated he would probably get 20 years for the episode.[17]

On March 9 Graham and approximately 50 of his men attended a church service during which the priest cautioned his flock that France was not yet secure against future danger from Germany. The service was conducted in French, and it pleased Graham that his linguistic capabilities had come to the point where he could understand nearly all of the sermon without difficulty.[17] In closing, the organist played "The Star Spangled Banner," and those who knew the words sang along. Graham regretted that a good many of his men did not sing, and he hoped the French would consider their silence as being due to an inability to sing rather than a lack of knowledge of the words. This prompted him to order that every man in the organization learn the words of at least the first verse.

A bank draft of Fr 52 Graham's father had sent as a Christmas gift arrived on March 25, just as he received permission to go to England for a 10-day vacation to begin April 4; not wishing to run the risk of a delay in getting home he refused the vacation. Instead, upon hearing that Colonel Russell of the surgeon general's office and William Welch of Johns Hopkins were planning to be in Cannes for a Red Cross conference, Graham went to Cannes hoping to see Russell, to discuss his assignment on empyema and to use Russell's influence to be sent home immediately, so that he could begin writing and work where he pleased. He wished to see Welch about conditions at Johns Hopkins, with a view to a post-war appointment. There is no record of his having met with either Welch or Russell in Cannes, but he did spend 2 days at the Carlton Hotel overlooking the beach. His April 7 visit to Nice was "a beautiful drive, worth all the squalor of Curel."[17] He arrived in the evening, made a short stop at Monaco, and returned to Carignan/Bordeaux on April 9.

On April 30 the remnant of Evacuation Hospital No. 34, Graham, Runyan, Gamble, Smith, Cochran, Dexter, Kilroy, and slightly over 100 men, boarded the transport *Black Arrow* to arrive in Hoboken, New Jersey, on May 6. The officers were kept at Camp Dix for about a week, relieved of their men after 5 or 6 days, and all except Graham were discharged. Evacuation Hospital No. 34 had been in commission for 9 months, 6 of which were spent out of the country. It was never set up as a hospital, it never cared for a patient, and the only duty expected of its men was to care for themselves and their equipment and to police the area in which they lived. For Graham, it was an uninspired tour of duty.

Fort Sheridan

After the last man was gone, Graham received a request to see Colonel Moncrief in the surgeon general's office in Washington, and when asked about his experiences, Graham bared his soul about his many difficulties at Camp Sheridan with Fuller, and at Curel and Joinville with Hibbett and Jones. When he heard those names,

Moncrief threw up his hands saying that Graham had been up against the worst crowd of men that could be found in the medical services. Referring to Fuller, Moncrief said, "It is too bad you ran into him. Everybody knows that he is the worst S.O.B. in the Army." Graham then asked, "Why in the world then didn't you tell me something about him when you offered me the chance to go to Camp Sheridan to be the Chief Surgeon of Evac of Hosp No. 34?"[25] Moncrief's reply was somewhat vague but relations remained friendly[v]. The visit, however, was not meant as a forum for Graham to discuss his difficulties but, rather, to tell him that he had been brought to Washington to prepare him to take over the surgical service at a general hospital in Williamsbridge, New York. Graham flatly refused; he was sick of the service. He felt he had done his duty and that his role in the army had been kicking around in the mud doing commanding officer work, a role for which he was unfit by training and inclination. He told Moncrief that he would go AWOL (absent without leave) if such an order were issued. It must have been an impressive display of temper, for Moncrief then asked if he would be willing to compromise by going to Fort Sheridan, Illinois, just north of Chicago. Graham acquiesced, but only if it were to be for a limited time and if his surgical services were needed. He would be unwilling to go and do the "innumerable non-medical chores of which the Army had found so many for medical officers to do."[w,25]

Graham reported to Fort Sheridan in mid-May, 1919, for what was to be a 4-month tour of duty; he lived with his parents and family in Evanston, commuting 12 miles to the fort each day. The camp hospital was staffed with many of Graham's Chicago friends, and he developed an interesting and active service among the 5000 patients in the hospital. His main task was to care for 134 patients with chronic empyema, 3 of whom died—1 of tuberculosis, 1 of pneumonia, and 1 of unknown causes. The army was still collecting information on all cases of empyema, and Colonel Dunham from the Empyema Commission asked Graham to enter his data into the final report. Graham was unable to comply with Dunham's request and apologized to his old friend and companion, saying that it was absolutely impossible to complete the special empyema reports. He had 100 surgical cases in addition to the empyema patients, and complained that he could not do even the absolutely necessary work, and that there was no clerical help provided to complete the empyema reports.[26]

---

v. The sons of Colonel Moncrief later became surgical house officers under Graham at Barnes Hospital.

w. In January 1920 Corbus, Weigen, and Bragg instituted a round-robin letter to renew associations made in Evacuation Hospital No. 34. Graham responded with a single-spaced, three-page letter detailing his activities in Carignan, his trip home, the interview with Moncrief, and duty at Fort Sheridan. He restated his discomfort at having been a commanding officer and expressed gratitude to every officer in the outfit: "At all times the spirit of our organization was most remarkable. I never questioned for a moment the loyalty of a single officer in the outfit.... such a spirit as that of course diminishes the responsibilities of the Commanding Officer."[25]

Soon after arriving at Fort Sheridan, Graham was appointed to the General Court Martial Board by General Leonard Wood, who was commanding officer of the central department and a candidate for the presidency of the United States. From 2:00 to 6:00 almost every afternoon, 13 medical officers of the board sat in judgment of deserters and others who, after having been picked up anywhere within the central department for various misdemeanors, were sent to Fort Sheridan for trial. Graham suggested to Bispham, Fort Sheridan's commanding officer, that it was unrealistic to have his highest ranking medical officers removed from their medical duties and selected for court martial purposes that could be done just as well, if not better, by "a group comprised of any of the forty or fifty convalescent line officers who were patients of the Fort, who would have been only too glad for some job to relieve their monotony."[25] When General Wood turned down the suggestion, a wrathful Graham wrote that he was "a cut-and-dried type of army officer whose chief thought in life is force and discipline and that his speeches as an active candidate failed to show any great vision." Graham continued: "I do not mean to bring in politics ... but have seen enough of the Army ... to be unwilling to have an old hard-boiled Army officer as President of our Country ... particularly at a time when the utmost tact, poise and intimate knowledge of European affairs is necessary."[25]

During the summer of 1919, Graham's duty at Fort Sheridan was interrupted by the visit of a trio from Washington University—Philip Shaffer, dean, Canby Robinson, internist, and Eugene Opie, pathologist—who asked if he would join the Faculty of Medicine as its professor of surgery. Graham was the only surgeon approached for this position, and he who had complained to James Mitchell in France, "I have no home, no practice, no hospital or teaching position, no money," landed a department chairmanship without even searching for it.[25]

The time that Evarts Graham spent with the Empyema Commission was probably the most significant period in determining his professional surgical life. There is no record of a thoracic surgical experience in either Chicago or Mason City, and the clinical and experimental obligations posed during duty with the Empyema Commission thrust his interests forever into the realm of thoracic surgery. The reduction in deaths due to empyema brought him fame, and his research in the physiology laboratory made thoracic surgery possible.

His army experiences gave Graham an intense dislike of the authoritarianism, the lack of imagination, and the misuse of personnel by his military seniors. Offended by the actions of Fuller, Jones, and Hibbett, he had used his influence with higher officials to either challenge, confront, or bypass them. Although Graham resented his role as CO of the evacuation hospital, he carried out his duty with great skill and perhaps even some enthusiasm. It was a lesson in command, responsibility, and authority that provided him with an experience not afforded many surgeons, and one that may well have been influential in the manner by which he subsequently led his Washington University department.

It is fascinating to speculate on how Graham would have responded to being forced to spend 6 months as chief of surgery in a hospital that was never used as a hospital and that never saw a patient. He would have held a position with no duties. However, his months as CO offered him opportunities for development that would never have occurred had he been chief of surgery. They helped to develop a more mature, serious, purposeful Evarts Graham.

The 4 years in Mason City and the army were, in many ways, distasteful and uncomfortable, but these experiences became indelibly stamped in his mind, soul, and psyche—they were determinants for many of his subsequent actions.

THE AFTERMATH: DISPELLING DISBELIEF

Graham's experiences with the Empyema Commission propelled him not only into the realm of thoracic surgery and physiology, but also into the thoracic surgery literature as author and speaker. Publications prior to 1918 showed his interests to be the effects of chloroform or ether anesthesia on phagocytosis, some features of the immune system, and fetal movements related to anoxia. These interests were dropped, and, in the years following the summer of 1918, he produced 17 publications[x] on the treatment of empyema, pulmonary dynamics, and the consequences of an open pneumothorax. The first was the 23-page report prepared for the surgeon general summarizing the experiences of 27 camp hospitals as recorded in the replies to the Moncrief questionnaire.[6] The second publication was the preliminary report prepared with Dunham on the management and study of empyema cases at Camp Lee.[8] The third publication of 1918 resulted from the 8 weeks that he and Bell spent at Johns Hopkins investigating the effects of open pneumothorax, the experimental production of pneumonia, and the timing of operative drainage. This 32-page report was almost finished when Graham left for Camp Sheridan. Published in December 1918, it became Graham's definitive work on respiratory physiology and open pneumothorax. Even though Bell was coauthor, Graham's role is

---

x. Topics of articles arising from Graham's experience with the Empyema Commission: Review of replies to Moncrief empyema questionnaire (1918); Report on treatment of empyema at Camp Lee (1918); Results of open pneumothorax lab experiments with Bell (1918); Maximal nonfatal opening in chest wall (1919); Principles involved in treatment of empyema (1920); Importance of vital capacity (1920); Influence of respiratory movement on pleural exudate (1921); Principles underlying intrathoracic surgery (1923; in French); Reconsideration of question of open pneumothorax (1924); Principles involved in treatment of acute and chronic empyema (1924); Surgeon general's report on surgical treatment of empyema (1924); Significance of alterations of intrapleural pressure (1924); *Empyema thoracis* (1925; the Gross prize essay); Significance of changed intrathoracic pressure (1925); Detailed response to criticism regarding findings in Baltimore and conclusions from Camp Lee (1930); Principles vs details in treatment of empyema (1933); Work of the Empyema Commission (1948; reminiscences 30 years later).

obvious, for the references are surgical, not biochemical; the style is that of Graham; and the topic is surgery and pulmonary physiology, not biochemistry.[16] This report was Graham's most conspicuous contribution, and it became a focus of contention for the next 12 to 15 years, for the concepts of pulmonary dynamics as contained in the Graham-Bell report were not well received by many leading surgeons of the day. MacCallum had alerted Graham to the list of prominent disbelievers and suggested that he be prepared to defend himself upon his return from France.[23] It was a classic confrontation between laboratory research findings and conventional clinical wisdom—a confrontation that Graham could not and would not avoid. The contest of ideas was held in surgical publications, in private conversation, and at scientific meetings. Soon after arriving in St. Louis, Graham published a short article on his calculations regarding vital capacity and the maximum permissible opening in the chest wall, in which he illustrated that the opening could be unilateral or bilateral. In this article, Graham returned to the mobility of the mediastinum and acknowledged that if it were rendered relatively immobile by induration or adhesions, his formulas would not apply.[27]

Graham's St. Louis appointment provided an experimental laboratory for further research on pulmonary dynamics, and, bit by bit, he added new information to buttress his arguments. In January 1920 he spoke before the Chicago Surgical and Medical Societies, again describing the three principles involved in the treatment of empyema. Here, he took issue with a depiction of open pneumothorax as presented by Moschcowitz (a colleague from the Empyema Commission), who used drawings that showed a rigid mediastinum with one lung collapsed to a small mass about its hilum and the other lung of normal size. He repeated the findings of his Baltimore experience and emphasized that "former prevalent conceptions of the mechanism and action of an open pneumothorax are incorrect."[28] In April he spoke to the American Medical Association about the importance of an adequate vital capacity in thoracic surgery, introduced the advantage of using a spirometer to determine vital capacity, and restated his and Bell's experiments with dogs and their results. He also noted that thoracoplasty operations result in a permanently marked reduction in vital capacity and should be reserved for the "rarest instances and only after other methods have been given an intelligent trial for at least many months."[29] In March 1921 he published a small piece reporting on the influence of respiratory movements in the formation of pleural exudates. The report outlined a study of isolated dog lungs in a system that permitted variation of the pressure surrounding the lung while the trachea was open to the atmosphere. He was surprised that "contrary to expectation most of the fluid poured out of the lungs at the end of expiration rather than at the end of inspiration." He performed similar experiments on a human lung removed at autopsy.[30]

During 1920 to 1922, several articles were written by authors who took exception to the work of Graham and Bell regarding the integrity of the pleurae and the mobility of the mediastinum. It was felt that the dog differed from man by having a communication between the two pleural cavities, and that air could move from one pleural space to the other. Pierre Duval of Paris, relying on personal observations made during the war, was particularly critical of Graham and Bell's work. He published two articles in *Presse Medical* (Paris) regarding what he considered to be fundamental truths about open pneumothorax: communication between the two pleural cavities is present in the dog but not in man, and the creation of a wide open pneumothorax in a calf is not fatal.[31,32] Graham responded with his own article in French in *Presse Medical* (Paris) refuting Duval's criticism of the anatomic similarities between dog and man, adding observations of his own on the fatality of pneumothorax in a calf, and attacking Duval's criticism of Graham's calculations on the theoretic maximum nonfatal opening. Once again, he buttressed his arguments with the findings that he and Bell had obtained in Baltimore.[33]

In May 1923 Graham responded to mounting criticisms with a major presentation to the American Association for Thoracic Surgery and a subsequent lengthy manuscript that reconsidered all aspects of open pneumothorax. Graham's talk led to a great deal of argument at the meeting, and, after defending the original Graham-Bell experiments, Graham introduced some new data from studies on the mediastinum of 25 dogs, in which he attempted to but could not find the pleural communications described by others. He also reported that in human cadavers the normal mediastinum is almost as flexible as is that in the dog. In his presentation and subsequent publication, Graham took pointed exception to Duval's criticisms. After adding evidence that he had obtained about the density of roentgenograms and modifications of pulmonary blood flow, he concluded: "No theory of the mechanics of pneumothorax so readily explains all the facts as the one based on our experimental results. ... The original observations on open pneumothorax made by R. D. Bell and myself and published in 1918 were true in principle."[34]

In October 1923 Graham made a presentation before the Clinical Congress of the American College of Surgeons on the treatment of acute and chronic empyema, in which he restated the principles that had been defined by the Empyema Commission.[35]

Graham's magnum opus that he prepared while at Fort Sheridan appeared in 1924 in the official history of the medical department in the World War. In 34 pages he discussed the physiology of respiration, the history of open pneumothorax, the studies in Baltimore, and calculations regarding the size of chest openings. He gave an extensive survey of the literature, and, in a footnote obviously added 2 or 3 years after the war, he named a list of surgeons who inferred that conclusions drawn from experiments on the dog were not applicable to the human.[5]

On February 9, 1924, Graham spoke to the Harvey Society of New York to discuss at length the consequences of alterations of intrapleural pressure. He reviewed the Empyema Commission experiences and the dog experiments performed with Bell, and presented evidence contrary to the opinions of his detractors, including some new material on canine pneumothorax and observations on five human cadavers that had not been presented previously.[36]

The year 1925 saw the appearance of a small book containing Graham's essay that had received the Samuel D. Gross Prize of the Philadelphia Academy of Surgery in 1920. This monograph is a succinct description of his experiences with the Empyema Commission, the laboratory experiments in Baltimore, and his clinical experiences at Fort Sheridan following his return from overseas. It closes with a lengthy addendum in which Graham again discusses personal differences of opinion about pneumothorax and the mobility of the mediastinum.[37]

In a 1929 presentation to the American Association for Thoracic Surgery, Graham extensively reviewed the cardiac, vascular, and pulmonary consequences of increased intrathoracic pressures, with particular emphasis on the effects of thoracoplasty.[38]

Even in 1930 the issue was still debated and Graham, coeditor of the text *Surgical Diagnosis*, in writing the section on thoracic diseases, summarized and responded to criticisms made by surgeons Rudolph Matas, Pierre Duval, John L. Yates, and J.W. Schneider. However, the basic physiologic principles of the Graham-Bell experiments were beginning to hold true and become important in the developing field of thoracic surgery—a field that was to explode 3 years later following his successful pneumonectomy.[39]

In 1933 Graham presented the results of empyema management at the St. Louis Children's Hospital, reporting a total of 116 cases with 13 deaths—a 12 percent mortality rate.[40]

His final publication on this topic, made 30 years after the war at the request of Nathan Womack, detailed reminiscences about his time spent with the Empyema Commission. It is a short overview without specific details, except for his three oft-repeated conclusions: late drainage, early sterilization, and maintenance of nutrition. Of these, he still considered the first to be the most important.[41]

During the decade of the 1920s, Graham's major thrust was the physiology of open pneumothorax; his successful pneumonectomy was yet to happen, and thoracic surgery was still only for the strong and daring. Graham must have sensed that an understanding of pulmonary and vascular responses to an opening of the chest was essential to the upcoming development of thoracic surgery. In the face of criticism from leading surgeons, he stubbornly defended conclusions drawn from his laboratory experiments (which were correct), overturning impressions gained from clinical experience. His struggle foreshadowed the conflict that occurred during World War II when Meleney's observations on the lack of benefit of the use of sulfanilamide in wounds were opposed to the clinical observations of I.S. Ravdin and surgeons at Pearl Harbor.

Chapter 5

WASHINGTON UNIVERSITY
AND
BARNES HOSPITAL

RECRUITMENT

The Process

Unbeknownst to Evarts Graham in the fall of 1916, he was beginning a lifelong romance with Washington University. At this time reorganization of the Medical School was well under way, and Philip Shaffer had become its dean. Shaffer later claimed that he was "perhaps the first of our faculty to discover Graham, although I can claim only a tiny credit for his selection."[1] At the request of George Dock, Shaffer had gone to Chicago scouting for a full-time instructor in medicine; he visited with H. Gideon Wells (director of the Otho S.A. Sprague Institute), Ajax Carlson, and Rollin Woodyatt of the University of Chicago. They told Shaffer about the son of a professor of surgery, a brilliant young man who, after an internship at the Presbyterian Hospital, proceeded to study pathology with Wells and Hektoen, chemistry with Nef and Steiglitz, and clinical physiology with Woodyatt. Shaffer learned that Graham was no longer available since he had gone into the wilds—a town called Mason City in Iowa—to establish a clinic patterned after the Mayo Clinic. Woodyatt thought it of no use to attempt to recruit Graham for this internal medicine position because he was a surgeon, not an internist. However disappointed he might have been, Shaffer, with his usual diligence filed Graham's name for future reference.[2]

During these early years, the chairman of surgery at Washington University was Fred T. Murphy[a], who, in 1911, had been recruited from the Massachusetts General Hospital by Robert Brookings. As the commanding officer of Base Hospital No. 21, Murphy went to France in 1917 with Drs. Clopton, Allison, Fischel, Opie, Veeder, Lehman, and others, a move that considerably depleted the staff of Barnes Hospital. Upon his return in the spring of 1919, Murphy was unwilling to accept a full-time position. He resigned his professorship and, soon thereafter, left for Detroit to administer financial affairs for his family.[1] At the executive faculty meeting of May 7, during which Murphy's resignation was accepted, Philip Shaffer moved that a committee consisting of Canby Robinson (dean), Eugene Opie (professor of pathology), and Joseph Erlanger (professor of physiology) be appointed to bring suggestions regarding a head of the Department of Surgery. Shaffer remembered a young surgeon from Chicago whose name he had forgotten; his files disclosed the name of Evarts Graham, who was located at Fort Sheridan, north of Chicago. Shaffer convinced the search committee to visit Fort Sheridan within the next 2 weeks, and, shortly after the visit, Graham was asked to attend an interview. He was proposed to the executive faculty on May 26 and immediately approved by both executive faculty and chancellor. There were no other candidates.

Graham's visit to St. Louis on June 6 and 7, 1919, permitted him to meet most of the members of the newly reorganized faculty. Major Graham was an imposing figure with a remarkable military record and in military uniform during this visit.[1] The visit culminated with a dinner at the newly opened Bevo Mill restaurant[b] in south St. Louis. Conversation during dinner was filled with attempts to convince Graham that he would have an unusual opportunity for personal development in

---

a. Fred Towsley Murphy (1872 to 1948), born in Detroit, was educated at Phillips Andover, Yale, and Harvard, where he obtained his doctor of medicine degree. After serving 2 years as a surgical preceptorial trainee, he became a member of the staff of Massachusetts General Hospital. Realizing the importance of laboratory experience, he collaborated with Walter Cannon, Beth Vincent, and Joseph Pratt to contribute to their studies of the physiology and pathology of the gastrointestinal tract. After moving to St. Louis in 1910, he was responsible for acquiring the services of Vilray Blair (plastic surgeon), Ernest Sachs (neurologic surgeon), Nathaniel Allison (orthopedist), John Caulk (urologist), and Malvern Clopton (general surgeon)—the basic team inherited by Graham. Murphy organized and supervised the equipping of Base Hospital No. 21 and went overseas as its commanding officer. Returning to St. Louis at the end of the war, he found the university to be heavily influenced by Rockefeller Foundation concepts of full-time clinical chairmanships, something he felt unwilling to accept. Leaving the practice of surgery, he returned to Detroit to administer the Murphy Family Trust for the next 30 years; he also served as director of large banking, manufacturing, and real estate corporations. He gave generous support to organizations that rendered civic service, but he retained membership in several surgical societies. His strong personality, tempered by kindliness and generosity, was such that it evoked at first an impression of austerity, which almost always changed to a feeling of profound respect and affection.

b. *Author's note:* Bevo Mill restaurant still exists.

the newly refurbished Washington University School of Medicine and the newly opened Barnes Hospital.[2]

Having explored some of the newer developments in medical education, particularly those in Chicago and Baltimore, Graham appreciated the opportunities that St. Louis afforded and, on the evening of June 7, verbally accepted the position. On June 10 the corporation formally appointed him as professor of surgery and chairman of the department, effective July 1, 1919. Fate had placed this opportunity in Graham's path through the resignation of Fred Murphy and the discerning memory and political skill of Philip Shaffer.

After his September 9 discharge from the army, Graham moved to St. Louis to begin 38 years with Washington University, as one among many who were to develop the institution into what Pritchett[c] had hoped would be "the Johns Hopkins of the Southwest." Less than a week after arriving in St. Louis, Graham wrote a complimentary letter to Fred Murphy, commending him for the work he had done as chairman of the Department of Surgery during the preceding 7 years.[3,4]

An "Ideal" Medical School in the Making

The rapidity with which Washington University accepted the resignation of Fred Murphy and moved to offer the position to Evarts Graham (34 days), and the alacrity with which Graham accepted the offer during his visit to St. Louis (2 days) serve as commentaries on both Philip Shaffer's vigor and Evarts Graham's desire for a position. There is no record of correspondence or other effort on the part of Graham to prepare a post-war career during his Fort Sheridan days, except for earlier correspondence with MacCallum at Johns Hopkins, which brought no response. It is probable that, at the very least, Graham was planning a return to Chicago to become a member of the Department of Surgery at Presbyterian

c. Henry S. Pritchett (1857 to 1939) was born in Fayette, Missouri, and received his bachelor's degree at Pritchett College in Glasgow, Missouri, in 1875. He became interested in the stars and, after working at several institutions, he became professor of astronomy at Washington University (1883 to 1887). During this period he spent a year in Munich earning a doctor of philosophy degree in astronomy. From 1900 to 1906, he served as president of the Massachusetts Institute of Technology; he then became the first president of the Carnegie Foundation for the Advancement of Teaching to improve the conditions for scholarship. Pritchett held this post from 1906 to 1930, during which time he also served as trustee for the Carnegie Institute and for the Carnegie Endowment for International Peace. He was instrumental, perhaps almost directive, in two visits to St. Louis by Abraham Flexner, and he was extremely influential in directing Robert Brookings and David Houston in their involvement in and understanding of the process of change in medical education. He maintained close contact with Flexner after the latter moved to the General Education Board of the Rockefeller Foundation, and he was very supportive of the generosity that the board offered Washington University. Becoming entranced by some of Brookings's ideas about government, politics, and education he promoted Carnegie Foundation money to assist in establishing the Brookings Institution. Throughout his life he received 20 honorary degrees and national honors from France, England, and Greece.

Hospital, with a renewed attachment to Rollin Woodyatt and the Otho S.A. Sprague Institute. A return to the practice of surgery from offices shared with his father was always possible; this would have led to a life devoted to the practice of surgery, something that would have been less than exciting to him. Developments at the University of Chicago also were on the horizon. Following his acceptance of the St. Louis chairmanship, Graham was approached with regard to a position as associate professor of surgery at Cornell, a post he easily refused in favor of the position at Washington University.

By 1919 the Washington University School of Medicine was completing a reorganization that, in many ways, was a pioneering effort in the United States—one that was to place it in the front ranks of American medical schools.[5] It had become the Rockefeller prototype for medical school development, and there was an air of excitement and enthusiasm among the faculty; Graham was attracted to this intellectually stimulating group.[6]

The effort in medical education at Washington University began through affiliation with the two oldest medical colleges west of the Mississippi—the St. Louis Medical College in 1891 and the Missouri Medical College in 1899. Both of these were proprietary enterprises owned and operated by a cluster of physicians in what was the common, almost universal, approach to medical education in the United States at the turn of the century. It was a period in which the need for university affiliation was becoming apparent to both universities and medical colleges.[7]

The St. Louis Medical College, founded in 1841, was the medical department of St. Louis University. William Beaumont, a pioneer gastrophysiologist, was included on its faculty roster. In 1855 the college severed ties with Roman Catholic St. Louis University, became independent, and remained so until 1891, when it became the medical department of Washington University. It continued to manage its own curriculum, tuition, salaries, and physical plant until 1906.

The Missouri Medical College was founded in 1840 by Joseph Nash McDowell, a nephew of Ephriam McDowell who had performed the first ovariotomy.[8] The college was the medical department of Kemper College until 1845 when it became a department of the University of Missouri. It remained so until 1857 when a reorganization required all instructors to devote themselves full time to education.

In 1899 Missouri Medical College made a final alliance with the St. Louis Medical College and became a copartner as the medical department of Washington University. The combined schools converted the Missouri Medical College building at Locust and Jefferson Streets into the 125-bed Washington University Hospital.[9] The 1899–1900 bulletin of the Washington University medical department announced the union, the faculties of both schools resigned, and a new Washington University faculty was appointed, mostly from the same individuals. The first Washington University doctor of medicine degree was granted in 1900, but the combined schools continued to operate as a proprietary school, with the Medical Fund Society as its financial authority and owner of its property[10] until May 31, 1906, when the medical faculty placed its affairs in the hands of the chancellor and board of directors of Washington University.[9] This change gave Washington University the control of its budget, appointments, and policies and prepared it for the momentous events that were to unfold 3 years later with the visits of Abraham Flexner.

Flexner paid two visits to Washington University as an agent of the Carnegie Foundation for the Advancement of Teaching (chaired by Henry Pritchett, ex-professor of astronomy at Washington University). After his first visit, Flexner classed the medical department of Washington University as "a little better than the worst but absolutely inadequate in every essential respect."[11] This led Robert Brookings, patriarch of Washington University and president of its corporate board, to turn his attention to the Medical School. Pritchett sent Flexner for a second visit with Brookings, who then began to pour his and others' efforts and financial resources into the Medical School development. Brookings recruited the nucleus of a new medical faculty and proceeded to construct buildings to house it, spending much of his wealth in this effort. After visiting the east coast to contact Flexner at the Carnegie Foundation, Welch at Johns Hopkins, and Edsall at the University of Pennsylvania, he interviewed and recruited eager and energetic young men to the opportunities and excitement that a new medical school could offer. Flexner regarded David Edsall as the "man with the right stamp," and he and Brookings planned that Edsall should become dean. Although a Department of Preventive Medicine was created especially for him, Edsall was impatient for hospital development and stayed only 1 year before leaving to become the architect and builder of the Harvard Medical School.[12]

It was not difficult to fill the major chairs with recruits. The new chairmen were Robert Terry in anatomy (from St. Louis), the only holdover from the previous school; Joseph Erlanger in physiology (from Johns Hopkins and the University of Wisconsin); Phillip Shaffer in biochemistry (from Harvard); Eugene Opie in pathology (from Rockefeller Institute); George Dock in medicine (from Tulane); John Howland in pediatrics (from Columbia); Fred Murphy in surgery (from Harvard); and David Edsall in preventive medicine (from Pennsylvania). They collectively became known as the "Wise Men from the East."

The first meeting of this faculty occurred in September 1909, at which time they decided to constitute themselves as an executive faculty made up of departmental chairmen; on an annual basis, they would elect one of their members to be dean. This placed governance of the school in the hands of the executive faculty, and the dean was expected to continue his duties as department chairman. In 1943 Shaffer and Graham arranged that the financial affairs of the Medical School would become equally separate from the parent university.[9]

By 1910 to 1911, the reorganization of the faculty was underway, and a physical plant that would include laboratories and patients was the next order of business.

To move the school and hospital from its midcity location, money from Brookings, Busch, Bixby, Mallinckrodt, and other St. Louis businessmen began to flow in. Plans were made for three basic Medical School buildings and for affiliations with the yet-to-be-built Barnes Hospital and a rebuilt St. Louis Children's Hospital. The first Rockefeller money that Brookings obtained with the help of Flexner was a major influence in designing the salary structure for the clinical faculty; more Rockefeller money helped to finance construction in the years following World War I. The "hero" of the reorganization was Brookings[9] (see appendix G). By 1919 Graham was ready to join.

The Coming of Full Time

During the first two decades of the twentieth century, clinical research was becoming laboratory based; Graham must have sensed this in his post–medical school preparation. Development of the new preclinical sciences of biochemistry, physiology, pathology, and bacteriology created demands that were unable to be met by proprietary schools faculty members. They were practicing physicians who gave some of their time to teaching, received reimbursement from clinical practice and tuition fees from students, and returned some of their money to support the school. For the proprietary schools, financial resources for laboratory development, the payment of preclinical professors, and comfortable educational relationships with hospitals were in short supply; university affiliation became the order of the day.[12]

The concept that a university would pay a salary to its clinical instructors as well as its preclinical instructors was broached in 1902 by Lewellys F. Barker[d], then an instructor in anatomy at the University of Chicago and, later, Osler's successor at Johns Hopkins. The concept of full-time clinicians became important when Frederick Gates, the philanthropic advisor to the Rockefellers, posed an innocent question to Flexner: "What would you do with a million dollars?" The immediate answer was, "I should give it to Dr. Welch." Abraham Flexner had found that most medical faculties were composed of busy practitioners who had little time for teaching; Johns Hopkins was the only school that had control of a hospital and its staff. Flexner's Carnegie report[11] put to death more than half of the medical schools in the United States, and since Johns Hopkins was the one school that most fulfilled Flexner's criteria, it became his prototype for US medical school development. To Flexner, Welch possessed the greatest vision, and he was the one most worthy of Rockefeller philanthropy.[12]

After hearing of Gate's question and Flexner's answer, Welch arranged a dinner at the Baltimore Club for Flexner, Franklin P. Mall, professor of anatomy, and

---

d. When Johns Hopkins established full-time positions in medicine, surgery, and pediatrics, Lewellys Barker, who had first proposed the idea, was now its professor of medicine, with such a large income from private practice that he resigned his position as chairman rather than accepting the offered salary.

William H. Halsted, professor of surgery, at which time Flexner asked the group the million-dollar question. Mall was adamant that every penny of the million dollars should be used "for the purpose of placing upon a salary basis the heads and assistants in the leading clinical departments,"[13] a position with which Halsted concurred. Soon thereafter, the Rockefeller Foundation offered $1.5 million to Johns Hopkins to place its medical, surgical, obstetric, and pediatric clinicians on a full-time basis (also known as the *university plan*), with reversion to the university the fees derived from private practice.[12] The Flexner proposal, which was approved by the board of trustees at its June 1911 meeting, led to the most bitter controversy in the history of the Johns Hopkins medical school.[13]

William Osler, who had left Johns Hopkins in 1904 to become the Regis Professor of Medicine at Oxford, led the fight with open letters of protest against the effort to institute full-time instructors. As a Baltimore clinical practitioner, Osler had developed a large private practice and felt that success in clinical practice created fitness for the chair. He feared that full-time clinicians would be cut off from their patients, and expressed the opinion that such a move would shrink them into the dimensions of the laboratory, away from the glories of bedside teaching, resulting in a faculty of "Halsteds"—"a very good thing for science but a bad thing for the profession." He felt it would lead to "the production of a set of clinical prigs ... whose only human interest would be research."[13] There were 2½ years of acrimonious deliberation on the proposal before the Hopkins faculty finally reached an affirmative decision in October 1913; the General Education Board contributed $1.5 million to Johns Hopkins for this purpose. Halsted had accepted the concept from the beginning and, in 1913, was the first US surgeon to become a full-time professor. MacCallum, a pathologist, close friend, and Halsted's biographer, felt that the move invigorated Halsted and "made him feel a new responsibility, not only for the active prosecution of his experimental and other studies, but more especially for the vigorous encouragement of his assistants. ... it was the basis of a flare-up in his activity which became really intense about this time. ... the new plan released him from much routine operating. ... he was one who worked to a much greater advantage when he had leisure."[14]

Belief in the correctness of full-time positions for clinical faculty dominated Rockefeller philanthropy for the next decade, and, although the Great War delayed the development and reorganization of American medical schools from 1917 to 1919, the policy became a significant feature of Rockefeller support of medical education. Through its 1913 action with Johns Hopkins, the General Education Board entered into and shaped a wide arena of medical education by providing salaries for clinical professors—$10,000 to professors and chairmen—at a time when busy practitioners were capable of making $25,000 to $30,000 per year. Harvard Medical School's refusal to acquiesce to the board's definition of full time resulted in its being denied Rockefeller money. Although a decade later the

General Education Board began to modify its rigid definition of full time,[12] the growth, development, and design of Washington University under the leadership of Brookings, with concurrence of the executive faculty (particularly Shaffer and Erlanger), held firmly to the concept and accepted all of the consequences of full time as it was initially defined by Gates and Flexner.

Upon hearing of the Rockefeller proposal to Johns Hopkins, Robert Brookings made an immediate approach to Flexner for similar treatment; the development of his Medical School was costly, and Brookings was willing to receive help from any source. In 1914 the Rockefeller Foundation offered $750,000 to Washington University and later proposed more if the full-time system was introduced. The issue was debated by the executive faculty for less than 1 hour, and all of the members except F.T. Murphy, chairman of surgery, expressed willingness to accept these salary arrangements as a part of the condition for Rockefeller support. Murphy stated that he "could not believe in or work under the full time idea." Full-time departments for Washington University were formally adopted on June 23, 1916, following an agreement between the General Education Board and Washington University, in which Rockefeller increased its commitment to $1 million dollars as long as Washington University contributed $500,000. This would create sufficient endowment to support full-time professors of medicine, surgery, and pediatrics. The date for compliance on the part of Washington University was January 1, 1919.[9,15] The agreement[e] was signed by both Brookings and Gates, on June 5, 1916, 1 year prior to the entry of the United States into World War I. Fred Murphy set aside his reservations regarding the plan for full-time professors until his return from France and his discharge from the army in May 1919.

Strongly in favor of the plan for full-time instructors that was accepted so readily without debate by the executive faculty, Brookings became widely recognized as one of its driving forces. He received a special invitation from the Society of Clinical Surgery to attend a formal luncheon on April 1, 1917, to meet with Drs. Charles Mayo, George Crile, J.M.T. Finney, and Arthur Dean Bevan, four leading US

---

e. On June 1, 1916, the General Education Board agreed to give $1 million dollars to Washington University if it would raise $500,000 for an endowment to support full-time departments in medicine, surgery, and pediatrics. The income would accomplish the following: "create and maintain departments on a full-time basis, i.e. ... [have Professors] paid for their full time and to hold their posts on condition that while engaged in the service of the university and the hospitals connected therewith they shall accept no fees for professional services ... that they will receive no pecuniary benefit ... and that fees charged ... for professional services will be used to promote the objects for which the fund is created."[15] The date for completion of the agreement was January 1, 1919. Robert Brookings and the St. Louis financial community rose to the challenge, raised the money, and established the basic principle of full-time departments in Washington University for the subsequent 80 years.

surgeons. During their round-table discussion, Brookings defended the experiment of full-time instructors. Bevan (of Chicago), the chief interrogator and opponent, was strongly supported by Finney (of Baltimore), but Brookings did not waver and later wrote to Flexner that no "argument advanced ... had any fundamental value."[16,17]

The issue of titles for full-time versus part-time faculty became of significance and received extensive consideration by Shaffer, Opie, and Erlanger. They did not wish to divide the faculty, but they did want to identify differences in the nature of the appointments. On March 27, 1917, Shaffer made the following proposal:

> a scheme which defines the distinction between those who are teachers on the university basis and those who devote the greater part of their time to clinical work and incidently assist in teaching and research. It is this distinction which all those medical educators, who have supported the full time scheme, have emphasized. The term "clinical" carries no suggestion of reproach and its introduction modifying the name of the department makes no change in the rank of the teacher. It has the advantage of long accepted precedent and its significance would be understood by the large number of educators throughout the country who are interested in the success of the new plan of medical teaching. It is no more than a frank statement of the principle of organization as it has been agreed to by the University. ...
> In our judgement this is a serious question and we hope that it may be decided by unanimous agreement.[18]

The plan was adopted, and designations such as *professor of surgery* and *professor of clinical surgery* continue to this day.

Graham's agreement to join Washington University was greatly influenced by the opportunity for full-time instructors, and he became the second full-time surgical chairman in the United States. Although he appreciated its value from several viewpoints, the arrangement was immediately attractive since he would not be required to establish a private practice to survive. He appreciated its long-term rewards in regard to the use of faculty members' time and efforts and defended it to colleagues around the country. A decade later he wrote J.J. Morton, who was then establishing a Department of Surgery at the University of Rochester in Rochester, New York:

> In regard to the questions which you ask ... the only men who are on full time besides myself are some of the younger men. It is not my policy to encourage men to stay on full time indefinitely. My reasons for this opinion are that such an arrangement blocks the way for the development of a constant stream of promising young men and ... is ...

unjustifiably expensive. Ordinarily, after a man has been on full time for perhaps four or five years I encourage him to begin a private practice limited to the hospital. As his practice increases I reduce his salary so that funds will be made available for other young men who come up. Most of these young men are encouraged to take up a practice limiting their work to practice in the hospital, occasionally one of them will open an office outside. Fees collected by the full time staff are turned in through the office of the Treasurer of the University to the Department of Surgery and are therefore expendable for departmental purposes.[19]

These ideas dominated Graham's activities regarding staff development throughout his tenure as chairman of surgery, and almost a quarter century after his arrival in St. Louis, Graham was still convinced of the advantages and correctness of the full-time system. In response to a request by John Fraser, dean of McGill University, Graham wrote:

There is no question in my mind about the soundness of the full-time principle. The job of properly conducting a large clinical department is certainly a full-time job if any job is. The many duties involved and the responsibility of a large clinical service, the teaching of undergraduate students, the organization and conduct of a program of graduate teaching of the house staff and the business of providing facilities for and lending inspiration with ideas of critical judgement for research projects all combine and more than use up the entire day. If the Director of the Department is harassed by the constant demand of private practice he must sacrifice some of the important aspects of the job itself. There are not sufficient hours in the day nor does anybody have sufficient vitality, to run the kind of department which I have in mind and at the same time be basically engaged in private practice. In spite of the remarks which I have just made I think it is unwise, and in fact unfortunate, to cut off the full-time professor completely from seeing private patients. If he develops an interest in a special field of surgery, he will very naturally and very properly wish to accumulate a large clinical experience in that field. ... The main thing is to get the right sort of man and relieve him of the harassing annoyances of making his living by private practice.[20]

Graham turned all of his private practice earnings over to the Department of Surgery, and, by the late 1940s, he accounted for 22 percent of the department's funds. Although at times Graham encouraged some of his specialty chiefs to accept full-time positions to devote more effort to research and teaching, Graham never planned to have the entire surgical staff of Barnes Hospital work on a full-time basis. He did, however, vigorously defend the principle that only faculty members, either full time or part time, could receive hospital appointments. This was an issue that would explode a few years later.

Brookings, Buildings, and Barnes and Its "Closed Staff"

In 1909 Brookings[f] had been inspired by Abraham Flexner with the dream of an ideal medical school, and he became indefatigable in his efforts to collect money from others in addition to donating his personal wealth to his newly found cause célèbre to make the dream a reality.[21,22] By 1910 he began to think about the housing required for the Medical School: a basic science building, an outpatient building, and an inpatient (hospital) complex. Through Brookings's efforts, supported by major financial gifts from Bixby, Busch, and Mallinckrodt, one outpatient and two basic science buildings were constructed at the corner of Kingshighway and Euclid Avenue. They were dedicated in a 3-day ceremony in April 1915.[23] A hospital was needed to complete the Medical School development, and Brookings turned his attention to the proposed Barnes Hospital and the St. Louis Children's Hospital.[9]

The Barnes Hospital began in 1892 after the death of Robert A. Barnes, a wholesale grocer and banker who left $950,000 for the construction and operation of a hospital "for sick and injured persons without distinction of creed, under the auspices of the Methodist Episcopal Church, South." His will contained an insufficient $100,000 for construction, and the trustees postponed building until 1912, by which time the value of the trust had doubled, permitting the building of a hospital with an adequate endowment. Barnes trustees were studying hospital construction at the same time that Robert Brookings was studying medical school design, and it soon became apparent that the building of a medical school and the construction of a modern hospital were so inter-related that the purpose of each would be more successfully fulfilled by an affiliation with the other.[24] Conversations between the two institutions were simple since Samuel Cupples, chairman of the Barnes Board of Trustees, and Robert Brookings, president of the Corporation of Washington University, were business partners and close friends who shared ideas and wealth in the Cupples corporation[g].

The St. Louis Children's Hospital had been in operation since 1879 at 2834 Franklin Avenue; its board of managers was composed of interested women, with

---

f. The extraordinary life and accomplishments of Robert S. Brookings are too extensive to be captured in a short biographical sketch. A brief description of the man and his career is presented in appendix G.

g. Cupples Station was a huge freight transfer depot located in mid–St. Louis in the area of Eighth and Spruce Streets on the west bank of the Mississippi River. The opening of the Eads Bridge in 1874 permitted railroad traffic from the east coast to cross the river and bypass the Illinois Terminal in east

the exception of Samuel Cupples, the lone male member on the board. Brookings courted Mrs. Grace McKittrick Jones, president of the hospital board of managers, whose husband, Robert Jones, was not only a personal friend of Brookings but also a member of the Washington University Committee on Reorganization of the Medical School. The Children's Hospital Board made plans to build a new St. Louis Children's Hospital on Kingshighway, adjacent to the property Barnes Hospital had purchased, and an affiliation agreement with Washington University was consummated in 1912.[25]

By 1905 the Barnes trustees had acquired a building site on Kingshighway, an action that led the university and St. Louis Children's Hospital to acquire adjacent property. Theodore C. Link, architect of the St. Louis Union Station, was named to design Barnes Hospital and the three Medical School buildings, all of which were done in a similar stark grey brick Assyrian motif. Construction was started in 1912, and all were completed within 2 years, with common facilities that would be shared and maintained. The Medical School buildings were opened in 1914, and, in that fall, Washington University Hospital patients were transferred to Barnes. When the St. Louis Children's Hospital moved its patients to the new building in the fall of 1914, the complex was complete. Only Johns Hopkins Hospital (owned by the university) had shown the degree of sympathy to the needs of medical education and research as did these two St. Louis hospitals.[25]

St. Louis. Coupled with the city's location at the mouth of the Missouri River, the Eads Bridge made St. Louis the gateway to the west (thus, the Arch). North-south trade on the Mississippi River became connected to railroads in St. Louis for east-west shipment, to barges going either up or down the Missouri River, and to the sea routes that connected New Orleans to the rest of the world. There was no transcontinental rail line, and all freight from east of the Mississippi required transfer to one of the 17 railroads operating to the west. In 1882, with his partner Samuel Cupples, Robert Brookings elaborated a scheme for a freight depot-warehouse complex that would receive, store, and trans-ship goods. They secretly purchased land immediately adjacent to the southern mouth of the railroad tunnel that ran under the eastern margin of St. Louis and then to the railroads going west. Brookings's project took more than three decades and, when finally completed in 1917, it consisted of 18 multistory warehouses of intricate architectural detail that spread over eight city blocks with a large rail marshalling yard. It permitted the transfer of goods from one railroad company to another or to St. Louis consignees without drayage from one station to another. The Cupples Station had a monopoly on all freight transport and trans-shipment at the focal point created by the crossing of the Mississippi River. Brookings's idea revolutionized the handling of freight; the Bush terminals in New York, the Pittsburgh terminal warehouses, and the Central Manufacturing and Warehouse District in Chicago became the most conspicuous adaptations of the project that he had conceived and developed. Capital stock of the St. Louis Terminal Cupples Station and Property (estimated to be $3 million) was transferred to the Washington University Corporation in May 1900—half from Cupples and half from Brookings. In addition, income from the station supplemented Washington University coffers for almost the next half century. Brookings retired from active business in 1896 to spend the remainder of his life and most of the wealth created by Cupples Station in philanthropic efforts directed to Washington University in St. Louis and to the Brookings Institution in Washington, DC.

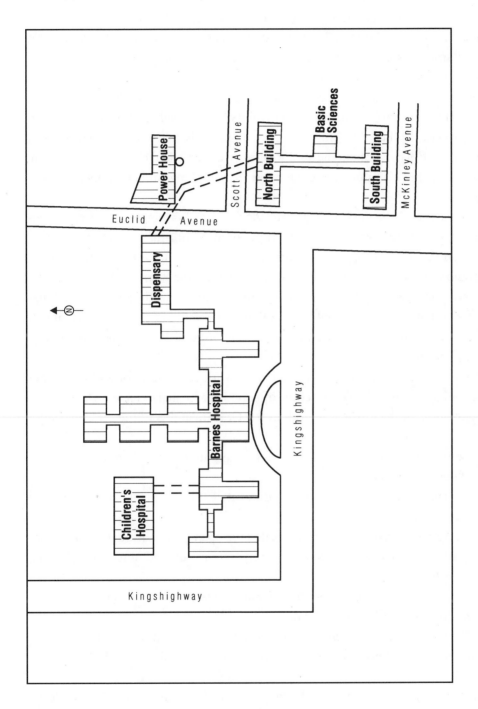

The 1914 location of St. Louis Children's Hospital, Barnes Hospital, and the four buildings of the Washington University Medical School.

Through terms contained in the St. Louis contracts, the trustees of the affiliat-ed hospitals agreed "that the medical staffs of the hospitals would consist solely of the teaching corps of the Medical Department of the University and that the Med-ical Department would have the right to use patients in the hospitals for medical research and clinical instruction to the students of the university."[9] The agreement with Barnes Hospital was signed on October 28, 1911, and with the St. Louis Chil-dren's Hospital on July 8, 1912.[26,27]

Control of the hospital staff (appointment, promotion, and discipline) by the Medical School gave Graham an opportunity that he had been denied in Mason City, where any licensed practitioner automatically had hospital privileges. A "closed staff" gave Graham the ability to select, appoint, and choose his own team, one that shared his values in regard to research, teaching, and other liberal educa-tional ideas.

By the time the United States entered World War I, Washington University Med-ical School was regarded as the prototypical example of a medical school's reorga-nization in accord with principles advanced by the Carnegie Foundation for the Advancement of Teaching and the General Education Board of the Rockefeller Foundation. It was visited by educators from around the world. In 1920 Brookings declared that the medical center had offered "a combination for the teaching of medicine, for medical research and for the care of the sick" that was "unsurpassed in any country."[9]

As does the conjunction of three planets with the moon portend auspicious happenings, so did the conjunction of several particulars create an auspicious opportunity for the fortunes of both Evarts Graham and Washington University:

1. Graham possessed an educational background unlike that of any other surgeon in the United States.
2. Graham's practice experience in Mason City left him suspicious and hostile to many actions of US physicians.
3. The resignation of Fred Murphy created the opening at Washington University.
4. Shaffer's efficient filing system and good memory allowed him to find Graham at Fort Sheridan.
5. The vigor and enthusiasm of the reorganized young faculty at Washington Uni-versity was appealing to Graham.
6. The full-time salary system made Graham independent of his private practice.
7. The closed staff hospital arrangements were almost unique.

Due to these unique occurrences, Graham found a home that he would never leave, even though attractive offers from other institutions would be made in the following years. He savored his educational role at Washington University, his surgeon-in-chief role at Barnes Hospital, and the opportunity to develop a new type of laboratory research within his own clinical department. Ludvig Hektoen, one of Graham's Chicago mentors, wrote to him: "As I look back I note that you proceeded from the beginning in what I think is the right way to go ... in order to make the most of the opportunities in medicine as a science and as a practical service. You persisted in the face of little recognition in places where you would most expect recognition and encouragement and you went out of your way to gain experience. Now your reward has come and I wish you success and satisfaction and happiness."[28]

Within months Washington University had the first canine research laboratory west of the Mississippi River, and a graded residency system of surgical education was in place within 7 years. Graham had found a niche to which he would bring great honor. His appointment permitted realization of the three goals he had expressed as a sophomore at Princeton: major surgery, research, and a clinic of young men. It also fulfilled Mitchell's prophecy made when the two were in Curel, France: "Graham when you get home you will be offered things on a silver tray."[29]

LEGACY

The Family Home

Evarts, Helen, and 2-year-old David moved to St. Louis immediately following Graham's discharge from the army. He came prepared to take charge of the three "homes" in which he would live for the remainder of his life—family, academic, and clinical.

During the weeks preceding their St. Louis arrival, Graham and Helen purchased a house at 4711 Westminster Avenue, six blocks north of the Medical School. Built in a classic turn-of-the-century Midwest fashion, it was a square brick home with an open front porch and small yard. The living room, dining room, and kitchen filled the first floor; three bedrooms and a bath were on the second; and Tillie Hecht's room was in the basement. This house, on the same block as the home of McKim Marriott, became the place where Graham entertained visitors from within and outside St. Louis, always with Helen as his social hostess. He also enjoyed evenings in the company of just his male friends. Graham soon became acquainted with many intellectual and financial chiefs of St. Louis, and they met monthly in an informal gathering in one of their homes for an evening of free-ranging and spirited discussion of the issues of the day. The group included Bishop Scarlett of the Episcopal Diocese, Stuart Symington of Emerson Electric (he later became a US senator), Edward Mallinckrodt Jr. of the chemical company, and Fred Eiseman of Rice Stix textiles. These evenings were warm, friendly, and provided Graham with the opportunity to develop a particularly close business acquaintance with Ted Mallinckrodt and a special social acquaintance with Fred Eiseman. Mallinckrodt and Graham would call each other to discuss topics of personal interest or financial support for the Department of Surgery, or topics of greater social or political import. Fred Eiseman and his wife, sons, and daughter became personal friends of the family who shared with them dinners and evenings of interesting and controversial discussions on the status of the world and the future of surgery. Dr. Ben Eiseman remembers one particular episode during which David Graham, on his way to becoming an internist, challenged his father by proposing that advances in medicine would make the surgery of tuberculosis obsolete. A spirited encounter, with Helen as moderator, ensued.[30] Time proved that David was correct.

Barnes Hospital

Two clinical homes were available to Graham. Appointed as surgeon-in-chief to both Barnes Hospital and St. Louis Children's Hospital, Graham carried the titles throughout his tenure as professor and chairman of surgery at Washington University. Barnes Hospital became his main base, and its acquisition of land on Kingshighway determined the location of Washington University's Medical School buildings on its left and those of St. Louis Children's Hospital on its right rear. When he arrived Barnes Hospital had existed for barely 5 years; for 2 of these years, it had functioned with a diminished staff due to the departure of Base Hospital No. 21.

By the time of Graham's arrival, all arrangements for a closed-staff teaching hospital had been completed. Washington University was to make all nominations for staff appointments to the Barnes trustees; students were permitted to see patients; teaching beds were supported by an endowment created by Robert Brookings and his brother. Barnes Hospital began its operation with approximately one teaching (ward) bed for every four paid beds. The charge for a ward bed was $1.50 per day, and no physician was allowed to charge for services. Semiprivate beds cost $2.50 to $3.00 per day, and a physician's fee was acceptable. Private beds cost $4.00 to $8.00 per day; again, a physician's fee was permitted. The Washington University Dispensary served as the Barnes outpatient department, and some faculty members served only in the dispensary, whereas others also carried appointments to the staff of Barnes and/or the Children's Hospitals. The radiology department, physically located in Barnes but maintained by Washington University, was held in the Department of Surgery for administrative purposes. The metabolic department and clinical laboratory were similarly administratively held in the Department of Medicine. A member of the executive faculty was selected to meet with the three members of the Barnes Hospital Board of Trustees,[31] and Graham became the university's voice.

Fred Murphy had been recruited by Brookings in 1911, and, from among the members of the two proprietary schools, he had selected men for Washington University faculty appointments and awarded operating room privileges at the Washington University Hospital. This meant that when the staff was transferred to Barnes, only faculty appointees were moved.[31]

Twenty months after the opening of Barnes Hospital, Base Hospital No. 21 was formally commissioned, barely 1 month following the completion of a memorandum of agreement between the General Education Board and Washington University to initiate full-time appointments in medicine, surgery, and pediatrics starting January 1, 1919.[32]

The Children's Hospital of St. Louis

Graham's interest in St. Louis Children's Hospital was peripheral to his interests and activities at Barnes. William McKim Marriott, Washington University's professor of pediatrics and pediatrician-in-chief of St. Louis Children's Hospital, became the university's voice at the Children's Hospital. David Barr, professor of medicine, became the university's voice in the dispensary. At the time of the 1910 Medical School reorganization, St. Louis Children's Hospital was located in an old building on the corner of Jefferson and Adams. John Howland, the first Washington University professor of pediatrics was its pediatric medical consultant. Howland left St. Louis after a 6-month stay, impatient with the progress of new construction and the conflict over the hospital's refusal to admit Negro[h] children as inpatients, even though they were cared for in the outpatient dispensary. Dr. Bordon Veeder, a St. Louis physician, served as interim pediatric chief until the coming of Marriott in 1917. By that time the formal affiliation with the university was in place, and its physician-in-chief, Marriott, became the spokesman to reflect university's interests in hospital policy. About that time Phillip Shaffer, dean, was instrumental in having a physician rather than a nurse appointed as administrator. Dr. Louis H. Burlingham assumed the post until he moved to Barnes Hospital as its director.

Even as surgeon-in-chief, Graham played only a little role in Children's Hospital affairs. His Barnes Hospital staff constituted the Children's Hospital surgical staff. The Children's Hospital did not possess operating rooms, and children were transported through an underground passageway to Barnes for all surgical procedures. Graham had little interest in pediatric general surgical problems that were becoming metabolic rather than infectious. His chief interest was in the care of thoracic infections. Within 6 years he had collected a series of cases of chest infections sufficiently large to warrant a report in the *Journal of the American Medical Association*.[33]

---

h. *Negro* was the term generally applied to the black people of St. Louis in the 1910s through the 1940s. It is used here as it was then since it captures the flavor of the correspondence and dialogue of the day.

Graham's views on the issue of segregation must be derived from occasional brief comments in his voluminous correspondence—he never addressed it in a formal statement. Although a constant and stalwart supporter of black physicians and concern for their people, his frame of reference was that of "separate but equal"—a standard, but not avant-garde, position during the first half of the twentieth century. The concept of an integration of races never appears in his correspondence.

The specialty of pediatric surgery was not developed during Graham's era, and he considered surgical capability in the adult acceptable for the surgical treatment of children. Not until Moyer's 1959 appointment of Dr. Jesse Ternberg did a surgeon who limited her practice to the surgery of children arrive.

Inherited Staff

In 1910 Brookings had been assured by President Houston that Harvey Cushing of Johns Hopkins was ready to move and would probably be interested in developments in St. Louis, but when Cushing left Baltimore, he went to Boston's Peter Bent Brigham Hospital, not to St. Louis. Attention was then turned to the Massachusetts General Hospital, where Fred Murphy was found and recruited, arriving in 1911 as chief of surgery to the Washington University Hospital on Eighteenth and Locust. Murphy worked with physicians carried over from the two proprietary schools, and he collected several competent surgeons who were willing to join in the reorganization effort by confining their practice to the Washington University Hospital, then becoming the surgical staff of the new Barnes Hospital.

Murphy's list began in 1910 while he was still in Boston. He persuaded Ernest Sachs[i] of New York to be his first assistant in the operating room and his executive

---

i. Ernest Sachs (1879 to 1958) was born in New York City into a family that was counted among the eastern seaboard Brahmins—an intellectually stimulating world of wealth, scholarship, and the arts. His father was a classical scholar, his uncle was a neurologist made famous by his description of Tay-Sachs disease, and his cousin was a professor of fine arts at Harvard. Sachs began to play the cello at age 6 and was a member of string quartets throughout his life. The wealth that came through his mother's (née Rosa Goldman) side of the family supported much of Sachs's Washington University efforts. He was educated at Harvard and Johns Hopkins (earning his doctor of medicine degree in 1904). Three years as a house officer at Mount Sinai in New York City were followed by 2 years in Vienna, Berlin, and London, where he studied with some of the greats of those cities, particularly Victor Horsley at Queen Square Hospital in London. Sachs was extremely pleased to be the first professor of neurosurgery in the United States, after having moved from training in general surgery with special interest in neurosurgery to full-time neurosurgery.

Sachs was a short, stocky man, who was extremely intelligent, crisp in speech, and challenging in his statements. Basically a clinical surgeon and preceptor, he was not an investigator except in his microscopic pathology laboratory. Dedicated to the care of his patients; gracious, thoughtful, and gentle as he hosted guests in his own home; he was a demanding, forceful, and critical chief to his house staff and fellows. In the operating room, he would shout and throw instruments when things were going poorly. Arriving at the hospital at 6:30 am, he expected his house staff to have seen all of his patients and completed the appropriate laboratory work before meeting him at the door. As a founder of the American Board of Neurosurgery and member of the Neurological Society and the American Neurological Association, he was a true pioneer in neurosurgery in the United States and was proud of the 30 fellows he trained, 10 of whom became professors of neurosurgery. His final years at the Yale Historical Library did not have the demands of patient care and permitted him time for reflection and intellectual creativity. He is buried beside his wife and daughter at Keene Valley, New York, in the eastern foothills of his beloved Adirondack Mountains.

officer for the department. Sachs became the pioneer neurosurgeon west of the Mississippi River and the first professor of neurosurgery in the United States. Vilray P. Blair, a St. Louis trained surgeon, had been associated with Washington University since 1894 and was well on his way to becoming a founder of the field of plastic surgery. Malvern Clopton, also a St. Louis native, was a man of considerable wealth and social prominence, with interests in the surgery of children. A loyal member of the staff, he later became president of the corporation of Washington University. Hugh Young of Johns Hopkins alerted Murphy to the presence of one of his urologic trainees who had moved to St. Louis, and, in 1911, the flamboyant John R. Caulk was induced to develop the upcoming specialty of urology. From Halsted's program at Johns Hopkins came Arthur O. Fisher and Barney Brooks. Fisher, who was to stay in St. Louis for the remainder of his professional career, introduced Halsted's surgical techniques, and Brooks organized a subdepartment of surgical pathology along the lines that Joseph Bloodgood had developed at Johns Hopkins. He eventually left to become the surgical chairman at Vanderbilt but retained a keen interest in Graham and the efforts at St. Louis. Many of these men performed military duty during World War I.

Barnes Hospital was opened on December 7, 1914, and the initial surgical staff that Murphy presented to the Barnes Hospital Board of Trustees on behalf of the Washington University Executive Committee consisted of Ernest Sachs, Vilray Blair, Nathaniel Allison, Malvern Clopton, John Caulk, Arthur O. Fisher, and Archer O'Reilly. Omar T. Sevin was appointed as resident surgeon, the first of three such men trained during the Murphy-Sachs years. The two other men were Barney Brooks and William Wilkening (see appendix C).[34]

One year following the opening of Barnes Hospital, Murphy began a 6-month leave of absence to the American Hospital in Paris, with a lengthy side trip to Alexis Carrel's experimental station hospital situated at Compiègne, 5 miles from the front. Upon his return, Base Hospital No. 21 was commissioned, with Murphy as its commanding officer and Malvern Clopton as its chief of surgical services. On May 16, 1917, the unit left St. Louis for 2 long years.[34] On May 7, 1919, the hospital was demobilized, and Murphy resigned as chairman of surgery and surgical chief at Barnes and Children's Hospitals. Murphy turned down an appointment as professor of clinical surgery, gave up the active practice of surgery, and moved to Detroit. Ernest Sachs had been acting chairman of the Washington University Department of Surgery and acting surgeon-in-chief at Barnes and Children's Hospitals during Murphy's 6-month leave of absence in France, during his time overseas with Base Hospital No. 21, and then, again, between Murphy's departure in May and the arrival of Graham in September. For the 1918 to 1919 Department of Surgery budget of $33,500, Sachs listed 21 people: secretaries, technicians, and two surgeons—Murphy at $10,000 (in absentia) and Sachs at $4000.[24,35]

With Murphy's departure and Sachs's continuing role as acting chairman, Sachs naturally expected to become the successor chairman. There is no indication in executive faculty minutes that Sachs was ever considered for the permanent position; however, in his autobiography, Sachs states that he withdrew his name because he objected to the full-time plan and, furthermore, did not care to do general surgery.[36] It was the impression of Frank Bradley that Sachs was very interested in the chairmanship and deeply resented the appointment of Graham. Relations between Sachs and Graham, although always formal and punctually correct, were never cordial (both were strong characters), but the development of neurosurgery did not suffer.[37] During his years at Washington University, Sachs was the only man to maintain his office (a research laboratory; Ms. Gertrude Mogle, his secretary; and Ms. Jessie Lindsey, who doubled as anesthetist and research technician) in the North Building at the opposite end of the hall from Graham's office. Sachs was always given teaching obligations with medical students, and his Thursday noon conferences with third-year students became legendary. In these conferences he occasionally made veiled remarks critical of other surgeons, including Graham, but there was never a formal face-off between the two. Graham refused to eliminate Sachs from the teaching system and wisely declined to take issue with his comments. He disapproved of, but did not dispute, Sachs's inappropriate use of ward beds for private patients.

From 1921 until 1946, Sachs was permitted to appoint fellows as preceptorial trainees for training in neurosurgery, always with Graham's pro forma approval. Sachs maintained a private practice in partnership with Dr. Leonard Furlow. He was fiscally independent of Graham and the Department of Surgery,[4] for Sachs's mother, Rosa Goldman, was the daughter of Marcus Goldman, the founder of the investment company Goldman-Sachs. Goldman-Sachs money was always available to Ernest Sachs and, when added to his private practice income, permitted him to provide fellowship stipends for the men who came to train with him. It provided him with a secretary, a technician, and an anesthetist, and covered expenses incurred in his neuropathology laboratory.[1,38,39]

The appointment of Evarts Graham as full-time chief of surgery created hard feelings among some of the surgical staff that had been collected by Murphy, and a small faculty group attempted to drive Graham away; Drs. Sachs and Fisher were active in this attempt, and only two members, Drs. Glover Copher and L.H. Burlingham (superintendent of the hospital), openly stood by Graham during this period.[2] Graham kept Fisher and Sachs on the faculty and the Barnes staff for the next three decades. A.O. Fisher became a well-known, socially prominent surgeon with a large private practice who was minimally involved in teaching; in his latter years, he moved to St. Luke's Hospital. Glover Copher, who was a resident when Graham arrived and then a staff member and colleague in the cholecystography effort, remained more loyal to Barnes Hospital than to Washington University. He built a large private practice and was generally regarded as the exquisite, ultimate general surgical clinician by students and house staff, until there was a major falling out with Graham during World War II. Burlingham, the hospital director, became deeply involved in the 1935 to 1940 conflict between the university and Barnes Hospital. Half of his salary came from Washington University and half came from Barnes. He became unable to withstand the stress of his position, underwent an emotional breakdown, and, after his resignation in June 1939, was succeeded by Dr. Frank Bradley.

Barnes Hospital[j] was officially opened on December 7, 1914. For the calendar year 1916, the average census was 115 patients. Eighty-three percent were patients used in teaching, 23 percent of which were free (ward). Seventeen percent were private patients. Negroes were originally housed in two Victorian style houses adjacent to Barnes Hospital, but within a year they were moved into the main hospital (Ward 0400). Barnes Hospital had four operating rooms, a cystoscopy room, a pathology laboratory, and a recovery room. During the 1918 calendar year, before Graham's arrival, there were 1900 operations—1138 by the surgical service, 260 by the gynecology service, 390 by special services, and 112 cystoscopies. The cost per patient-day was $2.96, of which 30¢ represented the cost of food.[24]

Graham's surgical department headquarters, staff offices, and research laboratories were across Euclid Avenue on the second floor of the North Building. At the east end of the corridor was his office and the laboratory for general and thoracic surgical pathology. Three-quarters of the floor was devoted to research laboratories, canine facilities, and offices for Ernest Sachs and others who would be recruited by Graham in the next few years (Heinbecker, Cole, Womack, and Key). Graham's Department of Surgery provided the organizational home for radiology and a half-time salary for an arrangement that, with the coming of Sherwood Moore, would be especially fortuitous for the development of cholecystography 5 years later (see chapter 6).

---

j. Barnes Hospital was designed with four open wards—two medical and two surgical, male and female of each—each containing 24 patients, with cloth curtains between them for separation and privacy. These beds were under control of the chief residents, men of 3 to 5 years' experience, whose responsibilities in determining admission, treatment, and discharge created the educational setting. The patients were indigent or occasionally had low-paying jobs. There was no private physician in charge except as supervisor of the chief resident, and no professional fee was collected. The costs of care were borne either by the hospital or were from a special endowment fund donated by Robert and Harry Brookings. The hospital also had private (single) and semiprivate (double) rooms for paying patients. As the fame of Barnes Hospital increased, the need for private beds created a constant pressure to reduce the number of ward beds or to admit private patients to them. Private physicians and surgeons devised several expedients to escape the arrangement that gave the ward service and ward beds to the house staff.

The "Town-Gown" Conflict

The staff hired by Murphy also experienced strained relations with surgeons of St. Louis, for the appointment of full-time chiefs of service and a closed hospital staff were new and poorly understood features. St. Louis, with its several medical schools, was a hotbed of professional rivalry, and many distinguished physicians staffed the two schools that had become Washington University Medical School. The appointment of outsiders as clinical faculty for the school and its affiliated hospitals, along with accompanying shifts in titles and appointments, brought resentment that was aimed more at Barnes Hospital than at the Medical School. Only Henry Schwartz, as the obstetrician-in-chief, was retained from the old St. Louis cadre.[31] Graham was a young man imported from afar, and he easily fit into the eager, newly reorganized faculty that felt a sense of personal responsibility for the success of their enterprise. They hoped Washington University would serve as a model, and that their experiences might benefit not only the local area but inspire other schools to raise standards and lift the level of medical education in America. Theirs was an idealism and enthusiasm that traditionally belongs to youth with a sound training and a devotion to standards of excellence.[31]

Graham chose to keep the surgical staff he had inherited and to bring new men onto his staff from his own training program, rather than importing or making more town appointments. Shaffer recalled that "Dr. Graham's tact and good judgement were at once evident in his success in that feat of adjustment, ... he decided to utilize fully the existing staff and to train young assistants from local men rather than to import ready trained new associates. ... He trains young surgeons in the department from the bottom up ... and a strong loyalty to his staff, junior as well as senior associates, are the qualities which laid the foundation for the admiration and loyalty of this group."[1]

In January 1920, after nomination by Ernest Sachs and G. Canby Robinson, Graham was elected to membership in the St. Louis Medical Society and became active and visible in their scientific programs. Throughout his St. Louis tenure, Graham made presentations, presided over panels, and organized clinics for the society's benefit, but after serving as chairman of its program committee for 3 years, in February 1925, he asked to be relieved of his chairmanship. He always maintained an arms-length relationship with the society, even though it conferred upon him and his associates Cole, Copher, and Moore an Award of Merit[k] for their

---

k. Evarts Graham and his co-workers were singularly honoured by the St. Louis Medical Society for their research leading to cholecystography. Graham received a Gold Medal specifically designed for this event and a Certificate of Merit, which also was awarded to Warren Cole, Glover Copher, and Sherwood Moore. Dr. Louis Behrens, the president, made an address that began with a brief outline of the work and ended with letters and telegrams of congratulations from the Mayos, Crile, Bevan,

"epoch making work on gallbladder function and visualization."[40] The presentation was made on Tuesday evening, June 8, 1927, in the Medical Society auditorium on Lindell Boulevard.

Just 2 days after Graham received the Award of Merit, the "town-gown" discord in St. Louis between the full-time clinical faculty of Washington University and the practicing physicians of St. Louis surfaced in the medical society bulletin. Its editor, R.B.H. Gradwohl, penned the first of two lengthy editorials expressing his dislike of the Washington University salary system, its qualifications for appointment to both the Washington University faculty and Barnes Hospital staff, and its management of the dispensary. Gradwohl was a pathologist in the process of developing the laboratories that analyzed blood and urine specimens received from doctors offices throughout St. Louis, to which they subsequently reported. Gradwohl was more of a businessman than a physician. His laboratories became a significant feature in the St. Louis medical community, and, as editor of the medical society bulletin, he wrote:

> The full-time teachers are supremely selfish. ... men accept these full-time jobs with the full consciousness that if they continue to do good work they will have life-time positions. Consequently they care but little for the future of the practitioner ... for their own future only. Most of them, by the way, would be incapable of securing a remunerative and living private practice. Some of them become full-time teachers because they are too TIMID to face the hardships of acquiring a private practice. Their job is a life of ease ... they live in a nice apartment, own a Ford or a Dodge or even a Buick and take part in the social life to which their professorial positions entitle them and become rather self-satisfied personages in the community.[41]

Five months later he continued his attack:

> It's all very baffling and incomprehensible, a situation grafted upon us out of the most commendable enthusiasm. But hasn't it gone far enough now to indicate that it won't do? Why not discharge all the full-time men, put them back in training under the clinical professors who after all are doing the real work in medical teaching and once and

---

Horsley, Finney, and others. The award read: "In recognition of this accomplishment, which is a most valuable contribution to the science of medicine, your society has unanimously voted you a medal, a ribbon and a certificate of merit. In conferring this single honour upon you your society is also honored by this effort—making it an achievement of a group of its members."[40]

for all do away with this fetish which the Rockefeller Foundation and other misguided but well meaning organizations have visited upon our profession and public? … Universities cannot engage the services of accomplished and skillful physicians as full-time teachers of clinical medicine. First because they don't want them. Secondly, because they can't get them. The years of experience as a clinician is not nearly as much of a recommendation to become Head of Surgery as three or four years of extricating spleens … or puncturing … guinea pigs in an experimental surgical laboratory. Ten years in clinical medicine … and private practice is not as good as twelve months in biological chemistry. … One thing protects these laboratory men who overnight become heads of medicine or surgery. … the walls around the teaching hospital are very high; they tell no tales. These operators probably work in sealed operating rooms until the operator graduates from a "mouse surgeon"[l] into a "man surgeon."

Were our profession a labor union, the situation could be remedied overnight. All clinical professors, all clinical assistants and underlings would walk out or … [the University should] … pay every man jack of them a good salary. Why not? … The ultimatum then would be 'fire the full-time professor, let him go to work as we are doing,' let all clinical instructors work for nothing as they formerly did and all will be well. Better work would be done in the teaching hospitals, better operations performed and the public would be better served because we could give them better doctors. The evil of free clinics would be corrected because the men in practice would have a hand in their correction and would naturally be more sympathetic than the men now in the school who naturally have no interest in the man in the street.[43]

---

l. Several generations of Barnes Hospital house staff and faculty have propagated the story that Graham was called a "mouse surgeon" by a prominent member of the St. Louis Medical Society. The date, the circumstances and name of the caller have never been identified with as much conviction as that such name calling had occurred. The editorials of R.B.H. Gradwohl are almost certainly the origins of this legend. Although there is no specific reference to Graham as a mouse surgeon, it was obvious to everyone that Graham was the target of the attack. Seven years later Graham paid a visit to Princeton, and, during a conversation with Abraham Flexner, the latter asked for a clinical opinion regarding discomfort in his shoulder, something a bit out of order in that setting. A few days later as a half-apology, Flexner wrote: "I think I paid you a high compliment when I asked you about my shoulder. It shows that I have as much confidence in a mouse surgeon—perhaps more—than in surgeons who are supposed to limit their attention to human beings."[42] Graham never forgave Gradwohl, and his subsequent relations with the medical society were exceedingly cool and very proper.

The Washington University full-time faculty received the Gradwohl comments without overt protest, but the issue continued to simmer, with the feeling that full-time clinicians and the dispensary were stealing patients from town practitioners. The society became increasingly concerned about the Washington University Dispensary in regard to whom might be seen there and whether the dispensary would accept patients who were able to pay.

One year later Graham received a letter from Dr. J.M. Ball asking if he would be willing to become president of the St. Louis Medical Society: "The Society is in the situation where it needs—not a politician—but a strong man at the helm. You are that man."[44] It is unclear as to how much authority the executive group of the medical society had given for this invitation, but a couple of statements in the letter suggest that Ball was uncomfortable with the society's leadership and wished to provide a strong alternative candidate.[44] Three days later Graham outlined his reasons for refusal:

> I have never been the least bit interested in political offices in medical organizations: in fact, I always shudder at the thought of such things. ... If my name should be announced as a candidate for President I should at once become a storm center of politics. This would be so distasteful to me that I cannot even think of it. ... Finally, I would say that the majority of the members of the St. Louis Medical Society are not interested at all in the things in which I am chiefly interested and that fact would constitute one reason why I would be a poor selection.[45]

In 1931 the Washington University Board redefined the nature of dispensary management, having recognized that it functioned as the outpatient activity of Barnes Hospital more than it did as an outpatient doctor's office. It was reorganized under a board of managers as a distinct, affiliated unit, functioning within the medical group in a fashion analogous to that of the several hospitals.[46] On April 19, 1932, 4 years after the second of Gradwohl's editorials, the Washington University Dispensary officially changed its name to the Washington University Clinics.

In October 1933 the St. Louis Medical Society appointed a "Code and Contract Board" that was to create a policy regarding hospitals, dispensaries, interns, and patients who may be able to pay.[47] The board met with representatives from the hospitals and the two medical schools, and by 1934 had prepared a "Proposed Declaration of Agreement between the Code and Contract Board of the St. Louis Medical Society and the Hospitals."[48] The proposed declaration only vaguely hid the medical society's concerns regarding the Washington University Clinics and its apparent failure to exclude anyone who might be able to pay a fee. The declaration defined who is and what constitutes an indigent, evinced concerns as to whether or not an individual had seen a private physician, and was critical of care given by interns. It clearly stated its "intention to retain within the private practice of individual physicians as many patients as possible," a principle somewhat at variance with the ideas of many on the medical faculty. The document specified that an intern or house officer could not give professional service to a patient paying any fee whatsoever unless the patient was assigned to a practicing physician who was appraised of all services rendered by the intern or house officer and who had the right to collect a proper and just professional fee; there was an obligation that any patient treated in the dispensary, later found to have been able to pay, would be charged. The intern or staff physician was obligated to "refer such individuals to the care of the patient's private physician."[48] The document specified that each hospital would send two members to a Code and Contract Committee that would act to oversee and ensure the cooperation of the hospital.[48]

Graham had major objections to the Code and Contract Committee document and was invited to make presentations to the board, not in his role as department chairman but as surgeon-in-chief of Barnes Hospital, to make his position known. Coerced, he met with this group on January 26, 1934, and submitted it with a four-page, 2000-word letter that outlined his objections. He stated that interns and house officers should have free and easy access to all individuals who come to the clinics or to Barnes Hospital, and that they should care for them without an obligation to return them to a community physician. He wrote the reasons for his reluctance to cooperate: "If it had not been for the insistence of both yourself and the members of the Board I should not have spoken. I was fearful that my remarks, given extemporaneously, might be misunderstood ... that they might be interpreted as an expression merely of personal spleen." His letter concluded by saying that the medical society was "seeking to gain a control over the hospitals, the medical schools and even the individual members of the medical profession of the City which is, frankly, intolerable. The various threats of coercion which were both stated and implied in the resolutions ... can have no other implication than that [the] administration is seeking to place the St. Louis Medical Society in a position of dictatorship ... to go so far as to influence the medical schools of this city with reference to policies of education."[49] An agreement embodying medical society conclusions that was sent to Barnes Hospital to be signed by three members of the Code and Contract Board, two officers of the society, and six representatives of Barnes Hospital was never signed.[50]

Undaunted, the St. Louis Society began to send members to surrounding county medical societies. In early 1935 a visitor to the South East Missouri Medical Society in Cape Girardeau, Missouri, asked that they pass resolutions boycotting the Barnes Hospital Clinic as well as all doctors associated with Barnes Hospital. No action was taken at that time, but 3 months later the Cape Girardeau Society was asked to send a speaker to a meeting in St. Louis devoted to a discussion of clinic abuse. In October eight men from the St. Louis Medical Society went to Cape

Girardeau and, after directing remarks toward clinic abuse at Barnes Hospital, proposed a resolution to the South East Society that it should boycott Barnes and all doctors connected with it. The resolution was muted by the time it was passed at a business meeting on the next day, but the episode demonstrated the determination of the St. Louis Society.[51]

The failure of the January 26 meeting of hospital representatives with the Code and Contract Board was largely due to the fact that almost all of the hospital representatives felt that the society was attempting to form an organization similar to a trade union. Graham commented that "the only difference between those rules and regulations and those of a trade union was that it was not stipulated how many hours a member of the Society would be permitted to work per day."[52] The agreement of the Code and Contract Board with the proposed boycotts was never formalized, and the effort was taken over by the society's Medical Economics Committee that had been studying free and part-pay services rendered by hospitals and clinics, and the methods of payment for such services. After consultations with an advisory group, the Medical Economics Committee decided that a greater service could be rendered to St. Louis doctors by adopting certain control procedures. It submitted an outline for a "Central Hospital and Clinic Admitting Bureau" that would review all patients seen in the Washington University Clinics and the Barnes Emergency Rooms with specific regard to ability to pay and assignment to a private physician. It proposed that all clinic patients first be sent to a private practitioner who would then become the gatekeeper for either clinic or dispensary care.[53] This proposal also failed to accomplish its desired ends. The Washington University Clinics continued to function, and, as war clouds gathered, the issue became less prominent.

Town-gown friction resurfaced during World War II but in a different venue. It was now between members of the Washington University clinical faculty (part-timers) who brought their patients into Barnes Hospital (the *town*), against members of the Washington University faculty (full-timers—the *gown*). The clinical faculty organized itself as the Barnes Hospital Society to counterbalance the academic interests of an executive faculty that was felt not always to move in the best interests of the clinicians of the hospital. The psychological factors in this conflict were related to social values, political attitudes, economics, and, above all, to the different philosophies of the full-time teacher versus the clinical practitioner.[31]

In mid-1941 David Barr, professor of medicine, proposed a group practice from the Washington Clinics that, by contract, would give medical or health care to social organizations, unions, institutions, or business corporations in the St. Louis area. After several months of discussion, the plan was dropped, and Barr left St. Louis to become professor of medicine at Cornell.

In April 1943 the Washington University Clinics separated itself from the control of Washington University and became incorporated as a free-standing agency with representatives from Washington University and Barnes and Children's

Hospitals on its board of managers. In April 1944 Dean Philip Shaffer proposed a clinic operated with a full-time, full-salaried staff that would care for private (paying) as well as indigent patients, with the net income from this enterprise reverting to the Medical School. The Washington University's full-time faculty now began to think of a clinic patterned after that of the Mayo brothers. Shaffer proposed the construction of a building to house 150 doctors and clinic areas for patients. Although in favor of the proposal, Graham thought that 1944 was not the proper time for the construction since most of the hospital staff were in military service. He thought it would be a misplaced trust to make such changes before they returned. By October 1944 plans had been laid for a clinic building to house both full- and part-time faculty, and, although Graham felt this was probably desirable, he also felt it had to be well thought out before it was done.[2] In November 1944 the board of clinic managers presented the proposal to what was left of the Barnes Hospital Society saying that the new clinic would be a self-supporting institution and its administrative trusteeship would be a charitable nonprofit corporation.[54] In January 1945 Shaffer presented a resolution to the executive faculty that would deny appointments to the staff of the proposed clinic to any except full-time physicians. Graham and others protested and, following a motion by Graham, discussion of the resolution was postponed. The issue now became the paramount topic of conversation between physicians at Barnes and Children's Hospitals. At mid-1945 a filibuster meeting was held by the part-time faculty, and, over the next 6 months, they managed to kill Shaffer's proposal when it was presented to the Washington University Corporation Board. In February 1946 Graham met with Frank Bradley, the hospital director, to inform him, "we took a licking at the Corporation meeting. Several errors were made. ... Shaffer made errors in the entire matter by being too persistent and impatient."[2] The clinic issue did not disappear. The members of the Barnes Hospital Society became proactive, hired a public relations agency, and extensively lobbied the administrative chiefs of the university. In a long letter to Evarts Graham, the society formally outlined its reasons for opposing the full-time clinic and listed seven points of concern as to why such a clinic could not succeed.[55] By February 1948 after 3 years of internal turmoil, the clinic effort was abandoned. The Medical School then turned to the making of hospital affiliations with construction of Barnard, Renard, and Wohl Hospitals in proximity to Barnes, and an expanded roster of clinicians.

An all-university clinic for patients of all economic classes became a reality in 1952 when the Wohl Clinic Building was built, containing clinic space and offices for the full-time medical and surgical faculty. The Washington University Clinics on Euclid Avenue was closed, and the space was converted to rehabilitation uses. Even though the closing of the clinics occurred concomitant with an increase in hospital and medical insurance and fewer indigents, the faculty had become divided, full time versus part time—and suspicion and distrust between the two groups lingered for years. Graham's hopes for a Mayo Clinic type of practice that had taken him to Mason City failed to materialize for him in St. Louis.

The proposed full-time clinic exacerbated friction between part-time and full-time men in Graham's department. By 1947 there was an overt confrontation about the group practice concept, and several outstanding part-time surgeons moved from Barnes to St. Luke's Hospital, threatening to build a doctor's hospital that would compete with the Barnes/Washington University Medical Center.[38] Graham filled the vacancies with his own resident trainees.

In December 1949, shortly before Graham's upcoming retirement, J. William Thompson, president of the medical society and a previous chairman of the Code and Contract Board, wrote to Graham, indicating Graham's election to honor membership in the St. Louis Medical Society. This honor, given to a distinguished member of the profession by a vote of the society, was a major tribute to Evarts Graham from a hostile St. Louis Medical Society.[56]

Chapter 6

CHOLECYSTOGRAPHY

THE START

The cholecystography saga began in the spring of 1923, when Evarts Graham summoned Warren Cole[a], a first-year resident, to his office in the North Building. Upon receiving the call, Cole entertained thoughts that many residents subsequently experienced: "These are my walking papers." He felt sure that Dr. Graham's mind was no doubt completely made up about his dismissal.[1] It was unnecessary apprehension, for Graham's greeting was friendly, and Cole's concerns disappeared when Graham offered a 1-year job in the laboratory, after which he would resume his residency.[1] Although a year in Europe at an operative clinic was not unusual, a year in an experimental laboratory was, but Cole accepted Graham's offer, and that year became a significant event in Cole's subsequent rise as a major figure in American surgery.

---

a. Warren Cole (1898 to 1990) was born on a farm near Clay Center, Kansas, and his education began in a one-room school 1.5 miles from home. He entered high school at the age of 12, the University of Kansas at Lawrence in 1914, and, following 2 years of undergraduate and 2 years of medical school in Lawrence (a 2-year school), he enrolled in Washington University and received his doctor of medicine degree in 1920. After a medical internship under Dr. Thomas J. Boggs at the Baltimore City Hospital, he spent a year as a surgical intern at Barnes Hospital before spending 4 years as a surgical resident, one of which was his year of cholecystography research with Graham. Cole became an instructor in surgery in 1926, and, between 1924 and 1928, he coauthored 16 articles with Graham

Conversation about the project began with Graham's observations on the 1910 report by Abel[b] and Rowntree that chlorinated phthalein compounds were excreted by the liver and would be concentrated in the gallbladder.[2] Phenolphthalein was being used as a cathartic, for many years sold as Ex-Lax, and Abel was investigating its laxative properties. Later Rowntree and others noted its color properties and suggested it could also be used as a liver function test.[3] In the first Alvarez lecture, Graham stated it was difficult to recall exactly how the idea of possibly visualizing the gallbladder by using phenolphthalein presented itself, but he gives the date as sometime in the winter of 1922 to 1923.[4]

In all of his writings on this topic, Graham credits the Abel and Rowntree observations, yet speculations frequently arise as to the role that his wife Helen may have played in the evolution of the idea that iodine or bromine attached to the phenolphthalein molecule might make the gallbladder opaque to x-rays. Helen had

---

and/or Copher on studies of the biliary tree. After refusing positions at Vanderbilt University in Nashville, Tennessee, and the University of Kentucky in Louisville, he accepted the chairmanship at the University of Illinois College of Medicine in 1936. This full-time position was in contrast to the clinical tradition of his predecessor J.B. Murphy ("Stormy Petrol") and permitted very productive years. His interests turned to infections and the study of cancer cells shed into the blood stream. He became president of the American Cancer Society, the American College of Surgeons, and the American Surgical Association before he retired in 1966.

A lean, wiry, quiet, and reticent man, he had an unpretentious dignity and a capacity for long and hard work, and, although socially insecure, he was certain of himself in an unassuming way. His ability to make keen and astute observations was an outstanding talent. As a result of a childless marriage to Clara, students and residents became his family. The Warren Cole Society has a worldwide membership of unusual size and exceptional personal loyalty. After retirement to Ashville, North Carolina, he continued to fish, write, and interact with his many pupils. In May 1990 he died quietly, leaving a noteworthy record of teaching, research, and clinical practice.

b. John Jacob Abel (1857 to 1938) was born on a farm near Cleveland, Ohio, and, after teaching high school Latin, mathematics, physics, and chemistry in La Porte, Indiana, he obtained a baccalaureate and a doctor of philosophy degree from the University of Michigan. From 1884 to 1891, he studied chemistry and medicine at Leipzig, Strassburg (now Strasbourg), Heidelburg, Vienna, Berne, Würzburg, and Berlin. After obtaining a medical degree from Strassburg, he returned to the University of Michigan as professor of materia medica and therapeutics. In 1893 Abel was called to Johns Hopkins Medical School, where he served as professor of pharmacology until his retirement in 1932. His Department of Pharmacology was the first in the United States, and many of his graduate students created departments of their own. He established pharmacology as a special discipline within the field of biochemistry, and he was an influential figure in the developmental years of the Johns Hopkins Medical School, standing alongside Mall in anatomy, MacCallum in pathology, and Howell in physiology. He was interested in the manner by which an organism reacts to agents isolated from various tissues, and he explored the possibility that histamine was the active principle elaborated by the pituitary. During 1918 to 1919, when Evarts Graham was in Camp Lee with the Empyema Commission, Helen Tredway Graham served as a special graduate student working with histamine in Abel's laboratory. She undoubtedly became conversant with the work that Abel and Rowntree had performed 8 years earlier on the excretion of chlorinated phenolphthalein.

worked in Abel's laboratory 8 years after the initial work on the phthalein deriva-tives, and, while she was there, one of Abel's students was studying the rate of disappearance of tetrachlorophenolphthalein from the blood. Evarts never acknowledged an indebtedness to Helen for his idea, so it is unlikely that she was a direct influence, for he certainly would have given her due credit. It is always pos-sible that he was subliminally prepared through discussions with Helen, but it seems as though the idea was solely Graham's.

Warren Cole spent the 1923 to 1924 year in the laboratory, and in 1924 he pub-lished the first of a number of papers on successful visualization of the gallbladder. Cholecystography became known as the Graham-Cole test, and Cole achieved international fame before he had completed his surgical residency. Graham had spent little time in his laboratories that year for the National Research Council, numerous medical meetings, and department responsibilities kept him busy; how-ever, he always consulted Cole when he returned from out-of-town trips, and they established a personal bond of friendship that lasted throughout Graham's life.

By 1922 it was known that ingested phthaleins appeared in the bile, first in con-jugated form, and 20 minutes later in free form; some time later they were excret-ed in the urine. In the bile the compounds were concentrated[c] at least 8 to 10 times,[5] something that was demonstrated by adding dilute alkali to bile and mea-suring the depth of color in a colorimeter. Many years later in a conversation with Rowntree, Cole asked why Rowntree and Abel had not carried their observations to the discovery of cholecystography. Rowntree replied that it was "an example of being so close to the forest that he could not see the trees."[6]

Cole initially consulted catalogues of various chemical firms to see if brominat-ed or iodinated phenolphthaleins were available. Tetraiodophenolphthalein from

---

c. Phenolphthalein has three properties of interest. The first is the laxative property that Abel and Rowntree were studying; the second is that the acid and alkaline forms are different in color; and the third is that tetraiodophenolphthalein has antiseptic properties resulting in its use for many years as a dressing powder to introduce iodine into a wound. The two phenol side chains contain four sites (the phthalein moiety also has four) to which iodine atoms may bind (see the figure on page 104). Phenoltetraiodophthalein has an intense blue purple color at body pH and visibly stains the serum. Tetraiodophenolphthalein is not visible at body pH, but its concentration may be determined by the addition of sodium hydroxide that converts it into a measurable purple form. Its use as a liver func-tion test was later replaced by the use of sulfobromophthalein sodium (Bromsulphalein; BSP).

The observation that the liver would concentrate and excrete phenoltetrachlorophthalein was made with almost as much serendipity as was the development of cholecystography by Harry Riedell's oversight. Abel and Rowntree were studying phenolphthalein's laxative effects on dogs when, one day, the diener, Charles Kampnis, noticed red bile coming from a bile duct that he had acciden-tally severed during the autopsy he performed after an experiment. He called this to Abel's attention, who then switched his research efforts from the cathartic activity of phenolphthalein to its modes of hepatic excretion.

Phenolphthalein
$C_{20}H_{14}O_4$

Tetraiodophenolphthalein   Phenoltetraiodophthalein

**Similar compounds may be made using either
chlorine (Cl), bromine (Br), or iodine (I)**

the Eastman Kodak Company was obtained and injected into several dogs to see if their gallbladders could be visualized. The compounds were unpredictable; in several instances animals died after receiving doses considerably smaller than those given to animals that survived. Iodine compounds were found to be more toxic than their bromine homologues. After the trials with Eastman Kodak phenol-phthaleins, Graham enlisted the services of Mallinckrodt Chemical Works of St. Louis, and it began to supply Cole with halogenated phenolphthaleins. Edward Mallinckrodt Jr. (a comember with Graham in the St. Louis Round Table) developed a personal interest in the problem and assigned Dr. N. Drake, a chemist, to work on the manufacture of tetraiodophenolphthalein and tetrabromophenol-phthalein. The former has a molecular weight of 822 and contains approximately

61 percent iodine, whereas the latter, with a molecular weight of 634, contains 54 percent bromine[d].

Cole initially used acidic compounds that he would neutralize with a weak alkali, and in later attempts he used strontium or calcium salts rather than sodium, in the belief that heavier cations would increase x-ray density. Sensitivity to iodine was well known, and there was always concern as to whether an iodinated compound would have an unacceptable rate of systemic reactions. Although the bromine effort was pursued because it was believed that there would be fewer side effects, Drake continued his efforts with iodine. It was ultimately found that adverse reactions to iodine were due to impurities in preparation, and, after these were eliminated, Drake produced a purified tetraiodophenolphthalein that was safe for intravenous administration. The material was delivered as a dry powder, and Cole was required to mix, titrate, and sterilize the compounds each day before use.

THE SETTING, THE DOGS, AND THE FIRST SHADOW

The second floor of the north wing of the basic science building housed the offices and laboratories of the Department of Surgery. A crawl space between the fourth floor and the roof was used to store surgical pathology specimens, and the roof had kennels and an open dog run. The departmental office (Graham's) was at the east end of the second floor, and members of his faculty (Heinbecker, Womack, Sachs, Key, Cole, and Elman) had research offices on the second floor. There were also two small dog operating rooms, a conference room, and an L-shaped room in which dogs were housed in individual cages. Across from Cole's laboratory was a special room where four dogs were housed, fed, and prepared for the cholecystography experiments. Dogs on the roof were kept in a free-running, fenced-in area and were brought to the second-floor cages for experiments or other activities, as needed. Since there were no radiography facilities, Cole transported his animals through a tunnel under Euclid Avenue to Barnes Hospital, a chore that fell to him since surgical laboratory assistants ceased work at 5:00 pm. Walter Mills, the Barnes radiologist, was involved in the effort from its beginning until his death in 1924 (due to over exposure to x-rays), and his chief radiography technician, Miss K. O'Brien, cooperated by staying overtime, taking the radiographs, and making sure before

---

d. The halogens.

Name	Atomic No.	Atomic Weight
Fluorine	9	19.0
Chlorine	17	35.5
Bromine	35	79.9
Iodine	53	126.9
Astatine	85	210.0

she left that there were good films. The chief diener, Harry Riedell, obtained dogs from the pound, assigned them, supervised the operating rooms, and was in charge of the overall care and management of the animal facility. Two men were assigned to feed and care for dogs on the roof.

Each morning Cole prepared the compounds to be tested that day, injected the dogs or rabbits by 8:30 or 9:00 am, and obtained the radiographs after 5:00 pm. Feeding and cage cleaning usually occurred in mid-morning, but one morning the upstairs men, after feeding the dogs on the roof, failed to come down and feed those on the second floor. Mr. Riedell, busy with other things, fed some of the dogs but failed to feed one in the special cholecystography holding area. That afternoon the defining event occurred—the dog's gallbladder was seen on a radiograph, and an excited Miss O'Brien called Cole from the radiography dark room. She had spent so many hours helping with the project that she was about as anxious as was Cole for a positive radiograph. Around 5:30 to 5:40 pm, Cole called Graham's office hoping to find him there. As usual, Graham was working late; he went directly to the x-ray department. While the two were looking at the film, Cole said: "This shadow is so dense and so round that it looks like a golf ball. You don't suppose that one of my resident friends has placed a golf ball into the abdominal cavity of this animal do you?" Graham replied, "I confess that it would be a splendid joke to play on you, but I don't think it is a golf ball. I think it looks more like a muskie and if the line doesn't break we should land him."[1]

After visualizing the gallbladder in the one dog, similar compounds failed to reproduce the finding. A few days later, Cole approached Riedell to find out just what had happened on that fateful day, and he asked if there had been anything abnormal about that dog. Riedell hesitated, stammered a bit, and announced that he could think of no way in which it differed from the others. His apprehension melted when he learned that the dog was a favored one, and, very meekly, as if fearing a sharp reprimand, he muttered: "Well Dr. Cole there was one thing somewhat different. I forgot to feed that dog the morning you injected him." Certain that he would be fired, Riedell requested that Cole not mention it to Dr. Graham, even as Cole tried to express appreciation for the great favor Riedell had unknowingly conferred upon them. The lack of food during the test hours made this dog different from the others, and fasting became a basic requirement of cholecystography.[1] Cole had been aware of an observation that eating caused an emptying of the gallbladder.[7] but only now realized the significance of fasting. Three dogs were fasted following injection, and the gallbladder showed up on films from all three. Cole then moved immediately to develop the technique for use in human beings. Graham's and Cole's perseverance over 4 months of testing on approximately 200 animals testifies to their conviction that the basic concept was correct.

Shortly thereafter, Cole's log book on this initial episode and the x-ray film that showed the shadow disappeared. The loss coincided with a visit by an out-of-town guest, who later began to brag to friends that he held them. When Graham discovered the identity of the pilferer, the log book and film were soon returned. This film was used in the initial publication in the *Journal of the American Medical Association*, in which the gallbladder is seen as a round, black shadow rather than the now conventional white image[e], suggesting that a positive image was shown in this particular article.[9]

Harry Riedell died in 1937. His son, Harry Riedell Jr., had begun part-time work in the animal laboratories, and subsequent to army duty during World War II, became the director and successor to his father. At the elder Riedell's funeral, Drs. Graham and Copher visited the Riedell home to speak with his widow; after attending the wake, they stayed for about 2 hours to express appreciation for the service he had given during the previous two decades.[10]

GOING CLINICAL

The doses of tetrabromophenolphthalein that Cole used in dogs were close to the lethal limit of 0.3 g/kg of body weight; that first dog with which success had been achieved had received 0.28 g/kg. It was decided that patients would be given less than one-tenth of the animal lethal dose per body weight, and that calcium tetrabromophenolphthalein would be the drug of choice.

The first patient received 1 g without major incident, although three bowel movements within 24 hours supported the findings of Abel and Rowntree that, with intravenous administration, tetrabromophenolphthalein acts as a laxative. The next four recipients received increasingly larger doses. Finally, 6 g of the bromine compound was considered the maximum safe intravenous dose. Ten consecutive patients, all with symptoms of gallbladder disease, received the maximum dose before February 21, 1924, when a good shadow of a human gallbladder appeared in the film of a nurse who complained of right-upper quadrant pain, which was subsequently found to be of renal origin. Films taken at 4, 8, 24, and 32

---

e. The initial dog cholecystogram published in the *Journal of the American Medical Association* illustrates the gallbladder as a black circle; the ribs are also black, and the surrounding areas are gray or white. Current radiographic procedures show the reverse; areas opaque to x-rays are white. In cholecystograms published 4 years later in Graham's book on biliary tract diseases,[8] the gallbladder, ribs, and vertebral column appear black, and the surrounding areas are white or gray. The gallbladder is presented to the reader's right and the spine to the left, as if the patient were being viewed from behind. The section discussing radiographic technique stresses that all patients must lie prone, with the x-ray beam directed from back to front. Film techniques of the early 1920s were similar to current black and white techniques, in which a "negative" results from the deposition of free silver following the action of light or x-rays; this is then enhanced by chemical development, and a positive image is made. Modern radiographic techniques eliminate the second step, and images on films show the patient as seen from the front.

hours after injection showed no shadow on the 4-hour film; a large, faint shadow on the 8-hour film; and a dense shadow on 24-hour film. Persistence was attributed to the prolonged fasting.

Adverse clinical reactions to the test were not insignificant: approximately 10 percent of the patients experienced some nausea, diarrhea, or feelings of being unwell. However, severe toxic effects were few, and, according to Graham and Cole's data, there was only one possible fatality in some 3000 patients. Cole and Graham soon learned that the absence of a shadow was an indication of gallbladder disease, and since failure to visualize became the important diagnostic finding, a rigid routine for oral or injection administration of contrast material[f] was made with the assumption that a normal gallbladder would routinely be visualized.

Sherwood Moore[g] now became the dominant figure in the cholecystography effort. Walter Mills had died, and Moore, still a member of the Department of Surgery, began to devote more and more of his time to radiology. As the number of patients increased, he, Cole, and Copher continuously refined the clinical aspects of cholecystography.

Mallinckrodt Chemical Works soon began to prepare ampules of calcium tetra-bromophenolpthalein for intravenous use, something that Cole considered a great

---

f. A standard set of orders in the 1920s for the intravenous administration of contrast material follows:

1. Take 2.5 g of sodium bicarbonate every 3 hours, while awake, for 48 hours prior to the test.
2. Omit breakfast on the day of the test.
3. Omit lunch (a glass of milk is permitted if hunger is pressing).
4. Sit up or lie on the right side of the abdomen [Lying on the right side was thought to encourage filling of the gallbladder because of the effect of gravity.]
5. Take water if desired.
6. Omit protein from the evening meal on the day of injection.
7. Undergo radiography at 4, 8, 24, and 32 hours after injection.

g. Sherwood Moore (1880 to 1963) was born in Virginia and graduated from the Washington University School of Medicine in 1905. After an internship and 2 years of obstetrics and gynecology, he entered the private practice of surgery in St. Louis, where, from 1910 to 1913, he was an assistant to Malvern Clopton. In 1916 Moore became the first resident in radiology at the Massachusetts General Hospital, and in 1917 he returned to Washington University as an assistant in surgery and radiology. In 1924 Moore began his collaboration with Graham, Cole, and Copher and carried the radiologic portion of cholecystography research and its subsequent clinical demands. By 1926 he was an associate surgeon, and in 1927 he also became professor of radiology.

Moore was the founding chairman of Washington University's Department of Radiology, and he gave up surgery in 1930 to become director of the Mallinckrodt Institute of Radiology, the first such institute in the United States. President of the American Roentgen Ray Society and director of the American Cancer Society, he received the first honor award of the Radiologic Society of North America. Other certificates of merit and gold medals soon came his way. He was fluent in Greek, Latin, German, and French and held military offices in both world wars, from 1917 to 1922 as lieutenant in the US Naval Reserve, and from 1922 to 1942 as major and then lieutenant colonel in the Medical Corps of the US Army. In 1949 he retired to his farm in the Ozarks. He is buried in Lynchburg, Virginia.

boon, for he was no longer required to be a part of the preparation process. Oral compounds, which caused nausea and occasional vomiting, came next; the capsules were prepared with coatings of keratin over an inner layer of sodium bicarbonate that would not dissolve until passed into the small intestine. Phenolphthaleins soon began to be used in the role of indicator—particularly sodium phenoltetraiodophthalein, a compound whose fluorescent purple colors the blood serum. Using a color comparator box, it was possible to follow its disappearance from plasma or serum over 1 to 2 hours after injection or ingestion.

Mallinckrodt Chemical Works produced a total of 89 drugs, of which 13 were found to be sufficiently concentrated in the gallbladder to be useful. Four of these compounds were initially accepted for clinical use since others had disadvantages, chiefly toxicity and a staining of the tissues. Tetraiodophenolphthalein and phenoltetraiodophthalein were manufactured and sold by Mallinckrodt Chemical Works under the names Iodeikon and Isoiodeikon. Isoiodeikon was the superior compound because, as a dye, it allowed the determination of hepatic function simultaneously with its use in cholecystography.[6,8,11,12] Sixteen years passed before new compounds were developed, mostly for oral use, and during these years the most widely used compounds were Iodeikon and its isomer Isoiodeikon. In 1940 Schering introduced Priodax (an iodoalphionic acid) followed by Telepaque (an iopanoic acid) then Ipodate or Orografin (ethyltriodoalphonic acids), Teridax, and, lastly, Cholegrafin (an intravenous drug used for demonstrating the common bile duct rather than the gallbladder). All have been supplanted by the increasing sophistication of ultrasonography of the gallbladder.

LIVER FUNCTION TESTS AND THE FATTY MEAL

Two compounds were used in attempts to obtain a cholecystogram and test liver function simultaneously. Tetraiodophenolphthalein is a blue powder; when dissolved in a dilute alkali, it produces a blue solution but does not color the blood serum. Phenoltetraiodophthalein is a powder that yields a fluorescent purple color in the blood serum when a weak alkali is added. With practically no side effects, 2.5 g of phenoltetraiodophthalein produced good shadows of a normal gallbladder, and it could be given intravenously in less than 5 minutes. The adult dosage was 40 mg/kg to a maximum of 2.5 g. This dosage was larger than that possible with other liver function dyes in use at the time, and Graham and Cole believed that by inflicting a greater load on the liver, they would detect lesser degrees of impaired function. The amount of dye remaining in the serum at 30 minutes and at 1 hour was determined, and retention of 10 to 12 percent in 30 minutes and 5 percent in 1 hour was considered normal. They soon learned that the test was essential in jaundiced patients, for, within a few months, there were three operative deaths following cholecystectomy; all three had high serum retention (99 percent in one patient). Graham always used this compound since dye retention determined oper-ability, and he rarely operated on patients with greater than 40 percent retention.[8]

One of the early modifications of the test was the addition of a fatty meal. Sosman, Whitaker, and Edson[13] proposed the giving of a meal of egg yolk, but-ter, and cream after the first radiograph in the morning if the gallbladder was visualized. A film taken 1 hour later would invariably show the gallbladder shad-ow to be smaller, leading to the assumption that contraction indicated normal musculature. Sherwood Moore was never convinced that the fatty meal con-tributed anything not already known, for he felt that if the gallbladder was visu-alized, its coats were elastic, and any pathologic process sufficient to produce an inelastic wall was incompatible with preservation of the concentrating function. Time proved him right.

THE ISSUE OF PRIORITY

In November 1924 Harvey Cushing wrote to Graham that two of his young men, Whitaker and Milliken, had taken up the study of biliary cystography and had con-cluded that tetraiodophenolphthalein was a better drug than was tetrabromophe-nolphthalein—since the two drugs have almost equal toxicity, only half the dose of the iodine compound was necessary.[14] He informed Graham that they had written a brief paper on the subject.[15] Graham's response a few days later belittled the work: "I would not be aggrieved at what your men found concerning tetra-iodo-phenolphthalein, indeed I would not be aggrieved if later work showed that that was superior to the tetra-bromo. The chief claims which we are trying to establish is that the first successful demonstration of cholecystography has been made by us and that we think that we have also established the normal criteria in comparison with which pathological gallbladers can be interpreted regardless of what particu-lar substance may prove eventually to be the best."[16]

Three months following the Whitaker paper Graham, Cole, and Copher pub-lished a small article in the *Journal of the American Medical Association* in which they discussed cholecystography and the use of sodium tetraiodophenolphthalein, concluding: "equally good cholecystograms can be obtained with tetra-iodo-phe-nolphthalein in much smaller doses than with tetra-bromo-phenolphthalein" and the "purified product sodium tetra-iodo-phenolphthalein which we are now using is no more toxic in equal doses than sodium tetra-bromo-phenolphthalein."[17]

In September 1925, after meeting Cushing in Boston, Ed Lehman told Graham that Whitaker was upset about Graham's response. Graham wrote to Cushing about the impression that Cushing felt Graham hadn't given Whitaker the proper amount of credit: "Dr. Lehman desired to have the question straightened out ... so there would be no cloud between the feelings of the Brigham crowd and our crowd ... I do not wish to get into any priority argument, I would much rather chuck the whole thing." Graham's two-page letter in which he discussed the development of cholecystography and the use of the various chemicals ended as follows:

> I do not think that Whitaker and Milliken have any priority. Indeed I should say that in the light of subsequent events their work might have done great harm. In other words, the first published work of Whitaker and Milliken drew conclusions which were dangerous to draw at that time in the light of our more extensive experience. ... If we care to harp on questions of priority we might ask why Whitaker hasn't given us credit for establishing these criteria. ... This is the first time in my life that I have entered into an argument about priority on anything and I can assure you that it is most distasteful. ... Whitaker has already received much deserved praise for his work which has delighted us immensely. In fact many people think he originated cholecystography.[18]

The following week Cushing wrote to Graham that he felt it was "credible of Whitaker to have gone to work on his own lines and tried out the iodine salt. ... you are quite aware of my difficulties in keeping enthusiastic young men on an even keel without taking the wind out of their sails."[19] Nine weeks later Graham wrote to Cushing: "I have been tremendously pleased with the splendid work of Whitaker and the rest of your young men on the physiology of the gall bladder."[20]

The issue, however, was not quite put to rest. In June 1929 B.R. Kirklin, a radiologist from Rochester, Minnesota, sent a review article on cholecystography to the *Archives of Surgery*. In his introductory historic paragraphs, he wrote that it was "Graham who first ... visualized the gall bladder with the roentgen ray. ... As the calcium salt proved to be somewhat toxic Graham soon abandoned it for the sodium salt of tetra-bromo-phenolphthalein. Then Whitaker and Milliken, early in 1925, advocated the use of sodium tetra-iodo-phenolphthalein. ... Graham had tried the iodine compound almost at the beginning of his work but because of impurities the drug had proved unsatisfactory. Indeed, he and his coworkers experimented with an impressively long list of compounds before their first publications."[21] Graham was a member of the editorial board of *Archives of Surgery* and wrote to its editor, Dean Lewis, to express sorrow that he, Graham, had not personally reviewed and discussed the article: "A certain amount of editing of many articles ... should be done ... [e.g.] Kirklin's article on cholecystography. This article gives all the credit for the use of tetra-iodo-phenolphthalein to Whitaker and Milliken. Our article on the subject of tetra-iodo-phenolphthalein is not even mentioned. In fairness to Cole and Copher I think that such a thing should not be permitted to appear in a journal of which I am one of the editors."[22] Lewis responded to Graham's feelings of insult and suggested that he place a letter in the correspondence section of the journal,[23] to which Graham responded: "I cannot find anything which led you to feel I consider Kirklin's paper insulting—furthermore, I certainly have no desire to enter into any controversy regarding priority. I have never engaged in such controversy and I hope that I never shall." He additionally included suggestions to Lewis about how to handle such articles.[24] Graham also wrote to Kirklin, claiming to be discussing a matter of editorial policy for the *Archives*, and he used Kirklin's article as text for his remarks, reasserting: "All the credits for the use of tetra-iodo-phenolphthalein were given to Whitaker and Milliken and ... our publications on it were ignored. I do not wish at all to stir up any controversy concerning priority because I abhor such controversies."[25] The correspondence ended.

Fifteen years later when John Fulton was writing the biography of Cushing, he came across Cushing's and Graham's letters on the issue and wrote to Graham about them. In a long response to Fulton, Graham stated: "It would appear that I am willing to give full credit to Whitaker and Milliken for their discovery of the use of tetra-iodo-phenolphthalein in cholecystography. For the sake of truth it is only fair to say they did not discover its use in that connection. I hesitate very much indeed to enter into any argument which concerns priority and for that reason I dislike to bring up the matter." After quoting several letters in his file, he continued: "If the correspondence on the subject is left as you have arranged it, everyone who knows nothing about the preceding experiences would infer that Whitaker and Milliken were the ones who first discovered the use of tetra-iodo-phenolphthalein for cholecystography. ... [it is] always a matter of embarrassment to me to raise the hideous issue of priority."[26] Graham sent Fulton some copies of his correspondence and suggested that if Fulton would "prefer to omit any reference to cholecystography, it would be entirely satisfactory."[26] Fulton expressed gratitude for the information and planned to either drop it entirely, as Graham suggested, or amplify on the lines he had indicated.[27] The episode is not mentioned in Fulton's biography of Cushing.

THE TRADE NAME

By 1926 Mallinckrodt Chemical Works was preparing to patent two cholecystography compounds and to provide trade names to establish the Mallinckrodt identity. The company proposed the use of *Bromeikon* and *Iodeikon* to the Council of Pharmacy and Chemistry of the American Medical Association, but it failed to ask Graham if the names were satisfactory to him. After receiving a letter from W.H. Puckner of the council asking for his comments on the use of these names, Graham wrote to Edward Mallinckrodt Jr.: "I would be willing to have those names used. It seems to me however that they are not good names and if I had known about the names in advance I would have made different suggestions. For example, I think that the name which the National Aniline and Chemical Company is going to use, 'Tetra-iodo,' is a more significant name than the ones which you have chosen."[28]

Mallinckrodt Chemical Works subsequently wrote to Graham: "We regret extremely that the names Bromeikon and Iodeikon were not submitted to you in advance. It was only through a misunderstanding that this was not done. ... you will, of course, understand that our only desire in placing the name on a product of our manufacture is so that we may try to bring to ourselves as many orders for the goods as possible."[29]

Dean McKim Marriott now became involved in the problem of the trade name. In error, he felt that Graham's letter to the American Medical Association Council expressed a wish to withdraw permission for the use of the proposed names. Graham wrote to Marriott: "I did not mean to withdraw any rights which I had in the matter of deciding the names for these substances whose use in cholecystography I had originated. ... It would seem to me that according to all of the rules of the Council with which I am familiar, Mallinckrodt Chemical Works should be entitled to the use of both Iodeikon and Isoiodeikon inasmuch as they certainly were the first manufacturing chemists to produce these products for cholecystography."[30]

Twenty years later the Schering Corporation patented Priodax tablets and, in their advertising literature, gave credit to Graham for the concept of cholecystography. Graham wrote to Schering: "As the originator of cholecystography I wish you to know how much I appreciate the consideration which you gave me and Cole. ... it has been somewhat of an astonishment to both of us that nineteen years were required to find a better agent. ... I am particularly pleased at your courtesy in calling attention in your advertising literature to the fact that we never regarded a phenolphthalein derivative as being entirely satisfactory. Too often manufacturers and others are not very careful to carry out the amenities by giving proper credit."[31]

THE MALLINCKRODT INSTITUTE OF RADIOLOGY

Following the clinical and commercial success of cholecystography, Edward Mallinckrodt Jr. asked Graham to list the most critical needs of the Medical School. At that time the Department of Radiology was housed in cramped and antiquated quarters, and most of its equipment was obsolete and unequal to the developments taking place in the diagnosis and treatment of gallbladder and chest diseases. Graham knew that Sherwood Moore and his predecessor, Walter Mills, urgently needed and wanted a new department and that they had prepared plans and tentative sketches for a radiology institute that would serve all of the affiliated hospitals in the medical center. Graham convinced Abraham Flexner that some medical school should have a model radiologic institute. Flexner proposed that if Washington University could obtain a donor for a building, the General Education Board would endow it. Graham appraised Edward Mallinckrodt Jr. of Flexner's response and

persuaded him to give the $250,000 for the building, to which the General Educa-
tion Board gave $5 million as endowment. Graham's initiative took the project to
Mr. Mallinckrodt with a recommendation regarding its priority, and Moore was
prepared for Mallinckrodt's decision to build the institute that has since been called
"the house cholecystography built," even though, upon completion, only four of
the eight floors could be filled. Mallinckrodt later commented on how little it cost
to have his family name on a Washington University building.[32]

GRAHAM'S VIEW OF THE EFFORT

Four years after the cholecystography success, Dean McKim Marriott prepared a
submission on Graham's behalf to the Nobel Prize Committee, and he requested
that Graham prepare a statement about the development of cholecystography. Graham responded with his concepts of hepatic and biliary tract pathology in addition
to the development of cholecystography:

> For about ten years I have been much interested in the question of the
> origin, development, diagnosis and treatments of infections in the bil-
> iary tract. One of my first contributions to this subject was work pub-
> lished in 1918 which showed that with practically every case of
> cholecystitis there is also an associated hepatitis, that this hepatitis
> shows itself by a leukocyte infiltration of the periportal structures and
> that it seems to be a lymphatic pericholangitis. Subsequent develop-
> ments of this work … have shown … a strong probability that many
> cases of cholecystitis begin as a hepatitis and that the infection spreads
> to the gallbladder from the liver by way of the lymphatics. On the
> basis of this theory it is easy to understand the well-known fact that
> cholecystitis is very often associated with other inflammatory lesions
> of the portal system such as typhoid fever, duodenal ulcer, appendici-
> tis, etc. … The development of cholecystography came about through
> a deliberate desire to obtain some method which would improve our
> ability to diagnose gallbladder disease. It seems to have accomplished
> that purpose. Whereas formerly it was necessary to do much guessing
> and surmising about the presence of the less severe grades of gall-
> bladder disease, cholecystography has now made it possible to diag-
> nose these conditions with an accuracy considerably above 95% and
> in our own hands 98%. Since gallbladder disease is one of the most
> common ailments that inflict adult humanity this method of accurate
> diagnosis has had a beneficial effect on a large part of the world. …
> enthusiastic reports of its diagnostic success have come from Great
> Britain, Germany, Denmark, France, Canada, Argentine Republic as

well as from all over this country. In addition to providing a method for more accurate diagnosis it has also enabled us to learn much about the physiology of the gallbladder because it is possible to watch with the X-ray all the changes which take place in the gallbladder under various conditions without the necessity of operative interference on the experimental subject. ... this same method has also been used by others in a study of the physiology of the gallbladder.

A newer development of cholecystography has been our introduction of the use of sodium-phenol-tetra-iodo-phthalein which, because its color shows in serum to which alkali has been added, makes it possible to carry out cholecystography and a test of liver function simultaneously with the same agent. As a result of this we have obtained much new information about the value of liver function tests. ... By means of this agent ... we can in the majority of instances differentiate between biliary obstruction due to carcinoma and that due to stone in the common duct. ... [It] also has provided us with a fairly accurate means of determining the operative risk on a patient with biliary tract disease.[33]

Graham's lengthy response to Marriott was a detailed report of the solving of a clinical problem rather than an analysis of the intellectual process that led to it. Evarts Graham had combined observations made by others and arrived at the idea that heavy atoms attached to phenolphthalein might make visualization of the gallbladder possible, and it is this synthesis for which Graham deserves credit and for which he was given so many accolades. The clinical successes were probably not worthy of a Nobel prize, but the intellectual exercise may well have been.

Graham's interest in the biliary tree, as is evidenced by his publications with Cole and Copher, continued for the next 15 years, and, on several occasions—at times almost defensively—Graham attributed his intellectual capability to the special training of his post–medical school years. He became a world figure and received many honors and awards for this effort; his decade-long apprehension over whether Whitaker would be given credit for the use of tetraiodophenolphthalein is not easy to understand, unless it reflects a deep-seated desire for personal recognition. Graham and Cole had tried this compound but had found it too toxic for human use and, after using the bromine form, returned to the iodine compound, which had become more purified. Whitaker reported on the relative x-ray densities of the iodine and bromine forms and concluded that the iodine form was more x-ray dense, something that Graham and Cole knew all along. Whitaker's contributions to the literature of the day are not those of an innovator, and it seems unworthy of Graham to have paid so much attention to a publication that was interesting and important but not basic to the development of cholecystography.

Graham's text *Diseases of the Gallbladder and Bile Ducts*[8] is a comprehensive work that presents the understanding and treatment in 1928 of liver and biliary tree disease. Seventy years later it continues to be interesting and enjoyable reading, containing many ideas which, after great refinement, are still current.

Chapter 7
———————

THE PNEUMONECTOMY

THE ARRIVAL OF GILMORE

On February 27, 1933, Dr. James Lee Gilmore, a 49-year-old obstetrician from Pittsburgh, Pennsylvania, was admitted to the Medical and Surgical Chest Service (the chest clinic) of Barnes Hospital, accompanied by his referring physician Dr. W.T. Mitchell. Little did anyone realize his registration that day would initiate a series of events that would make him the central figure in a surgical melodrama that would last for years. His operation, recovery, and survival marked a new epoch in the development of thoracic surgery.

Dr. Gilmore underwent four hospitalizations at Barnes; the first lasted for 6 days; the second, on March 9, was for 1 day; the third, on March 13, lasted for 11 days; and his final admission, on April 4 for an operation on April 5, ended with his discharge on June 18, 10 weeks later.

In January 1929 Dr. Gilmore had had pneumonia of the right lower lobe that required several weeks before full recovery. He was then well until July 1932, when he experienced general discomfort, chills, fever, and an elevated white blood cell count. One month later a chest radiograph revealed a "fan-shaped shadow in the region of the left axilla" (the upper lobe of his left lung) that regressed over the next few days; this condition recurred in October and, once again, soon subsided. An attempted aspiration of a suspected lung abscess in December 1932 resulted in a pneumothorax that persisted until his February 1933 admission to Barnes Hospital. His December symptoms had abated somewhat, but, 10 days before admission, fever and chest discomfort recurred, and he arrived with a tentative diagnosis of lung abscess.

Gilmore, who was of medium build, had restricted movement of the left chest. A chest radiograph showed collapse of the upper lobe of his left lung. A biopsy taken during bronchoscopy by Dr. M.F. Arbuckle failed to establish the presence of carcinoma. An iodized oil (Lipiodol) bronchogram[a] showed an obstruction in the left upper lobe bronchus, with satisfactory visualization of the left lower lobe bronchus.

There is no record of the events that occurred during Gilmore's 1-day admission of March 9. A visit to the chest clinic with some procedure seems likely, although it may have been merely an opportunity to be seen and have his case reviewed. His third admission, on March 13, was for further work-up. Dr. Arbuckle bronchoscoped him again and, after visualizing the left upper lobe bronchus, stated that its lumen was larger than it had been at the prior examination. He saw walls lined with a dark red membrane that bled easily, but was unable to distinguish[b] whether these were chronic inflammatory changes or malignant growths. In the main stem bronchus, just at the opening of the upper lobe bronchus, a mass the size of a pea with similar dark red characteristics was noted, and, after attempting to biopsy both the mass in the main stem and that in the upper lobe bronchus, Arbuckle felt that the biopsy material was not sufficient for diagnosis. Nonetheless, Dr. W. Dean Jr., pathologist for the Ear, Nose, and Throat Service, reported the condition to be squamous cell carcinoma of the left upper lobe. Dr. Arbuckle's third bronchoscopy, on March 21, showed abnormalities in both the upper lobe and the main stem bronchi, and satisfactory biopsies taken from these areas showed squamous cell carcinoma.

Following discharge, Gilmore returned to Pittsburgh taking the biopsy slides with him for review. He had plans to re-enter Barnes on April 4 for a right upper lobectomy the following day. There is no record that Graham and Gilmore discussed the possibility that a lobectomy might be inadequate. In a 1948 restatement of these events written for the *Texas Cancer Bulletin*, Graham noted: "The patient had an unusually stoical disposition. He insisted on knowing exactly our diagnosis. … He stated that he would like to go to his home to get some things in order and would like to borrow our biopsy slides to show them to some pathologist friends. … I recommended the removal of the left upper lobe. It is of interest that he demonstrated himself to be not only a stoic but also an optimist, because while

---

a. Lipiodol, 40 percent iodine in poppy seed oil, was first used as a contrast material in 1922. After administration of topical pharyngeal anesthesia to a patient, Lipiodol was sprayed into the trachea. Radiographs taken subsequently revealed an outline of trachea, bronchi, and, occasionally, some bronchioles. The flexible bronchoscope made bronchograms obsolete.

b. In 1930 the bronchoscope was a rigid metal tube illuminated by a wheat seed lamp that was carried to its distal end. Poor illumination resulted whenever mucus or other secretions were encountered.

at home he had some cavities filled."[1] Years later Gilmore confided to Dr. Graham that he had not only visited his dentist[c] but that he had purchased a cemetery plot.

THE STATE OF THE ART

In the decade following World War I, surgeons became increasingly interested in surgical intervention for diseases of the chest; the illnesses of the day were empyema, lung abscess, bronchiectasis, and tuberculosis. Medical literature of the 1920s contains few accounts of primary carcinoma of the lung. In 1919 Dr. George Dock, professor of medicine, had Alton Ochsner's class witness the autopsy of a patient who had died of lung cancer. He told them the condition was so rare, they would probably never see another case as long as they lived. A 1922 review of 4362 autopsies at the University of Minnesota found only 13 cases of carcinoma of the lung, and the following year a publication from Britain reported four cases of primary carcinoma of the lung among 3183 postmortem examinations.[2]

The setting for pneumonectomy was primitive. Intrathoracic operations were fraught with morbidity and mortality rates that would be unacceptable 70 years later. In the words of Dr. B. Blades, the "lack of interest in chest surgery was not surprising to anyone who has been repeatedly exposed to the stench of a putrid empyema or to the malnourished, desperately ill patient ready to surrender his body to death after all conservative measures have failed. For two decades only the dedicated and very brave were willing to jeopardize their surgical practice with shocking mortality rates, to give their time and energies without regard of financial return and with only a guaranteed high incidence of bitter disappointment."[2]

Tuberculosis was treated by collapse of the lung, either by thoracoplasty or pneumothorax; surgery for bronchiectasis and lung abscess was open drainage, cautery excision, or an attempt at lobectomy; empyema was managed by closed catheter drainage or rib resection, occasionally followed by pleurectomy or Schede thoracoplasty. In 1922 Lilienthal reported treating 31 cases of bronchiectasis by resection of lung tissue, with a mortality rate of 42 percent. Seven of his 10 patients who underwent resection of more than a single lobe died. Rudolph Nissen reported that, in Sauerbruch's Clinic, 10 sequential lobectomy patients died before one

---

c. In 1929 Dr. Gilmore developed pneumonia and empyema. Following a rib resection and open drainage his weight had fallen from 180 to 155 lb; he went to Florida to recover but did not improve. Upon returning to Pittsburgh, he had four dead teeth removed, rapidly gained 20 lb and began to feel well. He became a radical advocate of oral care and carried it over into his medical practice. On a number of occasions when patients refused to have their teeth cared for he suggested they find another physician. His 1933 preoperative visit to the dentist is usually described as something done in a spirit of high expectations about the outcome of his operation, but actually it was an attempt on his part to ensure the most favorable outcome. This should be considered preventive dentistry at its extreme.

person survived. Lobectomy was a formidable procedure; in Graham's 48 cases of bronchiectasis treated by lobectomy, there were only eight successes, with an operative mortality of 52 percent.[2] In 1923 Graham described cases of bronchietasis that he treated with an operation he called *pneumectomy with cautery*. He performed seven of his cautery procedures in the 9 years that followed, with one operative mortality and postoperative survival that was measured in days. His procedure consisted of opening the chest, establishing fusion between the lung and the chest wall by using iodoform gauze packs, and then reopening the area several days or weeks later to insert a hot soldering iron into the lung. In the anteroom off the operating theater, Graham's nurses would warm two irons until they were red hot and bring them to him in a metal pitcher. Smoke and stench resulted from the procedure.[3] Bronchiectasis and lung abscess led to thin, wasted individuals who had chronic cough and foul-smelling, putrid sputum or frank pus that ultimately resulted in social isolation. Those who developed the disease must have been willing to undertake any chance of benefit[d].

A direct surgical resection for infectious intrathoracic disease was spurred in a report from Brunn of San Francisco, who described six one-stage lobectomies for bronchiectasis, with one death;[4] Shenstone and Janes of Toronto reported 15 cases performed under local or spinal anesthesia, with three deaths.[5,6] In an April 1933 article on the operability of carcinoma of the lung, the same month as Graham's operation on Gilmore, Carlson and Ballon (from Graham's chest clinic) described the options available for the treatment of lung cancer as being transbronchial radon seeds, external radiation, cautery pneumectomy, lobe sequestration, and lobectomy; they did not mention the possibility of total pneumonectomy.[7]

In the early twentieth century, investigators in anesthesia were beginning to study the delivery of a respiratory anesthetic agent by using positive pressure. In 1910 a simple practical method for the control of intrapulmonic pressures was placement of a tube into the trachea under direct vision through a laryngoscope. The cuffed endotracheal tube was first reported in 1928,[8] but endotracheal anesthesia was not generally accepted, and ether or nitrous oxide administered by face mask were the anesthetic procedures of choice.

Although by 1933 a satisfactory method for the administration of anesthetic gases had become available, its fullest implication required an appreciation of the physiologic principles involved in open pneumothorax that Graham and Bell had

---

d. Bronchiectasis is an infection with dilatation of the bronchioles, destruction of the lung, and formation of multiple small pus cavities that drain into the bronchi and trachea before being coughed out. In Graham's time, there was systemic sepsis that produced a continuous and finally deadly weight loss; afternoon fever was almost always present. The production of foul-smelling pus with constant coughing precluded a full night's sleep and was so offensive to others that the bronchiectatic patient became a social outcast. Both patients and their courageous surgeons were willing to try almost anything to treat a disease that is rarely seen today.

defined in their work for the Empyema Commission. During World War I, many chest surgeons believed that in healthy young men with open chest wounds, protection from temporary open pneumothorax might be unnecessary. Probably the most important single observation of the Empyema Commission was the finding that an open pneumothorax on one side exerted a deleterious effect on both lungs (although not to the same degree), an effect that depended largely on the fixation or mobility of the mediastinum. Success of pneumothorax when used for antituberculosis collapse therapy was dependent on the presence of a mediastinum made fairly rigid by a regional inflammatory response.

By 1935 Graham had used his cautery technique on 76 patients with bronchiectasis, with an operative mortality under 15 percent. He claimed that 70 percent of his patients had been returned to work symptom free.[9] Although the results of operations for bronchiectasis were poor, those for lung cancer were even poorer. Carlson and Ballon reported on 23 cases of attempted pneumonectomy or lobectomy for lung cancer;[7] all of the patients undergoing pneumonectomy died, whereas 11 were reported to have survived lesser resections. By 1933 two patients in the world had survived a two-stage bilobectomy/pneumonectomy for bronchiectasis. Nissen of Berlin and Haight of Ann Arbor[10,11] had placed a tight ligature around the hilum to create a sloughing lung that was removed 2 weeks later. No patient had survived total pneumonectomy for a malignancy of the lung.

GILMORE'S OPERATION

Accompanied by his lifelong friend Dr. Sidney A. Chalfont, also of Pittsburgh, James Gilmore was admitted to Barnes Hospital on April 4, in preparation for a left upper lobe lobectomy the following day. He was assigned room 3117 on the third floor of the east (medical) wing of the hospital, where medical or surgical semiprivate and private patients received care. The operative permit obtained that evening read: "I herewith request the performance of the required operation and such additional work as may be found necessary or advisable at the time. /s/ James L. Gilmore/Witness: s/ W. Erlich, M.D."[12]

On that evening, one of the house officers visited Gilmore and told him that, if he were in Gilmore's shoes, he would get out of the hospital right then and there because the mortality rate had been extremely high. He suggested that Gilmore sign out against medical advice. Gilmore did not report the incident to Graham, for he was sure that Graham would make life uncomfortable for the house officer.[13] Dr. Kenneth Bell's preoperative orders were as follows:

Routine prep for lobectomy "L."
Morphine 0.15 gm @ 9 A.M.
Atropine .0004 gm @ 9 A.M.

To OR when called in bed.

TPR q4h.

Bedrest with bathroom privileges.

Tub bath.

Light diet.[12]

On April 5, 1933, shortly after 9:00 am, Gilmore arrived in Operating Room No. 1. His blood pressure was 100/60; his pulse, 84 bpm; and his respiration rate, 20 breaths per minute. Anesthesia was begun at 9:35, and an endotracheal tube (probably a Magill tube[e]) was introduced 10 minutes later. Graham made the initial incision at 10:00 am and entered the chest with the removal of ribs no. 6 and no. 7. After cutting adhesions between the upper lobe and chest wall, he felt several hard nodules in the upper lobe, and he focused attention upon the hilum. Confirming that the main stem bronchus was involved and that there was no uninvolved area in the upper lobe bronchus, Graham turned to Dr. Chalfont, Gilmore's physician friend (who was accompanied by Gilmore's brother-in-law, Dr. Archibald Campbell of Montreal, Quebec) and said that it would be useless to perform a lobectomy. He strongly advised the removal of the entire lung and asked for Chalfont's opinion. Chalfont asked if such an operation had ever been done before. Graham replied that it had been performed successfully in animals, in fact, he had even done it himself, but he knew of no case of a successful one-stage removal of the lung in a human being. After a little more discussion, and particularly because Graham felt that Gilmore would want to take any chances that might effect a cure, Graham decided to perform the total pneumonectomy[f].[1] A rubber catheter was placed around the hilum to constrict the arterial and venous flow for 2 or 3 minutes. No cardiovascular collapse occurred. Graham then applied two clamps, cut between them, removed the lung with one clamp, and placed three sutures around the hilar stump before removing the second clamp. The stump was cauterized with heat and silver nitrate, radon seeds were implanted, and, aghast at

---

e. The Magill tube is a curved, firm, red rubber tube inserted through the pharynx with its pointed end positioned in the trachea distal to the vocal cords. It was designed during World War I by anesthetist Ivan Magill at Queens Hospital, Sidcup (an army institution that specialized in treating facial injuries). The tube permitted continuous insufflation, not controlled respiration, that was conducted without the aid of suction. Sometimes it was used with a bag and mask covering the face, but its major benefit occurred when it was connected to a long single tube through which anesthetic gases were blown, permitting the anesthetist to be outside the operative field.

f. Evarts Graham wrote "The First Total Pneumonectomy"[1] 16 years after performing the pneumonectomy. During its immediate and subsequent publicity, there had been many recountings of the event. It is impossible to verify the intimate operating room conversation of 1933, which may well have been embellished by frequent repetition.

the size of the cavity, Graham removed seven more ribs (nos. 3 to 5 and nos. 8 to 11) to let the chest wall collapse onto the mediastinum and bronchial stump. The entire procedure took 1 hour 45 minutes. Gilmore's blood pressure was recorded as 120/80 upon leaving the operating room, and he received a transfusion of 500 mL of whole blood. Dr. Kenneth Bell[g], chief resident, was Graham's first assistant, and Dr. William Adams[h] was his second. Listed also as members of the operative team were Drs. Hall and Erlich; Miss Moore, the surgical nurse; and Miss Lamb, the anesthetist. The anesthetic agent was nitrous oxide and oxygen (ether was never used when hot cautery was anticipated).[14]

Graham dictated a lengthy operative note to Ada Hanvey, in which he documented his intraoperative decision to remove the entire left lung. After the lung was removed, the mucosa of the bronchus was cauterized with a hot cautery as well as 25 percent silver nitrate solution before being transfixed with double no. 2 chromic catgut suture around the whole pedicle. A second ligature was placed distal to the first, and a third was applied before the tourniquet catheter and the remaining clamp were removed. The open end of the stump of the main stem bronchus was slightly less than 1 inch from the bifurcation of the trachea. Two enlarged mediastinal lymph nodes that seemed soft and unlikely to contain cancer were removed for microscopic examination, and seven radon seeds of 1.5 mCi each were introduced into the severed pedicle. Graham did not record the radon administration in his dictated operative note, but he did so in his later report.[1] After the thoracoplasty was completed and the space obliterated, a small catheter that fitted tightly

---

g. Kenneth Rush Bell (1902 to 1941) was born in Sanford, Florida, a small town near Jacksonville, and received both undergraduate and medical school education at Emory University in Atlanta, Georgia, from which he graduated in 1928. He spent the summer of 1925 at the University of Chicago and returned to Chicago to intern at Presbyterian Hospital. Bell spent 1 year as surgical resident at the Wesley Memorial Hospital in Atlanta before he became a surgical resident at Barnes Hospital (1929 to 1933). Later he returned to Atlanta, developed a large surgical practice, held an appointment in both the biology and anatomy departments of Emory University, and practiced surgery at four hospitals. After joining the US Army, he was sent to Camp Clairborne, Louisiana, where, on December 4, 1941, at 39 years of age, he died of heart disease.

h. William Elias Adams (1902 to 1973) was born in Nichols, Iowa. He received his medical degree from the University of Iowa in 1926. His surgical education, begun at the University of Chicago, was continued with Ferdinand Sauerbruch in Berlin and, finally, in the residency program at Barnes Hospital. During his time at Barnes, Adams was fortunate to be in the operating room with Kenneth Bell, Evarts Graham, and James Gilmore on the fateful April morning. After his Barnes Hospital years, Adams returned to Chicago as associate professor of surgery, where his interest in surgery of the esophagus led him to become the first director of thoracic surgery at the University of Chicago. He followed Dallas Phemister as department chairman for 6 years and, after retirement, became an assistant director of the American College of Surgeons. A devoted husband, father, and elder of the Fourth Presbyterian Church in Chicago, he was kind and self-effacing but never self-deprecating. He retired to his ancestral home in Hopkinton, Iowa.

through the skin was led into a boric acid solution below the bed to give underwater sealed drainage. The operation was completed by closing the chest in layers[i] (see appendix E).

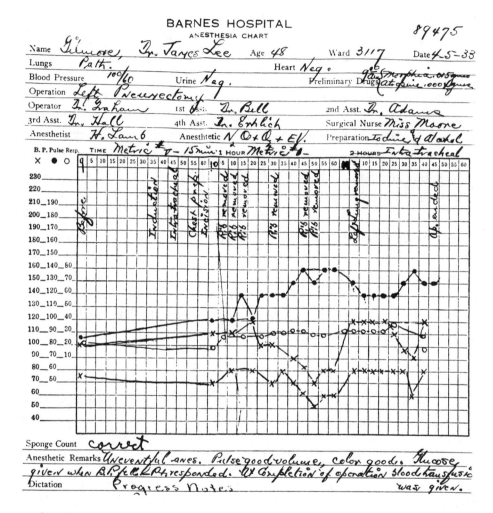

Anesthetist's chart of the operation of James Gilmore. (Courtesy of Barnes Hospital Records and Archives)

---

i. The official undated version of the operation reads as though it were dictated by Evarts Graham to Ada Hanvey, not prepared by First Assistant Kenneth Bell. There are, however, items in Graham's subsequent versions that are not in accord with this operative note (see appendix E):

1. The operative note does not document the insertion of the radon seeds.
2. The operative note contains no record of the conversation between Graham and Drs. Chalfont and Campbell regarding the advisability of proceeding with a total lung removal.
3. The operative note does not describe the removal of the third rib; however, notes from Gilmore's two subsequent operations document the presence of only ribs no. 1 and no. 2

THE ANESTHESIA

The operative record from Gilmore's operation contains the following remarks from the anesthetist: "Uneventful anes. Pulse good volume, color good. Glucose given when BP fell. Patient responded. At completion of operation blood transfusion was given."[12] There is a cryptic "N_2O-O_2-EV." (nitrous oxide, oxygen, expiratory valve) at the beginning of the record. The equipment was a ring of five gas tanks clamped to a three-wheeled stand—two each for nitrous oxide and oxygen, and one for carbon dioxide. Pressure gauges and flow valves on the tanks were jointly connected and led to a rubber breathing bag that was fitted with an expiratory valve, that permitted exhaled gases to escape under a variable resistance. The bag was connected to a face mask during induction and then, after entubation, to the endotracheal tube. The system had no soda lime cannister for carbon dioxide absorption; exhaled gases were discharged into the room. Induction and intubation with nitrous oxide require that oxygen concentration be severely restricted, and Miss Lamb's note indicating that "narcosis was induced in the usual way" means that the patient would have breathed a high percentage of nitrous oxide—perhaps 100 percent—until asleep, and then 95 percent nitrous oxide with 5 percent oxygen until relaxed for intubation. This procedure is the asphyxial nitrous oxide technique described by McKesson[j]. After the tube was in place, 800 cc of O_2 and 4000 cc N_2O per minute were administered, giving an oxygen concentration of 16.9 percent. Carbon dioxide stimulation and hand compression of the bag were used to ensure adequate respiratory activity. This nitrous oxide–oxygen technique was the only anesthesia method available to Graham whenever he anticipated the use of hot cautery.[15]

THE POSTOPERATIVE COURSE

Postoperative orders written by Dr. Bell were fairly sparse:

> Regular diet as tolerated.
> CO_2 routine[k].

---

j. E.I. McKesson of Toledo, Ohio, an anesthesiologist entrepreneur, was known in the 1920s and 1930s as the promoter of nitrous oxide anesthesia. His technique called for asphyxial induction, intubation, and then maintenance with oxygen concentrations of less than 20 percent. He designed the tripod anesthetic equipment that held tanks of nitrous oxide and oxygen, and through promotion of the tripod, he developed an equipment supply company, McKesson-Robbins, that became large enough to trade on the New York Stock Exchange.

k. Routine postoperative respiratory care consisted of intermittent stimulation with 5 percent carbon dioxide. A small tank containing 5 percent CO_2 and 95 percent oxygen was attached to a rubber tube; a red rubber funnel was used for a mask. Every 15 to 30 minutes, a nurse would cover the patient's face with the funnel and administer the gas mixture until breathing became deep and labored. The procedure was thought to be effective in preventing postoperative atelectasis.

Elevate foot of bed.
BP and Pulse q15 minutes.
May be turned.
Tight chest binder.[12]

By 3:15 the next afternoon, Gilmore was quite comfortable and had gone 8 hours without an opiate but had not voided. About 800 cc of fluid had drained through the chest catheter. Gilmore's temperature remained approximately 37.2°C. A moderately uneventful 2 weeks passed before the bronchus developed a leak. On April 18 Gilmore's temperature became 39.7°C, his pulse 134 bpm, and his respirations 32/min, with some respiratory difficulty. He coughed when he attempted to lie on his right side or upon talking. He was given Aspirin and codeine to lower his temperature and taken to the operating room for a thoracostomy and drainage of a pus cavity in the left upper chest. With Gilmore under nitrous oxide anesthesia, Graham removed a portion of the second rib and entered a cavity at the apex of the left chest, where he inserted a small tube. He planned to permit this drainage tract to seal, and then follow up with removal of the first and second ribs. From incision to closure, the procedure took 20 minutes. Once again, Dr. Bell was his assistant.

Nine days later, Gilmore was returned to the operating room for a two-rib thoracoplasty under nitrous oxide and oxygen anesthesia. In a 20-minute procedure, the prior incision was extended upward and the first and second ribs were removed. Dilaudid, Veronal, and codeine were the postoperative analgesics used. One week later Gilmore was permitted to get out of bed, and on June 18 he was discharged to go home.

Gilmore's activity had been increased gradually during his postoperative hospital period and, at time of discharge, he had been walking around for about 2 weeks, with moderate dyspnea on exertion. On admission his vital capacity was 3500 cc; at discharge, 1650 cc. His admission weight of 145 lb had fallen to 122 lb; a photograph published with the report in the *Journal of the American Medical Association* shows an extremely thin man with satisfactory motion of the left upper extremity.[12,16] Gilmore had undergone 44 days of hospitalization and three operative procedures, but he never needed to return.

THE PATHOLOGY

Gilmore's third bronchoscopic biopsy taken by Dr. Arbuckle on March 21 was unequivocally epidermoid (squamous cell) carcinoma. The operative specimen of April 5 consisted of the entire left lung, cleanly removed at its hilum. It weighed 535 g. The pathology report delivered by Dr. Nathan Womack, the surgical pathologist for the Department of Surgery, stated:

The upper third of the upper lobe was indurated but the rest of the lungs felt normal. ... The upper main bronchus contained some granular tissue whereas the lower main bronchus appeared normal. ... There was an enlargement of the peribronchial lymph nodes. ... A section through the upper lobe bronchus showed a granular papillary overgrowth of bronchial epithelium over a distance of about 4 cm. It represented the carcinoma which obliterated the lumen. ... There was a large abscess cavity containing yellow pus with miliary abscesses.[17]

The microscopic pathology showed that "the bulk of the mass was infectious material but throughout there were strands of malignant squamous epithelial cells containing rare mitotic figures. The lymph node sections showed pigment, endothelial hyperplasia, but no evidence of malignancy." The final diagnosis was "squamous cell carcinoma of the lung."[17]

The lung was placed into an earthenware jar measuring about 8 inches in diameter and 10 inches in height, filled with Kaiserling's solution, and with a cap that was sealed with Vaseline grease.

During the succeeding 15 years, as Gilmore lived and Graham showed him off at various conferences, other surgeons were having less success, and the nagging question began to arise: did Gilmore really have a carcinoma of the lung? By 1948 the question had become sufficiently pervasive that Graham felt a re-evaluation was in order, and he requested that Lauren Ackerman review the specimen. Ackerman was now accepting surgical residents into his surgical pathology training program for short periods of time, and Harrison Black, a chest service resident, was currently on rotation. The gross pathology specimens from prior years were stored in the crawl space—4 feet from floor to ceiling—between the fourth floor and roof of the North Building, and Ackerman ordered Black to obtain a flashlight and some sandwiches, and not return until he found the lung. With great fortune, Black found it in a jar that was so well sealed the fluid fixative had not evaporated. The specimen was redissected and a second report submitted, this time by Ackerman. The record room chart at Barnes Hospital contains the Ackerman report. Although the Womack report was discarded, a copy was kept in Graham's files. The Ackerman report dated November 11, 1948, described the lung as follows:

A tumor mass ulcerating into the upper lobe bronchus near the hilum ... is well delineated and measures 3 cm in its greatest diameter. ... There are numerous pin point abscesses, a markedly thickened pleura and the lower lobe appears essentially normal. ... The superior interlobar bronchial node ... adjacent to the tumor appears to be directly involved.[18]

Microscopic sections were taken of tumor, the lymph nodes surrounding the upper lobe bronchus, the lower lobe bronchus, and the thickened pleura. The surface of the tumor showed a

> fairly well differentiated pattern with numerous epithelial pearls ... [extending] ... into the lung parenchyma destroying bronchial cartilage and invading contiguous lymph nodes. In the deeper areas of the tumor it is extremely undifferentiated with practically no keratinization and numerous mitotic figures. In one area there is squamous metaplasia and epidermoid carcinoma in situ.[18]

The final diagnosis was "1) lung, bronchus—epidermoid carcinoma grade III; 2) regional lymph nodes—epidermoid carcinoma grade III; and 3) lung—bronchial pulmonary suppuration with multiple small abscesses."[18]

By 1948 Lauren Ackerman was becoming established as a prominent American surgical pathologist. Nathan Womack was seen as a surgeon with a side interest in pathology, not an expert pathologist, and Ackerman seldom failed to belittle his efforts. The finding of the lung, its re-examination, and the confirmation not only of carcinoma of the bronchus but of cartilage invasion and nodal involvement laid to rest the rumors that Gilmore's carcinoma operation had been performed for a benign adenoma and that this was the reason for his long survival. Ackerman was not to be challenged.

PUBLICITY AND PRIORITY

Evarts Graham must have realized the significance of his successful procedure, for 7 days later he wrote to H.A. Carlson[1] with comments about the upcoming publication of an article that Carlson and Ballon had prepared. Graham's letter was chiefly devoted to a description of the events in St. Louis, not the substance of Carlson's article.

> I wish you could have been here. ... I removed the entire left lung ... for an early carcinoma of the left [main stem] bronchus just where it bifurcated. ... The operation was performed a week ago and he has had a surprisingly little post-operative reaction. ... he looks like a patient recovering from a simple appendectomy or a hernia. ... I feel greatly

---

1. Herbert A. Carlson had been a fellow on the chest surgery service at Barnes Hospital and in 1933 was at the University of Minnesota. He was coauthor on a paper discussing operability of carcinoma of the lung, published simultaneously with Graham's operation on Gilmore.

thrilled about it. ... it looks now as if he would surely recover from the operation. This is the first time that a whole lung has been removed for carcinoma. ... I do not think it would be advisable to put a note about it in the article by yourself and Ballon on the operability of carcinoma of the lung because of course there is still the possibility of an embolus or something of that sort which might carry him off unexpectedly.[19]

The first public announcement of the event occurred at the sixth annual meeting of the American Association for Thoracic Surgery on May 9 to 11, 1933, less than 6 weeks following Gilmore's operation. Howard Lilienthal reported a pneumonectomy for sarcoma with a fatal outcome, and in the discussion Graham, elated about his patient who had survived a total lung removal, discussed Lilienthal's pneumonectomy. From a semantic viewpoint he stated: "Just a short time before I performed a complete pneumectomy and in my case, however, fortunately the result was successful. I do not call it pneumonectomy as Dr. Lilienthal does because I have the support of the *Oxford Dictionary* to call it pneumectomy instead of pneumonectomy."[20] Dr. Pol N. Coryllos of New York immediately rose to discuss the point of etymology, not surgery, and agreed with Lilienthal that it should be pneumonectomy, not pneumectomy as Graham proposed. He stated that pneumectomy means resection of air, and, if correctly constructed, it should be pneumonectomy.[20] This must have been a bitter moment for Graham, who prided himself on diction and grammar and was particularly superior about his knowledge of word roots. His earlier publication on removing the lung or lobes had been entitled "Pneumectomy with the Cautery,"[3] but in all publications and references after 1933, he used *pneumonectomy*. Despite the semantic problem, the verbal announcement of the operation had been made, even before the patient had left the hospital. It received immediate attention and galvanized the audience. The case was written up, submitted, reviewed, and accepted, and appeared in print in the October 28 issue of the *Journal of the American Medical Association* barely 4 months after Gilmore left the hospital.[16]

One year later, on the anniversary of the operation, Dr. William Adams, now with the University of Chicago, wrote to Graham asking about the results of their operation of the previous year. Graham replied:

I am pleased to tell you that Dr. Gilmore called me up on the telephone. ... he is getting along very well ... [can] carry on his practice without any abnormal amount of fatigue and has no more dyspnea on exertion than any other person of his age. ... I have removed the lung in two other cases for carcinoma but unfortunately they both died. ... I blame myself very much for the death of the first case because I believe he could have been saved by placing him in a respirator. ... I think now that this was a mistake. The other patient died very suddenly about fifteen hours after the removal of the lung. We were unable to determine satisfactorily what the cause of death was in spite of a post-mortem examination.[21]

Graham also referred Adams to the Carlson and Ballon article on operability[m] of cancer of the lung.[21]

Following the pneumonectomy performed by Graham, Drs. Rienhoff at Johns Hopkins and Archibald at McGill University independently described the technique of individual ligation of the hilar vessels and the bronchus.[2,10,22] Mass ligation of the hilar stump left a large amount of tissue distal to the ligature with an inadequate blood supply, that was expected to slough off and be dissolved or discharged through a chest tube or fistula. Within 8 months management of the hilum had been refined, antibiotics were appearing (this was the year of Prontosil [sulfanilamide]), the endotracheal tube had been given a cuff, and controlled respiration had been accomplished. Within a decade sodium pentothal induction replaced the use of the gauze mask and drop ether or asphyxial nitrous oxide induction. Graham, too, moved with the times, and 3 years later expressed his thoughts about operative technique: "I prefer to ligate the vessels and the bronchus separately. There are some cases, however, in which because of extensive induration of the hilus and of the mediastinum it is not possible to do anything more than mass ligation of the pedicle."[23]

Thoracic surgery was coming of age, but it did not come without detractors. For at least 50 years, the conventional wisdom/rumor of Barnes Hospital held that, following Gilmore's successful operation, there were 16 consecutive fatalities, and Graham became known as the "Butcher of Barnes Hospital." In 1970 I.Y. Olch remembered those years and felt there may have been 11 deaths.[24] In 1973 Brian Blades wrote that 3 years elapsed before a second survivor appeared, but he did not give the number of pneumonectomies attempted.[25] Graham's correspondence contradicts these remembrances. He acknowledged that in the 12 months following Gilmore's operation, he had attempted two pneumonectomies, and both patients died,[21] but that, at the end of 3 years, there were 5 cases in a row without fatality.[23] He summarized his 10-year experience as involving 56 pneumonectomies for carcinoma, with 22 deaths—a 40 percent operative mortality.[26] Although he never published his operative series, the rumors of 16 consecutive fatalities cannot be substantiated.

---

m. *Author's note: Inoperability* would have been a more appropriate term for use in Carlson and Ballon's article.[7]

It is probable that many of those early deaths followed operations for infectious diseases (bronchiectasis) since carcinoma was still a rarity, and Eastwood speculated on the possible role of inadequate anesthesia.[27] Those were daunting times that required courage and conviction. Graham had both.

FRIENDSHIP AND "SHOW AND TELL"

Following Gilmore's discharge from Barnes Hospital, he and Graham developed a friendship that was reflected in frequent correspondence, gifts, and occasional visits. This was partly based upon Gilmore's respect for and obligation to Graham, and partly upon the pride and pleasure that Graham felt at having opportunities to display to others the results of his handiwork. On several occasions Graham asked Gilmore's permission that he be shown to the audience when Graham was making presentations about the treatment of cancer of the lung.

Every year for 24 years, on the April 5 anniversary date, Gilmore telephoned Graham; it became such a ritual that Graham would comment about its regularity to anyone who would listen. In April 1935 Graham gave the Balfour Lecture at the University of Toronto. His subject was "Primary Carcinoma of the Bronchus," and during this talk he mentioned his successful case of 2 years prior. That evening, at the home of Dr. W. Edward Gallie, University of Toronto's chairman of surgery, Graham received his telephone call. Four days later he thanked Gilmore for his kindness, not only for calling Graham at Toronto, but because of the box of candy that Gilmore sent. Graham stated: "I do not feel that you need have any anxiety about a recurrence because it would seem to me that it should have shown some evidence of itself by this time if it were going to occur." He proudly wrote that he had a patient in the hospital, on whom he had operated nearly 2 months prior, who was making a very satisfactory recovery and would be ready to leave the hospital shortly.[28]

All of Graham's correspondence with Gilmore was quite formal. His salutations read "Dear Dr. Gilmore," until 1953 when Gilmore failed to make the standard April 5 call. Graham's 1953 letter read: "Dear Jim: … here it is the seventh of April and I haven't had any telephone communication with you. I hope the absence of my hearing from you has no special significance. I think however that this is the first time in twenty-two [sic] years that I have not heard from you. With best wishes, Cordially yours."[29]

Graham's correspondence with Gilmore started less than 1 month after Gilmore left the hospital. Graham had asked Dr. W.T. Mitchell, the Pittsburgh physician who cared for Gilmore, for a report on Gilmore, but he had failed to receive an answer. Gilmore himself gave the report in a July letter: "You enquire regarding dyspnea, energy, etc. Everything considered, I am improving; have gained 9 pounds in weight, am gaining in strength, dyspnea is much less than a month ago and morale is good. In fact I am so good I fear someone will send me as a foreign missionary."[30]

The dyspnea issue was of importance, not only to Graham and Gilmore but to others who had rarely, if ever, encountered an individual with only one lung. In November 1934, Dr. J. Edwin Habbe of Milwaukee, Wisconsin, at the suggestion of Graham, wrote to Gilmore asking about evidence of pulmonary dysfunction as the result of his lung tissue having been reduced by 50 percent. Habbe's interest was occasioned by Wisconsin's industrial compensation laws regarding silicosis; it was difficult to know the maximum or minimum amount of lung tissue that could be lost before an individual suffered impairment for work. Habbe wrote: "Any comment which you would be willing to make as to your own awareness of dyspnea or inability to exert yourself for your ordinary physical tasks would be of much value to me."[31] Two days later Gilmore responded: "I have not had a vital capacity done since leaving the hospital. I have some dyspnea on exertion, but not marked, in doing the ordinary things; … [I] can walk two flights of stairs rapidly and while it is noticeable, the dyspnea at the end of that exertion is not disabling."[32]

Graham and Singer's October 1933 publication in the *Journal of the American Medical Association* of the April operation and its successful outcome was preceded by speculation and comments in the news media. On October 29 Gilmore sent Graham a clipping from his newspaper that discussed what had happened in early April. To him it was a breach of patient confidentiality. Gilmore felt sure the information was not acquired in St. Louis, but he had the feeling that possibly Dr. Fishbein[n] should be censored. He also noted that he was back at work and feeling well, although not finding much work to do. He did not believe he could blame either Graham or Fishbein for that problem.[33] To this letter, Graham responded:

> In regard to Fishbein's connection with the newspaper accounts I can only say this. The newspapers here found out about your case while you were still in the hospital. Such information, of course, leaks out. For instance, the barber in the Chase Hotel, who I believe came over here to shave you, knew all about your case and told some people about it. The newspapers pestered me for months to give them a story. I told them that I would not do that but that after the article appeared in the *Journal of the American Medical Association* it would be more or less public property. They then began to pester Fishbein and I suspect that he had to yield to their insistent demands. At any rate, since your name was not mentioned, I do not think it had the same objectionable features that it might have had otherwise.[34]

---

n. Morris Fishbein of Chicago was the long-term, influential editor of the *Journal of the American Medical Association*. His editorialized opinions helped to shape the influence and certainly the public attitudes of the American Medical Association (AMA). Nominally he was subject to, but frequently functioned almost independent of, the AMA House of Delegates.

The public display of Gilmore began in 1934. M.F. Arbuckle, the broncho-scopist, wrote to Gilmore on March 13 to inform him that Arbuckle was to read a paper on the clinical diagnosis of primary cancer of the lung at an American Bronchoscopic Society meeting in Cleveland during the week of June 11, in company with the Laryngological Society and the American Medical Association. He asked if Gilmore would come to Cleveland on June 11 and be presented[o] to the Bronchoscopic Society, if it would not embarrass him. Arbuckle acknowledged: "I need not tell you that when I am feeling well I am jumping up and down with enthusiasm when I get thinking about this subject."[35]

After Gilmore agreed, Arbuckle wrote again: "I am looking forward to the pleasure of having you with us. ... I get a thrill every time I think about you and I am sure the men of the Bronchoscopic Society will do the same. The date is June 11."[36]

After presenting both his paper and Dr. Gilmore to the society, Arbuckle again wrote to Gilmore: "I have been meaning every day since I got home to write and tell you how glad I was to see you and how much I appreciated your coming over to Cleveland. I am delighted to see how well you are and I want you to know that not only did I appreciate your coming over but everyone else did. Time and again I heard expressions of appreciation and admiration on the part of many of the fellows. Please accept my thanks."[37]

The last public presentation of Gilmore occurred in 1951 when The American Cancer Society bestowed its annual award upon Evarts Graham. Ed Lehman, Graham's resident of 1921, now president of the American Cancer Society, planned to have Gilmore make the presentation on behalf of the American Cancer Society, and he wrote Graham to ask whether this would be appropriate. Graham responded:

> I am very much pleased that The American Cancer Society thinks I am worthy to receive its medal. I can't help thinking that in this case the American Cancer Society is one Ed Lehman. For that reason I am really doubly pleased. I would much rather be well thought of by you than some of the fuddy-duddys who occupy important positions in that society. ... I may say also that I cannot think of any very good reason why I have been selected for it unless it has been because of our old friendship and your desire to reward me with something which I don't deserve. The suggestion that you make about having Dr. Gilmore

---

o. The medical educational culture of the 1930s to 1950s was to demonstrate the effects of disease by showing afflicted patients to an audience. This was customary on "ward rounds" or "grand rounds," during which the professor would demonstrate signs or elicit symptoms from patients in front of large groups of 100 or small groups of 5 or 6. Results of therapy were similarly demonstrated by "showing" the patient. By the 1990s the custom had been replaced with the use of 35 mm slides or videotapes.

present is certainly a very interesting one. … He has a remarkably stoical disposition and that fact was one of the reasons really which made
me go ahead and remove his entire lung at the time I operated on him
on April 5, 1933. On the other hand I have asked him on two or three
occasions to come here and elsewhere for meetings at which I wished
to show him off. I would not want to overdo the business. … he is a
man of few words, certainly no speech could be expected from him
although he might be willing to speak very briefly. I don't think he has
the slightest inhibitions about exhibiting himself in public. All the
medical profession in Pittsburgh know that he had a cancer of his lung
and that he had his lung removed.[38]

After Gilmore received his invitation from the American Cancer Society, he
informed Graham, who replied: "I think it is very swell of you to be willing to go
there. I am very much afraid that I am a good deal of a nuisance to you. I might say
also that the business of asking you to be present was entirely their doings and not
mine. I should not have wanted to disturb you to that extent. It will be fine to see
you and again let me express my great appreciation to you for your kindness in
consenting to go to New York."[39]

The acquaintance between Graham and Gilmore was both friendly and fruitful.
The American Cancer Society meeting was the last such contact between the two,
although correspondence, Christmas presents, and telephone calls continued until
Graham's death.

NISSEN AND LUNG SEQUESTRATION

In 1948 Rudolph Nissen[p] of New York read a paper to the Historical Section of the
American Medical Association that was later published in the *American Journal of*

---

p. Rudolph Nissen (1896 to 1981) was a surgeon whose imagination and abilities led him to great
prominence. He began as one of the few special assistants to Ernst Ferdinand Sauerbruch in Berlin—
a man who collaborated with the Nazi regime and, after World War II, continued as chief surgeon in
East Berlin. In 1936 Nissen, a Jew, fled Germany and, with Sauerbruch's assistance, obtained a senior
position in Istanbul. Not particularly happy in Turkey, Nissen and his family moved to Boston in
1939, and in 1940 he became chief of surgery at the Brooklyn Jewish Hospital. It is rumored that he
performed his first fundoplication in Germany and a few in Turkey, but the official version claims that
the first fundoplication took place in 1946 in Brooklyn. In 1948 he wrapped cellophane around the
abdominal aortic aneurysm of Albert Einstein. In 1952 he accepted the chair of surgery in Basel,
Switzerland. His fame spread through the German-speaking surgical world, and his 70th and 75th
birthdays were acknowledged by multiple editorials in European medical journals. Nissen's life has
never been thoroughly explored in the English literature, and, although every surgeon seems to know
of the Nissen fundoplication procedure, few seem to know of Nissen.

Surgery.[40] After describing his 1931 two-stage removal of a lung and the similar operation by Cameron Haight, he stated that the third successful operation, that of Evarts A. Graham, performed in April 1933, had rightfully received much publicity because the pneumonectomy for carcinoma was done in one stage. Nissen spoke of Graham's brilliant operation and its splendid success, and stated that Graham's patient, a physician 48 years of age, was practising and in the best of health 15 years after the operation. Nissen then credited Rienhoff's individual ligation of the hilar structures[41] as being the major contribution in the development of pneumonectomy.

Three years later Graham received a letter from Dr. F. Homburger of Boston, who explained that Rudolph Nissen was being considered for the professorship of surgery at the University of Basel, Switzerland. He asked for Graham's opinion about Nissen's qualifications as a surgeon and his professional standing, particularly in thoracic surgery. Homburger indicated he was obtaining information at the request of friends on the Basel faculty, and he closed by assuring Graham that his communication was destined exclusively for the selection committee and would be kept confidential.[42]

In Graham's response to Homberger, he acknowledged that he had never met Dr. Nissen and knew very little of him. He continued:

> Dr. Nissen does not belong to any of the good surgical societies of this country but he ... is a member of the International College of Surgeons. ... the International College has some ethical members but is generally recognized as having a membership of men who certainly would not be of professorial calibre. ... the fact that the International College of Surgeons is the only surgical society to which Dr. Nissen belongs may be significant in regard to his practices. ... It seems strange that he does not belong even to the American College of Surgeons. ... I am not aware of the fact that he is doing any thoracic surgery. If he were doing much and were above criticism he would certainly be a member of the American Association for Thoracic Surgery. ... it would be very well for your friends on the Basel faculty to make further investigation of Dr. Nissen before appointing him to the Professorship of Surgery.[43]

Three weeks later Graham received a letter from Dr. A.L. Vischer of Basel that quoted a cable he had received from Homburger: "Evarts A. Graham, St. Louis, outstanding surgeon writes me devastating letter. Questions Nissen's ethics and qualifications."[44] Graham angrily wrote to Homberger that he had no definite knowledge of what Nissen was doing in this country nor about his ethics. He continued: "I wish you would get out my letter and read it again. Certainly I do not see how I could be quoted as writing a 'devastating letter' about Nissen's ethics."[45]

Homburger apologized to Graham but indicated that several others had given unfavorable or neutral comments and that his telegram had been quoted out of context. He quoted from Graham's letter and wrote, "I certainly feel that this implies questioning his ethics."[46] Nissen did receive the Basel appointment and, during the succeeding years, established himself as a leader in European surgery.

The cause of Graham's imprudent correspondence regarding Nissen is not easily understood, but there are several possibilities. First, Nissen was not in the mainstream of American surgery; he was not a member of the American College of Surgeons or other societies that Graham felt were important, particularly the American Association for Thoracic Surgery, even though entrance into those societies by someone with Nissen's background would have been difficult. Second, he was a prominent member of the detested International College of Surgeons. Third, there is a good possibility that Graham resented Nissen's claim of priority for pneumonectomy. Last, Graham may have been uncomfortable because Nissen was a trainee of Ferdinand Sauerbruch.[47]

Graham had visited Sauerbruch in 1926 and, after returning to the United States, had been informed that he would appear alongside Sauerbruch on a program of the Interstate Post-Graduate Assembly. Graham had written to George Crile opposing Sauerbruch's participation in the program:

> I cannot see why any American organization would extend any courtesy to him. ... he has been notoriously insulting and brutal to all Americans who have attended his clinic since the War. Even as recently as last July Phemister was publicy insulted by Sauerbruch. ... the feeling is so strong against him that the American Association for Thoracic Surgery has been unwilling to allow him to attend its meeting in Montreal. ... [It is] a great mistake that he has been asked to take part in this symposium and unless it should handicap you too much I should like to withdraw my name from the program.[48]

Graham also had written to the chairman of the program committee indicating his willingness to participate only if given the assurance that he would not appear at the same time as Sauerbruch:

> It is unfortunate that Sauerbruch was invited. ... Americans have gone crazy about the way they extend courtesies and lionize those particular Europeans who at home revile and despise us. ... Sauerbruch is the worst possible example. ... In July 1926 he publicly insulted Dr. D.B. Phemister ... who is an old friend of mine. I cannot see why anybody ... can wish to extend any courtesy whatsoever to a man like this. I am equally distressed to find that you have his name on your letterhead

and I … certainly suggest that unless you wish to arouse the animosity of many Americans who are familiar with the situation you remove
his name.[49]

Nothing of note had happened in the subsequent 20 years to induce Graham to
revise his opinion of Sauerbruch; his distaste was actually enhanced because of
Sauerbruch's World War II collaboration with the Nazis.

It seems most likely that Graham was piqued at Nissen's presumption of priority in pneumonectomy, and that Nissen's relation to Sauerbruch only made it
worse. In 1951 Graham was at the peak of his career, and the arrogance of power is
visible in this interchange.

THE ABBOTT LABORATORIES–*TIME MAGAZINE* CORRESPONDENCE

In February 1950 Abbott Laboratories reprinted an article Graham had written
for the 1948 *Texas Cancer Bulletin*[1] to accompany a special report on pneumonectomy in its publication called *What's New*;[50] in it Graham took credit for
having performed the first pneumonectomy. John Alexander of the University of
Michigan took exception to the claim and wrote to the editor, R.M. Wattrous,
requesting two changes: First, that it be stated that Nissen's operation was not
performed in the United States but in Berlin; and, second, that Evarts Graham
be asked to write a correction. Alexander felt that Graham's correction should be
a short statement and three bibliographic references to show that the first successful total pneumonectomy was performed by Rudolph Nissen in Berlin in
1931, the second by Cameron Haight at Ann Arbor in 1932, and the third by
Evarts A. Graham in St. Louis in 1933, contrary to the statements that were
made in the *What's New* article. Alexander claimed that the first two operations
were of great historic importance because they demonstrated that an entire
human lung could be successfully removed, and that Graham's operation was
also of great historic importance because it demonstrated that a cancerous lung
could be successfully removed.[51]

A copy of the letter was sent to Graham who immediately replied to Alexander:

> The main points in your protest are: 1. That I did not perform the first
> pneumonectomy and 2. That I should do something to correct the
> false impression that the Abbott Company has created. … Perhaps it
> will surprise you to have me say that in my opinion the operations
> performed by Nissen and Haight were not at all total pneumonec-
> tomies. In my opinion, therefore the Abbott statement is factually cor-
> rect. I do not know exactly what name to give the Nissen and Haight

operations. Perhaps it should be "sequestration of the lung". I really do not understand how anybody, wishing to be accurate, could call them pneumonectomies. ... To be strictly accurate you must limit the use of the suffix "ectomy" to the meaning of excision or cutting out. Neither Nissen nor Haight did that. I believe I was the first one to do it successfully. Would you think that a surgeon who ligated the base of an appendix and did no more to it than to remove the sloughed off necrotic organ two weeks later had performed an appendectomy or similarly one who ligated the gallbladder had performed a cholecystectomy? I don't think so. I don't think many surgeons would. In principle, however, the operations of Nissen and Haight are just like that. ... It is extremely distasteful to me to have to argue against the claims of two such good friends of mine as you and Cameron Haight. It is still more distasteful for me to have to blow my own horn in this way. Nevertheless, in the interests of accuracy I feel that I cannot duck the job of saying these things since your correspondence makes it imperative that I should reply in candour and frankness.[52]

Graham then asked Alexander:

What are we going to do about it? My answer to that question is very brief—I should like you and Dr. Wattrous of the Abbott Company to do whatever you like about any statement of correction, regardless of me. I do not want to engage in any controversy over this issue. I would much rather retain the friendship of yourself. ... If after reading this letter you still feel that Nissen's and Haight's operations were pneumonectomies, go ahead and claim the credit, however it is a little too much to ask me to agree with you on that designation. God bless you and pax vobiscum. I hate very much to send you a letter like this.[52]

Graham accompanied this letter with one to Fred Coller, chairman of surgery at Ann Arbor, in which he explained the situation with Alexander and stated that he would "tell the truth as I see it which is that according to my understanding of the word pneumonectomy, appendectomy, cholecystectomy, etc. I was the first one to perform a successful total pneumonectomy. John has forced me to make this claim, although I have avoided making it in the past at any time. ... I had hoped I might die peacefully without any priority squabbles."[53]

It was not to be. Five days later the issue arose again. *Time Magazine* published an article in its July 10, 1950, issue describing Graham's role in the development of pneumonectomy.[54] Graham immediately wrote to his friend Fred Coller: "I am sending you this letter because I wish to enclose in it a copy of the letter which I have just written to the editor of *Time*. Perhaps you have already seen how I was played up in the July 10 issue. I hope you will think I am acting properly in this very unpleasant matter. I am particularly anxious for you to see the copy of the letter which I wrote to John Alexander."[55]

Graham also wrote to the editor of *Time*:

> In your issue of July 10 you credit me with the first successful removal of an entire lung, in 1933. ... Out of fairness to others this statement requires some explanation. Although my operation was the first successful one in which a whole lung was cut out at one stage, two other pioneers in this field deserve such praise for their courage and success. Rudolph Nissen, then of Berlin but now of New York, in 1931 caused the lung of a child to slough out by operating on her in two stages in such a way as deliberately to shut off the blood to the lung. In 1932 Cameron Haight of the University of Michigan, an associate of John Alexander, performed a similar operation on another child, but a report of his case did not appear until 1934. Both patients recovered and were living and well several years later. In each case the reason for the operation was a severe chronic infection of the lung which probably would have caused the death of the patient without the surgical intervention. The reason for the operation in my case was a cancer of the lung. The patient is living and well more than 17 years later. This case, therefore, was the first successful removal of a whole lung for cancer.[56]

After reading Graham's letter to *Time*, Coller replied that he thought Graham's letter to the editor was a fair, accurate, and generous statement and that the matter should end there. He was concerned that Graham might feel that members of his department were not fully appreciative of his many contributions to surgery, and wrote: "I value you and your friendship more than anything that has happened to me in my professional life. ... The controversy is now over and can be forgotten. Nothing more can be added or detracted from the letter to *Time* in which you summarized the situation."[57] Graham returned home to find Coller's "very swell letter ... which was a great comfort."[58]

SUMMARY

Evarts Graham considered the first successful pneumonectomy for cancer of the lung to be his greatest achievement. His pride in this episode was probably related to criticism that he was a poor technical surgeon, a disapprobation that remained throughout his professional life.[59] His continuing friendship with Gilmore and continuing references to the event, particularly on the anniversary date, were topics he talked about far more than cholecystography. Gilmore's fortunate long-term survival added luster and perhaps even reverence to the event.

James Gilmore lived for 30 years after the pneumonectomy, long enough to attend Graham's memorial service. He continued to smoke and, at his death on March 6, 1963, an autopsy failed to discover any remnant of his pulmonary carcinoma. The operation, the fortuitous outcome, the publicity, and the dominant personality of Evarts Graham changed thoracic surgery from a specialty that dealt chiefly with sepsis to one that could now include the upcoming epidemic of carcinoma of the lung, first in men, then, 30 years later, in women.[60–62]

Chapter 8

FACULTY AND
STAFF DEVELOPMENT

BETWEEN WORLD WARS I AND II

General Surgery

Graham's development of faculty and staff reflected his belief that basic science research would underpin the surgery that would become more scientific and more technically refined in the twentieth century. Three months following his arrival in St. Louis, he reported to Dean G. Canby Robinson the status of the salaried surgical staff he had inherited, and from which he was to develop a department of his own making.

Names and salaries of all men...who are receiving salaries:

Professor of Clinical Neurological Surgery	(Sachs)	$3500
Professor of Clinical Orthopedic Surgery	(Allison)	1000
Associate in Clinical Surgery	(Fisher)	600
Associate in Clinical Surgery	(Brooks)	2500
Assistant in Surgery	(Alvis)	1500
Assistant in Surgery	(Staley)	1200
Assistant in Clinical Surgery	(Rainey)	500
Assistant in Clinical Orthopedic Surgery	(O'Reilly)	200
Associate in Clinical G.U. Surgery	(Caulk)	200

Fellow	(Chas. R. Fansher)	500
Student Assistants	(H. G. Peterman)	200
	(W. S. Priest)	200
Roentgenologist	(Moore, part of salary)	1000
Resident	(Lehman)	500
Assistant Residents	(Barnett)	250
	(Copher)	250

s/E.A. Graham[1]

Graham put his ideas regarding faculty development into words in a lengthy letter to Edwin Lehman, shortly after he became chairman at the University of Virginia:

> In an ideal department every member would be shooting off sparks. Unfortunately the ideal is difficult to attain and one of the things to avoid in building up a department is to add as little useless timber as possible. I feel that all of these new university departments should stand out predominantly for the contributions to knowledge which they have made. There are literally thousands of excellent clinical surgeons in this country. It would be a difficult thing, therefore, for a department to set up as its ideal a reputation for better technical work than is being done anywhere else. It would be almost impossible to realize such an ambition. On the other hand, it is not so difficult to make a department conspicuous for original work done in it if one is careful to choose for its personnel the type of man who has a real desire to accomplish something original. It isn't always necessary that the young man should have already accomplished something strikingly original. I have noticed … that oftentimes all that is necessary is to turn over an idea to such a young man and if he has the stuff in him he will develop the idea and go on with other things of his own.[2]

Graham soon began to appoint and promote individuals whom he considered creative because they had interests in one of the basic sciences: biochemistry, physiology, or pathology (not anatomy), as seemed pertinent during those early years. This was most clearly reflected in his appointments to the general surgery full-time faculty, for every man received laboratory space either in the north wing of the Medical School building or in Barnes Hospital.

During Graham's first 4 years, his unique staff development had become sufficiently visible nationwide that, in response to a request from Chancellor Hadley, Graham gave Robert Brookings a short report:

During this year I have traveled over the country from the Atlantic to the Pacific and I have found everywhere that this department of surgery is regarded very highly. I have been told by many surgeons of different types that this department is now the most productive department of surgery in the country. This is what I have been particularly striving for and I naturally feel gratified that it is being universally recognized that this department is turning out a lot of productive work.[3]

A decade following his monumental report on American medical schools, Abraham Flexner wrote to several individuals asking for impressions of what a modern medical school should be.[4] In an eight-page response, Graham expressed his philosophy of education, research, and the organization required for a successful Department of Surgery.[5] This letter led the Rockefeller Foundation to ask Graham to survey the English and Scottish medical educational systems with David Edsall (see chapter 15).

Graham's years at Washington University covered three critical decades of US history. The 1920s were years of post-war prosperity, growth, expansion, and new ideas. Graham's major players during this period were Barney Brooks, Edwin Lehman, I.Y. Olch, Warren Cole, Glover Copher, and Nathan Womack; the minor players were Duff Allen, Joe Gale, and William Hamm. The 1930s brought economic depression, restraints, contraction, and cutbacks that severely affected his staff. During these years his major players were Glover Copher, Robert Elman, Peter Heinbecker, Nathan Womack, and Brian Blades. Duff Allen, A.O. Fisher, and Franklin Walton moved from full-time academic activity into private practice. Heinz Haffner and Carl Lischer appeared on the scene toward the end of the decade, but, although Graham had hopes that both of these men would become a part of his full-time group, World War II and then discord surrounding the school's proposal for a full-time clinic left them on the sidelines.

The 1940s were years of war, faculty restrictions, victory, returning veterans, and the beginnings of new growth. Eugene Bricker, Charles Eckert, Henry Schwartz, and Thomas Burford joined Robert Elman, Peter Heinbecker, and Nathan Womack. Graham's department was re-invigorated with returning veterans as residents, even as Graham prepared for the vicissitudes in surgical education that would come with the Korean War.

During the first of these three decades—the 1920s—appointments came mainly from Graham's resident trainees. Graham's first resident was Edwin Lehman, who studied vascular surgical procedures and cancer, until he left in 1928 to become chairman of surgery at the University of Virginia. Glover Copher, who shared the cholecystography experiment with Warren Cole, remained on Graham's full-time roster. Two years later Duff Allen arrived—a young man who attempted to break into intracardiac surgery with his design of a cardioscope that would visualize and cut the mitral valve as treatment for mitral stenosis.[6] It was ahead of its time, and Allen soon left the core department to establish his private practice as a part-time faculty member. Warren Cole, after completing his year as chief resident in 1925 to 1926, became instructor then associate professor. Active in research on physiology of the biliary tree, he conducted canine experiments in that field until he left for the University of Illinois in 1936.[7] Cole was succeeded by Joseph Gale, whose interests in chest surgery led to an appointment at the University of Wisconsin, where, several years later, he became its chairman of surgery.

Peter Heinbecker worked in the fields of nerve conduction, neuroendocrine phenomena, and the treatment of hypertension. Without success, he attempted to elucidate the relationship between the three cell types of the pituitary gland and disorders of the adrenals. He supervised the chief resident and occasionally operated on ward patients, but he never established a reputation as a surgeon—he was always seen as a researcher.

Robert Elman, after training in surgery at Johns Hopkins and pathology at the Rockefeller Institute, became an assistant resident at Barnes and, in 1927, a full-time staff member. His operative ability reflected the fact that he never became chief resident. His interests lay in metabolism, nutrition, and diseases of the pancreas, and his laboratory in the Medical School building was supplemented by a laboratory and small clinical ward in Barnes Hospital, where he pioneered the use of intravenous nutrition with amino acids, and shared the initial work on pancreatic amylase with Michael Somogyi of the Jewish Hospital. Although widely acclaimed for his efforts in nutrition, he, like Heinbecker, was never asked to join another institution and remained at Washington University throughout Graham's tenure as chairman. External support for his work was generous, and there were always one or two fellows in his laboratory. Elman never accepted assistant residents on rotation through their clinical services, although he periodically supervised the chief residents.

I.Y. Olch[a], whose interests were general surgery, pathology, and endocrine interrelationships, spent 2 years as an assistant resident before being appointed to the

---

a. I.Y. Olch was born in Providence, Rhode Island, in 1896. After attending Brown University, he received his medical degree from Johns Hopkins in 1921, and then spent 1 year as one of Halsted's last surgical interns. He also had exposure to Joseph Bloodgood, Halsted's colleague, who was a pioneer in the field of surgical pathology. After heading to Washington University, Olch spent a few months with Eugene Opie in general pathology before becoming an assistant resident in surgery under Evarts Graham. Following his 1926 appointment as an assistant professor of surgery, he worked closely with Barney Brooks in the surgical pathology laboratory adjacent to Graham's departmental office. His major interest was the practice of surgery, followed by surgical pathology, and then the playing of the cello.

In 1935, with the support of Graham, Olch considered taking an appointment at the St. Louis Jewish Hospital or one at the Cedars of Lebanon Hospital in Los Angeles. He chose to go to California because of the respiratory problems of one of his children. He became chief of surgery as well as its surgical pathologist, and he held a clinical appointment at the University of California, Los Angeles. Olch continued in active surgical practice until an advanced age, and he died on January 26, 1985.

faculty as assistant professor. He shared the surgical pathology obligation with Barney Brooks, and then took it over when Brooks left for Vanderbilt. Olch was technically gifted and enjoyed surgery more than pathology. His surgical effort of historic note was an operation on Elva Dawkins, a farmer's wife from southeastern Missouri. After determining that her blood calcium was 16 mg percent (60% above normal), he removed a 3 cm parathyroid adenoma, the first US parathyroidectomy, preoperatively diagnosed and successfully removed.[8]

Nathan Womack[b], the 1927 to 1929 chief resident and a favorite of Evarts Graham, remained on the staff; his interests were the endocrine relationships between the pituitary and the pancreas, the lymphatics and infections of the gallbladder, and the response of the thyroid to systemic illness. His chief role was that of surgical pathologist for the department, and, to Graham, he was more of a pathologist than a surgeon. Womack was probably Graham's closest personal friend on the surgical faculty. The two would play golf together as well as attend St. Louis Cardinal baseball games with tickets given to them by the owner, Sam Breadon.[9]

The Rise and Fall of Glover Copher

Glover Copher[c] was one of only two residents from Graham's first 10 years at Barnes to remain in St. Louis for his entire professional career. (The other was Duff Allen.) After completing 4 years of training, in 1922 he became a member of the Department of Surgery, collaborated in the cholecystography project, and continued to work alongside Cole in the study of biliary tract physiology, infection, and obstruction, and portal vein hemodynamics. Graham was impressed with and supportive of

---

b. Nathan Womack (1901 to 1975) was born in Reidsville, North Carolina. He received his bachelor of science degree from the University of North Carolina, and his doctor of medicine degree from Washington University in 1924. Womack continued at Washington University as a resident to complete his training in 1928. Remaining in the Department of Surgery, he developed a special interest in surgical pathology and became pathologist for the department until 1948. He moved to the University of Iowa to become its department chairman for 3 years, and then home to the University of North Carolina in 1951 to become chairman, a position he retained until his death.

A soft-spoken man with an obvious mid-south accent, he was an inspiring teacher and an able clinical investigator. The faculty, and particularly the surgical house staff, were very aware of his warm personal charm. He was active in international and national organizations, especially the National Board of Medical Examiners; he was its president from 1960 to 1963. Womack's residents and associates admired and respected him, and he touched the lives of many individuals, particularly during his years at North Carolina.

c. Glover H. Copher (1893 to 1970) was born and raised in Troy, Missouri, a small town 30 miles north of St. Louis. At the age of 10, a home gunshot accident destroyed his right eye but not his desire for an education. Undergraduate and early medical education at the University of Missouri in Columbia (then a 2-year medical school) was followed by 2 clinical years at Washington University. Copher received his doctor of medicine degree in 1918. He spent the next 4 years as intern and resident at Barnes Hospital, first under Ernest Sachs (acting chairman), and then as Evarts Graham's

Copher, and with praise unequalled in his support for other members of his cadre[d]; he frequently recommended Copher to other schools as a candidate for chairman. In 1924, only 2 years following his residency, Graham suggested to G. Canby Robinson, who was looking for a chairman at Vanderbilt, that Copher was "one of those men who could probably swing such a position successfully," stating that Copher "would do very well indeed and would build up a strong department of the kind that you want."[10] Two years later Graham wrote to Barney Brooks: "Copher is developing very rapidly into an ideal type.... I should hate to lose him from here."[11] To C.C. Bass at Tulane, Graham recommended Copher for the surgical chairmanship: "My first choice and the one whom I would recommend above all others is Dr. Glover H. Copher.... He has a very strong bent for research and has an original mind together with an ability to see a problem through.... he has a sound knowledge of pathology and physiology and with it all is an excellent clinician and teacher....everyone connected with our institution is very fond of him."[12] Two years later Graham recommended Copher for professor at the Peking Medical College.[13] His fondness for Copher continued through 1929, when he responded to a request from G. Canby Robinson (now at Cornell) about possibilities for chairman: "I know both [E.D.] Churchill and [John] Alexander.... I do not think that either presents qualifications... to the same extent as Glover Copher. Copher has done a lot of experimental work... [has] thoroughly acquired the habit of experiment... and has shown a marked ability to stimulate interest... on the part of students.... He has been my first substitute in running a service for more than a year and for several

---

second chief resident. Copher opened his surgical practice at Barnes Hospital, and he remained there for the rest of his life. As an associate of Warren Cole, he was involved in several experiments on the biliary tree that followed the cholecystography success.

In 1924 Copher married Marjorie Hulzinger, chief dietitian at Barnes Hospital. She was a woman with a remarkable career as the first dietetic intern at the Peter Bent Brigham Hospital before assignment to the British Expeditionary Forces in France where she introduced dietetics to the British Army. She received a decoration by King George V and a commendation from the French government. Sadly, Marjorie Copher developed bronchogenic carcinoma, and an examination by Graham and Arbuckle demonstrated tracheal involvement. She was declared inoperable and died in May 1935, following a brief illness. An annual Marjorie Copher Award, established by her husband, is now the most prestigious honor awarded by the American Dietetic Association.

Glover Copher was meticulous in dress, manner, and speech—always with a fresh flower in his lapel. As a perfectionist in clinical bedside medicine and operative technique, he paid attention to every detail, not only with his patients but with everyone around him—clerks, nurses, students, and residents—all of whom he treated with a quiet dignity and respect, although with some degree of condescension. Relatively insecure, he tended to denigrate and downgrade those medical and surgical colleagues who failed to measure up to his standards of surgical/operative technique or excellence in clinical medicine. A demanding taskmaster to his house officers, his affectations, mannerisms, and aphorisms (eg, "asepsis, hemostasis, gentleness") were copied by dozens of residents who came under his influence, as were the three tenets for a successful surgical career—"availability, affability, and ability." Copher was the most influential surgical teacher for almost three decades and, in this

prolonged periods he has taken charge of the entire service including the teaching as well as the work in the hospital.... I would place him without any hesitation at the top of the group of young men of his age in the country."[14]

In 1930, when Graham was asked by the Rockefeller Foundation to examine the future of surgery, he wrote: "The following men are most likely to constitute the surgical leaders of the next generation: Glover H. Copher, Warren H. Cole, Edward Churchill, Edmund Andrews, Alfred Blalock, Claude Beck."[15] Graham's regard for Copher's capabilities peaked in 1931, when he was asked for names of possible successors to Harvey Cushing. After listing Brooks, Cutler, Holman, and Churchill, Graham suggested Glover Copher, Warren Cole, and Alfred Blalock of Nashville.[16] A strong personal friendship developed between Graham and Copher, and Eugene Bricker recalls an invitation to a Sunday lunch at Copher's house and then a football game with the two of them.[17] Graham depended heavily upon Copher during the decade and, when out of town, left his patients in Copher's care, never that of Heinbecker, Womack, or Elman. Also, Graham frequently gave to Copher patients that were sent to him. Glover Copher became his clinical support in patient management and operative assistance, and he served as Graham's unofficial vice-chairman. His stature in Graham's eyes was also apparent by Copher's office allocation. When the fourth floor of the Rand Johnson Building opened in 1931, it contained three surgical offices: a large one for Graham and two smaller ones for Malvern Clopton and Glover Copher. The remaining full-time men were housed across Euclid Avenue in the Medical School building. Graham's promotion of Copher, unmatched in his support for other members of his staff,

---

respect, was a complement to Graham and the other full-time surgeons who, though better known nationally, were less skilled as surgeons.

During those decades Barnes Hospital was a personal, friendly, intimate, and cohesive institution that became the social and professional focus of Copher's life; after he ceased to operate, he still paid daily visits to the physician's lounge.

Although a dominant character in Barnes Hospital's medical life, Copher played a minor role at Washington University and in national surgical affairs. His focus was entirely on his surgical practice and the local political and social events of the St. Louis area, little of which he missed. He was not only a surgeon to but also a friend of many families of the civic and business leaders of St. Louis and, following the death of Mrs. Copher, he devoted as much time and energy to his surgical practice as he showered on his daughter Marjorie. An institution in his own right, he failed to understand Graham's thrust in research as he, himself, pursued excellence of surgical care. Copher left an indelible imprint on the operative technique and clinical skills of three decades of surgical residents who were trained at Barnes Hospital.

d. *Author's note*: Graham's support for his full-time staff and specialty chiefs did not waver, except in the cases of Glover Copher and Ernest Sachs. In this book, extra space and detail is given to his relationship with these two men, as it reflects on Graham's management, not on the conflicts per se. These two men remained in the department throughout Graham's tenure, but he never achieved a satisfactorily comfortable working relationship with either. Everyone in the institution knew of the discord, but few knew the details, many of which are made public here for the first time.

bespoke a special, blind fondness for and admiration of Copher, of which Copher proved unworthy.

Graham's respect and dependence upon Copher continued through the mid-1930s, but, as Copher's private practice grew, his interests in the laboratory slackened, and he became Barnes' pre-eminent busy clinical surgeon, its most superb technician, and a man devoted to the minute aspects of patient care. Following the death of Mrs. Copher in 1934, Copher's life began to revolve around his daughter Marjorie, whom he overindulged, and a private practice that soon included the financial and social elite of Protestant St. Louis. He arrived at Barnes Hospital every morning at 6:30 am, in a contest with Ernest Sachs to see who would sign in first. He expected his assistant resident and intern to meet him at the door, and they would see all of his patients before starting to operate, promptly at 8:15. Copher's clinical practice gradually pre-empted half of the private general surgery beds, and he dominated Operating Room No. 3 almost every day. His clinical success inevitably produced resentment on the part of Elman, Heinbecker, and Womack, who began to press Graham to restrict Copher's clinical activities and to remove him from the full-time staff. Graham responded by first eliminating Copher's contacts with medical students and his supervision of the chief residents. Then, to Copher's dismay, Graham stepwise reduced his annual stipend and removed him from the Rand Johnson office.[18]

Elman, Heinbecker, and Womack, the full-time group, never established clinical practices of any size, and the resident staff never considered them to be surgeons of master caliber. To Graham, their academic and research productivity took precedence over technical capability. To Glover Copher, the operating room was the ultimate home of surgery, and for 25 years he imprinted Barnes residents with his attention to detail and surgical technique. Graham failed to appreciate Copher's role in the clinical education of residents as something that complemented his own intellectual idealism and research values. To Graham, Glover Copher was a highly eligible candidate for a major US academic position, but, despite his promotion by Graham, there is no record that Copher ever received an offer to visit, much less, take a position at another institution. Others must have recognized that Copher lacked the requisite qualities of academic leadership, something Graham failed to sense. Copher was self-centered and penurious, and, although superb at what he did, he was not a leader of men; his capabilities and limitations were a major miscalculation on Graham's part.

The episode that created an open schism in mid-summer 1944 concerned a patient, "F.E.," a personal friend of Graham's whom he had seen for acute biliary colic. Graham advised F.E. go home and return in 6 weeks for cholecystectomy. Three weeks later, F.E. was admitted to the St. Louis Jewish Hospital under the care of Dr. Llewellyn Sale and then transferred to Barnes, where Copher, covering for Graham at the time, received the patient and prepared for an emergency cholecystectomy. Incensed, Graham excoriated Copher and wrote a letter throwing him out of the fourth floor office: "The question of your having a private office here on the fourth floor is still a sore point. I hope you will make a move in the near future to open an outside office and vacate the space which you now occupy.... I appreciate very much the good work you have done ever since I have been here and realize fully your loyal devotion to the institution.... It seems necessary to make these changes which I mention in this letter but it seems to me that they will be for your best interest as well as for the best interest of the institution."[19] Copher had practiced out of that small office on the fourth floor of the Rand Johnson building for 14 years, and, even though it was now denied to him, Copher did not open an outside office. He recruited patients from under the clock in the Barnes lobby, and he saw them in a doctor's office in the hospital that was available to any member of the Barnes staff. Feelings between Copher and Graham became so intense that the two could not speak when they met in the hall. However, although Copher began to make snide remarks about his ex-colleagues, the "ion doctors," and derogatory, sotto voce comments about their research activities, he never deprecated Graham. His sudden fall from grace that amazed and puzzled the returning veterans became a subject of discussion in the coffee shop and hospital corridors.

Moving Copher out of the fourth floor office did not solve all of Graham's pique. Four years later Graham wished to terminate Copher's faculty appointment, an action that would also deprive him of a Barnes Hospital appointment; however, Frank Bradley strongly discouraged this action, for, by now, Copher's clientele had become major donors to Barnes.[20] Frustrated, angry, and almost irrational, Graham wrote to Bradley:

> Dr. Copher has so many private patients... that it interferes with other members of the staff, not only in getting their patients into the hospital but also in obtaining the use of an operating room. ... he makes no contributions of any kind to the educational activities of the school, he makes practically no contributions to the literature. He is, therefore in the position of using the Barnes Hospital solely for his private gain ... in unfair competition with other members of the surgical staff. ... I should like to recommend... limiting [his] number of private patients at any one time to ten... and that the Admitting Office be so informed.... [however] I desire to make exceptions of the plastic surgical service and the orthopedic service.... both of these services have brought great lustre to Barnes Hospital. I cannot see however that Dr. Copher has.[21]

Thirty months later, as Graham retired as chairman of surgery, discomfort between the two had not been resolved. Copher still had a large private practice but no educational responsibilities other than the surgical assistant residents assigned to him. The two never became comfortable with one another, and verbal interaction was kept to a minimum.

Years later, portraits of the two were hung in the main corridor of Barnes Hospital, facing each other but still not speaking.

WORLD WAR II AND POST-WAR YEARS

The years of World War II were trying times for Evarts Graham, who was torn between commitments in Washington, DC, and St. Louis. The Barnes surgical staff was depleted; Graham struggled to keep the service going and surgical demands met by using interns as residents and medical students as interns. Heinz Haffner and Carl Lischer, upon completing their residencies in 1940 and 1942, did not enter military service, and Graham relied upon them to supervise ward patient care and to oversee student and resident education. Following the war both remained on the faculty but, during the turmoil created by the full-time clinic proposal, they moved their practices to St. Luke's Hospital. Charles Eckert, who completed the residency program in 1944, remained on the full-time staff to fill the vacancy occasioned by the Copher controversy. In addition to his obligations in surgical pathology, Eckert developed a special interest in the surgery for cancer of the breast, and problems of cancer in general. He and Mrs. Eckert became personal friends of Dr. and Mrs. Graham, visiting their home on many occasions, and, when Graham stopped operating (at the age of 70), his general surgery patients were referred to Eckert; thoracic problems were sent to Burford. In 1956 Eckert left to accept the chair of surgery at Albany, New York.

During World War II, Graham covered chest surgery activities with the aid of fellows from overseas. The return of Thomas Burford, who became counselor, advisor, and on many occasions his surgical assistant, was a welcome relief. Burford was an ambidextrous and extremely skilled technical surgeon, who became a national figure in the world of thoracic surgery. Following his wartime experiences, Burford remained full-time in the department until Graham retired.

Graham's penultimate full-time appointment to general surgery was Ben Eiseman, who completed his residency in 1950, the year before Graham's retirement. Eiseman left the department 3 years later, spent 5 years at the University of Colorado in Denver, and then accepted the surgical chair at the University of Kentucky. Dr. C.B. Mueller, this author and Graham's final appointment, served 5 years on the Washington University faculty before leaving for the State University of New York (SUNY) in Syracuse.

Graham measured the quality and productivity of his efforts by the men he trained at Barnes Hospital who subsequently became department chairmen elsewhere. He was inordinately proud of this group, and, in a long letter to friend and colleague Paul Hawley, he named the men who had passed through his program and expressed his pleasure at their successes.[22] To Graham, this list (see appendix D) ranked with his pneumonectomy on James Gilmore as one of the satisfying and significant features of his 30-year career.

SURGICAL PATHOLOGY

Upon Graham's arrival in St. Louis, autopsy-oriented Departments of General Pathology were gradually moving from pathologic anatomy to pathologic physiology, but the pathology of specimens derived from the operating room was not generally embraced, and interested surgeons moved into this area of study. Joseph C. Bloodgood (1862 to 1935), on Halsted's staff at Johns Hopkins, set the pace for the development of surgical pathology as a surgeon with a special interest in the subject, and it remained with surgeons for three or four decades. Subsequently, such giants as Ewing, Stout, Foote, Stewart, and Warren (nonsurgeons) developed it into a discipline of its own over three or four decades, and by mid-century it was beginning to find its way into the fold of general pathology. Graham's effort in pathology started with the appointment of Barney Brooks, a surgeon from Johns Hopkins, who reviewed all general surgical specimens and conducted a Thursday afternoon surgical pathology conference that continued until World War II, and was patterned after Bloodgood's conferences. After Brooks's departure, I.Y. Olch, another surgeon with a secondary interest in pathology, maintained Brooks's tradition until 1937, when he left for California. Nathan Womack then took over the pathology obligation until he left for Iowa in 1948.

At the time of Womack's departure, surgical pathology was split by departmental orientation. General and thoracic pathology was in the North Building, adjacent to Womack's office. Neurosurgical pathology was carried out by Ernest Sachs at the opposite end of the corridor. The services of ophthalmologic pathology and nose and throat pathology were in the Oscar Johnson Institute, but in separate laboratories, and were covered on rotation by members of the Department of Pathology. The Department of Obstetrics and Gynecology maintained its own pathology laboratory on the third floor of the maternity hospital, headed successively by gynecologists Henry Schwarz, Frank McNally, and John Hobbs.

At the completion of his surgical training in 1944, Charles Eckert joined Nathan Womack, to be groomed for the surgical pathology role. Eckert was a meticulous, expert technical surgeon, patterned after Glover Copher and equally expert as a bedside clinician; however, for Eckert, surgical pathology was an "add on" to his surgery. With the fall of Copher, Eckert was required to assume Copher's role as a supervisor on the ward services and to give clinical support to Graham's general surgery private practice. It was a tall order, but, even though Eckert carried it satisfactorily after Womack departed, Tom Burford and Eugene Bricker insisted that

Graham recruit an individual whose sole responsibility would be surgical patholo-gy. They encouraged the appointment of Lauren Ackerman of Columbia, Missouri.

Graham had strong ideas about surgical pathology, the attitudes of surgical pathologists, and the administrative structures needed in its reporting relation-ships. He wrote to Warren Cole concerning the question of where surgical pathol-ogy belonged in the organization of the Medical School: "Of course I feel very strongly indeed it belongs in the Department of Surgery. I don't see how any real-ly adequate training of surgeons can go on if surgical pathology is taken out of that department and put into the Department of General Pathology."[23]

During the process of recruiting Lauren Ackerman, Graham wrote to Frank Bradley: "For many years it has been felt here that a very important part of the training of the surgical house staff is the creation of a proper feeling for surgical pathology. This feeling is much better developed in an atmosphere where the sci-entific spirit is encouraged than in an atmosphere in which the chief emphasis is placed merely upon routine diagnosis and the tagging of the specimen with the proper label."[24] Graham also wrote to Dean Robert Moore, chairman of pathology: "I regard pathology as one of the keystones in the training of surgeons. I do not see how anyone can be a really good surgeon unless he has a fair knowledge of pathol-ogy. ... after all, the surgeons have contributed greatly to our knowledge of pathol-ogy beginning with John Hunter. There must be no interruption of the activities between the surgeons and the pathologists."[25]

In 1940 the Washington University Department of [General] Pathology was a disease-oriented, autopsy pathology department with only a peripheral relation-ship to surgical pathology, and no relationship whatsoever to the operating rooms. However, other approaches were taking place half way across Missouri at the Ellis Fischel Cancer Hospital in Columbia. Dr. Theodore Eberhart, the medical chief of staff, had collected three men in a group remarkable for its quality: Eugene Bricker[e], the surgeon, would become internationally renowned for the operative treatment of advanced carcinoma of the uterine cervix; Juan del Regato, the radi-

e. Eugene M. Bricker (1905 to 2000) was born in Carbondale, Illinois. He attended its elementary schools and then the Southern Illinois Teacher's College before enrolling in Washington University from 1930 to 1934. A football scholarship in lieu of tuition, along with semiprofessional boxing in downtown St. Louis, supported his medical education. After internship and 3 years of residency at Barnes Hospital, Bricker became a faculty member whose first assignment, in 1938, was to the Ellis Fischel Cancer Hospital in Columbia, Missouri, where he stayed until he was called to join the army in 1942. After duty as chief plastic surgery consultant in the European Theater, he returned to Barnes Hospital in 1946 to supervise the expansion of Graham's residency program to accommodate returning veterans. With a lifelong interest in cancer, he focused on carcinoma of the cervix and developed the ileal loop that made pelvic exenteration an acceptable operation and brought him international fame. He retained an interest in athletic endeavors—tennis, squash, fishing, hiking, and mountain climbing—throughout life. His soft-spoken, confident demeanor endeared him to all

ologist, would move to the Penrose Institute in Colorado Springs and become a pioneer in radiotherapy for cancer; and Lauren Ackerman[f], the pathologist, would become the Doyen of American surgical pathologists. Bricker, del Regato, and Ackerman shared every patient, and Ackerman attempted to unify all the features that he saw—the patient, the operation, and the pathology, both gross and microscopic. His interests became the pathology and clinical manifestation of infections and malignancies, with no interest whatsoever in autopsy pathology.

Bricker and Burford persuaded Graham to ask Ackerman to be the pathologist for the Department of Surgery, a position that Ackerman accepted in 1948 upon the departure of Womack. Ackerman's appointment, however, did not easily resolve the complex issue of how he would relate to the Department of Pathology, headed by Robert Moore, who was also the dean. Ackerman's appointment was as a member of the Department of Surgery and a consultant to the Department of Pathology. He rejected overtures from Stanley Hartroft, Moore's successor, to become a member of the Department of Pathology. The arrival of Paul Lacey as pathology chairman, the departure of Sachs with the closing of his neuropathology lab, and an expansion of both ophthalmology and otolaryngology finally permitted a coalescence of all surgical pathology efforts; in 1960 Ackerman became a member of the Department of Pathology in charge of a surgical pathology section. His laboratory and office remained in Barnes Hospital, not in pathology department quarters

---

of his acquaintances. Never threatening or overpowering but generally at center stage in everything he did, Bricker was revered by his residents and fiercely loyal to all of them. A member of 18 organizations, he became president of the American Surgical Association and chairman of the American Board of Surgery. His 18-year membership on the Washington University Board of Trustees brought him an honorary degree in 1987. On January 1, 2000, death due to natural causes mercifully came, after 3 years of failing memory and increasing physical disability.

f. Lauren V. Ackerman (1905 to 1993) grew up in Auburn, New York, attended Hamilton College, and received his doctor of medicine degree from the University of Rochester in 1932. The next 7 years were spent in the study of tuberculosis, a medical residency, an assistantship in pathology and bacteriology at Rochester, and then a residency in pathology under Shields Warren in Boston, where he became interested in the histopathology of irradiated tissues. From 1940 to 1948, Ackerman served as pathologist at the Ellis Fischel Cancer Hospital in Columbia, Missouri. The next 25 years (1948 to 1973) he spent at Washington University/Barnes Hospital, where he established a residency program and an international reputation with his hands-on approach to surgical pathology. His first major publication Cancer,[26] coauthored with del Regato, became the period's premier textbook that covered diagnosis, treatment, and prognosis in one volume. He followed this work with Surgical Pathology,[27] which was probably the single most influential publication in the training of a generation of surgical pathologists. Honors poured in from around the world. Ackerman was a secure but self-effacing man who was rarely generous when discussing his colleagues, although his interesting commentaries were always done with extreme courtesy, touched with a good dose of humor. He was never excessively tidy in dress and often failed to tie his shoelaces. He was an intellectual oenophile, fond of chamber music, an engaging companion, and inordinately proud of his resident protégés. He died after a brief illness due to carcinoma of the colon.

in the Medical School. Ackerman continued to frequent the operating room (always when a frozen section was requested), and he developed a vibrant surgical pathology laboratory with its own residency training program, through which general surgical and thoracic surgical residents rotated at 3- or 6-month intervals.

Ackerman has vividly described to this author a conversation with Graham revealing Ackerman's initial attempts to develop a weekly clinical pathologic conference:

> "Dr. Graham, do you think it would be a good idea if we had a surgical pathology conference?" I said. "Yes Lauren, that would be a good idea." I said, "Well suppose I pick out a few cases and then maybe an intern will present the cases." He said, "Yes there is a room over there by the library, we can have it over there." I said "fine." So I picked some cases and went to the room at the appointed time. Dr. Graham wasn't there, and after 15 minutes he swept in with his retinue, saying, "Lauren you may begin now." ... The intern began the story. He got about two sentences in and Dr. Graham said, "Who did that? Did you do that?" The response: "Yes, I am afraid I did do that." Graham: "that's absolutely incorrect. I don't understand how you could do such a thing." We finally stumbled through that case [then] started the next case and it was even worse; ... I made two attempts to run a surgical pathology conference, but it was absolutely impossible with Dr. Graham because he would stop and tear the poor intern to pieces, [not only] for his presentation but particularly for what he did ... that is, the details of his technique. He would question him and then the poor fellow would not be able to continue; [Graham] would talk about the diagnosis, talk about why [and how] he did things, so that it was impossible to run the conference and show the pathology with Dr. Graham there. It was absolutely impossible."[28]

Ackerman solved the problem by keeping his conferences within the surgical pathology section—they were not clinical surgical conferences as such, even though they always carried a clinical context. One hundred people from all across the city would attend, and, when Moyer arrived, the surgical clinical-pathology conference was re-instated.

In the development of the Department of Surgery, Ackerman's laboratory was a shining, vibrant piece, generating its own air of excitement. He required his residents to spend half of their time in a research project, and the rotation through his service became a significant experience for general surgery residents. In 1973, as emeritus professor, Ackerman left St. Louis for State University of New York (SUNY) in Stony Brook, New York, to serve as pathologist emeritus until his death in 1995.

Ackerman was neither a surgeon nor an ordinary pathologist, but his selection was certainly one of Graham's great appointments. Ackerman—who was very egocentric, self-assured, brilliant, and constantly challenging his colleagues—was one of the brightest stars in Graham's crown.

ADMINISTRATIVE AND SECRETARIAL STAFF

After arriving in St. Louis, Graham worked with a sequence of secretaries and stenographers before he finally recognized the need for a central responsible figure; a firm secretarial–support staff arrangement in Graham's department finally happened in 1927, with the arrival of Ada Hanvey[g]. It was I.Y. Olch who suggested to Ada, a secretary at the medical society office, that she apply. (Olch was an active member of the society.) Hanvey, 21 years old, arrived at the North Building of the Medical School on Saturday afternoon, June 18 to spot a youngish man walking up the steps. After being escorted by him to Dr. Olch, Hanvey was introduced to her escort, Dr. Evarts Graham. After a brief interview, the two agreed that a 2-week trial period was in order. She impressed Graham with her ability to spell *tetraiodophenolphthalein*: she explained later that she had come across the word while working in the medical society office typing the material for Graham's 1927 Award of Merit, and when she knew she was coming for an interview, she had mastered its spelling.[29]

Ada Hanvey, the fourth of six children, was born in 1906 in Whitehaven, England. Her family moved to 397 Humphrey Street, St. Louis, when she was in her early teens. Her older sister, Lilian, became librarian for the St. Louis Medical Society and obtained a position for Ada, who worked for 4 years as a part-time librarian and general secretary.

The 2-week probation period was never again mentioned, and Ada Hanvey remained an integral part of the Department of Surgery until Graham's retirement. Within months, she had gained Graham's confidence and trust to the point at which she was able to allocate the three secretaries to the several full-time men in accordance with their secretarial needs, and then recruit new ones as needed. She became Graham's personal secretary as well as departmental executive administrator, and she relieved him of the management of the support staff that had begun to devolve on I.Y. Olch.

Graham was a prolific correspondent, dictating several letters to Hanvey every day. Salutations to his addressees varied with his degree of intimacy. He used "Dear Barney" (Brooks), "Dear Nathan" (Womack), and "Dear Warren" (Cole) to his

---

g. *Author's note*: The author's contacts with Dr. Graham and the Department of Surgery began in September 1938 and continued until July 1956 as medical student, National Youth Administration recipient, resident, research fellow, and faculty member. Contacts with Ada Hanvey also began in 1938. For 5 years the author lived next door to her sister, Lil Alderson, on Utah Avenue in south St. Louis. During that time, he developed a personal and friendly relationship with Ada that lasted until her death. Many comments in this section arise from personal observations as an 18-year affiliate or member of the department.

personal friends; "Dear Edsall" (David), "Dear Blades" (Brian), and "Dear Cushing" (Harvey) to his professional colleagues; and "Dear Dr. Flexner" (Abraham), "Dear Dr. Bradley" (Frank), and "Dear Dr. Bowman" (Isaiah) to recognize a more formal relationship. She took all of his correspondence in shorthand and transcribed it before leaving the office that evening. Many of his memoranda were written by Graham in longhand on lined yellow foolscap. Hanvey sent his manuscripts to subordinate secretaries, a system that kept her acquainted with his many activities. Graham made few revisions or corrections, and she monitored the accuracy of his correspondence to the point that retyping was seldom required. Once dictated, his scientific manuscripts were rarely revised more than once. Graham prided himself upon the precision of his English as well as the correctness of his grammar, and he kept a *Webster's Unabridged Dictionary* on his desk at all times. He even gave one to each staff member.

Graham was a hard taskmaster in regard to manuscripts from his department, and he insisted that each author submit everything for his review. One day Graham handed a manuscript back to Womack saying: "I don't like your usage of this word. …If you don't mind let's change it.… Why is it that nobody has to correct my papers?" Womack responded, "You never turn them over to us." Graham retorted: "Well God-dammit here's a copy of a manuscript. I'm leaving right now to give it at Princeton the day after tomorrow. You read it over and see if you can find an error in it." With delight, Womack took the manuscript home that night and, after considerable work, came across one error—a dangling participle. He immediately went to the Western Union office to wire: "For God's sake, don't dangle the participle in the first paragraph on top of page eight before the faculty of Princeton University. Signed: Galsworthy." Graham never responded, but Womack was sure he was quite "burned up."[9]

Ada cared for Graham's every perceived need, and she was "Miss Hanvey" to him until near the end, when she became "A.H." To her, he was always "Dr. Graham," with utmost deference. He became dependent upon her for most features of his academic life: his daily schedule; his conferences; and, to some extent, the relative importance of the many demands on his time and effort. He relied upon her judgment as to whom he would see and for what purpose. Within 6 to 7 years, she had become the doorkeeper to his office and, in some ways, his junior partner, sharing many facets of his responsibilities, particularly in thoracic surgery developments.

Although Ada's main purpose in life was her support of Evarts Graham, she did have other interests and demands. As a watercolor artist, her first studio was in the garage belonging to her parents, then a bedroom in one of her apartments. She traveled to mid-Missouri and Central American sites for inspiration. She enjoyed gardening and would bring flowers to the departmental office. Well tailored in an ultra-modern, almost arty style, her dress habits reflected her taste in the arts and in high culture.

A major extraprofessional obligation occurred in 1955, when both her sister Jo and her sister's husband, Barney O'Shields, died, leaving Ada to care for their 11-year-old son Patrick. These were trying times for the two of them. She was prim and proper, had never married, had many professional obligations, and was now almost 50, and he was a teenager of the late 1950s and early 1960s, the son of two US marines. They developed a working living relationship that was not necessarily strained, but not truly loving. Ada accepted Pat as her obligation and, to some extent, a burden. The two shared a three-bedroom apartment on Wydown Avenue, just south of Hanley Road, until Patrick reached 21 years of age.[30]

During Graham's retirement years and particularly with his translocation to an office in Wohl Hospital, her loyalty and dedication to "The Chief" never wavered. Graham had expressed to her his desire that Nathan Womack would become his successor as department chairman and, although not overtly hostile, she resented the coming of Carl Moyer, a chief with a very different and unusual administrative style. Sidelined and marginalized she disappeared from departmental activities.

After Graham's death, Ada Hanvey became public relations officer for Washington University, a role for which she was not well suited, and it was soon terminated. She spent 3 years organizing the Graham papers and memorabilia that now occupy 1568 folders in the archives of the Bernard Becker Library at the Medical School. She maintained a relationship with the American Association for Thoracic Surgery and the editorial staff of its journal, and was appointed special administrative assistant for the association, to care for the correspondence relating to its annual meetings (not local arrangements). She served for 14 years, from her first meeting in Chicago in 1957 through her last meeting in Boston in 1970. During these years major figures in the association were the acquaintances, friends, and colleagues she had acquired during the years in which Evarts Graham had been such a towering figure in the thoracic surgical world. In beating a path to his door, all had been required to pass Ada Hanvey's desk before entering the inner sanctum.

During the last 3 years of her life, Hanvey partially lost her sight, suffered lapses of memory, became a semi-invalid, and was placed in the Clayton-on-the-Green Nursing Home where, in 1980, she died after spending 4 months in a coma. Her nephews, Pat O'Shields and Harvey Alderson (Lil's son), cared for her fiscal and material needs.

Hanvey had dedicated her life to Evarts Graham, even to the point of babysitting his children and caring for his house in his absence. Ada Hanvey had played a significant role in shaping the culture and tone of Graham's office by giving to it her unique personal professional aura.

Chapter 9

THE COMING OF SPECIALTY SURGERY

Specialty surgery was barely visible on the horizon at the turn of the twentieth century. Surgery was generally all encompassing, but a few men became interested in special areas—chiefly defined by anatomic limits. This interest did not always restrict the scope of someone's practice; rather, it allowed a surgeon to work within a special area without restriction. Murphy's appointments acknowledged the trend.

Ernest Sachs, in his 1917 to 1918 report to the Barnes trustees, described how ward and dispensary cases were to be assigned: each surgical case would be assigned to a surgeon with an interest in the specific problem.[1] Evarts Graham, in his 1921 report to the board, re-inforced Sachs's initiative, pointing out that the Department of Surgery was organized on a plan by which "cases of certain kinds are assigned to specialists in these particular subjects while the remainder are cared for by surgeons on the general surgical service ... the orthopedic cases to Dr. Allison, the oral and plastic to Dr. Blair, the neurological surgical cases to Dr. Sachs and the genitourinary to Dr. Caulk. Laryngological and rhinological cases ... to Dr. Sluder, Otology to Dr. Shepleigh and the ophthalmological to the direction of Dr. Ewing. The general surgical cases in the St. Louis Children's Hospital [are] cared for by Dr. Clopton."[2] Surgical chief residents looked after these ward cases and reported to the appropriate specialist and, in return, would assist with private cases whenever assistance was either needed and/or served an educational purpose. With the opening of St. Louis Maternity Hospital, obstetrics was moved out of Barnes; however, gynecology remained at Barnes under the supervision of Dr. H.S. Crossen within the Department of Surgery.

Graham was concerned that specialization would reduce the field of vision of some of the specialists, even as he acknowledged the necessity for progress:

> The natural question which arises is does this scheme lead to ultra-specialization and is it justifiable because of its tendency to lead to narrow specialists? ... My answer to that is that the greatest progress ... is chiefly to be made by the men who are most interested in that particular line of work. Such specialists will bring into play an enthusiasm which cannot be expected from anyone who tries to cover too large a field. ... It has seemed to me that certain institutions, like properly equipped university hospitals and university medical schools should be places where a considerable amount of specialization ... [could] be carried out very properly even in spite of the fact that the need of the country is perhaps for more general ... [surgical] practitioners. The greatest danger to my mind in specialization consists in the fact that many specialists start in their specialties before they have had an adequate general training. ... We have taken the firm position that our young men shall not restrict themselves to a surgical specialty until after they have had several years experience in general surgery. ... an exception to this rule, however, is made in the case of ophthalmology, laryngology and otology.[3]

A decade later Graham wrote to the newly formed Advisory Board for Medical Specialties regarding the position it should take on specialty education: "With regard to orthopedic surgery, urology, gynecology and thoracic surgery...I am convinced on the basis of experience that a combined internship and residency of three years in internal medicine, general surgery and their branches followed by two or possibly three years work in a clinical specialty in a very active clinic far better prepares a candidate than would one year's internship and five years of special study and practice."[4]

As the 1930s progressed, Graham realized that thoracic surgery was moving to become a specialty of its own and began to wonder whether the field should be regarded as another branch of surgery requiring special qualification. Questions arose as to how much training in general surgery a thoracic surgeon should have, and whether thoracic surgeons should limit themselves exclusively to the thorax:

> There can be no argument ... over the fact that no matter to what special field one wishes to limit his work a sound training in the general aspects of medicine ... is essential. ... It has become more and more recognized that an experience in general surgery is helpful in the education of the specialist. Certainly anyone who undertakes the

practice of the more difficult sort of thoracic surgery must be acquainted with the fundamental principles of surgery [and] a considerable experience in general surgery would be most helpful.[5]

Evarts Graham considered himself a general surgeon first, a thoracic surgeon second, and, throughout his surgical career, accepted patients with gallbladder diseases, intestinal obstruction, colon cancer, and abnormalities of the pancreas. In collaboration with Alexis Hartman, professor of pediatrics, he was one of the first to identify and remove a pancreatic tumor of the islets of Langerhans (an insulinoma).[6]

Graham always opposed specialization in cancer surgery, feeling that organ orientation provided better surgery than the attempt to cover all cancers independent of recognized organ or tissue specialties. In 1937 a proposal for an Ellis Fischel Missouri State Cancer Hospital located in Columbia seemed inappropriate, and Graham wrote Governor Stark to encourage its location in St. Louis.[7] In an accompanying letter to State Senator McMillan Lewis, he outlined in greater detail his reasons for the St. Louis location: "Such an institution should not be undertaken unless it is going to be of educational value to the physicians of the state.... the primary intent is to accomplish the greatest good for the citizens of the state [who] will profit more by having a large number of the doctors well informed on the subject of cancer than if only a small group ... is so informed.... If however the hospital should be located at Columbia only an insignificant portion of the doctors of the state would get an educational advantage from it. Such a hospital would attract national and even international attention if it were in St. Louis. It could not do so at Columbia."[8]

The Ellis Fischel Hospital was finally located in mid-state Columbia, and Graham's nominee, Eugene Bricker, became its first surgeon. Medical students were permitted to go to Ellis Fischel for electives, but Graham refused to send his assistant residents for a 3- or 6-month experience. As chairman of the American Board of Surgery, he believed the board should acknowledge only 1 year spent in a cancer hospital as being worthy of training credit.

In 1938 Surgeon General Thomas Parran proposed that the National Cancer Institute support fellowships for the training of young men in the specialty of cancer—of all organs—thereby creating a new medical specialty. With the encouragement of his Chicago mentor, Ludvig Hektoen, Graham wrote a long letter to Parran opposing the project and recommending that he support an expansion of current residency training opportunities.[9] Graham wrote the following to members of the American Board of Surgery: "The government program on cancer is something... of vital concern to our Board.... the National Cancer Institute has organized a program for the training of cancer specialists. The Washington University Medical School was asked to accept 'trainees'. We refused to co-operate ... and I sent the enclosed letter to Surgeon General Parran.... I believe we ought to take action on the matter ... in order ... to prevent what I consider to be a pernicious influence on surgery."[10]

Graham also held firm opinions regarding the British custom of appointing a professor of surgical research in parallel with a professor of surgery. He disapproved of a Department of Surgical Research:

> Every-body connected with the department of surgery should be carrying on research and likewise…should be active clinicians.…It is a great mistake to relegate the research of any department to special individuals. In a university hospital, all of the clinicians should have a research type of mind because it is from such hospitals that new knowledge should be derived.[11]

By the late 1930s and mid-1940s, the thrust toward specialization was so well under way that Graham developed formal subdivisions and gave to each considerable autonomy in appointments, budgets, beds, operating room time, and research space. Relations with his specialty chiefs were generally very supportive, and he followed Halsted's example of picking men whom he considered competent and then leaving them pretty much alone. If a chief had any problem, he could go directly to the dean, even though ultimate decisions about finances and personnel rested with Graham who, each year, would inquire as to who and how many would be appointed and to what positions.[12]

In 1945 Eugene Bricker returned to take charge of the Washington University service at the St. Louis City Hospital, and to be responsible for the educational program for medical students and general surgical residents. Bricker left the full-time staff in July 1947 to enter private practice, a move that was a great disappointment to Graham, and one that brought a certain distance to their previously close relationship. Despite that, Bricker continued in his role with the residents until Carl Moyer took over their appointments, education, and promotion.

During Graham's 30 years at Barnes, his graduate program expanded to graded residencies in general surgery and five specialties. The format was 2 or 3 years of general surgical training followed by a residency or fellowship of variable duration[a]. At Graham's retirement his general surgery program consisted of 12 assistant residents and two senior co-residents.

a. Specialty residencies, 1946.

Specialty	Training
Thoracic	1 year as thoracic surgery resident followed by a 2-year fellowship—1 year each at Barnes Hospital and Koch Hospital (for tuberculosis)
Plastic surgery	1 year as plastic surgery resident, then a fellowship of variable duration
Neurosurgery	3 years as neurosurgical resident (available to three men at a time)
Urology	1 year as assistant urologic resident followed by 1 year as senior resident; occasional fellowships
Orthopedics	One orthopedic assistant resident and one chief orthopedic resident for 1 or 2 years each; no fellowships

THORACIC SURGERY

The development of thoracic surgery at Barnes Hospital, although natural for the times, was enhanced by the special arrangement between Evarts Graham and Jacob Singer. In 1920 surgery of the chest was the surgery of infectious conditions: bronchiectasis, lung abscess, tuberculosis, and empyema. Surgical procedures within the chest were compromised by lung collapse, asphyxia, and possible death due to the elastic recoil of the lungs and mobility of the mediastinum. Sauerbruch of Germany tackled the problems of intrathoracic surgery by designing an operating room with subatmospheric pressure that enveloped both the patient's body and the operating team; the patient's head was at atmospheric pressure outside the chamber.[13] This strategy predated the physiologic experiments of Graham and Bell that described the consequences of opening one side of the chest. This latter information, Magill's endotracheal tube, and a positive pressure breathing bag made routine opening of the chest possible but, as an extension of surgery of the abdomen, it had quite different physiologic problems. Evarts Graham saw himself as a general surgeon with a special interest in the chest—partly because it was the current frontier, but mostly because of his experiences with the Empyema Commission. To him, it was a natural addition to general surgery, not a specialty in its own right. On the national scene, Dr. Willy Meyer established a small group interested in thoracic problems, which later became the American Association for Thoracic Surgery.

Upon Graham's arrival in St. Louis, J.J. Singer[b] held a small clinic that dealt with the diagnosis and treatment of pulmonary diseases. The range of chest problems was becoming increasingly complex, requiring frequent consultations between internist, surgeon, and roentgenologist; a room for this purpose was sought, but the only available space in Barnes Hospital was a storage room for trunks. The trunks were removed, an exhaust fan and a few pieces of furniture were acquired, and the Medical and Surgical Chest Service came into being. Singer and Graham soon obtained a fluoroscope to operate at their daily meetings. Gradually members from the house staff began to attend the chest service conferences, and, as its fame spread, interested visitors from around the country came to spend varying amounts of time.

---

b. Jacob J. Singer, born in Leeds, England, in 1893, was brought to St. Louis as a child and later attended Washington University and its Medical School. After 3 years studying tuberculosis and other chest diseases, he became assistant and then associate professor of clinical medicine. From 1918 to 1930, he was chief physician at the Koch Tuberculosis Hospital in south St. Louis, and consultant in chest diseases for the United States Public Health Service. After his involvement with Gilmore, he collaborated with Graham and Ballon in *Surgical Diseases of the Chest*.[14] In 1941 he became medical director of the City of Hope Hospital in Duarte, California, and held an appointment as associate professor of medicine at the University of Southern California. A quiet, unassuming man, he died at his home on April 13, 1954, after a short illness that followed a heart attack.

Inpatient beds were available on either the medical or the surgical service, and initially these functioned separately; however, by the late 1920s, the unity of the approach was so apparent that a special service called *the Medical/Surgical Service*—otherwise known as *the chest service*—was established. It possessed an outpatient area, inpatient beds, and an ethos all its own. Admission to the service was through either Singer or Graham, and both medical and surgical residents participated in the care of these patients. By the end of its first decade, 26 men from all over the world had come to Barnes for special instruction and/or participation in the work of the chest service. In the academic year 1926 to 1927, there were 10 visitors, observers, and fellows.[15] Quarters were cramped, enthusiasm was high, and the reputation of the chest service was spreading.

In 1927 the Rockefeller Foundation awarded Graham $10,000 for each of 5 years to support his department and the chest service, and, upon its expiry, another $50,000 was given. Graham used some of this money to support the salary arrangements for his faculty, chiefly Elman and Heinbecker, but most of it was used for fellowship support for the chest service, which enrolled, among others, Charles Illingworth and then Russell Brock, who became close friends.

In a letter to the Commonwealth Foundation asking for funds for the chest service following its move to new quarters, McMim Marriott, the dean, concluded: "The organization here is probably the first of its kind in the world. In most other institutions in which the study of thoracic disease has been emphasized there have not been the intimate almost daily conferences and co-operation between medical, surgical and laboratory workers. The plan here has served as a basis from which have been modeled several other chest services throughout the world."[16]

Construction of the Rand Johnson Surgical Wing and the Mallinckrodt Institute of Radiology permitted expansion. The radiology department was moved from Barnes to the institute, and the chest service took over the vacated area. The chest service was fitted with two examining rooms, an office, a classroom, a conference room, and a fluoroscope room, with contiguity between it and the institute. A graduate nurse came from Barnes, a secretary looked after records and teaching paraphernalia, and a small library was acquired[c]. The battery of radiograph view boxes in the corridor became Graham's preferred backdrop as he discussed cases in front of his seated house staff and visitors.

---

c. In October, 1931, Volume I, Issue 1 of the *Journal of Thoracic Surgery* was published by C.V. Mosby, with Evarts Graham as its editor. He arranged for complimentary copies to be sent to editors of other surgical journals (eg, *Surgical Gynecology and Obstetrics*, *Archives of Surgery*, and *Annals of Surgery*) and, in return, received copies of their publications. As an editor, he also received copies of books pertaining to general as well as thoracic surgery, with requests for his review. These books and journals plus his own publications comprised the always open and available chest service library.

The new construction placed an emphasis on chest infections, and the semiprivate rooms with porch facilities on the second floor of the Rand Johnson Building (Ward 2200) reflected the treatment of tuberculosis as popularized by the Trudeau Sanitarium at Raybrook/Saranac Lake, New York. One advantage of the sanitarium-type construction was that it could also be used for general hospital needs, as happened after the advent of streptomycin therapy for tuberculosis. The solaria for each heated room had glass fronts that could be opened, while the inner rooms were used for bathing, feeding, seclusion, or isolation.[17] As tuberculosis and chest infections decreased, Ward 2200 became a general surgical, semiprivate ward, and an eight-bed surgical chest unit was opened on the fifth floor.

The chest service became the high point of Graham's clinical efforts. It was important to him both surgically and politically, and from it he derived a special sense of satisfaction. However, its physical location was in Barnes Hospital, not in the Mallinckrodt Institute owned by Washington University, and, as purse strings tightened during the 1930s, it was targeted for the creation of revenue for Barnes Hospital, even at the expense of the stellar reputation it had given to both Washington University and Barnes. On June 8, 1939, Frank Bradley asked Graham if he had heard anything concerning the chest service. After receiving a negative reply, Bradley referred to rumors that the chest service might be discontinued and the space converted into accommodations for patients in order to bring money to Barnes. Graham then admitted that he did know of a letter Mr. Westlake had written to his Barnes colleagues stating that the chest service was a financial liability to the hospital. He defended the status quo by noting that, since all the beds were filled and the service was busy, the hospital was receiving revenue, although he did acknowledge that many of the patients in the hospital were unable to pay the full cost of hospital care. He thought it "would seem to be wise to have the beds filled rather than empty and from that standpoint the Chest [Service] patients had been a good thing for the hospital."[18] Bradley suggested that a fee could and should be applied for the use of apparatus and personnel in the chest service, feeling it would be helpful in saving the chest service if Graham could show a direct revenue to the hospital from his activities. Bradley also suggested that charges be made for pneumothorax treatments, fluoroscopic examinations, and surgical dressings. Graham acknowledged that since the chest service had been a great asset to the hospital, he would be willing to help the hospital derive revenue from it, but he worried that while he was in England during the following 2 months, something might be done to destroy it. Bradley was unable to assure him as to whether the chest service would be there when Graham returned.[18] However, the trip to England did occur, the chest service was continued, and enough money was obtained from fees for services which, when added to a grant from the General Education Board, satisfied the Barnes trustees. The issue was dropped after Westlake ceased to attend board of trustees meetings.

The chest service functioned until Graham's retirement in 1951. It was his focal point for national and international contacts, and he prided himself upon the joint medical/surgical nature of the clinic, even though he did not replace Singer after his move to California, and Burford had assumed bronchoscopic activities previously performed by the otolaryngologists. It had become a thoracic surgery clinic.

The position of voluntary assistant that had been created in 1929 enabled Graham to appoint Thoracic Surgical Fellows to the service: Dr. Harry C. Ballon from Montreal, Canada, and Dr. Allan C. Gairdner from London, England, became the first two of a long line of fellows.[19] National and international fellows flowed through the chest service, and Graham became particularly friendly with C.F.W. Illingworth of Glasgow and Russell Brock of London, taking a personal pride in their subsequent accomplishments and achievements. His most important appointment, however, was Brian Blades[d], who, following a surgical residency at Bellevue Hospital, arrived on January 1, 1936, for a 2-year fellowship. Blades remained in St. Louis as assistant professor and shared the chest service with Graham—the first surgeon to become Graham's surgical partner and his obvious heir apparent.[20] Blades created a 2-year thoracic surgery residency and formalized the fellowship program before leaving for army duty in 1942. He served as chief of thoracic surgery at Walter Reed Hospital until 1946, and then he became chairman of the Department of Surgery at the George Washington University School of Medicine.[21] Blades's decision not to return to St. Louis, although a major disappointment to Graham, was equalled by Graham's pleasure that one of his trainees was now in a special position in the upcoming development of thoracic surgery. Graham wrote to Blades to express his personal feeling of disappointment that they would no longer be associated: "It was my expectation to slip out of the chest work gradually and turn everything over to you.... There is [no] hard feeling on my part or resentment at your decision to remain in Washington.... I know that you will be brilliantly successful."[22]

---

d. Brian Blades (1906 to 1977) born in Scottsville, Kansas, obtained a bachelor's degree from the University of Kansas, and a medical degree from Washington University in 1932. This was followed by an internship in Detroit and a surgical residency at Bellevue in New York City, before he returned to St. Louis as a Rockefeller Scholar for a 2-year fellowship with Evarts Graham. A faculty appointment was terminated due to World War II, during which he served as chief of thoracic surgery at Walter Reed Hospital in Washington, DC. Successful in his chosen field and comfortable in his chosen city, he remained as chairman of surgery at George Washington University School of Medicine until his retirement in 1970. He was consultant to the Veterans Administration, the National Institutes of Health, and the Air Force, and he received the award of Statesman in Medicine from the Arlie Foundation. Tall, suave, distinguished, and striking in appearance, Blades moved easily in the social circles of Washington, DC, and acquired friends and admirers outside the field of medicine. His charm, poise, and natural sense of leadership were such that his residency attracted large numbers of men who went on to leadership positions of their own in the developing field of chest surgery. He was a prolific writer, an effective speaker, and a particular favorite of Evarts Graham, who supported him throughout his life. Blades died of cardiovascular disease on September 28, 1977.

Graham's admiration and fondness for Blades continued throughout life; the two corresponded frequently, and the ultimate measure of Graham's respect was a willingness to let Blades become editor of the third, fourth, and fifth editions of his major work *Surgical Diseases of the Chest*.

Graham offered Blades's former position to Thomas Burford[e], who had been an intern and assistant resident on Graham's service after graduation from Yale Medical School. In 1940 Tom Burford and Larry Shefts had become the first two thoracic surgical residents in Blades's program, and Burford returned on a full-time status at the completion of a distinguished military career in the European theater. He became Graham's intimate professional associate, his support in the operating room, his confidant, his counselor, and his critic. At Graham's retirement Burford inherited a large clinical thoracic service and changed its thrust from an emphasis on pulmonary diseases to cardiac surgery, with the appointment in the next few years of two of his own trainees, Drs. Thomas Ferguson and Charles Roper. The influence of the chest service on the referral of patients to Barnes Hospital continued to the end of the century.

An interesting footnote to its history is that the chest service, founded by Evarts Graham, the surgeon who first accomplished the removal of an entire lung by resection, is now headed by Dr. Joel Cooper, the Evarts Graham Professor of Surgery, who first accomplished an entire lung replacement by transplantation.

NEUROSURGERY

All facets of neurosurgery—its practice, research, and education—at Barnes were dominated by Dr. Ernest Sachs during the 20 years between the two wars. His training program was an apprenticeship-fellowship based on his large private practice,

---

e. Thomas H. Burford (1907 to 1977) was born in New Franklin, Missouri, and, after premedical study at the University of Missouri, he obtained his doctor of medicine degree from Yale in 1936. He went to St. Louis as intern and resident, and in 1940 was one of the first two fellows in Graham's thoracic surgery training program. World War II brought him military service in North Africa and Italy, where he became a pioneer in the management of thoracic wounds. During the Sicilian and Italian campaigns, Burford developed operations for decortication of the lung for hemothorax and empyema, foreign body extraction, management of chest wall defects, and management principles for chest wounds. In 1946 he returned to Barnes Hospital as Graham's first full-time associate, becoming chief of thoracic surgery when Graham retired in 1951. He was a member of almost all of the major surgical societies and a constant contributor to the literature of the day. A man of forceful demeanor, he was admired by many and disliked by equal numbers, for he was short of temper, with high expectations of perfection and disdain for the mediocre. He was a visible, debonair, almost flamboyant, figure in the Barnes corridors and operating rooms, where he was an ambidextrous, highly skilled surgeon. An inveterate smoker, he succumbed at age 69 to pulmonary emphysema and cardiovascular disease, leaving behind a legacy of more than 50 trainees. He had redirected the chest service from pulmonary to cardiovascular surgery.

to which individuals would come for varying periods of time to work with him and Dr. Roland M. Klemme, and later with his formal partner, Dr. Leonard Furlow, in shared offices in the University Club building at Grand Avenue and Delmar Boulevard. Sachs had considerable fame as a neurosurgeon, and many wished to work with him. They spent some of their time seeing patients in the University Club office, but mostly assisted at his operations, wrote orders, and otherwise cared for patients in Barnes Hospital. The program started in 1921. The trainees functioned as assistants to Sachs or his associates and were expected to learn by observing and helping. Rarely did Sachs permit them to perform a major operative procedure with him as assistant; it was a role for which Sachs, with his intense personal commitment to every patient, was temperamentally unsuited. Several of his trainees left St. Louis without ever having performed a major operation on their own. This traditional educational philosophy was quite the opposite of that held by Graham, and it was undoubtedly a factor in the disharmony that led to Graham's desire to replace Sachs with someone whose educational concepts were more in keeping with his own, that is, had an emphasis on basic sciences, and were more actively experiential and less passively observational. Sachs recognized these differences in educational philosophy in a letter he wrote to his wife[f] following a dinner meeting of the surgical specialty chiefs: "[Graham] thinks that surgical education should really be taught from the physiological point of view. ... he and I differ completely. ... that's not going to get us anywhere. ... It was the most boring, stultifying meeting I've ever attended—a waste of time."[23]

Any description of the development of neurosurgery at Barnes Hospital during these years would be incomplete without acknowledging the lack of cordiality between Evarts Graham and Ernest Sachs—two proud and domineering men from very different cultural and social backgrounds. The origins of the discord are unclear, but it was sufficiently visible by 1922 that Harvey Cushing became aware of it and wrote to Graham: "Sachs is doing admirable work and should be a great credit to you. Do support him all that you can. ... I hope the day will come when you will let him have his own anesthetist."[24] This request suggests one issue that created difficulty between the two—one that was soon resolved when Sachs obtained his own anesthetist and was able to bypass the nurse anesthesia training school.

As Sachs's neurosurgical practice grew, his list of patients outnumbered the private beds available to him, and soon friction between Sachs and Graham centered around the use of ward beds designated for the residents. Some patients referred to

---

f. Henry Schwartz possessed the voluminous, loving correspondence between Ernest Sachs and his wife, who frequently spent time in Keene Valley, New York. Sachs wrote long endearing letters every other day that the two were apart, describing intimate details of his professional life and his enduring affection for her.

Sachs needed care somewhat outside of his area of neurosurgery, and he placed them in ward beds; yet he wished to look after them personally rather than supervise the residents assigned to him. He also desired the privilege of referring these patients to specialists of his own choosing, rather than following the accepted rule that, for ward patients, he should call the head of the appropriate specialty, who would take the referral and then direct the care through his own resident staff. Sachs wrote to Graham: "I am supposed to call in the head of the particular department into which they fit even though I may feel that someone else can handle that particular case more satisfactorily.... this old rule might well be changed. ... Would it not be possible to change the rule... so that private patients may be admitted to ward beds and carry the same privileges that they would if they were in a higher priced space?"[25] Graham was unwilling to elevate the issue to a major interpersonal challenge, and Sachs's letter lay on his desk for 4 months before it was finally filed, unanswered. The problem remained unresolved until Sachs's retirement and the arrival of Henry Schwartz.

Throughout his tenure as professor of neurosurgery, Sachs held a position on the teaching roster. Medical students did not receive a clerkship assignment to neurosurgery, but Sachs did see them for 1 hour each Thursday in the old operating amphitheater of Barnes Hospital. It was a tour de force of verbal and visual observation followed by clinical reasoning. Fearful students were called at random into the pit to face Sachs's grilling, and the direct, aggressive, and occasionally abrasive encounter was indelibly imprinted on everyone. The centerpiece was always a surgical patient, rarely neurosurgical, and Sachs discussed care and management in a critical, imperious manner by elucidating what he thought were errors in diagnosis or management. Criticisms of his general surgical colleagues, including Graham, were thinly veiled.[26] Sachs felt this hour to be the highlight of his teaching,[27] and, even though he was aware of the comments, Graham steadfastly, prudently, and silently refused to chastise Sachs or remove him from the teaching roster.

The correct but distant arrangement between Graham and Sachs broke into open hostility at the end of World War II. In 1940 the board of neurosurgery held its first examinations, and, although eligibility criteria were lax at that time, it was apparent that higher standards were needed. The simple recommendation of a practicing neurosurgical preceptor such as Sachs would not meet new requirements. Sachs was now in his sixties, his replacement was soon to be in order, and Graham desired an academically oriented residency training program in neurosurgery, rather than Sachs's fellowship.

The mid-1940s presented Graham with opportunities to make some new appointments, and, with the support of Dean Shaffer, he prepared to increase his cadre of full-time surgeons. As the war wound down, funds became available for three full-time surgical positions for military returnees, and Graham looked to Eugene Bricker in general surgery, Thomas Burford in thoracic surgery, and Henry

Schwartz[g] in neurosurgery. The simmering feud between Graham and Sachs flared into outright confrontation with the appointment of Henry Schwartz and the 6-month premature retirement of Sachs. A final insult occurred in 1947 when Schwartz refused to appoint Sachs's son, Ernest Sachs Jr., to the Barnes staff as a special Neurosurgical Fellow and partner in practice with Drs. Sachs and Furlow.

In July, 1936, Dr. Henry Schwartz, fresh from Dean Lewis's surgical program at Johns Hopkins and an instructorship at Harvard, became Sachs's fellow in neurosurgery. After 2 years in this role, he was appointed instructor in surgery, an active member of the Barnes Hospital staff, and, from 1938 to 1940, he was a partner to Sachs and Furlow, functioning more at Barnes Hospital than in the University Club office, but sharing their practice arrangement. In addition to his surgical activities, Schwartz developed interests in research with Elman and Heinbecker of the Department of Surgery, and O'Leary and Bishop, neurologist and neurophysiologist. Through O'Leary and George Bishop, he made the acquaintance of Evarts Graham and frequently lunched in the basic science building with him, Bishop, Erlanger, and others who gathered at the faculty table in the cafeteria. Uncomfortable with his partnership with Sachs and Furlow, in 1940 Schwartz moved out of the University Club building to share offices in the Beaumont Building two blocks away, with Cyril McBride, an internist, and Oscar Hampton, an orthopedist. He developed a fledgling private practice before he entered the army in 1942. Schwartz was

---

g. Born in New York City, Henry G. Schwartz (1909 to 1998) attended Princeton to obtain his bachelor's degree, and Johns Hopkins for his medical degree in 1932. Summer of 1931 was spent in Breslau, Germany. After graduation he became an intern at Johns Hopkins and then a National Research Council Fellow for 2 years at Harvard. During this period he married Edith Robinson, a classmate at Johns Hopkins, who became interested in pediatric psychiatry. Two years as an instructor of anatomy at Harvard were followed by a fellowship in neurosurgery under Ernest Sachs at Washington University (1936 to 1938). His 2 years in practice with Sachs were unharmonious, and he opened his own practice of neurosurgery. His early years at Washington University permitted him a close relationship with the neurophysiology group in the Departments of Pharmacology and Physiology, and he emphasized research interests in these arenas throughout his academic life. World War II saw him with the 21st General Hospital (the Barnes unit) as its chief neurosurgeon, and as neurosurgical consultant to the United States Army. He returned to St. Louis as head of neurosurgery and remained so until his retirement in 1988. He then continued to be active in a department now composed of neurosurgeons and neurologists.

Schwartz was a wiry, high-strung individual and, in many ways, dominated an intellectual environment that was made up of O'Leary, Bishop, Elman, and Heinbecker. He was as demanding of himself as he was of others and, like Sachs, became impatient and intemperate in the operating room when problems arose—behavior that was abandoned during his years in the military. With his wife Edith, he was a gracious host, open, pleasant, and very sociable. Many honors from across the United States came his way, and his vigorous residency program emphasized laboratory research as much as surgical excellence. He was the acknowledged dean of US neurosurgery during his latter years, and remained influential in medical school affairs as well as events on the national scene. Schwartz died on Christmas Eve, 1998 (at age 89), after a period of disabling emphysema.

appointed as a neurosurgical consultant to the Army of the United States and was sent overseas. His wife, Edith, who remained in St. Louis with their two children, was befriended by Helen Graham, who took the family under her wing.

In 1945, at the completion of war hostilities, Graham met with Fred Rankin and Barnes Woodhall in the surgeon general's office to arrange for Schwartz's early discharge. He wrote to Schwartz at the Kennedy General Hospital in Memphis, Tennessee, to report: "[In] a long talk with Sachs a few days ago [I was] much pleased at his reception of the news that you are coming back. ... Much to my astonishment there was no storm at all. ... he acted as if he did not know anything about it but there is so much talk about your return that I can hardly believe he did not know something. ... He was delighted that you will be back and [said] he would do everything he could to help you along."[28] Graham's letter detailed four points about Schwartz' return: (1) Schwartz would become a full-time associate professor of neurosurgery with the privilege of private practice; (2) Sachs would continue to be professor of clinical neurosurgery and head of the section, until such time as he became professor emeritus, and Schwartz would be groomed to take Sachs's place in the Medical School as the head of the section of neurosurgery; (3) Sachs would be allowed to continue in his partnership with Furlow; and (4) the most recent Neurosurgical Fellow, Ed Smolik, now in the navy, would not be returning. In addition, the question of the City Hospital arose, for Sachs's role in the caring of their neurosurgical patients had become a thorny issue.[28] The following day Graham wrote to Sachs to inform him of his letter to Henry Schwartz, quoting verbatim the above points that he had written about to Schwartz. He added a short paragraph to the effect that Schwartz might wish to have some of Sachs's laboratory space in the North Building, but he stated that neither he nor Schwartz would dispossess Sachs, as Cutler had done to Cushing at the Peter Bent Brigham Hospital.[29]

One week later Graham wrote again to Schwartz: "I regret that Dr. Sachs seems now not to be so thoroughly pleased with the arrangement which has been made. ... When I sent him a memorandum with material taken from [my letter to you] he seemed to become greatly disturbed. ... Recently rumors have been floating around the place that I have kicked him out on the street. I understand that the source of such rumors was none other than Dr. Sachs himself."[30]

Schwartz returned to St. Louis, became reunited with his family, and made preparations to move the educational effort from a fellowship program to a graded residency and to introduce research time in the training. Some of Sachs's rancor toward Graham spilled over onto Schwartz, much to the latter's dismay.[12]

The issue of Sachs's retirement became the next point of contention. Sachs was to reach 68 years of age in January 1947, and 1 year earlier Graham had written to Sachs: "It seems desirable to have Dr. Henry Schwartz take over the active direction of the teaching and of the administration of the Section of Neurological Surgery on July 1, 1946. ... It would be difficult to make necessary arrangements ... in the middle of the school year. On that date therefore he will assume charge of the Ward Service, the teaching and other university aspects of Neurosurgery.... Any arrangements about your having private patients in ward beds after that date should be discussed with him."[31]

A disgruntled Sachs was making plans for his son, Ernest Jr., to become a fellow at Barnes, complete his neurosurgical training, and then take over his father's practice at Barnes. In March 1947, Ernest Sachs Jr. wrote to Graham from the Lahey Clinic about his appointment. He requested permission to return to St. Louis in the fall of 1948 for 18 months of clinical neurosurgery training as a fellow with his father and Dr. Furlow. He hoped to be in practice with them, first as a fellow, then as an assistant, and finally as a partner. Becoming a fellow at Barnes Hospital required an appointment from the Medical School, and Sachs Jr. asked Graham for such an appointment.[32] Two weeks later Graham wrote to Sachs Jr.: "Henry Schwartz is arranging a long term program for the development of the field which includes intimate co-operation with biophysics, nerve physiology, neuroanatomy, clinical neurology and psychiatry. I have left to him the responsibility of initiating all new appointments in ... neurosurgery."[33] The following day Henry Schwartz wrote to Sachs Jr.: "With the present plans for the long range academic development of the Section of Neurosurgery here I regret that it will not be possible to give you the Medical School appointment which you have requested."[34] This episode severed all civil contact between Graham and Sachs. Sachs Jr. spent that next academic year with John Fulton, professor of physiology at Yale, and in late 1948 Sachs Sr. received an invitation from Fulton to become the Honorary Research Fellow in Physiology (with an office in the Yale Historical Library), a position previously held by Harvey Cushing.

Sachs's resignation as professor emeritus of clinical neurological surgery was tendered to Arthur Holly Compton, the university chancellor, not to Evarts Graham, his department chairman, or to Robert Moore, the dean. The inappropriate resignation caught Graham's attention, and, in a note to Moore, he wrote: "According to my understanding of the title Professor Emeritus, it is a position which one holds for life regardless of where he may go or what he may do. There is no question of resigning from such a position unless the individual feels that it would be harmful to him to continue the connection."[35]

In mid-1949 Sachs, his library, his pathology specimens, and his laboratory moved to New Haven. He was now close to his family in New York City and his summer home in Keene Valley, New York, at the foot of Mount Marcy. In his autobiography, Sachs reflected upon his St. Louis years, and, although generally happy, he had one major disclaimer: "My trying times were due solely to the personal animosity of one man who had always resented the fact that I had been present years before when the Dean, now dead, had criticized his work unfavorably.... One day out of a clear sky two years before I had reached retiring age my successor was announced. This was an absolutely unprecedented procedure and contrary to all custom. I was deeply hurt that I should be treated in such a way. I did think I might have been informed before the announcement was made public[h]."[27,36]

In the succeeding years, with interdisciplinary cooperation between surgery, physiology, neurology, and neurophysiology, Henry Schwartz developed one of the outstanding neurosurgical residency programs in the United States, and he became a highly recognized and decorated senior neurosurgeon. His selection was one of Graham's major triumphs.

ORTHOPEDIC SURGERY

The development of orthopedic surgery began with Murphy's 1919 appointment of Nathaniel Allison[i], a distinguished St. Louis surgeon, so well respected by the executive faculty that he served as dean from 1919 to 1923. Upon Allison's departure for Massachusetts General Hospital, Archer O'Reilly served as acting head of orthopedics for 2 years, before moving to St. Louis University. At the Shriner's Hospital, built in 1922 to 1923, just two blocks south of the Medical School, orthopedics was led by Dr. LeRoy Abbott, who was joined 1 year later by J. Albert Key[j], director of research.

At the time of Graham's arrival in St. Louis, the specialty's chief concerns were fractures, dislocations, sprains, special types of bone trauma, and osteomyelitis.

---

h. *Author's note*: The extant correspondence suggests that, with the exception of Dean Shaffer, Sachs knew before anyone else that Henry Schwartz was returning to Washington University to become head of the Division of Neurosurgery, to place it on a full-time basis, and institute a graded residency system.

i. Nathaniel Allison (1876 to 1931) was born in St. Louis, Missouri. He went east to Harvard to obtain a bachelor of arts degree, and a doctor of medicine degree in 1901. After spending 1 year at Massachusetts General Hospital as a rotating intern and 1 year as a fellow in orthopedic surgery, he returned to St. Louis. He remained there for the next 20 years, with the exception of overseas duty as chief of orthopedic services with the American Expeditionary Forces First Army. Returning in 1919 with a Distinguished Service Medal, he became an associate professor of orthopedic surgery at Washington University. After serving as dean from 1919 to 1923, he accepted a position as professor of orthopedic surgery and chief orthopedic surgeon at Massachusetts General Hospital. In 1925 Allison left Boston for the University of Chicago as its chief of orthopedic services, a position he held until his death 6 years later.

j. J. Albert Key (1890 to 1955) was born on an Alabama farm and attended the Alabama Polytechnical School to obtain a bachelor of science degree in 1913. Two years after entering Johns Hopkins Medical School, financial strains forced him to spend 1 year teaching anatomy at the University of Chicago. In 1917 the Johns Hopkins Hospital Unit No. 18 was sent overseas, and, while still a medical student, Key served as an intern with the unit and received his doctor of medicine degree by mail in France in 1918. His next 3 years were spent in graduate training at the Boston Children's and Massachusetts General Hospitals, after which he became an instructor in orthopedic surgery at the

Reconstructive orthopedic surgery in St. Louis had its origin at the Shriner's Hospital, with the management of postpoliomyelitis deformities in children. The Shriner's Hospital maintained a close educational relationship with Barnes through the friendship of Graham and Abbott. Upon Abbott's 1930 departure for the University of California, Clarence Crego assumed the chiefship at Shriner's and maintained the educational relationship established by Abbott. Under Crego, the hospital developed a training program in children's reconstructive surgery to which young surgeons would go to spend 2 or 3 years. With the success of antipolio vaccines, orthopedic rehabilitation surgery was unnecessary, and the Shriners turned their attention to the treatment of burns.

In 1926 Graham recruited Key to a clinical professorship in charge of orthopedic developments at the Medical School; he provided him with an office and research laboratory in the North Building. Key established a private practice with partners Drs. Fred Reynolds and Lee Ford.[37,38]

Orthopedic surgery was initially an integral part of general surgery, and general surgical residents served on rotation with the orthopedic faculty. In 1945 Key established an orthopedic training program whose first resident, Dr. Richard Odell, became the first full-time orthopedic surgeon in Graham's department. Key's training program became known nationally, partly for its quality and partly for Key's personal charisma and spontaneity. It attracted many fellows for varying periods of time. General surgical interns rotated at monthly intervals through the Shriner's Hospital; general surgical assistant residents spent 3 months on the Barnes Hospital orthopedic service, until they were supplanted by full-time orthopedic residents in the late 1940s and early 1950s.

J. Albert Key was never fond of Evarts Graham or the idea of a full-time salary. He became even less so when the Washington University Clinic was proposed, and his dislike was apparent even to his residents. However, when he developed acute

---

University of Maryland, until his move to St. Louis in 1924. The Shriner's Central Office appointed him as director of research for all Shriner's Hospitals, with his headquarters in St. Louis. This brought him into contact with LeRoy C. Abbott and led to a lifetime association with Washington University.

Key was a round-faced, short, stocky man, and in any gathering he was the center of attention, with a remarkable ability to start a conversation and then control it. He was generous of his time, efforts, and money, particularly in support of students and his fellows. He had a ready wit and a sharp tongue, but a friendly attitude that endeared him to all. He was a central figure in St. Louis, regional, and national orthopedics, and was the man who established and defined the Washington University Orthopedic Surgery Program, partly because of his infectious personal mannerisms but chiefly because of the voluminous research that resulted from his laboratory and clinical practice. Key's relations with Graham were always formal and proper, but his dislike of the full-time system and the proposed clinic colored their relationship. He died of cardiovascular causes at the "Key Hole," his country retreat near Steelville in the Missouri Ozarks.

cholecystitis, he turned to Graham for help and then blamed him for what he felt was a delayed postoperative convalescence.[38] Following Key's death in 1955, Fred Reynolds developed and expanded the formal residency program. There was only one orthopedic assistant resident in 1947, but the next 50 years saw more than 200 surgeons receive all or part of their orthopedic training at Barnes. The division became an independent department in April 1993.[39]

PLASTIC SURGERY

Plastic surgery was dominated by Vilray Blair[k] when he returned after World War I as the pre-eminent American surgeon skilled in facial reconstruction. While developing his private practice of plastic surgery, he held appointments in both the Dental and Medical Schools. He and Graham became close personal friends and, in later years, lived as neighbors on the bank of the Missouri River. During the 1920s and 1930s, fellows came to Barnes to work as Blair's personal assistant for a variable length of time. A man of considerable wealth, Blair, like Sachs, provided for his fellows from his personal fortune as well as his practice income.

James Barrett Brown arrived on Blair's service in 1925, 2 years following graduation from Washington University Medical School. Brown started as a Plastic Surgery Fellow, became a partner to Blair, and the two were later joined by Louis

---

k. Vilray Papin Blair (1871 to 1955) was born in St. Louis. His mother (Papin) came from a French family to whom the King of Spain had given a large tract of land that subsequently became some of the most elegant residential property of suburban St. Louis. Blair attended Christian Brothers College and, in 1893, graduated in Medicine from Washington University. An interest in anatomy that continued throughout his life led him to England. Then, short of money, Blair took appointments on two ships of the Royal Navy that sailed the coasts of West Africa and South America, before he returned to St. Louis in 1901 for a career in surgery. In 1918, as chief of oral and plastic surgery, he led a US contingent to Britain. He later returned to the United States to establish, with the aid of dentists, several centers for the treatment of face and jaw injuries. He became a lifelong friend of his new chief, Evarts Graham. A member of the dental faculty as well as the medical faculty, he published papers on the technical/anatomic features of facial reconstruction. He collected a group of plastic surgeons and became a pre-eminent figure in the development of the specialty and its social and scientific organizations. As a major figure in the founding of the board of plastic surgery, he rejected a position as its president, preferring to be its secretary. He was a quiet, confident man with a sense of personal worth and competence. As an innovator in plastic surgery, his teaching and practice brought him honors from all of his colleagues. Neither aggressive nor assertive, but with a quiet posture, he became a dominant and respected figure. A tall, gangling man, he moved in the operating rooms with a gauze strip tied around his nose and head, rather than the usual surgical mask. His attentive, quiet demeanor was exemplified in the care he took of his wife during her last 5 years, following a disabling stroke. He purchased and redesigned a bus so that the two could travel together. Devastated by her death, Blair remained in relative seclusion for another 5 years until he died of natural causes in 1955.

Byars, Frank McDowell, and Minot Fryer. As the only plastic surgeons in Barnes Hospital, this group was served by a 1-month rotation for surgical interns and a 3-month rotation for assistant residents. The stipend for residents was changed to a university origin, but fellows continued to appear. During World War II, army medical officers were sent to St. Louis for plastic surgical instruction of variable duration. Following Brown's return from military service in 1945, a formalized plastic surgery residency of 2 years' duration was established, with trainees accepted only after an internship and 3 years of general surgery. The plastic surgery service became a mecca for junior and senior surgeons from many parts of the world who came to observe the surgery and exchange ideas. The contributions of Blair, Brown, and Byars extended beyond the education of residents and fellows—almost every aspect of plastic surgery was enhanced by the writings of these three men.[40]

UROLOGY

John Caulk (1881 to 1938), an original Murphy recruit who came from Johns Hopkins, was the first urologist at Washington University. In the early twentieth century, urology was concerned with postgonorrheal urethral strictures, and urinary retention due to benign prostatic hypertrophy. Caulk became a pioneer in the transurethral approach to the prostate by developing a cautery punch that would remove tiny bits of the obstructing prostate through a urethroscope. Despite an untimely death at age 57 due to a brain tumor, Caulk lived long enough to see his initially despised approach improved by technologic advances and become generally recognized.

Caulk was succeeded by his preceptorial trainee and partner Dalton K. Rose, a man of considerable personal wealth who became an early proponent of cystometrography. The two persuaded Edgar Queeny Sr. and Jr. to donate money to develop a small operating room and a cystoscopy suite in the Mallinckrodt Institute of Radiology. In 1941 D.K. Rose accepted Dr. Carl Wattenberg as his first and only fellow. Two years later the two formed a partnership, which dissolved after 3 acrimonious years.

The urology service was initially covered by surgical interns who rotated monthly through it, and later by a 3-month rotation from the assistant resident roster. An accredited residency in urology began in 1946. It had been long in coming—11 years after the 1935 establishment of the American Board of Urology. Justin Cordonnier, trained by Rose and Wattenberg, joined the service as Graham's first full-time urology appointment, and he developed a formal graded residency by 1953. Its first chief resident was Robert Royce, a Washington University graduate who remained on the Washington University faculty until retirement as a distinguished and respected St. Louis urologist.[41]

GYNECOLOGY

The opening of Barnes Hospital divided Henry Schwarz's Department of Obstetrics and Gynecology. Its headquarters and most of the obstetrics remained in the cramped and shabby quarters of the maternity hospital at 4518 Washington Street. A few semiprivate beds for obstetrics and all of gynecology was transferred to Barnes Hospital. The arrangement was unworkable, and in 1921 gynecology became a division of Graham's Department of Surgery. Intra-abdominal diseases facing the gynecologist in those years were ovarian cysts, uterine fibroids, tubo-ovarian abscesses, and cervical carcinoma. Surgical interns and assistant residents were rotated through the service in conjunction with gynecology residents. Ward patient care was to be given by the general surgical chief resident, supervised by H.S. Crossen.[42]

Crossen found himself in a Department of Surgery under Graham, rather than in a Department of Obstetrics and Gynecology under Schwarz. He complained to Graham about the nature of his appointment and his designation as clinical professor of gynecological surgery: "It seems to me that the activities of the specialty are much better expressed by the simple term Gynecology … which is shorter and more convenient and by long usage has acquired a clear meaning which precludes misunderstanding. It is a more comprehensive term and covers *all* the activities of the specialty, whereas the term gynecologic surgery covers only a part of the work." Crossen followed this with a full-page explanation of his reasons for requesting the change in terminology and the subtle change in scope of gynecologic activities.[43] Ten days later Graham responded that the title had been conferred by a vote of the trustees of the university, and that he did not understand Crossen's objection. He asserted: "A considerable portion of gynecology is surgical work and I think that it is of the utmost importance for men to be well-trained in surgery as well as in obstetrics before becoming gynecologists. I do not see why gynecology is not a specialty of general surgery." He then went on to explain that surgery is more than operative activity, and he expressed his sorrow that a misunderstanding had occurred about it, and hoped that any arrangement that was made would be in the best interest of the whole school. "That is my only idea in taking an active part in this proposed change."[44]

The arrangement lasted for 6 years, during which time the trustees of the maternity hospital raised money and built a new St. Louis Maternity Hospital on Washington University property, immediately east of Barnes Hospital. In 1927 Graham transferred gynecologic surgery out of the Department of Surgery and back into the Department of Obstetrics and Gynecology, now headquartered in the new Maternity Hospital. Patient beds and the operative surgery continued in Barnes Hospital. The interchange of residents and interns between the two departments was continued for a time with divided responsibility and discontent on both sides.[45] All educational co-relationships ceased after World War II.

EYE, EAR, NOSE, AND THROAT

The specialties of Rhinology, Ophthalmology, Otolaryngology, and Otology were initially housed in the Department of Surgery, supervised by Graham. From the outset, Graham recognized these activities as distinct specialties on their own—and that surgery was not a major part of them. He saw them as mainly office practice specialties, with the operative treatment of mastoid bone infections being the major surgical effort. Graham gave these specialties an academic as well as a clinical home until the 1932 construction of the McMillan Hospital and the Oscar Johnson Institute, which provided space for what became the Departments of Ophthalmology and of Otolaryngology, separate from surgery and with no student, intern, or resident educational interchange.

RADIOLOGY

At the opening of Barnes Hospital, Dr. Walter Mills was listed as the staff radiologist for a hospital activity that had no overtones of education or research. It was a service concerned with radiography and fluoroscopy of bony disorders, and radiography of the chest. Fluoroscopy was used more widely than was film imaging. A deep therapy unit was installed in March 1922 after the department acquired 125 mg of radium.[19] Demand for radiologic services was small, and it was not even considered a medical specialty in its own right; it was an activity of special interest to some surgeons or physicians in addition to their chief clinical interest. Sherwood Moore, a surgeon (see chapter 6), was an example of such. With improvements in equipment, the advent of cholecystography, and the introduction of barium contrast studies of the gastrointestinal tract, the demand for radiologic services rapidly increased. The arrangement between the hospital and the university required that the Medical School have a parallel structure, and radiology was placed within the administrative domain of surgery, thus becoming Evarts Graham's responsibility. Clinical laboratory activities similarly went to the Department of Medicine.

The participation of Sherwood Moore in the cholecystography success prepared radiology for its status as an independent department in the Medical School in 1925. Its growth was dramatically facilitated by the construction of the Mallinckrodt Institute of Radiology. Sherwood Moore became the director, and the institute permitted the specialty to become medical, not technical, in character. Under Moore's leadership, education and research contributions were given high priority. Upon his retirement in 1949, the equally brilliant and capable Hugh Wilson (from Yale) continued the Moore tradition at the institute and prepared it for its next major expansion. At no time were interns or residents from the surgical service assigned to the Department of Radiology unit.

Graham's 30 years at Barnes Hospital saw specialty surgery grow from a list of seven interested surgeons to a large complex organization involving eight residency programs with upward of 100 residents and fellows. General surgery was losing its role as an end in itself and was becoming a preparatory experience for some of the specialties. Interpersonal confrontations had been kept at a minimum, and Washington University/Barnes Hospital was readied for the next half century of further surgical development.

Chapter 10
_____

ANESTHESIA:
AN UNFULFILLED DREAM

THE COMING OF NURSE ANESTHETISTS

A satisfactory development in the field of anesthesia evaded Graham during his entire time at Washington University. In 1911 Fred Murphy brought a nurse, Miss Gladys Farrar, from the Massachusetts General Hospital to administer anesthesia for him at the newly opened Barnes Hospital. At this time anesthesia was administered by many individuals with varying degrees of training and competence—an occasional nurse who was self-trained, medical students or interns, dentists, general practitioners, and referring doctors—always under the supervisory responsibility of the surgeon. Graham defined his position in his first report (1920) to the trustees of Barnes Hospital:

> Another important need concerns the question of the anesthetists to the hospital. The whole matter of the administration of anesthetics should be under the immediate supervision of a graduate in medicine who will devote his entire time to the work. Considerable progress is being made in the subject of anesthesia and there is still much to be learned about it in order to safeguard the patient as much as possible. It would be desirable to secure as Chief Anesthetist someone who not only is an expert in the administration of anesthetics but who is also qualified to carry on investigation in this field in addition to teaching and training other anesthetists. Such a person would require a fair

salary. At present this splendid opportunity for doing high grade work of this sort is being missed because of lack of funds for the purpose.[1]

Despite his efforts, an MD anesthetist did not appear on the scene until 30 years later, with the coming of Douglas Eastwood.

When Graham arrived in St. Louis, ether, chloroform, and nitrous oxide ("laughing gas") were the inhalants in general use.[2] General anesthesia was induced by dropping ether onto a gauze face mask, with an oropharyngeal airway in place. Graham's studies in Chicago had shown the deleterious side effects of chloroform, and he prohibited its use at Barnes except as a short-term pain reliever during labor. In the 1940s ethylene and cyclopropane became available and, following this, intravenous thiopental for induction and curare for muscle relaxation appeared. Spinal and caudal anesthesia were used occasionally in the practice of obstetrics. In the mid-1930s a visiting physician from France administered a spinal anesthesia as a demonstration, but, tragically, total paralysis resulted and, despite vigorous resuscitation attempts, the patient died. Graham then banned the use of spinal anesthesia at Barnes, until the late 1940s when surgical assistant residents were permitted to administer low spinal anesthesia for lower limb amputations or anorectal procedures. A few staff surgeons solved their anesthetist problems by hiring their own anesthetists, a policy that caused strains between surgeons and hospital. Blair and Brown used the services of Everil McDavitt, Alice Gronewald, and Matilda Katerhenry; and Sachs used Jessie Lindsey's services. All were dedicated nurses who worked at the hospital until their surgeons retired from practice.

A formal development in anesthesia began with the arrival of Helen Lamb, RN[a], in 1927, 8 years after Graham's arrival. The increase in number and complexity of surgical operations, coupled with an inadequate number of available physicians, made the training of nurses a necessity.[3] Through the efforts of Drs. Burlingham and Graham, a school for nurse anesthetists opened in 1929 under the direction of Ms. Lamb, a talented and dominating woman who had come from the School of

---

a. Helen Lamb (1890 to 1979) was born in Bolivar, Missouri, where she received her nursing education before moving to Lakeside Hospital in Cleveland as a student nurse anesthetist. She remained on its staff until her recruitment in 1927 to Barnes Hospital to become director of the Nurse Anesthesia School, a position from which she retired in 1951. The formal opening of the school occurred in 1929 with the enrollment of one student.

Ms. Lamb was a founding member of the American Association of Nurse Anesthetists, was a consultant to Richard von Forreger in the development of his anesthesia machine, and is credited with being one of the first nurse anesthetists in the United States to use endotracheal anesthesia. In 1929 her student nurse anesthesia program was 4 months in duration; by 1963 it had become a 24-month program. The school was closed in 1970; in the 40 years since its inception, it had graduated 939 nurse anesthetists. Lamb earned the respect of her students, staff anesthetists, and all who had the opportunity to observe her work. She made significant contributions to the field of anesthesia.

Student Nurse Anesthetists at the Lakeside Hospital in Cleveland, Ohio. Lamb was a department chairman on the hospital roster but never carried a medical school title, and, although she was an employee of Barnes Hospital, her contacts, activities, and alliances became closely related to Evarts Graham and his surgical staff. She was brilliant and created an outstanding teaching program with her good understanding of physiology and pharmacology, especially as it related to anesthesia. She did not permit variations from her ideas on how to manage patients, and, with the passage of time, she recruited a small cluster of full-time nurse anesthetists as her teaching staff. Her trainees were in constant demand, and the training, which varied from 4 months to 2 years, was terminated when Ms. Lamb felt that her student was responsible and competent. Charges for anesthesia services and supplies were made by the case, independent of length of time, complexity, or risk involved. In 1950 the hospital charged $30 per case,[4] sufficient to provide a net cash flow to the hospital budget.

Helen Lamb became the personal anesthetist to Evarts Graham, administering and overseeing all of his anesthesia needs for more than 20 years. Student nurse anesthetists administered anesthetics to ward patients and to patients of some of the surgeons on the full-time staff, but rarely, if ever, were they permitted into the operating rooms of Graham and those who employed their own nurse anesthetists, such as Vilray Blair and Ernest Sachs. Endotracheal intubation was a novelty initially performed only by Lamb. It involved the use of a flexible plastic-covered spiral wire with a firm stylette (the Woodbridge tube), inserted by using a laryngoscope, which did not permit good visualization of the larynx or the vocal cords. By 1950 all of Lamb's students were trained in the technique.

Although Graham had placed himself on record in 1920 as desiring an anesthesiologist with a medical degree to head a training program, little happened to this effect until 1944, when Graham began to look seriously for someone who would develop an MD anesthesia program, supervise the nurse anesthestists, and direct the nurse training program. He first approached Francis Foldes of Boston, who had been recommended by Henry Beecher, and invited him to come and investigate the position. In the words of Douglas Eastwood: "Foldes had been doing some work on potassium which at that time had just begun to be measured in the flame

On Christmas Day 1951, Lamb married Walter S. Powell, a director of the Brown Shoe Company and a figure skating referee. He died 10 years later in a plane crash in Brussels that took the lives of all members of the US Olympic figure skating team. Lamb's second husband was John Coleman, who died of lung cancer 9 years after their marriage. Lamb later married John Frost, a man 25 years her junior, who, it was rumored, had hoped for but failed to obtain her fortune. The Powell estate provided more than $1 million that, held in trust until Helen's death, financed the remodeling and reconstruction of the St. Louis Theater (a movie house at 718 North Grand Avenue), which became Powell Hall, the permanent home of the St. Louis Symphony Orchestra.

photometer. He was interviewed by Graham in the presence of Alex Hartman…
[and] at the conclusion of the interview Foldes asked Graham 'Who was that?'—
'Well that was Dr. Hartman'. Foldes did not know that Hartman had probably done
more work on potassium than anyone else at that time and the interview did not
come over very well."[4] Enthusiastic support for Foldes was not forthcoming from
the Massachusetts General Hospital surgeons, and the search was terminated.[5]

As World War II came to an end, a consensus was reached between the executive faculty, Graham, Bradley, and the board of trustees of Barnes Hospital that an
MD anesthetist had to be recruited. At the suggestion of Ralph Waters, who had
been an associate of Graham's at the Park Clinic in Mason City and had moved to
become chief of anesthesia at the University of Wisconsin, Graham contacted
Steven J. Martin, a lieutenant colonel still in the army. Martin indicated his willingness to develop an all-MD department, and, in a letter to Martin, Graham cautioned that this was a new venture and that he felt the changes that Martin had in
mind should come about gradually rather than suddenly: "For example, we have
been dependent upon nurse anesthetists, it would be impossible for us to carry out
the necessary work here if all of them are to leave immediately."[6] Martin proposed
a position for himself, a second anesthesiologist, and 14 residents. He visited St.
Louis feeling that he had accepted an appointment, even though one had not been
formally offered, and indicated his wish to develop a department with only MD
anesthesiologists and residents, who would have no contact whatsoever with the
nurses. When Graham asked, "How do you plan to cover the service without the
nurse anesthetists?" Martin responded by saying, "That's your problem."[4] Thus
ended Martin's interview and the search. Five years later Martin was again recommended, this time by Stuart Cullen of Iowa, to whom Graham responded, "We have
no confidence in Dr. Martin's judgement."[7]

ETHER AND HUMBUG

On October 16, 1846, in the operating amphitheater of the Massachusetts General
Hospital, William Morton, a dentist, administered ether to Gilbert Abbott, a patient
of Dr. John C. Warren, who subsequently operated on Abbott's left neck to remove
a mass of unknown nature. Although not entirely free of pain, Mr. Abbott was rendered sufficiently insensible that he did not move or cry aloud, and, at the completion of the procedure, Warren turned to his audience to say: "Gentlemen, this is no
humbug." It was an event that would transform surgery and surgeons, and the
episode is captured in a heroic painting by Robert Hinckley[b].[8]

---

b. *The First Successful Public Demonstration of Surgical Anesthesia*, painted by Robert Hinckley in
1882, hangs in the Francis A. Countway Library of Medicine, Boston Medical Library, Cambridge.

One hundred years later, J.H. Means, professor of medicine at Harvard, requested that Graham be one of four speakers at an Ether Centenary to be held in the Sanders Theater, Cambridge, on the anniversary date, October 16, 1946. Graham's speaker companions would be Raymond B. Fosdick, president of the Rockefeller Foundation; Henry K. Beecher, professor of anesthesia at Harvard; and Karl T. Compton, president of the Massachusetts Institute of Technology. Graham accepted the challenge and chose as his title, "Ether and Humbug." He opened with a definition of *humbug*, then spoke of the state of medicine in 1849 and how much humbug existed in the then-accepted medical doctrine. He proceeded to explore the uses of ether in the relief of pain during operations on human beings, and the research on animals that made possible a greater understanding of the physiology of both animal and man. "We of a later age whose privilege it has been to see medicine established on a firm scientific basis can scarcely appreciate its state at the time at which Morton and Warren conducted their successful demonstration."[9]

Believing that two contributions stood alongside the discovery of ether as the three great contributions to surgery during the previous century, Graham complimented Joseph Lister for his adaptation of the work of Pasteur on infections, and George Crile for his many years of attempting to explain surgical shock. He then returned to the subject of anesthesia and stated that Morton "could hardly have foreseen that a century after his momentous demonstration there would be many substances available…and many techniques…necessary for the different use of anesthetic agents requiring knowledge by those who would use them for their complicated actions on the living body."[9]

The closing section was colored by his previous contentious dealings with American anesthesiologists and the difficulties he had encountered in recruiting MD anesthesiologists to Barnes Hospital. He continued:

> For more than half a century after the demonstration of ether anesthesia its practice was regarded as so simple and free from danger that it was considered that no special knowledge or training was necessary in order to "give an anesthetic". … the youngest and most inexperienced interns were entrusted with this complicated and dangerous performance. In retrospect it seems incredible that this could have been so. … In order to obtain better anesthesia than that provided by the unskilled interns about 1907 Dr. George Crile and the Mayo Brothers trained specially selected graduate nurses to take charge of the anesthesia in their clinics. Shortly after the first World War a school for the training of nurse anesthetists was established at the Lakeside Hospital, Cleveland. Later, similar schools were created elsewhere and hundreds of nurses were trained in the art of administering anesthetic drugs. No one can deny that the creation of the nurse

anesthetist resulted in a vast improvement in the quality of the anesthesia and of the surgery throughout the country. The slipshod practice of having it conducted by interns, and still worse by the referring physicians gave way to the employment of professional anesthetists, albeit nurses.... For some strange reason the profession of physician anesthetist or anesthesiologist did not make a strong appeal in this country until very recently. The physician, because of his superior education in the science of medicine is better qualified than the nurse ... and he is more likely to advance our fundamental knowledge of the field.... There are some prominent anesthesiologists who would eliminate completely the nurse anesthetist. They have even supported legislation in some states which would make it illegal for a surgeon to engage the services of a nurse anesthetist. This, it seems to me, is a most unrealistic attitude to take. There are seven thousand hospitals in this country but at most only a few hundred professional physician anesthetists. They can conduct only a small fraction of the anesthesias. Who will handle the rest? Shall we return to the old custom of having the inexperienced intern or the doctor who refers the patient to the surgeon administer the anesthesia? God forbid! The best solution to the problem is to encourage the training of the nurse anesthetist until there are enough physician anesthesiologists to fill the demand.

If we are to continue to have nurse anesthetists for at least an indefinite period, where are they to be trained? Should they not receive their instruction in this dangerous art in our best teaching hospitals where they can have the benefit of the teaching of the best professional anesthesiologists, or should they be compelled to seek their instructions casually in doctors' offices? I think there can be only one answer to this question. Yet again there are those of great influence in this new profession of anesthesiology who would, if they could, abolish all opportunities in our hospitals for the nurse, or for that matter, anyone not possessing the M.D. degree, to obtain instruction in the art of anesthesia. What would Morton, the dentist, think of that, the man whose epoch-making work we are celebrating today? Let us not have any humbug in affording the benefit of that work to all the people[c].[9]

---

c. *Author's note*: During the year 1946 to 1947, the author was a Rockefeller Scholar in the Department of Biochemistry at Harvard and, through the courtesy of Dr. A. Baird Hastings, received two tickets to the Ether Centenary event. He and Mrs. Mueller sat in the balcony, awed by the academic pomp and circumstance. Graham's talk seemed straightforward and correct, for he was stating what seemed to us to be ideas of the rational world.

The speech stunned the anesthesiologists in the audience. Verbal comments, letters of protest, and editorials in medical journals subsequently appeared. The term *art of anesthesia*, used by Graham, was particularly offensive to anesthesiologists who considered anesthesia to be a part of the practice of medicine and, therefore, to be done only by or under the direction of a physician, not a nurse. Graham soon realized the need for a printed version of his speech and, after receiving a note[10] to the effect that Harvard was not planning to publish the talk, he sent it to Morris Fishbein, editor of the *Journal of the American Medical Association* with the following comment: "My reason for sending it is that I think something should be said which would perhaps start a discussion on what is to be done about the nurse anesthetist technician."[11] He mailed the manuscript on November 18, the galley proofs were ready by December 20, and its publication appeared in the January 11, 1947, issue of the *Journal*.[9] Indeed, it did start a discussion, which continued for more than a decade. Although initially agreeing to write an accompanying editorial, Fishbein failed to do so.

Before its publication complimentary notes were received by Graham from several sources—Churchill, Beecher, Means, and others. John Fulton, the Yale historian, wrote a critical letter after hearing derogatory reports on the speech from Yale anesthesiologists,[12] to which Graham suggested that he wait to read the published version. He then gave Fulton a personal lecture: "They are unwilling to countenance the existence of the nurse anesthetist technician. Waters has told me on several occasions there is no place for them at all and Lundy [John S. Lundy, Mayo Clinic] has written to me in the last few days...that he is opposed to a school of anesthetist technicians."[13] To Churchill, he wrote: "I did not intend to get into another fight, but now that my hat is in the ring I suppose I shall have to carry on. ...I came away from Boston with a sort of bad taste in my mouth feeling that I had not done very well and that, entirely unconsciously on my part, I had apparently aroused the ire of the anesthesiologists in the audience."[14]

During the Ether Centenary event, Graham and Beecher[d] struck up a friendship that was to move in two directions: first, in the politics of the training of anesthetists,

---

d. Henry Beecher (1904 to 1976) was born in Wichita, Kansas, and, after obtaining a master's degree in chemistry at the University of Kansas, obtained a doctor of medicine degree from Harvard in 1932. His surgical internship was followed by a year's traveling fellowship in Copenhagen, after which he spent 2 years as assistant resident in surgery at Massachusetts General Hospital. Interested in anesthesia, he became an instructor at Harvard and anesthetist-in-chief of Massachusetts General Hospital in 1936. His main interest lay in the physiology of anesthesia. One of the initial certificants of the American Board of Anesthesiology, he pioneered the development of physician anesthesiology education at Harvard and elsewhere in the United States. Beecher concluded his anesthesia/pharmacology career with writing and public speaking, making a major impact in the field of medical ethics and research on human beings.

both nurse and physician and, second, in the recruitment of someone for Barnes Hospital. Graham asked Beecher if he would be interested in a move to St. Louis, an invitation that Beecher declined. Beecher did, however, suggest a young man from Michigan—Dr. Carl A. Moyer—who, after 6 months in Beecher's laboratory, had recently moved to Dallas, Texas. Beecher wrote to Moyer a month later to alert him of the nomination to St. Louis, and he stated his own reasons for not going: "This place [Harvard] is still in the throes of post-war turbulence and I am afraid if I left it now it would all fall to pieces and ten years of building would be wasted."[15] Concurrent correspondence with Rovenstine at New York University failed to produce a likely candidate, but Graham found Rovenstine to be understanding in regard to training nurses alongside physicians, at least for the near term, although he felt it was not an ideal goal for medical schools.[16–18]

Carl A. Moyer was Graham's next prospect. He had had surgical training at the University of Michigan before spending time with Beecher to learn about fluids, electrolytes, and the pharmacology of drugs, although not clinical anesthesia. In those years Harvard's greatest strengths in that area were James L. Gamble, pediatrician, and A. Baird Hastings, biochemist. Moyer's position as professor of experimental surgery at the Southwestern Medical School in Dallas was out of the mainstream of Texas surgery, and within 3 months he was willing to consider offers from elsewhere. Three weeks after the Ether Centenary, Graham approached him via a letter written on his behalf by Nathan Womack, who outlined the scope of a new department that would be in and out of the operating theaters, with responsibility for all forms of inhalation therapy as well as such things as fluid balance, electrolyte balance, and the care of surgical patients. Womack alerted Moyer to the fact that only a well-trained physician could meet these requirements, but that such a man would also have to continue to supply well-trained nurse anesthetists. It was an impossible dream.[19] Moyer responded with a show of interest,[20,21] and Graham invited him for a 3-day visit, which occurred from January 20 to 23, 1947.[22] By mid-February, Moyer was ready to leave Dallas, with the proviso that, if an opening should occur under Dr. Fred Coller at the University of Michigan, Moyer would accept a position in Michigan, even though Coller had advised him to consider carefully the anesthesia offer at Washington University.[23] Moyer closed another letter to Graham by listing several surgeons he had had as teachers and wrote, "to count you among them has been a secret wish, sometimes wishes come true."[24] The correspondence continued until April, when Moyer decided he would move to St. Louis. Graham was ready, for by now he knew that his friend Ted Mallinckrodt Jr. was planning to endow a Mallinckrodt Department of Anesthesia in honor of his son Henry, who died in Europe in 1945. Graham outlined to Moyer the money to be donated by Mallinckrodt, suggested a title of professor of surgery and anesthesiology, and proposed a salary of $10,000 per year. There was money for one or two assistants, and Graham wrote to Moyer,

"Much of the routine load can very well be covered by the nurses and I am sure they will be enthusiastic about working for you."[25] Three weeks later Graham explained that the position would be that of associate professor since, in the opinion of the faculty, Moyer had not demonstrated his ability as an anesthesiologist. A budget of $24,300 was proposed, of which Barnes Hospital would contribute $13,000, and Mallinckrodt would donate $4,400. Graham also alerted Moyer to the planned arrival of James Elam.[26]

The issue of his relationship to the nurse anesthesia training program became important to Moyer after he received cautionary telephone calls and adverse comments. His academic appointment was to be Washington University; his directorship, the nurses, and the nursing program were associated with Barnes Hospital. On May 6 Moyer wrote to Graham indicating that the nominal director of the Department of Anesthesia should have complete control over the nurse anesthetist training program. He had explored the issue with John Adriani of New Orleans, who did not have such control, and Moyer felt that Adriani was in a position for which Moyer, himself, would not care. Moyer was critical of the competency of nurse anesthetists in Dallas, but he expected that this could be improved by having the nurses attend lectures and perform experiments. Aware of one of Beecher's studies, he wrote: "An anesthetic death rate of 1:270 major surgical procedures cannot be excused."[27] He demanded that the director be chairman of the committee charged with the selection of nurse and physician trainees, and that the school for nurse anesthetists be conducted with its primary goal being the training of nurses, not the saving of or making of money for the hospital.[28]

The Washington University faculty approved Moyer's appointment, active as of December 1, 1947. Graham acceded to all of the concerns Moyer had expressed in his May letter and, after conversing with Frank Bradley, decided that three MD resident positions would be made available when the right candidates were found. A salary of $5,000 was available for an instructor in anesthesiology, and $5,000 for a chemist, with additional money for a secretary, expenses, and equipment.[29,30] Moyer next voiced concerns about his expected arrival date, and he postponed it for 1 year. Five months later, Moyer resumed the correspondence and, after complaining about rumors in Dallas that he was leaving, he brought up the issue of salary, which he thought was too low. He stated that $15,000 to $17,000 was in order. He presented a family budget to justify his case, and explained that he also had a duodenal ulcer that sometimes gnawed at him: "I therefore cannot honestly accept $10,000 per annum at Washington University.... I want the job but cannot move now because I cannot see my way clear financially with a fixed salary, a growing family and progressive inflation."[31] It had been almost a year to the day since Graham had first talked to Beecher about Carl Moyer, and it was 5 more weeks before Graham could bring himself to acknowledge that Moyer was not coming.[32] He made no attempt to meet Moyer's salary demands.

At about that time, Nathan Womack was in the process of accepting the professorship of surgery at the University of Iowa, and in December Graham reopened communication with Moyer inquiring about the possibility of his coming to St. Louis in the Department of Surgery to fill the spot created by Womack's departure. He wrote: "You are probably not too enthusiastic about the anesthesia program which we were previously considering. I should like to talk to you about coming here to join the Department of Surgery on a full-time basis." Graham then proceeded to describe the position.[33] Moyer did not respond to the letter or accept the invitation to visit. Three years later the committee searching for a replacement for Evarts Graham as chairman invited Moyer back to St. Louis and, in July, 1951, Moyer became chairman of the Department of Surgery.

By mid-1947, after almost 9 months of correspondence with Moyer, Graham had begun to sense that Moyer did not wish to come to St. Louis, and he began to look at local talent. Graham approached at least three individuals. The first was Lawrence W. O'Neal, a Washington graduate and assistant resident in surgery who had been sidelined for 2 years with a pulmonary illness. Graham was prepared to send O'Neal to Harvard to work with Henry Beecher for 1 or more years and then have him return as professor and chairman of anesthesia. However, O'Neal wished to be and subsequently became an important and outstanding surgeon in St. Louis.[34]

The next candidate was Robert Glaser, chief resident in medicine. In June 1947 Graham explained to Glaser that, for some years, he had been looking for a full-time professor of anesthesiology. He finished by telling Glaser of his desire to have Glaser become the Mallinckrodt Professor, something Glaser in his "wildest dreams could never have envisioned—being offered a named professorship while still a chief resident."[35] Once again, Graham proposed to send Glaser to Beecher for 1 or 2 years and have him return to be professor of anesthesiology, but Glaser preferred a different career—one in infectious diseases. He remained on the Washington University faculty until 1957, before moving to Denver to become dean of the Medical School, and then moving to Stanford. Glaser became the editor of *Pharos of Alpha Omega Alpha*, a member of many boards and councils, and a distinguished member of the Washington University Board of Trustees.

In November 1948 Womack and Graham together approached Seymour Brown, a Washington University graduate and director of anesthesia at St. John's Mercy Hospital in St. Louis, to request that he consider moving to Barnes. Brown demurred because of the nursing school and his own comfort with the cooperation he experienced from the staff and sisters at Mercy.[36]

In February 1948 the chancellor announced a permanent professorship of anesthesiology, endowed by Mr. and Mrs. Edward Mallinckrodt Jr. with a gift of $100,000 to honor their son Henry, but there was no named incumbent, and no one to fulfill its objectives to "teach the subject of surgical anesthesia to undergraduate and post-graduate students but also supervise the administration of anesthetic drugs and use of oxygen and other gases as therapeutic agents in the hospitals of the Washington University Medical Center…also train resident physicians and nurse technicians in the practical applications of anesthesia and…engage in research."[37] A special Research Laboratory of Applied Physiology related to respiration was formed to be integrated with the new professorship.

OF EASTWOOD AND ELAM

Graham's search for a physician to head the anesthesia program made its first positive but faltering move with the arrival of James Elam in 1947. After graduation from Johns Hopkins, Elam interned at the US Naval Hospital in Bethesda, and followed this with 1 year as a fellow in physiology with Maurice Visscher at the University of Minnesota. During this time he pursued his studies of an oxygen analyzer (oximeter) and carbon dioxide absorption systems. In order to set up the research laboratory, Graham proposed that Elam come as a special surgical intern, with most of his time to be spent in the laboratory rather than with usual internship activities. His operating room time was to observe anesthesia, and in the laboratory he was to perform experiments with the oximeter. After this year he would become instructor in anesthesia, with the expectation that he develop the research laboratory and perform duties limited to research and teaching. Albert Roos, from the Department of Physiology, worked part-time in the laboratory, and fellows began to arrive for varying lengths of study. In January 1949 Elam was sent to Harvard for a 2-year fellowship working with Henry Beecher. Discord between the two soon arose because Elam's interests were more in laboratory work than in clinical anesthesia, and within 3 months Elam requested that Graham relieve him of the Harvard obligation. Elam then moved to Iowa to complete 2 years as a resident in anesthesia under Stuart Cullen. The surgeons at Washington University were under the impression that he would return as the Mallinckrodt Professor and head a Division of Anesthesia in the Department of Surgery. In reality, Elam returned in April 1951 as research director in anesthesia and stayed for 2 years before leaving in July 1953 to become chief anesthetist at the Roswell Park Hospital in Buffalo.

During Elam's Iowa sojourn, general dissatisfaction with Helen Lamb, the nurse training program, the complexity of surgery with less than adequate anesthesia, and Graham's inability to recruit an individual to direct an MD program led a group of 13 surgeons, headed by Tom Burford, to challenge Graham to greater effort. They assembled for a full and free discussion of the problem, and to explore methods and means whereby their critical anesthetic situation could be improved.[38] Burford informed Graham of the meeting in a letter that contained three paragraphs outlining the pressing necessity for and condemning the level of anesthetic efficiency. He pointed to "a deterioration in administration to the point where petty jealousies, gossip and even character assassinations made for a totally inefficient and unstable department."[38] With unanimous agreement that the current state of affairs should be corrected, the group made three proposals: first that a *male* physician supplant Miss Lamb as the administrator of the department; second, that there be an increase in the number of nursing supervisors; and, third, that the rotation of supervisors and students through the various surgical specialties be reviewed.[38]

Soon after writing to Graham, Burford contacted Nathan Womack, then chairman of surgery at the University of Iowa, where a well-respected anesthesia program headed by Stuart Cullen was housed. Womack recommended Douglas Eastwood[e], a young staff anesthetist who had done some research work with him, and arranged for Burford to pay a visit to Iowa City. Eastwood and Burford got along well; Burford presented a good picture of the condition of and opportunities in St. Louis, and, as a consequence, Eastwood accepted the position at Barnes, with an idea that it was a place where he could do something significant. While a resident, Eastwood had surveyed the country to identify places where he might wish to go at some future time. He had picked those places that were good institutions but had the worst anesthesia arrangements. His list included Johns Hopkins, Ohio State University, the University of Michigan, and Barnes Hospital: "Each place had some

---

e. Born in Ellsworth, Wisconsin, in 1918, Douglas Eastwood obtained a bachelor of science degree from Coe College in Cedar Rapids, Iowa, before his 3 years at the University of Iowa Medical School. In 1943 he graduated with a doctor of medicine degree and then interned at the Detroit Receiving Hospital. Contacts with the field of anesthesia began with Dr. Stuart Cullen's lectures in the pharmacology course, and Eastwood earned a master of science degree in pharmacology in 1946. Because of a shortage of nurse anesthetists and physician anesthesiologists during his last 2 years in medical school, he began to administer anesthetics during nights, weekends, and summer vacations. As a result of this experience, when Eastwood became an army officer in 1945, he was assigned chief of anesthesia for the 97th General Hospital in Frankfurt, Germany. He was one of the many individuals who returned from military service after an experience in which they were in charge of the operating room, the emergency ward, and the direction of nurse anesthetists.

Following his discharge from the army, he returned to the University of Iowa as resident and then instructor in anesthesia, before moving to Washington University in 1950. Three years later he returned to Iowa. He next became chairman of anesthesia at the University of Virginia, a position he held from 1955 to 1972, before moving to Cleveland, Ohio.

Eastwood is a man of agreeable, pleasant demeanor, with an outgoing, engaging personality that makes it easy for him to befriend and charm everyone. His interests extend beyond the fields of anesthesia and anesthesia research to include the intricate problems of medical student education, and assistance and education in developing countries. During 1972 to 1973, he served as consultant to the World Bank with a United Nations program in Tanzania. In 1972 Eastwood moved to Cleveland, Ohio, to engage in medical education research with Dr. Hale Ham at the Case Western Reserve University Medical School. As professor in the Department of Anesthesia, he received the Outstanding Clinical Teacher award from the medical students. Since becoming emeritus professor in 1989, Eastwood continues as special consultant to the Veterans Hospital and director of the Wright Surgical Center in Cleveland.

good people doing clinical anesthesia—nurses—but they weren't contributing so I wanted to go to one of them. Washington University was the first opportunity and I thought it was a pretty good one."[4] In retrospect, Eastwood stated that he had made a very serious error in accepting the position at Barnes.[4]

Eastwood arrived in October 1950 to find himself assistant professor of anesthesiology at Washington University and director of anesthesia at Barnes Hospital. His relationship with Helen Lamb was strained from the beginning; she had been there for almost 25 years, while he, as a newcomer with many new ideas, assumed the direction of anesthesia in the operating room, leaving to her the directorship of the nurse training program. Lamb retired 1 year later. Soon after his arrival, Eastwood was invited to a meeting of department chairmen and, after being introduced, found that the other chairmen headed pharmacy, maintenance, nursing, purchasing, and other hospital divisions. Recognizing that his department was a hospital function and not related to the practice of medicine, he never attended another department meeting, sending, instead, one of his senior staff nurses.[39,40]

Eight months later Elam returned. The two had been together in Iowa and knew each other intimately, and a satisfactory working relationship was established, with Eastwood in the operating rooms and Elam in the research laboratory. However, 20 months later Elam left for Buffalo. Upon his arrival Eastwood had prepared a 3-year plan consisting of the establishment of an MD residency program, recruitment of residents, enhancement of faculty, and an integration of the nurse program with the MD program—even though the two were basically different, one a technical service the other an academic exercise. Jack Elder, a well-trained anesthetist who was chronically ill with emphysema, bronchitis, and recurrent pulmonary infections, was recruited from Robert Dripps's program at the University of Pennsylvania.[4] After an initial review, Eastwood's residency program received a 2-year probationary approval for the training of MD anesthesiologists. The following year, two residents appeared.

In July 1951 Carl A. Moyer arrived in St. Louis, and changes were in order. Graham had tried hard and had succeeded in winning the confidence of Eastwood through frequent formal conferences, and a friendly relationship that included home invitations had developed. This was about to change. Moyer showed that he cared little for Elam or the nature of his research, and he was a factor in Elam's departure. It was a destructive move to Eastwood's plans. Although Moyer and Eastwood had many conferences, Moyer was unable to bring himself to press for a Department of Anesthesia or a Division of Anesthesia in the Department of Surgery, an element essential to Eastwood's 3-year plan. Frank Bradley and Carl Moyer refused to consider such a move. Bradley cited the financial needs of the hospital and the support that the hospital's anesthesia efforts gave to the budget. Moyer was his usual indecisive self. The lack of a resolution satisfactory to

Eastwood was his reason for returning to Iowa in October 1953. He later stated, "It was a big mistake to go there before I was ready for the *big time*."[39,41,42]

Jack Elder remained as temporary director of anesthesia for the next 18 months, after which Moyer recruited Robert Dodd from Dallas, who established and maintained an MD residency program alongside the school for nurse anesthetists until the school was closed in 1970. A Washington University Department of Anesthesiology was then established under the direction of Dr. Ronald Stephen, the first incumbent of the Mallinckrodt chair.

In the attempts by physicians to establish anesthesiology as part of the practice of medicine, Graham's defense of the role of the nurse anesthetist was interpreted as being against physician anesthesiologists, even though he believed in physician participation in teaching, research, and clinical practice, as well as the supervision of nurse anesthetists. He received encouragement and help from some of the anesthesiologists—Stuart Cullen, Robert Dripps, and Henry Beecher—but most of the others were highly critical.[43] Graham did not live to see the achievement of the anesthesia goals that he described in his report to the board of trustees of Barnes Hospital 37 years earlier.

THE BOARD, THE COLLEGE, AND THE SOCIETY

During the late 1930s and early 1940s, the introduction of short-acting barbituates replaced drop ether induction and its associated time-consuming episodes of vomiting. The coming of curare, a muscle relaxant, made intra-abdominal surgery easier, but it also required that the anesthetist breathe for the patient by intermittent manual compression of a rubber bag. It was easy to give a lethal dose of ether in just a few breaths, and a study by Henry Beecher suggested the occurrence of one death in approximately 300 cases when curare was also used, as opposed to one death in 3000 cases without it.[4,27]

During World War II, medical officers without prior training had been assigned to anesthesia in the military hospitals, and after the war some of these experienced men began to recruit candidates into the new specialty. The leaders of the movement held to the principle that they should have the same relationship with patients as did other physicians, but they went a step further to insist that anesthesiologists should not receive remuneration from a hospital or medical school for their services; they should practice only on a fee-for-service basis, with submission of their bill directly to the patient. It was a rallying point for the new specialty.

In 1938 the American Board of Anesthesiology established training and practice criteria for admission to their examination. Six years later the American College of Anesthesiologists was established, with its own set of training and practice requirements. This effectively created two paths for the certification of competence. Under the presidency of Douglas Eastwood, this second path was discontinued in 1977.

A third organization, the American Society of Anesthesiologists, was developed. It had no entrance requirements other than an interest in the practice of anesthesia and membership in a medical society. It was an open-ended society whose initial interests in upgrading the practice of anesthesiology were later changed to political and economic interests.

In addition to training requirements, the American Board of Anesthesiology had a clause regarding revocation of its certificate. It considered that being refused membership in the American Medical Association (AMA) or the local county medical society constituted a violation of ethical principles, and, if a man were to be refused admission or expelled, the board's certificate would be revoked. Interlocking directorships between the American Board and the American Society made it easy to discipline and punish those who believed it their right to practice their specialty and receive remuneration for services as they pleased.[43] In 1953 the American Board of Anesthesiology finally withdrew the clause requiring membership in medical societies as a requirement for certification. The anesthesiologists' wish to take over such responsibilities as fluid balance, drug administration, and pre- and postoperative resuscitative measures created friction with surgeons who felt that they bore the primary responsibility for the care of the patient.

Graham's 1947 "Ether and Humbug" article[9] brought into the open the issue of how nurse anesthetists should relate to physician anesthesiologists. Although Graham received many complimentary letters, there were disparaging editorials in several medical journals and lay magazines. Some physicians went so far as to suggest to would-be patients that they would be risking death if they let their surgeon use a nurse as an anesthetist. There were attempts in several states to pass legislation making it illegal for anyone other than a licensed physician to administer an anesthetic. The relationship between the society and the board was so close that threats were made to young men associated with nurse anesthesia programs that they would not be allowed to pass the examination of the board unless they renounced the association. Some attempts were made to revoke the board certification of anesthesiologists who worked in collaboration with nurse anesthetists. The two salient features seemed to be that salaried arrangements for anesthesiologists were unacceptable, and that no one could ethically work alongside or in association with a nurse anesthetist. Graham's "Humbug" speech brought this latter issue into focus. Rovenstine (of New York University), Waters (of the University of Wisconsin), and Lundy (of the Mayo Clinic) were vigorous spokesmen for the hard-line anesthesiologists, whereas Beecher (of Harvard), Cullen (of the University of Iowa), Papper (of the University of Columbia), and Dripps (of the University of Pennysylvania)— with Graham on the sidelines—were spokesmen for moderation and time. In 1950, when Eastwood was planning to go to Barnes Hospital, he was informed that he would never pass the examinations of the American Board of Anesthesia because Barnes Hospital had a nurse anesthesia program.[39]

The anesthesiologists' attack was six pronged:

1. Refuse to admit individuals associated with nurse anesthetists to membership in societies, or disqualify them from eligibility for board certification.
2. Decertify those who used or worked with nurse anesthetists.
3. Get states to pass laws declaring nurse anesthetists illegal.
4. Declare that hospitals using nurses are in the corporate practice of medicine.
5. Require fee for service (not salary), and establish the medical—not technical—status of anesthesiology.
6. Use public scare tactics.

Publicity in lay magazines became sufficiently pronounced that in December 1947 the Southern Surgical Association at its annual meeting passed the following resolution:

> The Association heartily disapproves of the publicity given by certain newspapers and popular lay magazines to the statements sponsored by a group of anesthesiologists who are seeking to discredit the well-trained nurse anesthetist and to compel surgeons to operate only if anesthetics are administered by physician anesthetists. ... This attempt to persuade the public that there is a grave danger in a surgical operation if the anesthetist is not a certified medical specialist is already decreasing the number of efficient, well-trained nurse anesthetists and forcing surgeons to perform recently developed complicated operations with anesthetics administered by young hospital interns or general practitioners, neither of whom have special training or experience. s/Alfred Blalock[44]

The American College of Surgeons (ACS) became involved in the issue, and Harold Foss, a regent from Danville, Pennsylvania, chaired a committee that, in April 1952, recommended the admission of anesthesiologists as fellows or associate fellows of the ACS. Foss's committee received contrary advice from Henry Beecher, who believed that his specialty must develop itself from within, and that it would suffer in stature by legislative measures of the American College of Surgeons regarding training and practice, even though the ACS measures were designed to help give maturity and dignity to the fledgling discipline. Graham, now chairman of the ACS Board of Regents, was enthusiastic about assuming an obligation for the college to assist, if not to police, the development of anesthesiology. He established a second committee, under Loyal Davis, to look further at the problem and to offer a possible solution. The Davis committee suggested that requirements for fellowship in the American College of Surgeons for anesthesiologists be 2 years of residency, 4 years of practice, restriction to that practice area, and the experience of anesthetizing at least 2000 hospital patients. After Davis acknowledged that the pledge of the college created for surgeons would not apply to the anesthesiologists, Graham prepared his own draft for submission to the regents[f]. The longer pledge that was finally drawn consisted of four paragraphs specifically designed for anesthesiologists, and a required signature.

A third committee of the regents attempted to introduce ethical qualifications for the admission of anesthesiologists to fellowship in the ACS, but this committee's recommendations were unacceptable to the board of regents, then chaired by I.S. Ravdin. Graham, however, continued to pressure the regents to create a fellowship for anesthesiologists, using the special pledge, and in April 1956 the ACS conducted a review of the anesthesia fellowship proposal. Henry Beecher of Boston and Robert Dripps of Philadelphia testified that the proposed pledge was one that the best anesthesiologists in the country would never sign. Even worse, the ACS proposed that anesthesiologists be taken in as associate fellows and not as full fellows. This, too, the anesthesiologists were unwilling to accept, and, after a long discussion, the regents decided they should not proceed with the idea of an ACS Fellowship for anesthesiologists.[43] From afar, Graham dissented, and Ravdin presented Graham's ideas to a board of regents who felt that the American Society of Anesthesiologists was now in the hands of a better group than it had been before, and that these men needed to work out their own difficulties within their own society. Ravdin wrote to Graham: "If we are to take them in we must take them in as full Fellows and without the obligation of signing the pledge which was, in my opinion, a distasteful one."[46] He offered Graham an invitation to appear before the June 1956 meeting, but Graham did not accept. He realized that the American College of Surgeons was not going to exert any effect whatsoever on the development of anesthesiology's board or societies.[43] Formal activities of the American College of Surgeons in the developing field of anesthesiology ended.

---

f. Fellowship pledge for anesthesiologists (Graham's version):

> In accepting fellowship in the American College of Surgeons I pledge my support of the purposes and high ideals of the College as expressed in the Fellowship Pledge for Surgeons. The anesthesiologist and the surgeon must realize that they constitute a team whose only purpose is to make an operation more efficient and safer for the patient. This concept transcends any ideas of pecuniary reward.
>
> Believing that trade union methods and concepts are out of place in the practice of medicine and surgery I shall not lend my support to a dictation of how any qualified anesthesiologist may receive his compensation, whether as a salary from an institution or on a fee basis.
>
> Until an adequate number of physician anesthesiologists exist to fill the needs I shall not oppose the training of anesthetist technicians provided that their training is under the supervision of a recognized and qualified anesthesiologist and provided that proper safeguards are taken to protect the safety of the patient.[45]

L'AFFAIRE MOUSEL: A MATTER OF PRINCIPLE

The vendetta between Evarts Graham and physician anesthesiologists continued until the end of his life. He had been deeply wounded by their failure to understand his position on nurse anesthetists, their restrictive position on practice and salary arrangements, and their resort to personal deprecation. He was ever ready to continue a battle in which he felt bruised, and in 1953 he enthusiastically accepted the challenge posed by Lloyd Mousel who had just been appointed to the Swedish Hospital of Seattle, Washington. Mousel was to establish a closed staff of physician anesthesiologists working in conjunction with some nurse anesthetists, excluding other hospital staff members who, on occasion, gave anesthesia. It was this latter action that angered the local part-time practitioners of anesthesia. Mousel was informed that he would not be admitted to the local medical society and was expelled from the AMA, setting the stage for revocation of his certificate from the American Board of Anesthesiology. He was aware of the interest on the part of the American College of Surgeons and requested that he be able to present his case before the board of regents. As chairman of the board, Graham was encouraging. Mousel appeared before the board on April 4 and 5, 1953, and the regents received his complaints but took no action. On February 1, 1954, the King County Medical Society formally refused to admit Mousel to membership. Two features of his Swedish Hospital appointment concerned the physicians who led the society to reject his application. First, his appointment placed him on salary from the hospital, and fees accruing from his activities would revert to the hospital. Second, he was to be in charge of a department that contained nurse anesthetists working with physician anesthesiologists. The society never questioned his professional qualifications or ethical conduct apart from the fact that he received a salary and supervised nurses. Mousel appealed the medical society's action to the Judicial Council of the AMA on the basis that his membership application had been refused solely on the ground that he had a salary for administrative work at the Swedish Hospital. He indicated that, in the event the AMA did not reverse the action of the local county society, he would commence court action.[47]

Mousel's appeal was rejected on the grounds that the AMA did not have jurisdiction over the actions of a county society, and Mousel immediately filed suit in the Superior Court for King County against the American Society of Anesthesiologists and six other organizations. At that time, he again contacted Evarts Graham.[48] Although Graham was no longer on the board of regents, he was still interested in the special anesthesiology fellowship, and Graham accepted the responsibility for college action. He wrote to Mousel explaining the position of the American College of Surgeons and sent a copy of the pledge drawn up specifically for anesthesiologists. In Graham's letter to Mousel, he explained: "Just as the surgeons have always had to sign a pledge that they will not engage in unethical practices so we have drawn up a pledge for the anesthesiologists who will be admitted as Fellows in which we stress the point that they pledge themselves not to interfere with properly conducted courses for the training of nurse anesthetists until such time as there will be enough physician anesthesiologists to take care of the needs of the country."[49]

A few weeks later, Graham wrote to Paul Hawley, director of the American College of Surgeons, advising him of the activity in Seattle and stating: "He [Mousel] was put out of the Anesthesiologists Association and they even went so far as to try to take away from him his Board certification.... In my opinion this is a very important case. I hope you will be willing to supply him with whatever information we may have that will be helpful to him in winning his case. The whole thing has been a wonderful example of the measure to which some of the lunatic anesthesiologists who have power will go to enforce the union rules."[50]

Five months later Mousel asked Graham if he could and would appear as a witness: "If I am not supported by people of national stature I am very apt to be defeated in my defense of this position."[51] Graham indicated his willingness to go to Seattle to testify at the trial set for September 20, which was later postponed to October 10.[52] Graham then called Paul Hawley and I.S. Ravdin to report that he was planning to go to Seattle. Both felt this to be an important matter, felt that the college should be involved, and that the ACS would underwrite the cost of his trip.[53] Graham contacted Frank Bradley to ask if he would contact hospital administrators and the American Association of Nurse Anesthetists on his behalf.[54] From this effort, Bradley found that of the 7000 general hospitals in the United States, 52 percent used members of the American Association of Nurse Anesthetists, alongside members of the American Society of Anesthesiology, in their operating rooms. The executive director of the nursing association presented a list of 15 leading hospitals with formal training schools for nurse anesthetists,[55] and Graham submitted all the information to Mousel's legal firm in Seattle. Three days before the anticipated trial, with a settlement in the process of being reached between Mousel and the professional societies involved, the trial was postponed to January 3, 1956.

The requisite trip to Seattle never occurred for, on January 2, 1956, the parties announced a complicated out-of-court settlement. Mousel would continue to work on salary, supervise nurse anesthetists, and institute a physician residency training program. The hospital would charge for the services of nurse anesthetists, and Mousel's salary would cover teaching, training, and any other legitimate function except for supervision of nurses in the actual administering of anesthetics; this exception was made to eliminate the contention that such supervision amounted to the corporate practice of medicine by the hospital. Mousel would send a bill to the patient, and the hospital would reduce the service charge of the nurse anesthetist by an equal amount.[56] It was an arrangement that Graham would have eagerly embraced for Barnes Hospital two decades earlier. However, at this time, Graham was disappointed at the settlement, feeling that it avoided fundamental issues

regarding the role of nurse anesthestists, nurse training schools, and the relationship between physicians and nurses. To him, it avoided what was an overarching
principle, the role of a medical society in defining practice policies rather than
practice quality. His response to the Seattle settlement contained overtones of his
discomfort of many years before with Mason City practitioners, his satisfaction
with the principle of a full-time salary, and his general resentment of anesthesiologists for their failure to help him during his search for a middle ground solution
at Barnes. He wrote to Mousel's lawyer in Seattle:

> My spirit of frankness compels me to tell you that I am very much dis-
> appointed in the terms of the proposed settlement. . . . in fact I am
> inclined to think that such an agreement as you have mentioned
> would be regarded as a great victory for the anesthesiologists and as a
> defeat for Dr. Mousel. . . . The fundamental issue to which I object very
> seriously is the one of having any medical society or group dictate to
> a respectable and competent member of the profession how he shall
> earn his livelihood. . . . there is no place in the practice of medicine for
> trade union rules. When, at the insistence of the Washington State
> Society of Anesthesiologists, Dr. Mousel agrees to change his usual
> practice and customary procedure in submitting a special bill for his
> services for the supervision of a nurse anesthetist I think he lends his
> support to an idea which, in my opinion, is intolerable and is to be
> utterly condemned. The motive behind all this kind of action is one of
> pure greed. . . . I had hoped that this case would stand out as a shining
> example that there are members of the medical profession, even anes-
> thesiologists, who were willing to stand up for a principle and there-
> by to show the public that the motive of financial profit and greed is
> not the one that dominates the practice of medicine. . . . Nevertheless
> . . . he has made a very disappointing surrender to the worst element of
> the anesthesiologists in this deal.[57]

Graham continued:

> I have always very strongly resented the idea that any group of doctors
> can tell me how I shall make my living provided that what I do is hon-
> orable and legal. As a matter of fact I am accustomed to a struggle with
> the medical profession about all this because I was the first young
> man in the country to become a full-time professor of surgery work-
> ing on a salary in a university similar to a professor of chemistry,
> Greek or history. I was criticized and even cursed on the grounds that
> I was allowing myself to be used in a manner contrary to the best

interests of the medical profession. Now, however, the situation has changed to the extent that the Professors of Surgery in all of the first-class medical schools in the country are on full-time. Dr. Mousel could have had the same opportunity to set a splendid example in anesthesiology if he had resisted the efforts of his union in the state of Washington to make him go along with the crowd. . . . I am quite sure that in this case the other side does not wish to have the wide publicity which the court trial would bring. In my opinion they will settle for almost anything in order to avoid having the public point the finger of scorn at them. . . . I think it would have been far better from every standpoint if you had pushed this case to trial instead of making a settlement on such terms as you have indicated in your letter to me. I am very unhappy about the whole thing.[57]

The settlement, which was satisfactory to all parties in Seattle, resolved a specific case, but to Graham, who was standing on a matter of principle, the compromise was capitulation. Unfortunately for Graham, it came at the same time as the retreat of the American College of Surgeons on the issue of anesthesia fellowships. One year later, Graham would be dead. Barnes Hospital would have 12 staff nurse anesthestists with 33 students. Washington University would have no well-established MD anesthesia training program and an unfilled Mallinckrodt Professorship in Anesthesia that had been endowed 8 years before.

The Seattle-Mousel effort was the final episode in Graham's efforts to influence the training and certification of anesthesiologists, to upgrade the profession, and to protect the patient. His approach had been overly paternalistic and, acting individually or through the ACS, he had wished to impose his own ideas about training, qualifications, professional competence, and ethical behavior. Graham had wished to regulate the relationship between nurse anesthetists and a fledgling specialty that wished to stand independently, rather than in a role subservient to a surgeon. All of it had failed. It was undoubtedly the greatest effort Graham had made without any appreciably visible or positive results.

Chapter 11

SURGICAL EDUCATION

The keystone of Graham's educational effort was the general surgery service at Barnes Hospital, which, in its early years, was centered around the ward patients. Since medical students and interns were not permitted to see private or semiprivate patients, there was a continual demand for an increased number of ward beds, and a constant search for funds to support them. Graham's 1928 to 1929 report of the surgical service reveals his opinions about the educational opportunities in the Department of Surgery:

> There are several reasons why it is desirable for purposes of medical education to allot more teaching beds to the Department of Surgery than to the Department of Medicine. In the Department of Medicine a larger amount of profitable instruction can be carried out in the Out-Patient Department and also a larger amount can be carried out in the daily observation of the average medical patient in the wards. In the Department of Surgery however in most cases the chief educational value of the patient is concerned with an operation, not only with the operative technique itself but also with the study of the pathology revealed by the operation, etc. It often, although by no means always, happens that a patient who occupies a surgical bed for two weeks may have very little educational value except during one day of the two weeks[a].[1]

---

a. *Author's note*: During these years the most frequent operation was the repair of an inguinal hernia. Patients were kept at strict bed rest for 12 postoperative days, then allowed up for 2 days before discharge home, with limited activity for 6 weeks. Sixty years of age was the upper limit of eligibility for hernia repair.

During the last half of the nineteenth century, surgery was taught in a passive observational style in which the learners sat or stood in a circular amphitheater while the patient and the surgical team were gathered at a table in the center—a style reminiscent of the frontispiece of Vesalius's *de Humani Corporis Fabrica*. Modern versions are captured in three heroic paintings: one by Robert Hinckley, *The First Operation Under Ether*, in 1893; and two by Thomas Eakins—*The Gross Clinic*, in 1875, and *The Agnew Clinic*, circa 1910.[2–4] This observational style was adopted by the early clinical congresses of the American College of Surgeons.[5]

By the turn of the century, surgical education was becoming preceptorial. An aspirant would become an assistant to an established surgeon, work with him, assist at his operations when needed, and gain clinical experience until one or the other terminated the attachment. These learning activities were generally uncontrolled, unregistered, and unrecorded. Graham's training at Chicago Presbyterian Hospital was preceptorial, with his father and Arthur Dean Bevan as his chief preceptors. When universities entered the picture, these preceptorial traineeships became formalized as fellowships with a predetermined beginning and ending, and generally with some financial support for the trainee.

Early in its development, Washington University abandoned the rotating internship by which an intern would pass through all of the recognized specialties: medicine, surgery, pediatrics, and obstetrics. Subsequently, each intern was assigned to one of these specialties for a full year—a "straight" internship.

Graham's formal graded residency did not develop all at once, but evolved over a period of 5 or 6 years. The eventful year occurred in 1925 to 1926 when Graham selected Joe Gale over Nathan Womack to be his chief resident. I.Y. Olch remembered the occasion: "Up to that time the residency at Barnes was sort of a hit-and-miss thing. Graham hadn't really thought it out. He'd have an intern and pick a fellow for assistant resident [for one or more years] ... and then make him his resident for two years. ... Graham had two assistant residents who were anxious to stay on, one was Womack and the other was Joe Gale who [later went to] Wisconsin in chest surgery. Womack was ... disappointed and we were all disappointed too."[6] One evening Olch told Womack that he would get him a job, and he asked if Womack would be interested in pathology. After receiving an affirmative answer, Olch told Graham that Barney Brooks was becoming more active in vascular surgery, and that things in the surgical pathology laboratory were getting busier. He recited his own increasing student obligations and suggested that it would be worthwhile to get another man in the laboratory who could help with the surgical pathology. He could also assist Graham when the need arose. As a result, Womack was appointed to a year in pathology in Olch's laboratory, next to Graham's office. Olch discussed the outcome:

> Nathan was there and he [Graham] was able to see him and watch
> him at work. ... The second time around he suggested that Nathan

come back in the house as assistant resident and then promised that he would go on to the residency. After he did that with Nathan I told Graham that this thing worked out pretty well, why not do this as a regular thing? The next candidate was William Hamm who later became a prominent plastic surgeon in Atlanta, Ga. We started a stream of these fellows and it became routine for him to pick an assistant resident, with my connivance, and send him to the lab for a year. Well that made the residency a four year deal—assistant resident for one year, the laboratory, assistant resident for another year and then the residency. Up to that time, to my knowledge, there had not been a similar situation in the country. ... we developed this graded residency and then Sam Harvey put the same system in at Yale.[6]

In reminiscing upon his year at the Johns Hopkins Hospital as one of Halsted's last interns, Olch compared the Hopkins arrangement with the system that had developed at Barnes:

> Some guys were a resident for one year and some ... for five years. ...
> Halsted or the attending men never instructed the interns in anything
> ... except at the operating table when they were doing something if
> you had nerve enough to ask. ... you never dared to talk to [Halsted]
> because you didn't know what his reaction would be. ... By a graded
> residency I mean the resident and the assistant resident were instruct-
> ing the men below them. ... Graham was a very good teacher. ... From
> the student's and average intern's point of view ... [there was] little or
> no contact with [Halsted]. ... if you followed on rounds and listened
> carefully you could hear what he was telling the resident. What the
> people did at Washington University really was the prototype of the
> residency program as we know it in this country, everyone talks about
> Halsted's residency system but that's not it at all. ... Halsted's residen-
> cies were not regular residencies. The type of residency we have now,
> which is the one they have at Hopkins today was started by us and
> mostly Womack and myself ... not realizing what we were doing
> [while] we were doing it.[6]

The residency program at Barnes began by collecting surgeons with common interests who shared and supervised one or two trainees who had been assigned to them. Initially, the effort included only ward patients, but it gradually expanded to include private patients, and became formal when university and hospital joined as partners in the effort.

Graham's presidential address to the International Surgical Society in 1956 reflected his thoughts on surgery and the preparation of its trainees:

> The inside of the heart was the last anatomical frontier for the surgeon to pass [and] that frontier is now closed. But there is a wide and far-reaching physiological frontier which is just beginning to be explored. …The physiological frontier is capable of indefinite expansion if we think of a surgeon as one who is interested in something more than cutting and sewing.[7]

The year of laboratory experience under university auspices led to arguments as to whether or not this was really surgical education—the pathology laboratory was relatively easy; however, the biochemistry or physiology laboratories were less so. Even now with molecular biology, the debate still persists.

In mid-1920, 9 months after his arrival in St. Louis, Graham's surgical service had one chief resident, three assistant residents, and an unrecorded number of interns. Ten years later this had increased to one chief resident, six assistant residents, and five interns. By 1940 there was one chief resident, nine assistant residents, and nine interns. From the nine interns, three assistant residents were chosen each year to serve for 3 years, from which only one ultimately achieved the chief resident position. By 1950, in order to care for returning veterans, the system had been expanded to two chief residents, 12 assistant residents, and nine interns in general surgery (see appendix C). In addition there were several specialty residents and a variable number of fellows. Interns rotated through 12 defined services on a monthly basis. During their 3 years, assistant residents rotated on a quarterly basis through 12 services that included both private and ward general surgery, the outpatient clinics, surgical pathology, and several of the specialties. Interns were now permitted to see semiprivate patients but not patients in the private pavilion.[8]

By the late 1920s, the year in the laboratory had been introduced into the general surgical program. At first it was 1 full year in the pathology laboratory, but it soon became a year in any laboratory. In reminiscing about those years, Womack felt that "an entirely different approach to surgery was suddenly thrown into the surgical eye and it was attractive to bright young minds. It brought men from all over the country and influenced the organization of many Departments of Surgery. This was around 1924–1928 that saw the establishment of several new departments of Surgery such as Rochester, Western Reserve and Chicago and the reconstruction of several old ones like Minnesota."[9] The development was so important that men such as Owen Wangensteen would remember it as follows: "I think here is an idea that Graham put across.…It has had a tremendous influence on surgical education throughout the world and I would say far supersedes any single experimental or clinical contribution of Graham's. I think also that Graham would be a bit surprised to hear one say this because it was so ingrained in his approach toward surgery that he never recognized it."[9]

Ten years after his arrival in St. Louis, Graham began to elevate his sights in regard to the residents who would be trained on his service. He began to see his trainees not just as accomplished, educated surgeons but as leaders in the development of surgery in the country; this concept required that they do more than merely learn the craft of surgery. In 1930 he expressed these ideas in a letter to Richard Pearce of the Rockefeller Foundation:

> Leadership comprises so many qualities that it is difficult to estimate the likelihood of somebody's becoming a leader unless one has some personal knowledge concerning those qualities other than intelligence and good work.... The surgeon of the future will be much better trained and much more interested in fundamental science than his grandfather was.... For the first time in the history of the world a group of surgical leaders has appeared in this country who are really scientifically inclined and who are more interested in inquiring into the causes of disease in general than they are in the more mechanical aspects of surgery. Of course, in the past there have been shining solitary examples of surgeons of that sort as, for example, Lister, but there have never been so many at one time as there are now in this country. The surgical leader of fifteen or twenty years from now will be much better prepared in the fundamental sciences than men of my generation are but even so I doubt if they will institute so radical a departure from existing customs and traditions as the men of my generation have done. The graded resident system, the abundant opportunity for advanced study in any medical school subject ... has made it possible for these young men who are now growing up to prepare themselves in a manner that was impossible to the men of my generation except under most unusual circumstances and conditions.[10]

Graham followed this with a list of nine men whom he saw as potential leaders, and he concluded, "The subject always interests me and I think there is nothing as fascinating as to watch a group of hand-picked boys develop into mature leaders."[10]

The apprenticeship system of the early years of the twentieth century was a system destined to disappear, but it took several decades. At Washington University Graham developed educational units within the Department of Surgery, for example, general surgery, urology, and gynecology, and he moved his residents through these experiences. This setup would be imitated in most medical schools. However, even at Barnes, the move toward formal programs was gradual. Ernest Sachs and Vilray Blair retained fellowships until the end of World War II. General surgical residents rotated through the several specialty services, whereas, except for a pathology rotation, specialty residents rarely did so. Upon reflecting on those years, Womack asserted: "The function of the medical school—particularly the Department of Surgery [becomes one] to develop great minds, to teach, to stimulate. And those minds that are good will go out into their communities and establish proper medical care."[9]

In the early 1930s, there were less than 20 places in the United States that offered 2 years of postgraduate education in surgery. By the early 1940s there were over 400—a change that resulted from the entrance of universities into postgraduate medical education, the establishment of the American specialty boards, and the development of hospital credentialing and accrediting activities. By establishing these agencies, the profession was attempting to provide the American public with capable, competent surgeons trained in recognized institutions. Graham was a significant figure in this effort.

It was almost inevitable that when the American Board of Surgery defined training specifications, Graham's program would be the general prototype, although the laboratory year was deleted since not every training program was able to mount a meaningful experience. The chief resident year had an alternate provision—2 years of practice in association with a specially certified preceptor would be accepted in lieu of the chiefship year—an arrangement that made it possible to train candidates in institutions that did not care for ward/charity patients.

The number of training positions at Barnes was expanded by using fellows or voluntary assistants who would come for varying periods of time as accessories to the residents. Although these voluntary assistant positions were formalized in 1927, the hospital never gave to these men the authority or responsibility that it gave to a resident.[11] Barnes Hospital funded the intern positions, the university funded the residents, and all certificates of service were jointly signed. Funding for the fellows came from many sources and was usually funneled through Washington University, although, in some cases, private practice groups paid fellows from their own funds. In 1926 the General Education Board awarded Graham $50,000 to support fellows who were beginning to appear from overseas as well as from all parts of North America. When that fund expired, the board awarded funding for 5 more years, after which Graham obtained money for this purpose from the Commonwealth Foundation. During World War II, the Rockefeller Foundation agreed to support four general surgery veterans of Graham's choosing for 3 years.

Graham considered that training in general surgery was a basic preparation for any surgical specialty. He never relinquished contact with his general surgical chief resident, and he would spend an hour every Thursday afternoon making rounds on the wards with his resident and staff, to see all of the ward patients and discuss their problems. With a retinue of five or six, he would flow through the ward, stopping at each bed for a brief report on the history, physical examination, operation, and outcome, which was delivered by a chief resident who was then subjected to a quiz. Interns, assistant residents, and attending staff were generally silent unless one of them felt that the chief resident needed support from the pressure of Graham's questions.

During the 30 years in which Graham was surgeon-in-chief at Barnes, the hospital produced 20 department chairmen (see appendix D) and 26 heads of service or chiefs of specialty units in universities around the world.[12]

Graham displayed his idealism and expectations of medical education in his 1938 welcoming address to the freshmen class: "Clinical medicine after all is only applied anatomy, physiology, pathology and bacteriology.... A knowledge of the fundamental reactions of the structures of the body is useful practical knowledge to the clinician, [but] first of all on the list of requirements are those qualities which are usually embraced in the words Character, Honesty, Integrity and Moral Instincts.... The great doctor must also have wisdom and ... in the words of Paul, Faith, Hope and Charity."[13]

In response to a request from Elliott Cutler, who had just assumed the chairmanship of surgery at Western Reserve University in Cleveland, Ohio, Graham expressed thoughts on the specifics of medical student education:

> The important matters to teach the undergraduate are the fundamental principles, a rational and scientific approach to problems and a knowledge of tools. By the latter I do not mean surgical instruments but I mean all of those things such as methods of various kinds which enable him to obtain information, not only concerning a particular patient but also concerning what knowledge exists in the world on a particular topic ... of clinical work, concentration should be placed in the general processes of disease with special discussions emphasizing particular diseases and abnormal conditions as illustrative of general principles.... If possible also the student should be made to realize that many of the conditions within a special field are very properly beyond the realm of a so-called general practitioner and that for such conditions he should seek consultation with an expert.... the student should be made to realize the possibilities of modern diagnostic and therapeutic measures....[14]

Graham's contacts with medical students were not intimate, but during the latter half of his tenure, he gave a weekly lecture in the semicircular auditorium to the entire third year class. The lecture was always on a subject of surgical interest, but he never presented a patient, as was the habit of Drs. Barr and Wood. Graham's lectures were comprehensive, ordered, and covered an entire topic from a historic aspect to clinical presentation, operative management, and outcome. "His lectures to the medical students were lucid, simple and dealt with basic primary facts, [and the students] adored him as a lecturer. There was nothing difficult or obtuse about what he presented; it was clear and forceful."[15] He always started on time, covered his topic in a step-by-step fashion, and closed with a pronouncement. Then, as the students put away their notebooks, he left the amphitheater followed by his resident staff. His was a dramatic presentation followed by a dramatic exit.

A 1-hour written examination ended each clerkship and, coupled with staff observations, produced a numeric grade. It was a clerkship that was met with mixed reactions by the students, but Graham did not apologize for either its nature or the rigorous demands it made on students' time and effort.

Chapter 12

COLLEGES, SOCIETIES, ASSOCIATIONS, AND BOARDS

THE AMERICAN COLLEGE OF SURGEONS

Evarts Graham was a "joiner," even by standards of 50 to 70 years later. He was an active member of 17 societies, president of five, and an honorary member in 29 others (see appendix A). Although he made important contributions through many of these organizations, his influence in elevating the standards of surgery, improving the hospitals in which it took place, defining the nature of graduate surgical education, and making the case against unethical practices occurred mainly via the American College of Surgeons (ACS) and the American Surgical Association (ASA).

The American College of Surgeons was the last of four innovations of a Chicago gynecologist, Franklin H. Martin. Martin's educational concerns were with practicing doctors, not medical students, and his first enterprise was his Post Graduate Medical School of Chicago, which gave practical clinical demonstrations. The second contribution was a journal, *Surgery, Gynecology and Obstetrics (SGO)*, that was run by and devoted to the interests of medical practitioners. Its first issue was published in July 1905, and within 18 months there were 2800 paying subscribers. Within its 140 pages, more than half of all scientific articles pertaining to surgery, gynecology, or obstetrics published during that year appeared in *SGO*. Martin's third innovation was influenced by a visit to the operative clinics and discussions of a group called the "Society of Clinical Surgery." Founded in 1903, this group included, among others, Crile, Cushing, the Mayo brothers, Mumford, and Murphy. The members visited each other twice a year to share experiences.[1] By 1910

Martin decided to invite all 3500 subscribers of *SGO* to visit the surgical clinics and operating rooms of Chicago for an educational experience; the program was patterned after the one he had seen in the Society of Clinical Surgery. Martin's plan for the fall of 1910 called for a 2-week period of operative clinics sponsored by five local societies[a], with all expenses borne by *SGO*. Ten thousand invitations were sent, 200 visitors were anticipated, and 1300 doctors attended.

Before the first week was finished, the clinics had been so successful that Martin decided to create a new organization called "The Clinical Congress of Surgeons of North America." Plans were made for an annual meeting in a major American city, with membership composed of all subscribers to *SGO*. Philadelphia surgeons offered to host the second congress in November 1911, and, at the New York City congress in 1912, there were 2600 registrants. Some in the profession who were not supporters of Martin's organization circulated rumors that the $5 registration fee was a source of personal income for Martin. Even though the rumor was soon disproved, other rumors were initiated, leading to unfounded criticism of Martin and the American College of Surgeons Board of Regents.

Martin realized it was necessary to require some standard of surgical practice for enrollees; he felt that only qualified surgeons should be permitted to attend the Clinical Congress, and that a subscription to *SGO* was not a suitable standard. He planned a society built upon the successful Clinical Congress but that would require definite qualifications for membership. At the 1911 congress in Philadelphia, he asserted his five proposals[b] to develop an American College of Surgeons and received the enthusiastic support of J.B. Murphy of Chicago, who agreed to second their presentation to the membership. Martin stated, "I believe that this large organization of surgeons on the American continent, the Clinical Congress of Surgeons of North America, should assume the responsibility and the authority of standardizing surgery."[2]

Edward Martin of Philadelphia (no relation to Franklin), chairman of the 1911 congress, expanded the scope by asking Chicagoan Allen Kanavel to propose a committee on the standardization of hospitals so the public would know at which

---

a. Chicago Surgical Society, Chicago Gynecological Society, Chicago Neurological Society, Chicago Orthopedic Society, Chicago Medical Society.

b. Five proposals for the development of the American College of Surgeons:

1. A standard of professional, ethical, and moral requirements for every authorized graduate in medicine who practices general surgery
2. A supplementary degree for operating surgeons
3. Special letters to indicate fellowship in the college
4. A published list of fellows of the college
5. The appointment of a committee from the Clinical Congress with power to proceed with the plan

hospitals they were safe to receive treatment.[2,3] Thus was born the American College of Surgeons; its mandate was to elevate the standards of surgery by its requirements for fellowship, to use the Clinical Congress for the education of its fellows, and to raise the standards of hospital services by creating a commission to inspect and accredit hospitals.[1]

The issue of fee splitting arose at the initial meeting of the organizing group in 1911. A surgeon from Fort Wayne, Indiana, Miles F. Porter, questioned any eligibility requirements that failed to include an ethical statement, and he rose to say: "There are a great many men ... who from a ... moral standpoint are unfit. I refer to fee splitters[c]. Such men should not become members of this body."[1] Met with applause, his remarks initiated a discussion of the worst evil of the surgical profession, one that was to remain a cause of bitter controversy for many years. Four years later, Graham encountered it in Mason City, Iowa.

Evarts Graham was admitted as a founding member at the ACS Convocation of 1914. *Surgery, Gynecology and Obstetrics* became the official organ of the ACS. The Clinical Congress was held each year in conjunction with an annual convocation of the fellows, and ACS fortunes were directed by a group of clinical surgeons who strongly supported Martin—John B. Murphy, Allen Kanavel, Albert J. Ochsner, Charles and William Mayo, and George Crile.

In the early 1920s, the ACS consisted of more than 5000 fellows, its affairs were conducted by a board of 16 regents, and it was headed by an executive director with broad authority and responsibility. The regents established the requirements for fellowship, set fees, and supervised both the Clinical Congress and the Hospital Standardization Program. Day-to-day administration of the ACS was the responsibility of the director. The board of regents, composed of surgeons from the major clinics (particularly those of the Midwest), was dominated by Franklin Martin, the ACS executive director.

By 1924 criticism of the board arose from two sources. The Society of Clinical Surgery[d] sent a petition requesting a reduction in the number of fellows admitted, an elevation of the requirements for admission, and a development of methods to examine candidates' character, training, intelligence, and ethics. At the same meeting, a close associate and friend of Evarts Graham, Malvern Clopton of St. Louis,

---

c. *Fee splitting* is the practice in which part of the professional fee paid to a physician or surgeon is given (by subterfuge or otherwise) to a third party, usually the referring physician.

d. The Society of Clinical Surgery, initially a few men who shared their experiences through biannual visits to each others' clinics, was the stimulus for the Clinical Congress of Surgeons. Martin always credited the society, saying that he applied their ideas to a large group instead of a select few. By 1924 this society had become more formalized and included many of the professors of surgery who, although they endorsed the aims and objectives of the ACS, felt excluded from many of the policy actions taken by the board of regents, particularly its proselytizing for fellowship in the ACS.

read a similar, longer, and more detailed petition prepared by the Eclat Club[e]. Both petitions emphasized that the fellowship of the ACS included men who were fee splitters, charged that nothing had been done to get rid of them, and complained that the Hospital Standardization Program was not sufficiently stringent. Both objected to domination of the board of regents by Martin, and both criticized the length of term and the age of board members. Strong criticism was directed at Franklin Martin because of a perceived failure to issue a satisfactory financial statement.

After receiving the two petitions, the regents responded with a formal rebuttal, somehow failing to appreciate the differences in philosophy occurring between two generations of surgeons that was resulting in the evolution of a group of Young Turks. As one of these Young Turks, Evarts Graham was also interested in issues other than those contained in the petitions. He had plans for a surgical training experience that required adequate and special hospital support in addition to a defined training program. One year after the two petitions had been presented to the regents, he staked out his position on these issues in an address delivered before the Southern Medical Association. He decried the overemphasis on the purely operative aspect of a surgeons' work, and stressed that standards based on deftness of the operator, number of operations performed, and even the derived income often led to unwise operating and commercialism, with its accompanying evil of fee splitting. In his view, an original contribution to the science and art of surgery was the real measure of accomplishment, and the basis of surgical training was to give an individual the maximum opportunity to prepare his mind for the reception of ideas while developing manual skills. He emphasized the need for an understanding of pathology and physiology, and for individual research experience:

> Even in many of our university hospitals the organization, the type of facility offered to the young man and the whole atmosphere is too much that of a nursing home and too little of the kind of hospital which can offer the training which I have suggested. The program of standardization of hospitals carried out by the American College of Surgeons has been of very great value in raising the general average of the surgery performed but a hospital which merely meets these requirements will not be able to provide young men with the opportunity for superior

---

e. The Eclat Club grew from a close personal association in France of several young surgeons. According to one of its members, requirements for membership were that the candidate should have served at "the Front," been scared, and held a rank no higher than captain. Thirty-two charter members were elected, and Arthur Elting was its first president. Membership was limited to 50 people. Its members all matured in surgery at about the same time, and, in succession, five were elected presidents of the American Surgical Association. They were young, well-trained, active teachers in Departments of Surgery, and all were convinced that the board of regents needed an infusion of young blood.

developments which are likely to make them originators of important surgical thought and practice.[4]

Graham was voicing a problem that was becoming increasingly apparent, that is, the need for effective monitoring of surgical training programs in addition to the monitoring of hospitals.[5]

The 1932 Clinical Congress met in St. Louis, and events of that congress began the transformation of Graham's relationship with the American College of Surgeons from a quasiantagonistic position to one of strong unity of purpose. Prior to that time, Graham had not been deeply involved with the ACS, but he agreed to become chairman of the local arrangements committee, a position that was usually accompanied by the individual's election to office, customarily as a vice-president. Having accepted the task, Graham organized the activities of the week of Monday, October 17, through Friday, October 21. His local committee on arrangements was composed of 38 St. Louis surgeons in two subcommittees, one each for ophthalmology and otolaryngology. Allen Kanavel, Graham's long-time friend and supporter, was president of the ACS that year, and, in the invitation extended to the fellows, he wrote: "Evarts A. Graham, Professor of Surgery at Washington University School of Medicine, with a committee representing all the medical schools and hospitals, has prepared an extensive program presenting their clinical material, much of it unique in nature. Here will be found some types of surgical work not to be seen elsewhere in the United States."[6]

Graham's committee enlisted operating rooms and clinic areas of almost all St. Louis hospitals for daily operations, demonstrations, and clinics. In addition to operative surgery, there were surgical films, sessions on the teaching of surgery, two evenings devoted to discussions of problems of interest to the public at large, and sessions on cancer, trauma, and industrial medicine. The program included 4 full days of a discussion of the ACS Hospital Standardization Program. Barnes Hospital carried the bulk of the week's effort by providing 90 clinical demonstrations, five of which were by Evarts Graham. Graham's enthusiasm and willingness to organize and participate in the congress is visible in the daily operative clinics that he arranged—particularly in his own operative lists[f]. The scope of the program

---

f. Evarts Graham's operative list for October 19, 1932:

1. Thyroidectomy
2. Exploratory laparotomy for gastric hemorrhage, appendectomy
3. Cholecystectomy and gastroenterostomy
4. Second-stage resection of colon for carcinoma
5. Exploratory laparotomy for right upper quadrant tumor
6. Cholecystectomy
7. Excision of tumor of the back

reflected how the Clinical Congress had expanded since the early years when its program was centered around operations viewed by visitors on the floor or in the balconies. (In Chicago in 1910, J.B. Murphy had operated in a theater that held 50 visitors—tickets were required for admission.) The 1932 registration fee remained $5.00, and hotel rates for single rooms ran between $1.50 to $4.00. At the Annual Meeting of the Fellows and the convocation on Friday evening, Evarts Graham officially became first vice-president-elect of the American College of Surgeons and commenced 20 years of dedicated affiliation.

Prior to the convocation, Graham had not been consulted of his appointment, and he became aware of his election as second vice-president through a notice in the *St. Louis Post-Dispatch* that Friday morning. Angered by this, he held a long and heated discussion with George Crile, in which he also raised many criticisms of the ACS held by men of his generation. Crile contended that the election was an honor, to which Graham responded that, to him, it would be an honor to be made regent, not second vice-president. When all was done, Graham became first vice-president-elect, but he refused to sit on the platform for the convocation at Kiel Auditorium. Crile spoke to Martin who immediately discussed the issue with Graham, and, after returning to Chicago, wrote to indicate that the episode made him realize how little the rank and file of the fellows knew about the inner workings of the ACS. Martin explained that vice-presidents were ex-officio members of the board of regents, and he hoped that Graham would find it possible to attend each session of the board as well as meetings of the executive committee. He concluded: "I hope now that we have won your interest that you will become one of the future supporters, … your two years of service, of which I hope you will take advantage, will make you I am sure one of the staunch supporters of our organization."[7] The St. Louis meeting convinced Graham of the potential power of the ACS and the splendid work it had accomplished. Franklin Martin would not live to see his prediction come true.[1]

The invitation from Martin to attend meetings of the board of regents and the executive committee, in addition to the offer to present his ideas, was a challenge Graham could not refuse, and he prepared to confront the regents with several specific criticisms. A review of Graham's list reveals that Malvern Clopton's 1924 petition on behalf of the Eclat Society was influential in refining Graham's thoughts:

1. Martin was too powerful and essentially controlled the College.
2. The Regents were too old and had held office too long.
3. There was a glaring lack of medical school representation on the board of regents.
4. Standards for admission were too low.
5. Improvement in surgical training was not being fostered.
6. There were questions concerning disclosure of the financial aspects of the ACS.

For the fall 1932 and spring 1933 meetings of the board of regents, Graham planned a course of action he felt would produce more results than did the two petitions given to the regents 8 years earlier. Although the Society of Clinical Surgery, of which he was now a member, had a group of young men in academic positions, Graham chose to use his personal voice as the voice of dissent and the vice-presidency as his platform, and he prepared for a major presentation at the October 1933 meeting of the regents. Six of the 16 regents had held office since the board was inaugurated 20 years prior, and Graham felt keenly that younger men who had attained positions of leadership and held the most important chairs of surgery in the country lacked both voice and representation. A later communication from Martin chose to ignore this point, for he sent Graham a list of young men who had been elected to the board from 1916 until 1932, the majority of whom were private practitioners not university professors; all were handpicked by Martin.[7]

In preparation for his confrontation, Graham contacted 20 surgeons[g] whom he considered to be leaders in American surgery, to point out that he had certain criticisms to make of the ACS, and that he had been invited to express his views. He asked for their candid opinions on the policies of the ACS and requested any constructive ideas:

> I am writing to ask you to give me some suggestions. ... I have been invited to attend the Board of Regents next Fall to express my views concerning the College. ... I hope to present a program which will put it somewhat more in touch with the men of our own generation who have now come into positions of leadership in surgery. ... I feel that we have been neglected, that our opinions have neither been asked for nor received in a proper spirit. ... the College has lost the enthusiastic support of the men who at the present time occupy the most influential positions in American surgery and who want to be enthusiastically behind it. ... I wish to show, as I believe to be the case, the ideas which I have suggested from time to time really represent the ideas of the most influential surgical leaders of our generation ... so I can state that after canvassing twenty of the influential leaders I have found that certain criticisms stand out.[8]

Graham also wrote to J.M.T. Finney asking for his support in the effort.[9]

---

g. Barney Brooks, Frederick A. Coller, Elliott C. Cutler, Samuel C. Harvey, Carl A. Hedblom, George J. Heuer, Emile Holman, E. Starr Judd, Frank H. Lahey, Dean D. Lewis, John J. Morton, George P. Muller, Howard C. Naffziger, Alton Ochsner, Dallas B. Phemister, Erwin R. Schmidt, Allen O. Whipple, Edward D. Churchill, Edwin P. Lehman, and Mont Reid (the latter three were not fellows of the ACS).

Graham's presentation to the board of regents during the meeting of October 10, 1933, summarized the replies he had received that were unanimously critical of the fact that the younger surgical teachers did not have an intimate connection with the ACS. They were disassociated; no one cared what they thought. His contemporaries felt that a John B. Murphy oration at the Clinical Congress was ludicrous since Murphy was not a good surgeon and should not be held up as an ideal to the young surgeons of the country. Graham stated categorically that the dues were too high, the standards for admission to fellowship were too low, and an adequate financial statement had never been presented. He charged that fee splitting still existed among fellows of the ACS, but that the regents had done nothing about it: "Fee splitting keeps surgery in hands unfit and untrained to do it."[10]

The regents had heard similar criticisms 8 years earlier in the petitions of the Society of Clinical Surgery and the Eclat Society, and, in similar fashion, they prepared a detailed 12-page reply that they sent, on December 4, 1933, to each recipient of Graham's letter as well as to each regent. Meanwhile, Graham had written to his 20 contemporaries to summarize what he had gained during his meeting with the board, interpreting the discussions that resulted from his presentation as an indication of a belief on the part of "some of those in control of the affairs of the College that too much emphasis was being placed upon teachers of surgery."[11] In an attempt to forestall the rebuttal, Graham had included among his 20 surgeons Frank Lahey and E. Starr Judd (of Lahey Clinic and of Mayo Clinic, respectively) who represented large clinics with no immediate connection to an undergraduate medical school. The three-page letter to his contemporaries detailed the discussions between himself and the regents on each point he had raised.[11] In December Graham wrote to Martin restating his basic position: "I am arguing for a satisfactory representation of the men of my generation in the formation of policies and in some of the control of the College."[12] Martin, always sensitive to attacks on the ACS and to the possibility that criticism could be aimed at him, turned to Allen Kanavel for an opinion as to how he should respond. Kanavel replied: "I am delighted with Graham's letter. He has stated the case as fairly as anyone could.... I think we would be lacking in good judgement if we fail to meet him on his own grounds, without malice and without losing our own poise.... we must recognize that the men in the group he represents are important in the future if we only do not lose our heads and antagonize them. Graham is worth winning since he will probably be the strongest man in surgery ten years from now."[1]

The regents accepted Kanavel's temperate approach to Graham's concerns, and, on June 10, 1934, Samuel Harvey (of New Haven), Evarts Graham (of St. Louis), Alton Ochsner (of New Orleans), Dallas Phemister (of Chicago), and Erwin Schmidt (of Milwaukee) met with the board of regents for a free discussion of Graham's criticisms of the ACS. Kanavel felt that most of the criticisms were due to the fact that the critics did not know what the ACS was really doing. Graham repeated his arguments for and insisted upon an addition to the board of regents of three or four members from the group of younger surgeons. Later that year Sam Harvey was elected to the board as the first Young Turk to obtain a seat on the Supreme Court of Surgery.[1] Sixty years later, 80 percent of the regents were important academics, and between 1980 and 2000, 18 presidents of the ACS were academic chiefs of national and international stature.

Following the admission of the Founders' Group in 1913 to 1915, discussions continued to arise regarding requirements to be placed on applicants for fellowship. Organized residency programs were not available at that time, and to demand more than a rotating internship and 2 years of surgical apprenticeship would have markedly reduced the number of eligible applicants. Following World War I, a few prominent surgeons had acolytes for 2, 3 or 4 years; many of these were graduates of Halsted's department at Johns Hopkins. By the mid-1920s, an organized progressive residency training involving the services of a group of teachers, a yearly accrual of residents with a planned discharge, was limited to Halsted's service at Johns Hopkins, the Mayo Clinic, and Graham's service at Barnes Hospital. Perhaps interests of the ACS in graduate education should have been more forceful to ensure that facilities for residency education were developed, but the fact that this was not done was "probably based on a lack of awareness rather than the thought of keeping standards low so as to develop a large membership."[13]

By 1930 the issues of education and qualification for fellowship had become very heated, and in 1931 a special subcommittee composed of Drs. Elliot Cutler (of Harvard University), George Heuer (of Cornell University), and Allen O. Whipple (of Columbia University)—members of the ACS Committee on Undergraduate, Graduate and Postgraduate Education—were appointed by the regents to study the teaching of surgery. They were scheduled to give a three-part report at the regents' meeting in October 1933 but were refused the floor. The three men, shocked and angered, threatened to resign from the ACS, feeling that a lack of interest in or support for the subject was responsible for the last minute cancellation. They failed to recognize, first, that the interest of the ACS in education was chiefly toward the practicing surgeon, not the undergraduate or resident trainee, and, second, that at this meeting the regents were preoccupied with Graham's presentation of the criticisms stemming from his letter to the 20 surgeons. Somehow the regents had failed to recognize that improving surgical education was the ultimate route whereby the standards of surgery would be raised; it could not be accomplished by merely changing ACS eligibility requirements, something always within their purview.

The failure on the part of the regents to hear the panel of the three men effectively closed the window of opportunity for the ACS to play the major role in establishing standards of surgical competence. The venue was moved from the American College of Surgeons to the American Surgical Association.

THREE AMERICAN SURGICAL BOARDS

Three months after his October rejection by the regents, Cutler wrote to Graham to suggest that their presentation be given at a meeting of the American Surgical Association, with a preamble stating that the ASA was the only surgical organization of sufficient size and importance before which such a paper could be given since the ACS refused such papers and was not interested in education of the surgeon.[14] Although Cutler's recommendation for an inflammatory preamble was rejected, the educational panel that had been prepared for the ACS in 1933 was presented at the April 1935 meeting of the ASA. It followed a timely presidential address entitled "Higher Degrees in the Profession of Surgery," in which Edward Archibald of McGill reviewed the post–medical school activities of England, Germany, Australasia, Canada, and the United States. He observed that the ACS had been organized to upgrade the quality of American surgery, and that, as an educational body, it had been remarkably effective, even though (probably rightly for its times) it had not wished to make admission standards so stringent as to exclude a large body of surgeons.[15] At that time ACS membership required a medical degree, 1 year's internship (rotating), and 2 years as a surgical assistant.

In the subsequent panel presentation, Elliot Cutler reviewed the undergraduate teaching of surgery in the medical schools of the United States and Canada. He was followed by George Heuer who reviewed the graduate teaching of surgery in university clinics. Heuer noted that, in the previous 35 years, although the residency system had spread to 39 of 59 medical schools, 20 schools offered no graduate instruction at all and that, of the 39, six offered less than 3 years of instruction. Heuer suggested that all grade A medical schools be encouraged to adopt graduate teaching as a part of their educational program. Allen O. Whipple then reviewed the situation in nonuniversity hospitals, speculating that postgraduate teaching might well be done in some of these large institutions, with a system of 3 to 5 years of graduate training, under supervision, independent of whether or not a degree would be granted.[16]

The discussion that followed the presentation was summarized by Evarts Graham: "I think this is a momentous occasion for the American Surgical Association."[15] He described what he thought should be the minimum requirements for the training of a surgeon in order to protect the public, the profession, and the hospital, and to eliminate surgery being done by incompetents, and he stated his hopes: "Now something will be done about the whole matter. . . . The remarks made this morning, are excellent . . . yet nothing has ever come . . . in regard to the most important matter of establishing proper standards of qualification for those permitted to practice surgery. . . . I shall therefore Mr. President, propose that you, Sir, appoint a standing committee of this association to report next year and . . . study the question of the proper qualifications of the surgeon in order that something may be done about it instead of merely a reiteration of discussion."[15] Roy McClure of Detroit supported the idea and, at the subsequent business meeting, in time-honored tradition, Graham—who had complained and made the proposal—was appointed chairman of the Committee on the Elevation of Surgical Standards[h].

In his opening address, Archibald had pointed out weaknesses in the requirements for fellowship in the American College of Surgeons, and he had suggested that there be established a board of examiners that would create a strict examination in the fundamental principals and practice of surgery. In his presidential address to the ASA 13 years earlier, J.M.T. Finney had made a similar suggestion without avail, but times had changed. Through his motion, Evarts Graham led the American Surgical Association, as the teachers of surgery, to a duty and a responsibility to become active in improving the training of surgeons. Although the committee had been established to study surgical standards and to report back the following year, Graham turned his study committee into a working group with a defined goal—the creation of a qualifying board that was national in scope.

Graham's introduction to physician evaluation had come through the National Board of Medical Examiners (NBME), an organization dealing with medical students. In 1924 he began a 20-year stint as chief examiner for St. Louis, one of 11 National Board centers that conducted the Part III examination, consisting of a 1-day practical bedside oral examination that involved the candidate, the examiner, and a patient. Four years later, succeeding J.M.T. Finney (his colleague and mentor from World War I), Graham began a 6-year term as a member of the board.[17] When his membership ended in October 1934, Graham was succeeded by Dallas Phemister. The experiences Graham gained with these contacts became significant in his plans to establish something similar for the evaluation of surgical trainees, using both written and practical oral examinations. His years with the NBME saw the beginning of his friendship with J. Stewart Rodman[i], the medical secretary for The National Board. A few years later, Rodman became a colleague in the founding of the American Board of Surgery (ABS), and its first Secretary.[18]

---

h. American Surgical Association Committee on the Elevation of Surgical Standards: Edward W. Archibald, Arthur W. Elting, Thomas M. Joyce, Thomas G. Orr, Allen O. Whipple, Evarts A. Graham (chairman).

i. J. Stewart Rodman (1883 to 1958), born in Abilene, Texas, received a doctor of medicine degree in 1906 from the Medico-Chirurigical College of Philadelphia, where his physician father was chairman of surgery. An internship in Pennsylvania Hospital was followed by a fellowship at the Mayo Clinic. Rodman Sr. was convinced of the need for one examining body that would permit successful candidates to practice anywhere in the United States, and the son became active in the formation of examining boards, parallel with his attempt to establish a surgical practice in Philadelphia, which never flourished. He became the founding secretary and treasurer of the National Board of Medical Examiners when it was established in 1915, and in 1933 the founding vice-president of the Advisory Board

Ten days after the ASA meeting, Graham wrote to his five ASA committee members: "You are of course familiar with the general dissatisfaction which exists with the existing qualification of Fellows by the American College of Surgeons. The ASA feels that there is an urgent need for the creation of some mechanism by which properly qualified surgeons can be certified to the public."[19] His letter contained a series of questions and a statement of his views opposing the ACS as the certifying body, for, even though Franklin Martin had died a few months earlier, Graham did not wish to see the authority for certification placed in the hands of a group beholden to the executive director of the ACS. His committee agreed that a more representative body than the ACS should receive this authority, and they planned that other surgical societies be enlisted in the organization of a certifying board and then represented in its final directorship.[19]

George Crile, chairman of the executive committee of the ACS, paid a special visit to St. Louis to persuade Graham that the ACS was the one organization that should assume the functions of the proposed certifying board. In opposing this suggestion, Graham warned Crile that the ACS would be out of step if it did not participate with other surgical organizations in the founding of an independent board. As a result of this conversation, they agreed that a meeting would be held in Chicago in October 1935 at the headquarters of the college, with men from the the American College of Surgeons, the American Surgical Association, and the surgical section of the American Medical Association (AMA).[19]

The ASA group arrived at the meeting forearmed with Evarts Graham's resolution proposing "that a...National Committee for the 'Elevation of the Standards of Surgery' composed of twenty-four members be formed for the purpose [and] it was hoped the American College of Surgeons would co-operate in the proposed endeavor."[20] The Committee was to be composed of six members each from the American College of Surgeons, the American Medical Association, and the American Surgical Association, as well as two each from the Western Surgical, the Southern Surgical, and the Pacific Coast Surgical Societies. The New England Surgical Society was excluded because of the time it required to appoint representatives. An acrimonious discussion followed, pitting the ACS against the joint forces of the ASA and the AMA. Representatives of the ACS stated that such a proposal seemed

---

of Medical Specialists. As a founder of the American Board of Surgery (and its first secretary until his retirement in 1953), he served as a dedicated, faithful, and hardworking officer, spending much of his time and effort on the road pursuing ABS activities. His attention to minute detail made him an ideal secretary, and, as professor of surgery at the Women's Medical College, he was noted for meticulous preparation and delivery of lectures. He became sufficiently prominent in Philadelphia to become president of the Philadelphia Academy of Surgery. His final years were plagued by a persistent duodenal ulcer, prostatic difficulties, and three heart attacks that finally led to his death. Rodman is buried in Valley Forge, Pennsylvania.

unnecessary since the college had long been interested in improving surgical standards, but since the majority favored the resolution, they agreed to support a proposed National Committee composed of the six organizations.

The initial, and only, meeting of the National Committee[j] was held on February 15 to 16, 1936, at the Palmer House in Chicago. Its first act was to appoint Evarts Graham as chairman, after which he appointed two working groups to report back to the main committee the following day. The first group, Committee A, headed by J. Stewart Rodman, proposed that a 13-member American Board of Surgery be organized and gave some general guidelines. This committee on organization, on which Graham served, suggested that any organization must be acceptable to the Advisory Board of Medical Specialties and that it be composed of members of the major surgical societies including the AMA[k]. It proposed a method for selecting a founders' group, and the means whereby others could be certified by examination.

Committee B, a committee on the training of surgeons, under Sam Harvey's direction, focused on hospital accreditation programs and reviewed residency training opportunities. It recommended that the ACS and the AMA should jointly form a council to define a program for the training of surgeons in properly qualified hospitals, and then set training standards to meet requirements set by the proposed American Board of Surgery. Harvey's committee emphasized the need for adequate laboratories, an adequate amount of clinical material, and a surgical staff interested in and capable of teaching.[21] Residency review committees and the Joint Commission for the Accreditation of Hospitals would become the instruments to carry out these recommendations. The most significant recommendation adopted at this meeting was that all standards for the proper training of surgeons should be subject to the approval of the American Board of Surgery.

After the National Committee approved the reports of its two subcommittees, the members departed to report to their societies of origin. Graham delivered its recommendations to the 1936 annual meeting of the ASA, presenting not only a plan for organizing the American Board of Surgery, but also plans for increasing

---

j. Members of the National Committee for the Elevation of the Standards of Surgery present at its first meeting: Arthur W. Elting, Thomas G. Orr, Evarts A. Graham, and Allen O. Whipple, from the ASA; Irwin Abell, Donald Guthrie, Samuel C. Harvey, and Donald H. Munroe, from the ACS; Brian King, Roy D. McClure, Fred W. Rankin, J. Stewart Rodman, and Hugh Trout, from the AMA; Erwin Schmidt and Reginald H. Jackson, from the Western Surgical Society; and Robert Payne and Mont Reid, from the Southern Surgical Society.

k. The initial composition of the ABS: Arthur W. Elting, Evarts A. Graham, Allen O. Whipple, from the ASA; Donald Guthrie, Erwin R. Schmidt, Harvey B. Stone, from the ACS; Howard M. Clute, Fred W. Rankin, J. Stewart Rodman, from the AMA; Philemon E. Truesdale, from the New England Surgical Society; Thomas M. Joyce, from the Pacific Coast Surgical Society; Robert L. Payne, from the Southern Surgical Society; and Thomas G. Orr, from the Western Surgical Society.

and improving the facilities for training young surgeons. On behalf of the National Committee, Graham expressed the hope that "this Association (ASA) in which the movement had started would express its approval of the Committee's recommendations."[22] After unanimously approving the report, Graham, Elting, and Whipple were nominated as the three ASA representatives. The other surgical societies also accepted the recommendations made by the National Committee, and all prepared to send representatives to the founding meeting of the proposed American Board of Surgery.[23] Through Graham's efforts, the way had been cleared to organize the American Board of Surgery, with approval from the largest national and sectional surgical societies.

The first organizational meeting of the American Board of Surgery was held on January 10, 1937, at the Palmer House in Chicago, with the 13 members in attendance. As its first order of business, the group elected E.A. Graham as chairman, A.O. Whipple as vice-chairman, and J. Stewart Rodman as secretary-treasurer. As an executive committee, the three were given the mandate to develop a constitution and bylaws.

Graham appointed J.S. Rodman, T.M. Joyce, R.L. Payne, F.W. Rankin, and E.R. Schmidt as the board's first examination committee. He received a report from A.O. Whipple regarding the matter of improving the training of young surgeons, and appointed Whipple, D.M. Chute, and D. Guthrie as a committee of three to solicit cooperation of the newly formed American Board of Surgery, the American College of Surgeons, and the AMA's Council on Medical Education and Hospitals in order to build on the report of Harvey's subcommittee (Committee B) of 2 years earlier.[24,25] Five weeks later, Graham and Whipple attended a meeting of the Advisory Board of Medical Specialties (ABMS)[l], presented their plans, and received approval for membership of the American Board of Surgery on the Advisory Board of Medical Specialties, thus giving the ABS official sanction as the certifying agency for surgery. This broad base of support was later to be significant in Graham's

---

l. The American Board of Medical Specialties is an organization of 24 approved medical specialty boards. Originating in Boston in March 1933, it was a voluntary organization, with Louis B. Wilson as its first president and J. Stewart Rodman its vice-president. It became officially incorporated and obtained a full-time staff in March 1961. It serves member boards by providing an opportunity to discuss common problems, giving advice, co-ordinating their work, and attempting to introduce and use professional standards for evaluation and certification. It operates as a confederation of individual specialty boards and does not interfere with the autonomy of any member board. On November 4, 1937, Evarts Graham was appointed by the Advisory Board to be one of its representatives to the Commission on Graduate Medical Education, a joint effort of the Advisory Board and the AMA Council on Medical Education and Hospitals. The commission was charged to determine the following: "how the problem in this field [training of specialists] can best be solved,... to formulate educational principles involved in graduate and post graduate medical training... and to draw up standards of training which are of help to the Council on Medical Education and Hospitals and other agencies."[26] This was tailor-

opposition to attempts made by the International College of Surgeons to create its own certifying board.[26,27] Four more organizational meetings were held during the following 12 months. In addition to serving on examination committees, the 13 directors of the American Board of Surgery met 23 times during the first 5 years— a testimony to the dedication of the busy surgeons.

From the outset, it was agreed that the ABS should consider a candidate's moral and ethical standing in the profession, and that everyone should know that the matter of fee splitting was of major concern. Its first information booklet contained the statement, "The Board, believing that the practice of fee splitting is pernicious, leading as it does to a trade in human life, will reserve the right to enquire particularly into any candidate's practice in regard to this question."[25] This position expanded the board's evaluation of a candidate from one of ensuring surgical competence to one of ensuring a candidate's moral and ethical integrity. This move was quintessential Graham.

At the initial meeting, Graham invited Dr. Vilray P. Blair, a plastic surgeon and close associate at Barnes Hospital, to discuss what recognition should be given to other specialties of surgery.[28,29] Although, by now, several surgeons with experience during World War I had become interested in the reconstruction of facial injuries, plastic surgery of the day was generally within the province of oral surgeons, dentists, gynecologists, rhinologists, otolaryngologists, ophthalmologists, and orthopedic and general surgeons, as well as beauty parlor operators and individually defined specialists with inadequate medical qualifications and little or no training in surgery. It was time to "clean up the act," and Blair believed that a close relationship with the American Board of General Surgery would be the proper channel for qualification in oral and plastic surgery. On June 14, 1937, a committee from the American Association of Plastic Surgeons (AAPS)[30] consisting of Vilray Blair, John Staige Davis, John M. Wheeler, and George Dorrance met with Evarts Graham at Blair's home on the bluffs overlooking the Missouri River, to organize the American Board of Plastic Surgery (ABPS). Without Graham's permission, Blair had placed Graham's name on the stationary prepared for this new American Board of Plastic Surgery, and, after Graham remonstrated, Blair apologized in writing: "I need what you are doing for us and the use of your name is not the least part of this help."[31]

---

made to Graham's interests, and a report was filed 2 years later. The following year on December 29, 1938, Graham represented the Advisory Board to the National Advisory Cancer Council. In 1970 the board enlarged its secretariat, increased its coordinating activities, and changed its name from the Advisory Board of Medical Specialties to the American Board of Medical Specialties. Its mission is to assist member boards in their certification of physician competence; to give assurance of quality education in knowledge, skills, and experience; and to provide information to the public and the profession on issues regarding specialization in medicine.

After the ABPS was formally organized in 1938, Blair sent a list of proposed founders to Graham in his role as chairman of the American Board of Surgery. Not all of the men on Blair's list were certified by the ABS; one was an ophthalmologist, and four were dentists. This forced a decision by the ABS that individuals who were not medical doctors might be certified by the Plastic Surgery Board, if each case had received a satisfactory review by the American Board of Surgery.[32] By 1940 it became apparent that the Plastic Surgery Board could not function as a subsidiary board, and, with Graham's support, it reorganized, received approval of the ABMS, and in May 1941 became an independent major specialty board.

At the January 1937 meeting of the American Board of Surgery, there was also a group from the American Association for Thoracic Surgery (AATS), which held discussions with the ABS. Carl Eggers made the AATS proposal that thoracic surgeons should qualify only after prior certification by the ABS, and that the thoracic board would be subsidiary to, and an affiliate of, the American Board of Surgery.[33] When the AATS was formed in 1917, not one member considered himself a specialist in thoracic surgery. Twenty years later, of its 160 members, 97 (61%) were general surgeons with a special interest in thoracic surgery; 34 had had some special training, but only 18 (11%) restricted their practice to the specialty. Evarts Graham considered himself a general surgeon with a special interest in thoracic surgery.

The proposal to create a thoracic surgery board was not met with uniform enthusiasm. Edward Churchill of Boston wrote: "The chief idea seems to be to stop some sanatorium superintendents from doing thoracoplasties.... a Board is not going to accomplish this.... there are not enough people to do the thoracoplasties anyway....how can anyone have the temerity to call himself a thoracic surgeon in these days? The chest is a busy place.... the neurosurgeons are after the sympathetic trunk, the abdominal surgeons after the stomach and spleen and fellows like Al Blalock and Bob Gross are playing with the heart."[33] Graham felt: "At the present time thoracic surgery is so new that opportunities for strict specialization are very few [and] the chief question which concerns us is whether or not the field of thoracic surgery should be regarded as another branch of surgery and...how much training in general surgery the thoracic surgeon should have and whether or not the thoracic surgeon should limit himself."[34]

Graham continued to perform intra-abdominal operations as long as he was surgically active, attempting major biliary procedures, resections of the pancreas, and abdominoperineal resections of the rectum. Initially he felt that the AATS should create a special examination for qualification in thoracic surgery, thus functioning in an auxiliary fashion to the American Board of Surgery, and should consider only those candidates who had previously received certification by the ABS. It was agreed that thoracic surgeons, for the time being, should be certified by the American Board of Surgery with an extra title, and, if the time should come for the creation of a board in thoracic surgery, that it would be subsidiary to and an affiliate of the American Board of Surgery. Evarts Graham accepted this position until 1946, when John Alexander encouraged him to reconsider an independent thoracic surgery board. One year later, with Graham's approval, the AATS decided to establish the American Board of Thoracic Surgery (ABTS). Graham became uncomfortable with the educational provisions that shortened a candidate's experience in general surgery, but the board was now in younger hands, many of them his own trainees, and, although he remained aloof from the thoracic board, he was not in opposition. Graham frequently corresponded with William Tuttle of Detroit, the ABTS secretary. Evarts Graham was issued the ABTS Certificate No. 3—after Eggers and Tuttle.

In April 1937 the second meeting of the American Board of Surgery was held. By this time it had received the approval of both the Advisory Board for Medical Specialties and the AMA Council on Medical Education and Hospitals. Only 20 months after the ASA committee was appointed, the American Board of Surgery had received approval from organized surgery as well as organized medicine—a remarkable accomplishment. Three hundred twenty-two invitations to the Founders' Group had been accepted, certificates had been designed, and Evarts Graham was awarded Certificate No. 1. During its first 2 years, the ABS received 1570 applications for membership via the Founders' Group; 938 were accepted, 103 were deferred, and 315 were declared ineligible. The remainder were held pending receipt of additional information.

The second subcommittee, Harvey's Committee B, had been charged to look at the means to increase facilities for the training of surgeons. The committee's report concluded that the ACS and the AMA should jointly form a council to organize and carry out a program that would evaluate the training of surgeons in properly qualified hospitals. Committee B had earlier recommended that educational standards should be set that would meet the requirements of the proposed ABS, and had acknowledged that it would be necessary to have careful and competent periodic surveys of hospitals, but it did not specify an organization to do so. The ACS Hospital Standardization Program that began in 1918 was now in full swing, surveying 3596 hospitals in 1938; the AMA was also surveying hospitals but with criteria established for hospital management and internship training, not for the practice of and training for surgery. Its list of hospitals was similar but not identical to that prepared by the ACS.

In 1938 graduate training for surgery was still rather informal and unstructured. As chairman, when the ABS set down the board's requirements for training, Graham noted that relatively few hospitals had an adequate system for residency training. He felt that, to be effective, a program should include an annual intake, graded promotions from the internship, and not less than 3 years devoted to surgery. The experience should be distinctly educational and not a means of supplying cheap assistance to staff members, and, in its later years, it should include the performance of major as well as minor operations under supervision, as well as independently. This was the pattern of Graham's service at Barnes Hospital. Graham felt that the large public charity hospitals should also have responsibilities for graduate education; in this way, a patient could, by his own educational value, repay to the community the debt he owed.[34,35]

In 1938 Fred Rankin wrote on behalf of the AMA Council on Medical Education and Hospitals to note that surgical "training and post graduate education is distinctly chaotic"; he also noted that the council had recently declared its intention to make a comprehensive study of all facets of graduate education. He pointed out that the Division of Surgery had concluded: "The weakest link in the chain of medical education is in post-graduate surgery. It is well nigh impossible under present conditions to provide operative instruction.... A man cannot perform passably or safely as an operator without considerable experience."[36]

Four years after Archibald's address, Graham reported to the American Surgical Association on the origin, development, and progress of the American Board of Surgery. By this time 1570 applications had been received for the Founders' Group, and 423 candidates had been examined, with a failure rate of 29.3 percent. Graham described three hurdles: first, scrutiny by the board concerning a candidate's previous training; second, personal observation of a candidate's performance in the operating room by a member of the board; and, third, a written (Part I) and oral (Part II) examination of the candidate. In observing the performance of candidates in the Part II examination, Graham praised their anatomy knowledge but felt, "in pathology ... they are astoundingly weak to a degree which is almost unbelievable." After describing some personal experiences with candidates he noted, "We who are teachers ... and conducting graduate training in surgery ... must have a course of training with sufficient experience in gross pathology....I would not have thought it possible that young surgeons who otherwise have obtained a pretty good training could have been so deficient in one of the fundamental features of surgery, namely, pathology." Graham ended the report by describing the hard-working nature of membership on a board that met three times a year for periods of 3 or 4 days, noting: "Those of us who are ordinarily actively walking around and standing on our feet feel it a hard task to sit down for so long a period of time."[37]

Graham's term as an ABS board member expired in 1941. Having organized the board and served as chairman for 4 years, he felt he should not continue, even though, several months earlier, the board had unanimously voted that he serve for at least another year. Fred Coller of Ann Arbor, Michigan, succeeded him as a member of the board, and Allen O. Whipple became its chairman.

In his final address to the board, Graham stated that he hoped the organization would seek out young surgeons to serve as its members, for if it became an "Old Boys' Club," it would suffer the usual problems associated with older people not understanding the viewpoints and attitudes of the young. He indicated his hope that the constitution of the American Board of Surgery would not become so strong and inflexible that the board would be unable to respond to changing times.[24] It was another example of futuristic thinking from someone with leadership talents and devotion to a cause that was felt to be worthwhile.[25]

THE JOINT COMMISSION

Thoughts about inspection and accreditation of hospitals were in the minds of many surgeons at the inception of the Clinical Congresses that antedated creation of the ACS. As president of the 1912 congress, Dr. Edward Martin of Philadelphia had asked Allen Kanavel of Chicago to present a resolution to the members that "some system of standardization of hospital equipment and hospital work be developed"; he subsequently appointed a committee[m] to study its feasibility. The efforts of Edward Martin and Allen Kanavel made hospital standardization one of the original projects of Franklin Martin's American College of Surgeons, but within 3 years it was realized that hospital records were so poor that 60 percent of otherwise acceptable applicants for fellowship had been rejected because of inadequate hospital record keeping. The American Hospital Association (AHA), after being solicited for involvement in a hospital standardization program, offered cooperation but no financial support. The ACS director, John G. Bowman, then approached the AMA's representative, Arthur Dean Bevan, for help. However, the AMA, likewise, found the enterprise too daunting, and the ACS was forced to accept the obligation by itself. A committee on standards composed of 21 fellows of the college was formed, the Carnegie Foundation of New York provided $30,000, and in December 1917 the ACS Voluntary Hospital Standardization Program was launched. Upon application, hospitals were to be visited, reviewed, and possibly accredited. One thousand trial visits were planned for the year starting in April 1918, and the results of these field trials were presented by Bowman to a conference on hospital standardization held in New York on October 24, 1919. Bowman reported that 692 hospitals with 100 or more beds had been surveyed, but only 89 had met the standards. The numbers were made public, but to keep the list of surveyed hospitals from the press, all copies of the report that contained hospital names were fed into the furnace of the Waldorf-Astoria Hotel at midnight. Some of the most prestigious hospitals in the country had failed to meet the basic standards.[38] Following these field trials, the ACS Board of Regents listed some factors it considered essential to the proper care and treatment of patients, and it adopted five standards that became collectively known as the

---

m. Members of the standardization committee: Ernest A. Codman, chairman; Walter W. Chipman; John J. Clark; Allen B. Kanavel; William J. Mayo.

"Minimum Standard"[n]. Five years later Franklin Martin wrote: "The Minimum Standard has become to hospital betterment what the Sermon on the Mount is to a great religion."[1] Twenty years later the ACS was surveying 3600 hospitals annually, of whom 74 percent received approval.[39]

In 1949 the AMA received a resolution sponsored by its Section on General Practice that it should assume complete authority for medical student education and for hospital standards, and become the agency to set standards for intern and resident training. The AMA eliminated hospital standards from the resolution, commended the ACS for its prior 30 years work in this area, and accepted the remainder. Some months later the ACS began to rethink its role in the Hospital Standardization Program, for by 1950 the program cost the college $2 million annually, money drawn almost solely from dues paid by the fellows. In March 1950, when Paul Hawley[o] became the ACS's executive director, he faced the prospect of deficit financing unless the college could shed a major financial load—the largest of which was its Hospital Standardization Program. Hawley approached George Bugbee, executive director of the American Hospital Association, and the two tentatively agreed to transfer the ACS Standardization Program to the AHA, in return for an AHA guarantee to provide adequate funds by increasing dues. The agreement was to be consummated at the September 1950 meeting of the AHA.

Although these negotiations were thought to be confidential, trustees of the AMA became aware of them and, fearful of domination by hospital directors, appointed a committee to meet with Hawley as soon as possible. In August 1950 Elmer Hess, the AMA president, and six others met with Hawley and four regents

---

n. Abbreviated version of the Minimum Standard:

1. Physicians are to be organized as a staff.
2. The medical staff is restricted to graduates with medical degrees, with ethical standards that prohibit fee splitting.
3. The medical staff is to adopt a set of rules, regulations, and procedures, and to review clinical activities.
4. Accurate and complete records are to be developed and filed.
5. Facilities including the clinical laboratory and radiography department, are to be under competent supervision.

o. Paul Ramsey Hawley (1891 to 1965) was born at West College Corner, Indiana. He obtained a bachelor of arts degree in Indiana, and a doctor of medicine degree from the University of Cincinnati in 1914. He became an intern and house physician at Cincinnati General Hospital before World War I, and, after serving as a regimental surgeon, chose the army as his career. Between the two wars, he received a doctor of public health degree from Johns Hopkins; attended the Army Medical School, the Army War College, and the Command and Staff School of the Army; and held various military posts at home and abroad. In the summer of 1941 he was sent to England as a special observer, became the army's chief surgeon in the British Isles, and later became its chief surgeon in the European Theater, with offers to support the ACS program with adequate financing or to take it over. The AMA was unenthusiastic about suggestions for a cooperative plan that would include the AHA. The AMA representatives reiterated their position: the professional staffs of hospitals must not be placed under the control of hospital administrators.[40] Subsequent to this meeting, the ACS regents decided to explore methods that might include the AMA in some arrangement. Becoming aware of these moves, the trustees of AHA expressed dismay over the failure of the ACS regents to adopt the tentative proposal that had been prepared by Hawley and Bugbee. They proposed to establish a standardization program of their own and in September 1950 adopted a resolution to that effect. The impasse between the AMA and AHA continued throughout the fall. At its October meeting, the ACS regents declared that the college would continue with its Hospital Standardization Program, but this did not preclude consideration of proposals for the participation of other interested agencies.

Another element further confounding the issue at this time was a clause in the Hill-Burton Hospital Construction Act that stated that all Hill-Burton hospitals would be expected to meet the requirements necessary for ACS approval. Having originally demanded at least a 50-percent membership on any accreditation board, the AHA was now willing to consider a proportional representation of less than one-half, and it was moving tentatively to one-third. After acknowledging the pioneer efforts and success of the ACS program, the AMA indicated it was anxious to unite with the ACS against hospital administrators, whom they considered a common enemy. The fellowship of the ACS became disturbed by all of the discord, and

---

where he oversaw 203,000 hospital beds and 250,000 officers and men. Hawley rose to the rank of major general and was honored by five countries for his World War II activities. He belonged to medical and surgical associations within the United States and Britain. After retiring from the army in June 1946, he spent 18 months as chief medical director of the Veterans Administration (VA); he then became chief executive officer of the Blue Cross and Blue Shield Commissions. From 1950 to 1961, as director of the American College of Surgeons, he guided the college through turbulent post-war years.

While with the VA, Hawley promoted an association—Deans Committee Hospitals—between medical schools and Veterans Hospitals that would elevate the medical care of veterans; at the same time, he released the VA medical staff from its constraining bureaucracy. Becoming executive director of the ACS and being faced with a significant deficit due to its Hospital Standardization Program, he and Graham guided the college to the development of the Joint Commission for the Accreditation of Hospitals. He took a firm stand on fee splitting and the nature and development of graduate training, and he was instrumental in forming the International Federation of Surgical Colleges.

A stocky, well-built man with a round face, Hawley was jovial, polished, and extremely successful in interpersonal dealings. After some initial concerns regarding his military background, he achieved the highest respect of the board of regents, and all of those with whom he worked came to depend on his wisdom and judgments in regard to position and timing. He received seven honorary degrees, became an honorary member of 11 societies, and after retirement, lived in Maryland. Hawley died in 1965 and was buried in Arlington Cemetery.

indicated to the regents a desire that the college should continue with its program and control it single-handedly. A request to the 8000 fellows to contribute to a special fund for this purpose obtained only $19,700, a response that did not auger long-term success.[41] Despite this, the regents hoped that they could continue to finance the program, and they believed it would be wise to break off all discussions since the AHA and the AMA had created a stalemate due to their uncompromising attitudes. The Hospital Association wished to cooperate with the College of Surgeons but not with the Medical Association, and the Medical Association would not accept a program dominated by the Hospital Association.

At this time Evarts Graham was vice-chairman of the board of regents, and, in summarizing the situation, he identified three possible solutions:

1. The American College of Surgeons could continue its highly successful program and secure financial assistance on its own initiative or accept some from the AMA, but the AMA's demand for majority control was something impossible for the ACS to accept.
2. The program could be financed and administered by the American Hospital Association, with the professional standards aspect of the program controlled by the two medical organizations. The AMA was adamantly opposed to this plan because it put hospital administrators in control.
3. As the third option, Graham proposed that an independent commission be established, one that would be financed by contributions from each participating organization and be composed of representatives from each. The commission would administer its affairs independently. Corporate members of the commission would be the participating organizations, each of whom would be represented by appointees of its own choice, and the Canadian Medical Association (CMA) would be invited to become a member.

Although each organization had its own agenda, Graham's third proposal was acceptable to them;[1] it was a solution not unlike that which had led to the formation of the American Board of Surgery. The regents of the ACS appointed a subcommittee to establish a plan to provide representation by several agencies on a joint commission. It was finally agreed that the AMA and the AHA would have six representatives each, the ACS and the American College of Physicians (ACP) would have three each, and the Canadian Medical Association would have one. Hawley and Bugbee wrote a charter and bylaws for the commission, and by April 1951 the ACS, the ACP, and the AHA had approved them. The AMA, however, was not quite ready, for the American Academy of General Practice wished to have its own participating membership on the commission, rather than be represented by the AMA. The AMA finally acknowledged its own independent and sole role, denying the wishes of a general practice group that was desirous of performing surgery without special training or certification. By September 16, 1951, all four agencies—ACS, ACP, AMA, and AHA—had approved Graham's proposal, and the Joint Commission on Accreditation of Hospitals (JCAH) was incorporated and chartered in the State of Illinois. By March 1952 the JCAH was formally organized, with Evarts Graham of St. Louis, Arthur Allen of Boston, and Newell Philpott of Montreal representing the American College of Surgeons. Headquarters for the commission were on ACS property at 660 Rush Street, Chicago.

From the outset, accreditation was and continues to be voluntary on the part of all facilities, initially accredited by the ACS, then by the JCAH, and now by the JCAHO. In 1965, when Medicare was enacted, it used JCAH standards for hospitals as those necessary for the treating of Medicare patients.[42]

Transfer of the standardization program from the ACS took place after the commission agreed to accept the college's list of approved hospitals as its initial roster. The final (35th) list of ACS approved hospitals turned over to the Joint Commission showed that 3265 of 4111 hospitals housing more than 25 beds in the United States and Canada had met the Minimum Standard.

Formal transfer of the Hospital Standardization Program from the American College of Surgeons to the Joint Commission took place on December 6, 1952, in the J.B. Murphy Auditorium of the college. Dr. Hawley acknowledged the occasion as being of salient importance to all hospitals, second only to the inauguration of the ACS program 35 years earlier. Evarts Graham, as chairman of the board of regents, presided over the day's program and officially conveyed the ACS Hospital Standardization Program to the Joint Commission on Accreditation of Hospitals. In his speech Graham reflected on Allen Kanavel and his resolution of November 15, 1912. He referred to Bowman's report to the regents at the Waldorf-Astoria Hotel in New York in 1919, and to the burning of the files, noting: "The Regents decided...that if such shocking conditions in the report were disclosed the best thing would be to destroy the evidence in order not to weaken the confidence of the public in its hospitals."[42] He then stated:

> One of the most outstanding developments in the hospital world in recent years has been the recognition of an extension of the functions of the hospital. It is no longer merely a place for the sick to be treated. In its new place it is acting as the health center of the community from which radiate all the health activities. Medical schools could not exist without teaching hospitals. Nor could the education of nurses and paramedical personnel be carried out without their assistance.... The development of modern surgery put unusual temptations in the way of those whose backbones were none too rigid. At the turn of the century the pernicious custom of fee splitting and the use of other dishonest surgical practices reared their ugly heads.... we can all be

proud however that from its beginning the College has taken a firm stand against the dishonest practices of surgery.... it is to be hoped that the formation of this joint body will not result in any relaxation in the endeavor to protect the patient from dishonesty.[42]

Then, turning to Dr. Gunnar Gunderson, Graham stated:

It is a happy moment for me, the Chairman of the Board of Regents of the American College of Surgeons to turn over to you the Chairman of the Joint Commission on Accreditation of Hospitals this program of Hospital Standardization which for nearly a third of a century has been the child of the organization which I represent.... We hope that in the years to come the standards of the hospitals of North America will ever remain high.... May those hospitals realize to their utmost abilities their important responsibilities not only in the care of the sick but in the educational activities which are a function of every hospital.[42]

Dr. Gunderson, on behalf of the Joint Commission, accepted the program by acknowledging that it presented "a tremendous challenge to all who served the American public."[42]

At this time Dr. Hawley introduced Dr. Edwin L. Crosby, the newly appointed executive director of the Joint Commission, who introduced the Honorable Lister Hill, a United States senator from Alabama, and coauthor of the Hill-Burton Hospital Construction Act. In his speech of the day, Hill noted: "Within our generation the hospital has evolved from a refuge for the dying to a necessity for the living.... No longer do people fear hospitals." He commented on the unselfish services of the American College of Surgeons and noted: "How great is the power over hospitals that lies in the administration of the program. The American College of Surgeons has never usurped this power in its own interest; rather it has used it again and again in the interest of the public.... it has set an inspiring example.... it merits our tribute today."[43]

Four members[p] of the Corporation of the Joint Commission on Accreditation of Hospitals first met at the Drake Hotel in Chicago on December 15, 1951. Evarts Graham called the meeting to order at 10:30 am to adopt amendments to the bylaws that would permit Canadian membership.[44] That first meeting of the corporation lasted only 15 minutes and was immediately followed by a meeting of the 20 initial

p. Members at the first meeting of the Joint Commission: Evarts A. Graham, acting chairman, from the ACS; Gunnar Gunderson, from the AMA; Anthony J.J. Rourke, from the AHA; Leroy H. Sloan, from the ACP.

commissioners. Again, Evarts Graham called the meeting to order, briefly outlining the negotiations that had led to the establishment of the Joint Commission, and he predicted that December 15, 1951, would be remembered as a date that was an important milestone in the development of health services for the American people.

Starting small, in 1920 there had been seven visitors in the field to carry the message of minimum standards to the hospitals of the United States and Canada, in a voluntary program. Seventy years later, the Hospital Standardization Program had accredited 5000 of 6500 hospitals, had accredited 2800 other health care facilities, and had became the Joint Commission on Accreditation of Health Care Organizations.[3]

Graham served 4 years as a member of the commission. His major contribution was the breaking of the deadlock between the AMA and AHA. During 1952 to 1953, he served on a three-man special committee set up to look at the formation of Departments of General Practice within the hospital staff structure, an arrangement that he opposed for fear that general practitioners would acquire surgical privileges.[45] On April 18, 1953, the subcommittee recommended that the Manual of Hospital Accreditation direct that, if established, a Department of General Practice should be responsible for administration and education and not be a clinical service. Patients would be admitted only to the established clinical services, but general practitioners could have privileges given upon recommendation of the clinical service chief.[46] This satisfied the ever-vigilant Evarts Graham, who wrote to Dr. A.J.J. Rourke of the AHA about his concerns regarding the growing influence and importance of the Academy of General Practice: "I have spent my life, more or less, in an effort to protect the public from bad surgery... very few of the general practitioners have experience or training yet they are becoming more and more ambitious... to undertake a surgery which is beyond their ability...."[47]

Graham's appointment to the commission terminated abruptly, with a few terse letters between him and I.S. Ravdin, chairman of the ACS Board of Regents. In November 1955 Graham had written to Ravdin questioning his own tenure on the commission. The regents accepted this as a resignation from an unfilled term and immediately appointed Walter McKenzie of Edmonton.[48] Graham responded: "As far as I know I have never resigned.... how can he fill my unexpired term?... it is an ... occasion for the Board of Regents to regret.... the matter is so confused and involved... the only way out is to consider that I did resign.... I am sorry to bring up an unpleasant matter like this.... nevertheless I must get the whole thing straightened out so that I will know where I stand."[49]

Although he had been a dutiful commissioner during those years, Graham now found that research on smoking and lung cancer was intellectually more exciting, and his activity on the President's Commission on Health Needs of the Nation more stimulating. Having left his mark on the upgrading of hospital standards, he turned his attention elsewhere.

FEE SPLITTING: THE AMERICAN COLLEGE OF SURGEONS VERSUS THE AMERICAN MEDICAL ASSOCIATION

The fee splitting that Graham had encountered in Mason City continued to plague him throughout his professional life. Fee splitting in Iowa had occupied an inordinate amount of time at the very first meeting of the board of regents, and 40 years later it was still there. In March 1952 the Iowa State Medical Society took the position that joint billing was acceptable and should not be considered fee splitting, thus legalizing a position diametrically opposite to that held by the American College of Surgeons.

The ACS responded by deciding not to recognize any candidate from Iowa except full-time members of the University of Iowa faculty, and, after demanding that every fellow of the ACS from Iowa undergo a financial audit, 200 fellows voluntarily submitted their finances. Then, during Graham's tenure as chairman of the board of regents, the issue moved out of the closed medical arena into the glare of newspaper and magazine publicity. At the 1952 Clinical Congress in New York City, a round-table conference between 13 representatives of the ACS and eight science writers discussed ethical problems of medical and surgical practice. Discussion of fee splitting led to a wide-ranging debate in which the regents discussed the evils of the practice, stating that it tended to exclude the young, well-trained, ethically conscientious surgeon from establishing a strictly surgical practice. It worked not only against the best interests of the patient but also against the ultimate benefit to the public that would be derived by elevating the quality of surgical training and improving the results of surgery.

During this meeting Dr. Loyal Davis, speaking as a regent of the ACS, stated that fee splitting was on the increase in Chicago, even though hospitals in Illinois had been pressured to eliminate from their staff physicians who were found guilty of the practice. Reports of the conference appeared in 338 newspapers, 36 of which had accompanying editorials. Within 5 weeks, 150 members of the Chicago Medical Society petitioned the society to expel Dr. Davis, and pressured the Illinois Medical Society to institute similar action. The AMA became involved, held its own hearings, and in late 1952 reaffirmed its policy statement against fee splitting.[50] No punitive action was taken against Loyal Davis.

Upon hearing of Davis's allegations, the editors of *U.S. News and World Report* requested an interview with Paul Hawley, director of the ACS, to obtain background material on the topic. In an interview that was recorded and later published, Hawley discussed unethical practices in medicine and how they differed from legal ethics. He touched on fee splitting, unnecessary operations, selection of a qualified surgeon, the role of the family doctor, the rising standards of care in hospitals, the introduction of medical audits, and the aim of the entire medical profession to raise its level of patient care.[51] An unprecedented storm broke over

Hawley's head and around the American College of Surgeons. Eleven resolutions were introduced into the AMA House of Delegates at its New York meeting on June 1, 1953—all condemning both the ACS and Hawley. The AMA House of Delegates refused to pass any of these resolutions but very clearly stated that only they—the AMA—not the ACS, carried the sanction of the entire medical profession and regarded medical ethics as within their purview.

As chairman of the ACS Board of Regents, Graham, together with Hawley as executive director of the college, now became embroiled in media publicity and in a confrontation with the AMA regarding the ethical status of the entire medical profession. Graham decided to appoint a committee of three—Drs. Leland S. McKittrick, George V. Brindley, and Warren H. Cole—to meet with representatives of the AMA. Two meetings scheduled for mid-summer 1953 were postponed, and the first meeting was held on October 21 at the Drake Hotel in Chicago. Graham was present in his role as chairman of the board and as a keenly interested participant in the fee splitting issue.

In preparation for a second meeting planned for November, Graham outlined his thoughts in a three-page memorandum, highly critical of the AMA. He asked: "Does the AMA mean business in regard to fee splitting.... Have any members been expelled?" He noted the violence of the reaction against Hawley and suggested that components of the AMA did not want the existence of the practice to be made public, stating that he was "forced to the conclusion that the Trustees of the AMA are not interested in doing something positive to curb the unethical practice."[52] Graham felt that there should be an extensive publicity campaign, disciplinary action by the AMA against offenders, suspension of state medical societies such as the Iowa Society, and a concerted attempt to get state laws passed outlawing the practice.[52] He sent his thoughts to the three ACS members who subsequently attended the second meeting held at the Jefferson Hotel in St. Louis on November 27, 1953, where all agreed there were certain unethical practices that caused serious problems in the medical profession. After 4 hours they concluded that the situation was of importance, that something should be done, and the JCAH should be asked to join the effort. The ACS members drew up a definition of the four items discussed at the November meeting, and, on February 22, 1954, presented them to an AMA committee:

1. An *unjustified operation* is one in which either the indications were inadequate or the procedure was one which is contrary to generally accepted surgical practice.
2. *Ghost surgery* is that surgery in which the patient is not informed of, or is misled as to, the identity of the operating surgeon.
3. A *fee* is *excessive* when it is greater than the patient is reasonably able to pay or higher than justified by the service rendered.

4. *Fee splitting* is the refunding of any portion of the total fee for the care of a patient to either the surgeon or the referring physician. Moreover, when the surgeon or the referring physician submit [*sic*] a joint bill, itemized or un-itemized, it shall be interpreted as fee splitting according to the principles stated by the judicial council and approved by the house of delegates of the American Medical Association in December 1952.[1]

Graham did not attend the February meeting in Washington, DC, but Hawley reported to Graham that the definitions of ghost surgery, unjustified surgery, and exorbitant fees were adopted. However, the AMA refused to accept the definition of fee splitting and threatened to change their code of ethics to permit the practice. The meeting was adjourned without agreement as to future meetings. Hawley expressed to Graham that he had "great concern for the future of medicine in the country under the current AMA leadership….coupled with bad public relations… for not supporting us [it] will be enough to destroy completely the confidence of the public."[53] He concluded: "I am very very glad you were not here. You would surely have blown your top and the meeting would have ended in a grand free-for-all instead of upon a note of restrained hostility."[53]

The AMA House of Delegates subsequently restated its 1952 position condemning the splitting of fees, but the issue continued to simmer for the next many years, bringing the two organizations into continuous minor confrontation. Throughout this period, "Evarts Graham [as] a dynamic representative of the College vigorously championed the policy that the College should take the lead in presenting to the public the case against unethical practices in the medical profession. …Graham was aggressive and impatient with other medical organizations… that felt it was against the best interests of the profession to wash dirty linen in public. …He was equally antagonistic to any movement or belief which he thought tended to lower the standards of surgical care."[1]

THE AMERICAN COLLEGE OF SURGEONS AND SURGICAL FORUMS

At the second meeting of the Society of University Surgeons, in February 1940, Owen Wangensteen presented ideas on the dissemination of knowledge acquired through research, and then later wrote, "Societies will do well to lend serious consideration to the matter of the establishment of a surgical forum before which the best that is new in surgery each year may be presented."[54] As an honorary founding member of the society, Evarts Graham heard the call and, in his role as president-elect of the American College of Surgeons, arranged for Wangensteen to present his proposal to the regents at their June meeting.

The 16 regents were competent practical surgeons, but the majority disagreed with Wangensteen's idea, believing it could neither succeed nor hold an audience that was used to hearing experts speak. Four months later, at the October meeting held in conjunction with the Clinical Congress, Graham was inducted as president and arranged for Wangensteen to once again speak to the regents. This time the presentation was modified by the suggestion that his proposal be given a 1-year trial. With Graham's leadership, strongly supported by Dallas Phemister, this was an acceptable compromise, and a forum committee, with Wangensteen as its chairman, made plans for a surgical forum to be held in conjunction with the Clinical Congress the following year.

The first surgical forum held in Boston in 1941 consisted of three sessions of 3 hours each. The innovation was a success, for, in a national meeting place, young aspiring surgeons could now give expression to their scientific work. Its reception led Wangensteen to write: "A new flavor was added to the annual meeting. . . . there was a stir of excitement in the atmosphere which was communicated from listener to listener in the audience as sincere, keen and eager young men came successively to the platform to unravel their skein of thought upon subjects of current and material interest."[55] Presiding over that first forum was the forum committee: Evarts Graham, Owen Wangensteen, Frederick Coller, Alexander Brunschweig, and Michael Mason.[56]

Eight years later, on October 10 to 15, 1949, the Surgical Congress of the International Society of Surgery (ISS)[q] was held in New Orleans, with the last 2 days reserved for an American program whose content was delegated to Evarts Graham. He wrote to all American members suggesting that there be about 21 papers of the newer work for which American surgery had become well known: "It would be a good idea to acquaint members with our American custom of inviting non-members to participate."[57]

The trial was moderately successful but was not again attempted until Graham became president of the 16th Congress of the ISS, 6 years later. In preparation for its 1955 meeting in Copenhagen, Graham sent a letter to all members explaining

---

q. The International Society of Surgery was founded in Brussels by the Belgium Surgical Society on September 9, 1902. Under the auspices of the Belgium government, it had an international organizing committee consisting of representatives of the leading surgical societies, academies, and faculties of the Western medical world. The society was organized into national chapters and held a Clinical Congress every 3 years in one of its member countries. Its First International Congress, held in Brussels in November 1905, had 700 attendees. The secretariat remained in Brussels until 1979, at which time it was moved to Basel, Switzerland, under the sponsorship of Martin Allgöwer.

In 1954, when Graham began his communications with Leo Dejardin, secretary general, irregularities with some of the travel procedures and perquisites were becoming apparent. Officers of the organization had been taking advantage of a travel agency to such an extent that Graham instituted

the nature and purposes of a forum, and invited them to solicit the interest of young investigators. One hundred one requests for places on the program were received, 80 were accepted, and four sessions were held during the last 2 days of the meeting. "The part of the program which attracted the greatest interest was the Surgical Forum.... The Congress at Copenhagen was the first at which any real emphasis was placed on the importance of allowing young men, not members of the Society, to give short reports."[58] Attendance was large at all sessions, and the concept of a surgical forum for young investigators was introduced to Europe.[58] Graham had written to Leo Dejardin, secretary of the ISS, attempting to explain the difference between American ideas and European ideas in the construction of a program: "We do not select a topic and then invite people to speak on the topic. Instead, members of the [American Surgical] Association write...if they wish to be on the program, abstracts are submitted...and the final program consists of a miscellaneous presentation of topics...although it may happen that two or three papers are on the same subject.... We always encouraged young investigators who were not yet members of elite surgical societies."[59]

During his last year of life, Graham wrote to Wangensteen: "The creation of the Surgical Forum...has been one of the greatest things for the development of surgery through the stimulation of younger men that has ever happened.... One needs only to look around and see how many other organizations are imitating the Surgical Forum to realize the great success of the venture."[60]

Sixty-one years after it began, now named the Owen H. Wangensteen Surgical Forum, the forum has become a major feature of the ACS Clinical Congress, with 1500 authors having presented 360 papers.

---

a divorce of the secretariat and travel activities, requiring each individual to prepare his or her own itinerary and funding. It was later found that unpaid dues that were being carried as assets were creating a fiscal accounting imbalance not reflected at the bank. This impropriety led to its move from Brussels to Basel.

During the late 1930s and the early 1940s, the American chapter was dominated by Rudolph Matas and Elliott Cutler. The 1940 German occupation of Holland and Belgium precluded the use of Brussels as society headquarters, and a temporary arrangement was made with the American College of Surgeons to house the organization in its East Erie headquarters in Chicago. World War II created many difficulties, and there was a question as to whether the society would survive following the war. It became a "pet" society to Evarts Graham, who enjoyed its contacts and the honor of being a member—particularly the honor of being the president of the 1955 International Congress in Copenhagen, something that he relished and expressed in his voluminous correspondence with Leo Dejardin.

The American chapter of the ISS now consists of approximately 75 to 80 members, and its Clinical Congress every 3 years is marked by an emphasis on the meeting's social side and the culture of the country in which it is held.

THE AMERICAN SURGICAL ASSOCIATION

The American Surgical Association (ASA) was the inspiration of Samuel D. Gross (July 8, 1805 to May 6, 1884) of Philadelphia. Gross was a product of the sturdy, laborious Pennsylvania Dutch, who spoke both German and English, and at age 17 he began to study medicine as the pupil of a country practitioner. He graduated from Jefferson Medical College at 23, and, after years in Cincinatti and Louisville, during which he turned down several offers of chairs of surgery, he returned to Jefferson, where he subsequently founded the Philadelphia Academy of Surgery. He conceived of an American Surgical Association while attending the 1880 meeting of the American Medical Association in New York City, and he sent a letter, signed also by four other prominent surgeons, soliciting the cooperation of principal surgeons of the United States.

In his recollections Gross wrote of the need for consultation between surgeons: "Specialists have combined on their limited areas of observation. I desire to see the men who practice surgery in its truly comprehensive sense come together for consultation and social intercourse from every part of our great country—the men that represent the art of the nation.[61] Later he wrote: "I expect much from this association and it is proper here to add that it is an independent organization having no connection whatever with the American Medical Association. Its object is to foster surgical art, science, education and literature, to cultivate good feeling in the profession and to unite the prominent surgeons of the country in one harmonious body."[61]

Over the years, the association prospered. It continued to hold a two-and-one-half-day meeting containing papers frequently at the forefront of surgical endeavor. To be on the program was an honor, and its presidency was perhaps the most prestigious office in American surgery. Evarts Graham was elected to membership in 1920 and, after serving on the special committee that initiated the American Board of Surgery, was rewarded with the ASA presidency in 1937. Graham had his usual thoughts about changing the current state of the association, expecting to bring it up to date; this time he elected a conciliatory approach rather than a frontal attack, such as he had used with the ACS.

In 1938 Graham used the opportunity provided by his presidential address to express concerns about an organization that he felt was stodgy, old fashioned, and behind the times. He constructed a dialogue with Gross that was a mix of light humor and serious purpose, by inviting him to return from heaven via a radio beam. The two discussed the current expansion of surgery by the use of radiologic and chemical tests, the nature of surgical training, and the influence of surgical specialization. Gross commented: "Specialists might have run wild and pursued their specialties to the neglect of fundamentals if it had not been for the influence of the ASA." Graham was heavy-handed in his sarcasm about the association's failure to admit specialists, recommended an increase in membership, and commented that there was no clearly thought-out plan "as to what the purposes and functions of the Association should be in addition to providing a pleasant bit of social relaxation." He proposed a full 3-day meeting, sectional meetings, and a shortening of the time allocated for presentation. Gross agreed. Graham suggested changing the time of meetings since "June is the most inconvenient time of the year for teachers." Gross asked about a forum on surgical research that would attract young men, to which Graham responded that there was a need for a forum, "for the American College of Surgeons … has programs given almost entirely by well-known surgeons." He informed Gross of the newly formed American Board of Surgery and was vehement in his denial that the board would ask hospitals to appoint only board-certified surgeons to their staffs, stating "it is a privilege and an honor to have one of the certificates." Gross finally took his leave in order to "have a consultation with Galen about Hippocrates who had fallen coming home from a party and dislocated his halo."[61,62]

Elliot Cutler thanked Graham for his remarks and suggested the appointment of a committee to investigate a reorganization of the association. Arthur Elting, the incoming president, appointed Eugene Pool to head a committee that would explore and report back the following year on Graham's several suggestions. After circularizing all of the members, Pool received 45 responses. He reviewed the issues raised by Graham and printed an eight-page report suggesting the admission of younger members, specialty representation, a minimum of social activity, and the use of ASA influence to improve conditions in surgery.

Sixty years later the American Surgical Association remains much as it was in Graham's day. An exclusive society with 345 active, 530 senior, and 70 honorary members, it contains the surgical leaders of the United States and Canada, and holds an annual meeting with many social events added to the presentation of surgical research and clinical observations.

After its foray into the formation of the American Board of Surgery, the ASA remained aloof from the political and academic world until 1970 to 1975, when it participated in a national surgical manpower study conducted with the ACS, entitled the Study of the Surgical Services of the United States (SOSSUS).[61] The association remains a bastion of surgical conservatism, little changed from what it was when Graham attempted to introduce more openness.

THE INTERNATIONAL COLLEGE OF SURGEONS

The International College of Surgeons (ICS) was chartered in Geneva in May 1936, with its headquarters and secretariat in Brussels. It was covertly created by Max Thorek, a surgeon who, along with several Chicago colleagues, had been denied fellowship in the American College of Surgeons and membership in the International Society of Surgery. Drs. Thorek and John F. Pick, also of Chicago, attempted to

SCENES FROM THE GRAHAM
FAMILY PHOTOGRAPH ALBUM

The Bernard Becker Medical Library of the Washington
University School of Medicine is designated – BML

David Wilson Graham—father. (Courtesy of BML)

Ida Barned Graham—mother. (Courtesy of BML)

Captain Graham, US Army—1918. (Courtesy of BML)

Helen, David, and Evarts—1919. (Courtesy of BML)

With Barnes Hospital Surgery Staff—1920. (Courtesy of BML)

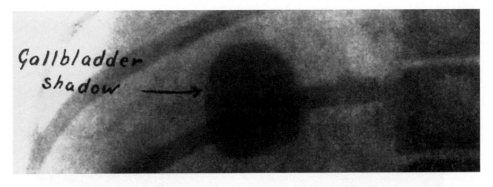

First cholecystogram as seen in a dog. (Reproduced with permission from Graham EA, Cole WH. Roentgenologic examination of the gall bladder. JAMA 1924;82:613.)

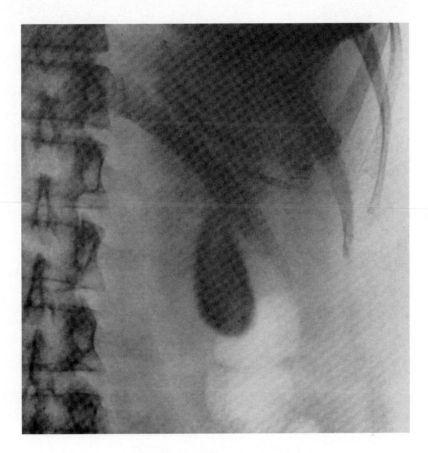

Normal cholecystogram in a human — 1925. (Courtesy of BML)

Circa 1925. (Courtesy of BML)

Atlantic City
MAY, 1925

With Sam Harvey—1925. (Courtesy of BML)

Circa 1930. (Courtesy of BML)

With Elliott Cutler and Harvey Cushing, circa 1933. (Courtesy of BML)

February 28, 1935.

Copher, Graham, Cole, Moore—1935. (Courtesy of BML)

Circa 1936. (Courtesy of BML)

American Board of Surgery—St. Louis, 1938. (Courtesy of BML)

Barnes Hospital—1919. (Courtesy of BML)

Children's Hospital, Barnes Hospital, Washington University—1950.
(Courtesy of BML)

A favorite pose in the Chest Clinic—1948.

With staff of the Chest Clinic—1950. (Courtesy of BML)

His favorite photograph—circa 1950. (Courtesy of BML)

With surgical resident staff—June 1951.

With Paul Hawley — 1951. (Courtesy of BML)

Circa 1952. (Courtesy of BML)

The Graham Medal—struck 1952. (Courtesy of BML)

In the smoking laboratory—1953. (Courtesy of Time/Life publications)

With Ada Hanvey—1953. (Courtesy of BML)

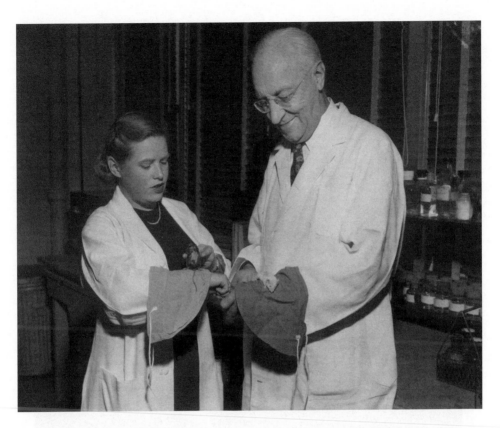

With Adele Croninger—1954. (Courtesy of BML)

Circa 1954. (Courtesy of BML)

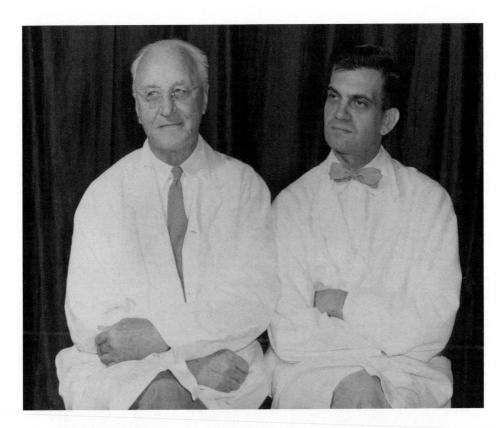

With Ernst Wynder—1954. (Courtesy of BML)

Circa 1955. (Courtesy of BML)

With James Gilmore—1955. (Courtesy of BML)

The last photograph—1957. (Courtesy of BML)

Helen Tredway Graham—circa 1958. (Courtesy of BML)

The home on the bluffs overlooking the Missouri River.

recruit prominent surgeons from around the world as founding members, and made many personal visits. Leopold Mayer of Brussels, secretary general of the International Society of Surgery, was one of those so visited, and Mayer informed Rudolph Matas of New Orleans about the visit. Matas, then president of the US chapter of the ISS, attempted to determine the nature and origins of the new college and, in so doing, uncovered the fact that Thorek was its founder. Matas and Cutler, secretary of the US chapter, wrote to the 44 ISS American members asking them to decline fellowship in what was seen as an unnecessary society.[1] Evarts Graham was one of the 44 members. Opposition to the International College by the International Society became intense and known worldwide; on May 8, 1936, the society adopted a six-point resolution decrying the new college.

Ten years later, in March 1946, the International College of Surgeons declared the existence of an International Board of Surgery (IBS). It awarded diplomas with a design similar to those of the established boards, and encouraged all members of the International College to consider themselves diplomats of the International Board of Surgery. This action, taken without the sanction of the Advisory Board for Medical Specialties, aroused the ire of the board of regents of the ACS, particularly Evarts Graham, who considered that such actions were not elevating the standard of surgery or reinforcing the qualifications for certification as a surgeon.

In 1951, 1 month after he became chairman of the board of regents, Graham appointed a committee of three to draft a resolution condemning board certification by the International College. The ACS Board of Regents, in passing Loyal Davis's nine-point resolution on December 3, 1951,[1,63] noted that standards fixed by the board of The International College of Surgeons were "not in accordance with generally accepted principles of education and training upon which competence in surgery was evaluated." The resolution deplored the establishment of certifying boards other than those approved by the Advisory Board for Medical Specialties, and regarded "such actions as constituting a menace" to the standards in the practice of surgery and to their further elevation.[1] The International College accepted general practitioners who performed some surgery—an anathema to Graham.

Graham began an almost personal crusade to eliminate the quasi–certification board of the International College of Surgeons. Within 1 month, Norman Littell, counsel for the International College, called Paul Hawley, the ACS director, to demand that the December 3 resolution be revoked. He threatened to bring an antitrust lawsuit against The American College of Surgeons as well as personal suits against Hawley and Graham. Littel did, however, indicate a desire on the part of the ICS to have a conference about the issue. As chairman of the board of regents, Graham would not agree to confer in the face of threats to sue, and all who knew Graham understood that "as Chairman of the Committee which organized The American Board of Surgery he would take the establishment of the International Board of Surgery as a personal affront and as Chairman of the Board of Regents was somewhat offended that the personal attack had not been made against him alone."[1]

The issue of the International College certifying board was also discussed by the AMA Council on Medical Education and Hospitals. Some members desired an elevation of the standards of surgery, whereas others were in favor of surgery being performed by general practitioners without special training or certification. Finally, in a December 1952 statement of policy, the AMA House of Delegates declared, "It is not in the best interest of medicine or the public for other medical organizations to establish certifying agencies."[1] By so doing it restated its original position that the American Board of Surgery was the one board that represented the surgeons of the United States.[1]

The issue became public in an unusual way. In November 1953 the Missouri State Medical Association journal, *Missouri Medicine*, announced that Evarts A. Graham had recently been elected president of the International College of Surgeons.[64] Graham immediately wrote to its editor, Vincent T. Williams, stating:

> I was horrified to read on page 876 of the November issue that I had recently been elected President of the International College of Surgeons. I am sure…you have no desire to make me suffer by gratuitously bestowing on me not only membership but the highest office in The International College of Surgeons.…I do feel my reputation has been badly damaged.…I cannot afford to let people think that I am even a member of The International College of Surgeons to say nothing of allowing my name to be put up as President of such an outfit.…I was elected President of The International Congress of Surgeons which meets every two years.…it is the regular meeting of the old and thoroughly respected Société Internationale de Chirurgie.[65]

Williams immediately responded to Graham stating that he was "mortified to death that we pulled this boner."[66] Two months later Max Thorek entered the fray with a full-page editorial rebutting Graham's comments. He elaborated on the origin of the International College, denied the statement regarding a lawsuit pending against the ACS or Graham, commented on Graham's fear of a damaged reputation, and then took up the issue of priority for pneumonectomy that he said belonged to Rudolph Nissen. He recommended that Graham give up all of his honors.[67]

One month later Graham responded with a two-and-one-half-page letter, which he sent for review to Beverly B. Vedder, the lawyer retained by the ACS, and to Paul Hawley, the director. Vedder had returned Graham's first version, concluding that Graham had made statements that were on the fringe of being libelous and as "close to calling Max a liar as you can get and still use light language."[68] Three days later Graham wrote, "It will be extremely hard for me to accept lying down the very irritating statements which Max made about me."[69] Two weeks later Graham wrote again: "I cannot let this opportunity go by to show him up as the liar which he really is.... my own reputation in Missouri is too important to me to let his statements about me go unanswered."[70] Graham wrote again on March 19, in response to another letter from Vedder: "There will be many people in Missouri who will assume that because of my silence against the recent blast of Max Thorek he has won the battle and all his allegations must be sound or I would answer them.... I have made up my mind to go ahead."[71]

Hawley responded to Graham's agony in a letter of March 16, 1954: "It pains me no end to see such a distinguished gentleman as you become involved in a urinary contest with a skunk. To do so you must descend to his level since he cannot possibly ascend to yours, ... there is danger of making Thorek a martyr despite the fact that he is an unconscionable rogue."[72] Graham's vehemence had now reached the point at which, on March 19, he wrote to Hawley and again turned down Hawley's recommendation that he not respond to Thorek, saying, "I think it is a unique opportunity... to show the public what a mongrel outfit the International College is—particularly its founder and leader."[73]

In a final editorial in *Missouri Medicine*, Graham again discussed the lawsuit, his own role in The International Society of Surgery, and the "vicious charge by implication that he had attempted to steal an honor from Rudolph Nissen."[74] Graham quoted in full the resolution originally adopted by The International Society of Surgery and, in closing, wrote: "I hope I shall not have to call upon your good nature again to devote space to this matter. Yet I think it is important to have the facts straight."[74]

The editor of *Missouri Medicine* had become an innocent bystander in a polemic, which threatened to become more and more personal. Graham, however, did have the last word in a battle precipitated by a typographic error. Quite unintentionally, a state medical journal had publicized the differences between the American College of Surgeons and the International College of Surgeons in regard to surgical training and the certification of competence. Loyal Davis commented on the episode:

> In the mind of Evarts Graham any attempt to lower the standards for training of young surgeons was in the same category with unethical surgical practices. Both were fought with strong frontal attacks. Graham believed that his predecessors as Chairmen of The Board of Regents were overly diplomatic and cautious.... He had always believed that The American College of Surgeons should be more aggressive in its opposition to fee splitting, unnecessary operations, ghost surgery, and other unethical principles. He had become impatient with the dilatory actions of The Board of Regents and his service as a Regent had not tempered

his patience so that when he became Chairman he aggressively took on some of these issues.[1]

Evarts Graham's distaste for the International College of Surgeons was preconditioned by his 1935 review of Max Thorek's application to the International Society of Surgery. The society members in the Chicago area had unanimously opposed Thorek because of unethical practices. His subterfuge in initially denying involvement in the formation of the International College was of no help, and, after exposing him, the ISS issued a seven-point resolution urging their members to withhold endorsement of support or alignment. Graham went so far as to reprimand members of the Barnes staff who participated in International College programs, and he vigorously discouraged such activity. In April 1951 he obtained a roster of ICS members and, to his dismay, found that 709 fellows of the ACS were also members of the ICS. He haughtily refused a request by the ICS to make a tape recording of his thoughts on carcinoma of the lung.

It was a further offense to Graham to discover that the April 1950 AMA Directory listed the International College but not the International Society, and Graham led a protest to the AMA for this discrimination. The International Society was a small exclusive society, whereas the International College was a large inclusive organization whose success, 7000 members by 1954, peeved Graham sufficiently that he made several disparaging remarks about the International College in his voluminous correspondence with Leo Dejardin as he prepared for the Copenhagen Congress of the International Society. The audacity of the ICS in calling itself a board and claiming examinations that did not exist was the final straw—a direct assault on Graham's ideas about the elevation of surgical standards. Graham entered into the fray with his usual intense determination, personal preoccupation, and almost personal vehemence. It was obviously a crusade for good against a dual evil— unethical practices by the founders and a reduction of the standards of surgery by claiming certification with nonexistent examinations.

The affair was closed on January 26, 1952, when the executive committee of the International College abolished the International Board of Surgery, and the words board and diplomate were removed from its certificates. The regents were now ready for the 1957 confrontation with the American Board of Abdominal Surgery, which had been organized by Blaise Alfano without the support of a major surgical society. It, too, failed to materialize.

GRAHAM AND THE AMERICAN COLLEGE OF SURGEONS

Evarts Graham became a founding fellow of the American College of Surgeons in 1914 but did not participate actively until the 1932 St. Louis Clinical Congress. By this time he was a major figure on the American surgical scene, destined to bring to the college his many thoughts and ideas that had been developed during his unique educational postgraduate experience, the Mason City years, his research for the Empyema Commission, his collection of a full-time faculty that emphasized surgical research, and his institution of a 4-year graded residency program. He had commanded the attention of the medical world for his discovery and development of cholecystography. Graham did all of these accomplishments by the age of 50. The fame that came from his first successful one-stage pneumonectomy in 1933 and then, 4 years later, from his creation of the American Board of Surgery only added to his luster.

Graham's first contribution to the ACS was his expansion of the program for the 1932 Clinical Congress with discussions of disease processes and disorders of physiology as well as demonstrations of operative procedures. His second contribution to the college followed Franklin Martin's 1934 request that he become chairman of the Missouri Committee for the Protection of Medical Research in Missouri[r]. This small committee was expected to be alert to impending legislation that restricted animal experimentation and to be informed of any antivivisection bills.[75] Graham prepared a position statement to be sent, as needed, to various members of the legislature, and he served on the committee for 5 years, but there was little activity.

The year he was elected president of the American Surgical Association, 1937, Graham became a member of the ACS Committee on Graduate Training for Surgery, and for 18 years he served under the chairmanships of Dallas Phemister and Fred Coller. In 1939 he became president-elect of the ACS, and, a year later, its president. During this year George Crile insisted on resigning from the board of regents with the stipulation that his seat be given to Evarts Graham, and Graham sat with the regents from October 1939 until November 1954 as president-elect, president, regent, and then chairman of the board of regents for his last 3 years.

In 1941 Graham sponsored Wangensteen's Surgical Forum. He failed in a 1943 attempt to fuse ACS fellowship requirements with training requirements of the several American Surgical Specialty Boards.[21,76] As a result of his severe dealings with fellows of the ACS who had been charged with unethical conduct, a judiciary committee of the college was formed to bypass him, for Graham was abrupt, harsh, and quite unsympathetic, even before he knew the defendants' side of the case.[63] In 1937 Graham was appointed by the ACS to the Commission on Graduate Medical Education, which, with the Advisory Board for Medical Specialties, was instrumental in establishing the Conference Committee on Graduate Training in Surgery.

In 1946 Graham sat on the Committee on Relations of the College with the American Boards, and in 1952 he served as the ACS representative on a special

---

r. Missouri Committee for the Protection of Medical Research: Evarts A. Graham (chairman), Vilray P. Blair, Malvern B. Clopton, William T. Coughlin, Minford A. Hanna, Father A. Schwitalla, Major S. Seelig, Frank A. Teachener.

committee to establish the framework for a conference committee on graduate training in otolaryngology that he hoped would be emulated by other specialty boards and ultimately lead to other residency review committees. Success was limited. He and MacEachern failed in an attempt to incorporate anesthesiologists into a special associate fellowship of the ACS. He and Paul Hawley had been key players in creating the Joint Commission on Accreditation of Hospitals, and the two led ACS opposition to the International Board of Surgery.

It was customary for the chairman of the board of regents to serve only a 2-year term, but in 1953 two issues facing the college were considered of such importance that Graham's term was extended. The first was the confrontation with the International College of Surgeons and its International Board of Surgery. Deeply involved, Graham felt that a change of leadership at this time would be seen as a sign of weakness, and he desired to remain chairman. The second issue was the old, ever-present issue of fee splitting. Loyal Davis had been propelled into a position of such high publicity that, although he was the logical successor as chairman of the board of regents, it was impossible to consider him for the position.

It appeared to the regents that if Graham's service to the ACS as a regent were terminated just at the time when the college was being severely criticized for its efforts to combat unethical practices, it might well be interpreted as a lack of confidence in his leadership and a reversal of the policy of the board of regents. Graham's dedication, loyalty, and devotion to the American College of Surgeons was in complete contrast to his attitude as a younger man. Davis wrote, "Franklin Martin must be laughing…in his grave to have seen the complete conversion of Graham."[63]

Graham was anxious to remain chairman of the board and urged the nominating committee to submit his name for election to an additional 1-year term. Bluntly outspoken and previously highly critical of the ACS, Graham had now become the most ardent, uncompromising champion of the college, an organization in which he had been a pioneer in elevating the standards of surgical care for patients.[1] Davis wrote, "He was harsh and dictatorial…could not stand opposition; [but] he and Arthur Allen brought stature to the Chairmanship of the Board of Regents."[63]

Although remaining as chairman of the board until November 19, 1954,[1] Graham departed with discord because of his desire to remain yet another year. He confided in Loyal Davis that by early 1954, he and Hawley were having a difference of opinion, and Davis guessed it was because of Graham's wish to continue for a fourth year as chairman, whereas Hawley opposed any extension of a regent's term. Although Owen Wangensteen had done his utmost to have Graham re-elected to continue as chairman, his efforts were strongly opposed by Willard Parsons of the board of governors, and Graham's term as regent was terminated.[63] In writing to Wangensteen, Graham disclosed his feelings of rejection and the dislike that had been shown to him by the regents and governors, saying, "I am sorry that the termination of my career with the College for various reasons seemed to be associated with a sour taste to many of the Regents."[77] "Evarts Graham reluctantly relinquished the Chairmanship of the Board. For thirteen years as a Regent he had unselfishly devoted his energy to the affairs of the College and had become identified in the minds of the public and the profession as the spokesman who dictated policies of the most influential surgical organization in the United States."[1] He was not sure that younger men among the regents could carry on since his activities as chairman of the board of regents included membership on so many councils or committees of the college.[78]

Graham's occasionally overbearing, authoritarian, and domineering demeanor as chairman of the board of regents was illustrated in an episode that occurred in preparation for a sectional meeting in the British Isles, when Graham singlehandedly chose four English surgeons for honorary fellowship, and then proposed that the regents approve his action. Only one regent (Loyal Davis) opposed him, on the grounds that Graham had not even had the courtesy to consult the committee that nominated honorary fellows. Graham became angry, and a shouting match ensued. The other regents were silent and unwilling to express their convictions; Graham's nominees were approved. After lunch that day, Graham handed Davis a rolled piece of white paper tied with a red ribbon saying he had conferred honorary fellowship upon Davis for stating his views and voting his opinions; then, smiling, he said "the action of the Board would stand."[79] Several regents felt that Graham would brook no opposition and insisted on being a dictator. He was influential in many of the college's activities and, at the end of his term, held membership on eight committees and was chairman of three of them[s].

As late as 1956, no presidential portrait of Evarts Graham had been hung in the Murphy Memorial Auditorium, and Graham responded to a request from Hawley by asking if a bronze bas-relief would be acceptable instead of a portrait. The bas-relief in question was 28 by 18 inches and weighed about 40 pounds. In 1941 Malvern Clopton had proposed to the American Surgical Association that a Graham Medal be given for exceptional contributions, and, even though the idea was rejected by the ASA Council, Carl Mose, professor of sculpture at Washington University, completed the medal. Clopton died, Mose went into military service, and the medal, after being placed in the care of Robert Elman, finally found its way to the Graham basement. The ACS rejected the proposal of the bas-relief sculpture, and nothing further occurred until 1988 to 1989. Eugene Bricker collected a fund,

---

s. Councils and committees of the ACS on which Graham served in 1954: board of regents, as chairman; executive committee, board of regents, as chairman; finance committee, as chairman; board of directors, Franklin H. Martin Memorial Foundation, as chairman; art (Daniel Catton Rich, chairman); public relations (Loyal Davis, chairman); Committee on Graduate Training in Surgery (Frederick A. Coller, chairman); Joint Commission on Accreditation of Hospitals (Newell W. Philpott, chairman); committee to study situation in Iowa.

and James J. Ingwerson, an artist who had painted several other prominent Washington University faculty members, painted a posthumous presidential portrait. Graham's son, Evarts Jr., posed in ACS robes for the painting of the body, and facial features were copied from photographs in the archives. The original painting hung for a year in the Becker Library of the Washington University Medical School, and in 1990 it was hung with other ACS presidential portraits in the Murphy Memorial Auditorium in Chicago. A reproduction now hangs in the university library, where it is framed between two brass plaques containing an account of his life and a list of donors to the Graham Professorship in Surgery.

Chapter 13

INTRAMURAL ACTIVITIES: PART 1

Graham's offices, first in the North Building and then, after 1931, in Barnes Hospital, were the foci of his administrative, intellectual, and editorial activities as well as a place for patients, operations, students, research, and faculty development. All of his actions relating to the Medical School, the hospital, and the university were monitored by Ada Hanvey. His contacts with the university were usually directly with the chancellor, rarely through the dean. There were local civic activities, an extensive correspondence, and many obligations outside St. Louis, for he could not refuse an invitation to be part of a happening—in or out of St. Louis.

THE EXECUTIVE FACULTY

Graham's early years in St. Louis saw governance of the Medical School placed in the hands of the executive faculty, a group made up of department chairmen. Following George Dock's resignation as dean in 1912, the executive faculty annually nominated one of its members for appointment as dean, and, although the chancellor and corporate board confirmed it, this effectively placed the school in the hands of the faculty, rather than the university chancellor.[1] Years later, Graham and Schaffer managed to place the school's fiscal affairs under the authority of the medical faculty, rather than the administration on the hilltop campus.

The executive faculty met on the first Wednesday of each month, and Evarts Graham, sitting as chairman of surgery, developed ideas about and accepted responsibilities that related to the entire school. Although nominally the surgical representative, he soon began to see the entire school as within his domain of responsibility, and with his positive approach and outspoken opinions, he achieved a pervasive role.

Graham became a close friend of William McKim Marriott, pediatrician and neighbor and the dean from 1923 to 1936. Upon Marriott's departure, in lieu of appointing a dean, the chancellor placed the school in the hands of an administrative committee composed of Philip Shaffer as chairman, Evarts Graham from surgery, and David Barr from medicine.[2] During this year Graham also held a position on the Committee on Financial Needs, was chairman of the Committee on the McMillan Hospital and Oscar Johnson Institute,[3] and was chairman of the Committee on Graduate Instruction.[4] The most significant feature of the administrative committee's responsibility was the tenuous and increasingly contentious relationship with the board of trustees of Barnes Hospital. After receiving a recommendation from Shaffer, Chancellor Throop invested "Dr. Graham with all of the authority and support that the Faculty and the Administration of the School" could offer. Throop stated, "It is felt that he is the one best qualified to co-operate actively with Dr. Clopton."[5]

Graham took the opportunity to strengthen the school's bargaining position with the Barnes Hospital Board, and he searched for ways to improve the increasingly strident conversations brought on by financial problems of the mid-Depression. In the spring of 1937, he prepared a six-page document detailing relations between the Medical School and Barnes Hospital. It opened with the statement that Graham had not been invited to Barnes board meetings for over a year, and noted that the affiliation must result in "a unit with divided but interdependent responsibilities."[6] He acknowledged that each institution was in trouble, but, although the hospital was filled and able to increase its income by increasing its fees, the university was dependent on a decreasing endowment income and was unable to cover some of the obligations for hospital services that should be charged as hospital costs but were assumed within the educational budget. He pointed out that the hospital's favorable position was due mainly to the prestige conferred by its affiliation with the Medical School. The contract between the two institutions provided for consultation and advice by the university in the selection of a hospital superintendent. Graham requested that the university eliminate its support for Dr. Burlingham, the hospital superintendent, because he had "aroused distress and suspicion" where confidence and understanding were essential. Graham encouraged that Burlingham be replaced with someone more understanding of the university dilemma. The document was typical of Evarts Graham and represented his frustration with the Barnes Board. It was approved and adopted by the faculty at its regular meeting on May 12, 1937.[6]

At the same meeting, Graham presented a resolution that Philip Shaffer be appointed dean of the Medical School. Five days later, in his response to the chancellor, Shaffer showed support for the actions of May 12 by stating that his willingness to become dean was contingent upon the acceptance of the Graham document of 5 days earlier. Shaffer asked the corporation to deny Burlingham his "wholly unjustified and unearned payment [because of his] refusal to permit the payment of certain items in the budget to be used specifically for surgery purposes."[7] Graham's role in selecting Philip Shaffer as dean of the Medical School was amply repaid, for it gave the school a strong leader during the critical coming 8 years, and strengthened a close working relationship between the two men.

In October 1945 Graham wrote to Arthur Holly Compton, the chancellor, outlining his thoughts on a successor to Philip Shaffer, who desired to relinquish the deanship. Graham was fully aware of the dean's role and stated, "Policy in the past has been to select one of the Departmental heads of the medical school [but] all of us feel that it would be a mistake to continue that policy." He alerted Compton of the need to discuss "the question of what sort of a salary would be paid to a full time Dean and how much of a budget could be prepared for the administration of the Dean's office." He closed by stating that he would like to "persuade Dr. Alan Gregg the Director of the Division of Medical Sciences at the Rockefeller Foundation to take the job."[8] As a follow-up to this letter, Graham was asked to serve as chairman of a committee consisting of Robert A. Moore (of Pathology), Harry L. Alexander (an internist), Barry Wood (of medicine), and Carl Cori (of physiology) to search for Shaffer's successor.[9] After a few brief discussions the committee decided to continue the policy of having a department chairman become dean, and Robert Moore was chosen.

An interesting feature of the Graham-Shaffer relationship occurred in 1941 and 1942 during the search for a professor of medicine that followed the departure of David Barr, who headed to Cornell. Both Shaffer and Graham felt that pediatrics and internal medicine should be combined, and the issue arose as to whether Alexis Hartman, the chairman of pediatrics, might become the professor and chairman of medicine, or whether Dr. Carl Moore, a professor of medicine, might additionally become a professor of pediatrics.[10] Wiser heads prevailed: the two departments were kept separate, the combined professorship never came to pass, and a young man from Johns Hopkins, Dr. W. Barry Wood, was recruited to chair the Department of Medicine. This event was underscored by Graham's belief that the surgery of children was not very different from the surgery of adults. He never accepted the idea that children's hospitals had different problems than did adult institutions.

DEALING WITH THE BARNES HOSPITAL BOARD

Upon his arrival in St. Louis, Evarts Graham immediately became the Medical School's liason representative to Barnes Hospital. It was a role that was never assumed by the dean until 1958, when a major confrontation occurred between Edward Dempsey, the dean, and Edgar Queeny, chairman of the Barnes Hospital Board of Trustees.[1] Although Graham was the assigned representative to the board, the dean was always its official spokesman, an arrangement that teamed Graham with Philip Shaffer during difficult years when Graham met monthly with the three Barnes trustees, Frank C. Rand[a], Albert Keller, and Joseph W. Lewis. Rand was by far the dominant figure on the board, and it was inevitable that tensions would develop between Rand and Graham. Through the encouragement and efforts of Graham, Frank Rand was appointed to the Washington University Corporation's Board of Trustees in February 1928, but, as acrimony developed between the two, and disagreements between Barnes and Washington University increased in bitterness, Rand resigned from the Washington University Board feeling that membership on the two boards created a conflict of interest. In its early years, the Barnes Board was occupied with investments, finances, hospital development, and operational concerns, until Graham's cholecystography success introduced the need to enlarge the medical center complex. An ever-increasing demand for ward beds,

---

a.　Frank Chambless Rand (1876 to 1949) was born in Marshall County, Mississippi, and educated at Vanderbilt University in Nashville, Tennessee. Both literally and figuratively, he followed in the footsteps of his cousin, Jackson Johnson (son of Helen Rand Johnson), who organized the Roberts, Johnson and Rand Shoe Company of Memphis, subsequently the International Shoe Company of St. Louis. Johnson became its chief executive officer and a member of the corporate board of Washington University. In 1898 Frank Rand started as a shoe salesman with the International Shoe Company; he later became a superintendent, vice-president, president in 1911, and finally chairman of its board from 1916 to 1930. He held directorships of the Mercantile Commerce Bank and Trust Company, the Union Electric Company, and Bell Telephone, was president of the board of trustees of Vanderbilt University, chairman of the board of trustees of Barnes Hospital, and a member of the board of Washington University. Feeling that the latter two positions created a conflict of interest, as a good Methodist, he resigned membership on the Washington University Board and confined his interests to Barnes Hospital. In the mid-1930s he and the descendants of Jackson Johnson donated funds to build the Rand Johnson surgical wing of Barnes Hospital. Following his reconciliation with Evarts Graham, he became his friend, associate, and patient. After developing carcinoma of the lung, he was operated upon by Graham, but, nonetheless, he died of his disease on December 2, 1949.

A few days later, Graham wrote a letter of condolence to his son Edgar in which he reminisced about his relationships with Frank:

> He and I had our differences at times which on occasion were rather serious.... After the Westlake turmoil... and after Dr. Frank Bradley became superintendent there was no occasion whatever on my part to have any difference of opinion with your father. ... We had a sincere mutual respect for each other which finally developed into a very warm friendship. I know that on many occasions he went out of his way to demonstrate his friendship to me. The responsibility of taking care of him in his final illness was a tremendous one for me because of my warm friendship for him.... I express to you what a great personal loss his death is to me.[11]

nursing care, and radiography services, and the growing importance of analytic chemistry created discord that ultimately led to outright hostility.

As early as the end of 1922, it was apparent to Graham that an enlargement of Barnes Hospital was essential if the university's teaching and research obligations were to be met. During the winter of 1923, he told Abraham Flexner that Rockefeller interests would be making a mistake if they spent large sums of money on the creation of laboratories and at the same time left medical schools crippled in regard to an adequate number of hospital teaching beds. Conversations on this point continued between the two until 1927, when Flexner finally asked Graham how much money would be required to make surgical facilities adequate for the Washington University–Barnes Hospital enterprise. Graham estimated that $300,000 would be enough to add a new floor over the entire hospital.

In the spring of 1928, the General Education Board (GEB) declared its willingness to contribute $450,000 as an endowment for surgery, if $300,000 for construction could be raised in St. Louis. The GEB policy was to give money only to universities, not to hospitals, and therefore the $450,000 would be given to Washington University, with its income reserved for the Barnes trustees to expend for surgical activities in Barnes.[12,13] The $300,000 raised in St. Louis came from two men: Jackson Johnson, chairman of the board of the International Shoe Company; and Frank C. Rand, its president. Johnson, then a trustee of Washington University, dedicated his gift to the memory of his son Jackson Johnson Jr., who had died in 1918 while in Europe with the American Expeditonary Forces. Rand's gift was in memory of his brother Edgar, one of the founders of the Roberts, Johnson and Rand Shoe Company, who had died in 1907.

An alternative to adding a floor over the entire hospital was that a three-story addition be placed on top of the surgical (west) wing; this was found to be impractical because foundations were insufficient to withstand the weight. Plans were expanded; more money from Rand and Johnson was supplemented by a gift from Malvern Clopton that permitted the construction of two floors to contain new operating rooms. The west wing was demolished and, in its place, rose an eight-story structure—the Rand Johnson surgical wing of Barnes Hospital—with a $450,000 endowment for surgical research and teaching.[14]

Graham's personal friendship with Edward Mallinckrodt Sr., combined with his connections with Abraham Flexner and the General Education Board, made possible the development of an institute of radiology, the first in the country. The GEB proposed to endow a newly formed Department of Radiology with $750,000 if St. Louis would raise $250,000 for a building. Gifts from Edward Mallinckrodt and his son Edward Jr. easily met this goal, and an eight-story Mallinckrodt Institute of Radiology was opened in 1931, with Sherwood Moore as its director. The radiology institute was a Washington University building, and it functioned as such, whereas the Rand Johnson Building was an addition to Barnes Hospital. The wrecking of the west wing—the surgical pavilion—at Barnes was begun on June 1, 1929, and on November 1 construction of the Mallinckrodt Institute of Radiology began. The Great Depression had not yet begun to take its toll.

At a meeting of the board on December 29, 1932, Graham sought $1900 for his Medical and Surgical Chest Service, and requested that it be taken from monies earned on the $450,000 GEB endowment given to Washington University. The Barnes trustees had generally assumed the Rockefeller endowment money to be a gift to Barnes Hospital that, by policy of the GEB, was conveyed through Washington University. Graham became upset because nothing formal had been arranged about this endowment and how the accrued income could be spent. He felt that he was the one who had secured the funds and that he somehow had a proprietary interest in them, but he had never been informed of whether anything had been spent and, if so, how much and for what purposes. During the course of a prolonged and heated discussion, Mr. Rand stated that it had been "his clear understanding with Mr. Flexner... that the funds were to be transferred to Barnes Hospital for expenditure by the Trustees of the Hospital and... he [Rand] considered that the agreement... between the GEB and WU was [an attempt] to get around the fact that it was against the policy of the GEB to give money to hospitals."[15] Graham insisted: "As Surgeon-in-Chief of the Barnes Hospital I should be consulted about the expenditures of these funds because I have been largely instrumental in obtaining this gift which is the largest gift to the endowment of the hospital that has ever been received."[15] Both Rand and Lewis were emphatic that Graham had no rights in the matter since he was not a member of the board of trustees, but Graham regarded it as at least a matter of courtesy to keep him informed. The board stood firm on the principle that Graham had no entitlement, but it directed Dr. Burlingham, the superintendent, to give Graham a statement from time to time. Heated discussions followed about the use of restricted and unrestricted endowments, and Graham left in a huff to dictate a memorandum about the affair.[15] The issue was concluded with Rand's opinion prevailing—that the gift of the GEB would support education and research, whereas St. Louis money would provide for new construction. The board did at least acknowledge that the GEB gift was in recognition of notable contributions to the progress of surgery by the Washington University Department of Surgery.[16]

By 1932 the three Barnes trustees were considering 5 and 10 percent reductions in hospital salaries, and in November the trustees voiced appreciation at Graham's report that one intern and one assistant resident position had been eliminated from the surgical quota as an accompanying Washington University economy measure. Financial difficulties were visible within the Medical School, and Graham requested that all semiprivate and private patients in Barnes Hospital be charged $3 for the procedures performed in the Washington University clinical laboratory. The trustees considered the request at a special meeting with Evarts Graham and

Philip Shaffer held on October 30, 1936. Graham began the discussion by stating that ever since Barnes Hospital opened, the Medical School had been operating the laboratories for all patients in the hospital free of charge. In the early days, this was easy, for there were relatively few patients, and a large part of the laboratory work available in 1936 had not even been in existence. In the space of 20 years, the new laboratory procedures that had become essential strained the school's budget, for it carried the cost of these procedures that Graham and Shaffer believed should be a hospital obligation. Discussion ranged back and forth regarding the hospital deficit due to teaching, and what obligation should be borne by the Medical School for patient care in the hospital. During the discussion Graham's temper flared, and he shouted his resentment at the stand of the trustees whom he felt were criticizing him and suggesting that he was trying to harm Barnes Hospital. Rand also was angry: "You take it on yourself, you talk about what you resent, the Board has cause for resentment too. You did not even let me finish what I have to say and I wish you would take a more tolerant attitude toward the Board at these meetings." Graham apologized. Rand continued: "We do not want a spirit of conflict. We have been operating for twenty years on the basis of trying to do what is right for the three parties concerned—the patient, the medical school and the hospital." The issue of the $3 laboratory fee led to personal invectives, and Rand faced Graham angrily:

> You and I have reached the point of friendly enmity Doctor. I want to say to you that I do not ask for your endorsement of my personal point of view. I reserve the right to discuss opinions independent of my own feelings. . . . it is dangerous to motivate another man's actions. . . . When a misunderstanding of this kind arises other things . . . take on a magnified importance that breaks down a normal friendly feeling. . . . I have talked some to Chancellor Throop about the question of your meeting with us. . . . It has been customary to discuss the mechanical and financial end of the hospital [among] ourselves. . . . We would be glad to have you with us, you remain if you like.[13]

After further discussion the trustees agreed to study the matter of the laboratory fee and finally accepted the $3 charge. Graham later remarked: "If the Trustees had not authorized the laboratory charge the relationship between the hospital and the university would have been in danger."[13]

The next confrontation came when Graham brought a request from Sherwood Moore to have the radiology interns live in the Barnes Hospital interns' quarters. After the trustees agreed, with certain conditions attached, Graham asked that the hospital also provide them with uniforms. This request was declined, thereby angering Graham, who, at this point, was ready to take offence on the smallest occasion. His displeasure was apparent at the meeting of May 6, 1937, when he said: "Since the laboratory fee of $3.00 was put into effect, the legally appointed representative of the medical school has not received a notice to attend meetings of the Trustees of Barnes Hospital.... I do not give a hoot what you [think] about me. The point is that it is true that I have received no notices and it necessarily destroys my confidence.... we cannot get along unless we discuss our problems together.... If you think that in any respect the University has not fulfilled its duty to the hospital, what proof would you ask more than the growth of the hospital?" Rand retorted: "Washington University did not amount to anything until its affiliation with the hospital [and] we take a loss of some $80,000 per year."[13]

The argument over the radiology intern uniforms finally became so bitter that it led to Graham being asked not to attend any more meetings of the Barnes trustees. On June 28, 1937, the Barnes Board met at the University Club to discuss a reorganization of the Training School for Nurses. Mr. Rand ended the meeting by again mentioning the cost of uniforms for radiology interns ($28.24), a charge the hospital was unwilling to bear. Graham produced three $10 bills from his pocket and placed them in front of Dr. Burlingham, the hospital director. Heat developed between Graham, Burlingham, Rand, and Keller, and the cash payment was refused.[17] The next day, when asked by Mr. Daniel N. Kirby, the legal advisor to the university and a member of its corporate board, not to attend the meetings of the Barnes Board, Graham was informed that Rand had requested it following the University Club confrontation. Graham thereupon wrote to Rand and enclosed a check for $28.24 for the intern uniforms, stating that if Barnes Hospital felt it could not undertake this expense, he would be pleased to make a personal contribution.[18] On July 1, 1937, Daniel Kirby officially replaced Graham as the university representative on the Barnes Board. He functioned with more diplomacy and tact than Graham had displayed, particularly during the following months, which were to see a major dispute about the selection of a successor to Dr. Burlingham, who was receiving half his salary from Washington University, even though he was the hospital director.

By late 1936 relations between the hospital and the university had developed to the point at which the executive faculty, in a move to reinforce its position, formally announced: "Negotiations toward improvement in hospital relations [will] be placed in the hands of Dr. Graham with... full authority. He is the one best qualified... to take the steps necessary.... [This] invests Dr. Graham with all the authority and support... that the faculty can confer."[5] The authorization was confirmed by Chancellor Throop,[19] and Graham was now the spokesman for the Medical School and the university, no longer merely a representative of the school on the hospital board. He became the focal point of university relations with the hospital—relating to the board not as a quasi board member, but as the university, with whom the board had to deal.

The issue of the radiology intern uniforms brought the Graham-Rand antagonism to the point of rupture. Three weeks later Graham wrote to William Darrach, dean of the Columbia Presbyterian Medical Center, alerting him to an upcoming visit by Rand, whom he described as a multimillionaire chairman of the board of the International Shoe Company and said: "Because of his success in the business world he has become impressed with the idea that he is always right. He is arrogant, obstinate and uncompromising. He does not have the least idea of what this … hospital ought to be, nor has he ever been willing to be told."[20]

The break of the cool but friendly relationship between Evarts Graham and Frank Rand over the issue of the radiology uniforms bothered both men, and each put out feelers hoping for an olive branch. For two proud and stubborn men it was not easy, and reconciliation required help from Hospital Director Frank Bradley and Dean Philip Shaffer. Graham and Rand met by accident in the operating room in November 1939, when Rand was escorted by Bradley to have a small skin cancer on the left side of his nose removed by James Barrett Brown. The two shook hands, and from then on they slowly became more friendly. It was Rand's custom to hold an open house on New Year's Day in his home at 7100 Delmar Avenue, and that year he invited Graham, a courtesy that had its intended good effect. Perhaps part of the reason that Graham was willing to make up with Rand was that he was beginning to transfer his animosity to Mr. James L. Westlake, who in October 1936 had become a member of the Barnes Board following the resignation of Joseph W. Lewis, due to ill health.[13]

Mr. Westlake's concept of Barnes Hospital was that it should give up its role as a teaching hospital, and he initiated moves to separate the hospital from the Medical School, pattern it after the Methodist Hospital of Indianapolis, and do away with teaching wards and negro patients. He demanded that the radiology department be turned over to Barnes and that the university take over the expense of the School of Nursing. He was critical of the rates the university charged the hospital for electricity, power, light, steam, and hot water, and he proposed that previous real estate transactions be reviewed.[13] Finally, he suggested that the hospital appoint a large courtesy staff, opening it to practicing physicians not members of the university faculty, a move that collided with the Medical School's desire for more full-time faculty and the maintenance of a closed staff. Westlake's move to enlarge the staff was supported by Hospital Director Burlingham, for the mid- and late 1930s were difficult years for the hospital; many beds were empty, there were few paying (private) patients, and ward beds were a burden on finances. Burlingham proposed to send a letter to all members of the St. Louis Medical Society offering them a position on the Barnes staff if they would admit their patients to Barnes. Graham's vigorous protests finally prevailed, but the issue became so heated that it led to Burlingham's emotional collapse and resignation, and the appointment of his assistant Frank Bradley[b].[21]

---

b. Frank R. Bradley (1900 to 1973) of Scotch-Irish descent, was born in LaClede, Illinois. After finishing high school in Mount Vernon, he became a brakeman on the Louisville and Nashville Railroad. He

Westlake convinced his two fellow trustees to pass a resolution that no negro patients would be admitted, an action that raised the conflict to the boiling point; then, in mid-1938, Westlake persuaded his two colleagues to place the University on notice that the Barnes trustees wished to have the present contract cancelled. On September 30, 1938, such a letter was written and sent. The most critical issues in the dispute were the monopoly of the Mallinckrodt Institute on radiographic services, the Medical School ownership of the clinical laboratories, the rates charged for utilities supplied by the university-owned power plant, and the costs born by the hospital for nursing education.[22]

Although Rand had voted for closing the hospital to negroes, he informed Kirby that he did not fully agree with Westlake on this issue. Philip Shaffer arranged for an emergency meeting on July 12, 1938, between Washington University representatives and the Barnes Board, at which time Shaffer presented a resolution framed to inform Westlake that his attempt to convert Barnes Hospital from a teaching hospital to a high-grade nursing home and to eliminate negroes was unwise. As the university spokesman, Graham reiterated the sense of Shaffer's resolution by stating: "Westlake will not understand what I am going to say but Mr. Rand is beginning to." Graham's opening comments dealt with the question of whether it was desirable to change the present broad character of Barnes Hospital in education, research, and patient care. Then second, and of equal importance, he emphasized that in St. Louis, a border community, the race relation question was always a live issue, and he had no doubt that getting rid of negro patients would be interpreted by the negro citizens as undue discrimination. A long discussion occurred regarding the status of negroes, and, finally, in a 2:1 vote, the trustees decided to retract their previous resolution and to continue to admit them as patients. Space was subsequently provided in the medical (east) wing, and a segregated ward was maintained until 1964.[13]

The September 30 letter of intent by the Barnes Board to terminate the contract between Washington University and Barnes Hospital was accompanied by a

---

graduated from Washington University with a doctor of medicine degree in 1928, working nights during his university and medical school years as a switchman for the Terminal Railway Association of St. Louis. A 3-month internship at the Veterans Administration Hospital in Jefferson Barracks was terminated with his appointment as assistant superintendent of Barnes Hospital. In 1939 he replaced Louis H. Burlingham as director, and he subsequently oversaw the transformation of Barnes from a small institution into a large complex involving several hospitals. He authored many articles, was frequently a featured speaker, and became president of the American Hospital Association and the American College of Hospital Administrators. He developed the Washington University Program in Hospital Administration and was the first to introduce airline-style food service to a hospital cafeteria. Popular with nurses and staff, he was particularly friendly with Barnes residents, often inviting them to his home or to other social or theatrical affairs. An affable, genial, intensely human person, he was forever concerned with the well-being of his hospital and the people who made it a great institution.

personal letter from Mr. Rand to Malvern Clopton, now president of the Washington University Corporation, indicating his belief that the Barnes Board really did desire a continued affiliation.[23] Five days later Clopton acknowledged the correspondence, and a redefinition of the affiliation was undertaken.[24] Tension was building between Westlake and his two co-trustees, and he ceased to attend board meetings between June 16, 1941, and mid-1943. A survey made by Dr. Basil McLean of Rochester, New York, led, in 1949, to a second affiliation agreement that would last until the early 1960s when another crisis led to an agreement that contained provisions for conflict resolution and creation of the position of first vice chancellor for medical affairs.[1]

In his 1924 report to the trustees of Barnes Hospital, Evarts Graham had presented his concept of a teaching hospital, in particular, Barnes. In reference to the growth of Barnes, he wrote: "The number of free beds is still inadequate for the accomplishment of one of the main purposes. The Barnes Hospital was established with objects and ideals somewhat different from those ordinarily adopted by hospitals. Its function is not merely to give the best possible care to the sick. It has a further object in being a place where experts of the future are to be trained, both doctors and nurses, and where new knowledge will be created for the benefit of humanity."[25]

Graham's view of hospitals was always with a broad horizon: "It is no longer merely a place for the sick to be treated.... today the hospital is the most important and most expensive factor in medical education.... Perhaps nothing has been more revolutionary in the past century in medical education in this country than the realization that the center of all medical educational activities is the teaching hospital."[26] As to trusteeship, he asked: "Who is responsible for the hospital? Do [the trustees] know what their responsibilities are? The trustee should be able to say: 'We guarantee to the people who come into our hospital competence and honesty.'"[26] Graham constantly challenged the Barnes trustees that their role was greater than the management of buildings and the maintenance of fiscal stability; there were educational and ethical aspects to their obligations.

By working together on many occasions during these tumultuous times, Hospital Director Frank Bradley and Evarts Graham became close friends, and Bradley recalled:

> Graham was very profound.... he was a unique individual.... From the standpoint of a hospital administrator... he understood the role that the hospital played in the medical school and medical education. ... He was a great protector of the hospital and thought that the medical school which was primarily interested in teaching and research tended to either ignore or override the hospital but Dr. Graham prevented that. Through his strength on committees and his knowledge of hospital operation... he helped to maintain the teaching wards and, in a sense, made the hospital group what it really is.[27]

For 30 years, Evarts Graham was the most important voice of medical education and research within the St. Louis hospital community, outdistancing other members of his faculty, and the accolades given by Frank Bradley—a hospital superintendent of national stature—acknowledged Graham's role in shaping the partnership of Barnes Hospital and Washington University. Bradley's vision was also a major factor in preparing Barnes Hospital to become one of the country's outstanding institutions by the end of the century, and he, along with Graham and Shaffer, helped to make Washington University the "Ideal Medical School" that was hoped for at the beginning of the century.

CHOOSING CHANCELLORS

Evarts Graham's stature within the medical faculty as well as in the national and international medical community made him important in several aspects of Washington University, other than just the Medical School. His official contacts with the hilltop campus were chiefly with the chancellor's office, but he also had acquaintances and close contacts on the science and engineering faculties. Evarts Graham and Arthur Holly Compton[c], as Princetonians and faculty colleagues who arrived at Washington University within months of each other, established a warm and

---

c. Arthur Holly Compton (1892 to 1962), born in Wooster, Ohio, obtained his bachelor's degree at Wooster College in 1913. Three years later he became the third of three brothers to obtain a doctor of philosophy degree at Princeton. His physicist brother Karl became president of the Massachusetts Institute of Technology, and Wilson, an economist, became president of Washington State University. Following his Princeton studies, Compton taught for 1 year at the University of Minnesota, before doing World War I research on aircraft instruments for the Westinghouse Lamp Company. Chosen as a member of the first class of National Research Council Fellows, he spent his fellowship year (1919) at Cambridge, United Kingdom, in the Cavendish Laboratory of Ernest Rutherford, discoverer of the atomic nucleus.

In 1920 a 3-year contract with Washington University saw Compton as head of the Department of Physics. During his years in St. Louis, his experiments conducted in the basement of the Eads Building led to his receiving the 1927 Nobel Prize in Physics for "the Compton Effect," which described an increase in the wavelength of electromagnetic radiation when scattered by particles whose size was shorter than the wave being scattered—it is also known as the "Compton-Debye Effect." He moved to the University of Chicago as chairman of physics (1923 to 1929), and remained in Chicago as distinguished service professor until 1945. From February 1942 until July 1945, he was director of the Metallurgical Laboratory of the University of Chicago, which supplied uranium for the first sustained nuclear reaction, a part of the Manhattan Project to develop the atomic bomb. For the 8 years following the expiry of his term as Washington University chancellor (1945 to 1953), he remained in St. Louis as a professor of natural history.

Compton belonged to the nation and to the world as counselor to high government officials, a member of many national and international commissions, and an active champion of humanitarian causes. Compton loved pomp and circumstance; he received 14 honorary degrees and nine medals of distinction. During his years as chancellor, Washington University was transformed from a local college to an institution of national and international prominence.

admiring friendship during Compton's 3 years as chairman of the Department of Physics. It was inevitable that at the end of World War II, Graham would be involved in the search for a chancellor, particularly when Compton, who was a "far-out" possibility, was being considered.

Harry Brookings Wallace, a nephew of Robert S. Brookings and president of the Cupples Corporation, served 32 years on the corporate board of Washington University—as president (1942 to 1951) and interim chancellor (1943 to 1945). Probably his greatest contribution was the recruitment of Arthur Holly Compton, accomplished by close collaboration with Evarts Graham. Conversations between Compton, Wallace, and Graham began in the early spring of 1944, and on July 6 Compton, as president of the Metallurgical Laboratory ("Met Lab") at the University of Chicago paid a short visit to St. Louis. His visit was partly to explore the chancellorship and partly a business trip to the Mallinckrodt Chemical Company to visit with its president, Edward Mallinckrodt, for at this time the company was purifying uranium nitrate for the Met Lab's atomic pile, the experimental incubator of the atomic bomb.[1]

Compton followed up the visit by writing to Wallace: "After careful consideration…I can only tell you that it is not feasible for me to consider an offer of a Chancellorship at Washington University at this time."[28] Copies of the letter were sent to both Mallinckrodt and Graham. In an accompanying personal letter to Graham, he indicated his sorrow that it had been necessary to confirm his negative response[d]. Graham continued the correspondence: "It would have been a grand thing for us if you had come here as the Chancellor. … I question very much whether you really wish to give up physics to become a university president. I did feel nevertheless that possibly you might wish to conquer some new world since you have already cleaned up so successfully in the scientific world."[29]

Not to be easily turned away, Wallace elected to send Drs. Frank Bubb and Evarts Graham to Chicago to talk further with Compton. Bubb was chairman of applied mathematics and in charge of the Washington University cyclotron that supplied plutonium for the Met Lab.[1] Graham and Bubb spent 2 hours with Compton on Saturday morning, July 29, and returned to give Wallace the impression that Compton was more disposed to consider the possibility of coming to St. Louis than he had been 3 weeks earlier. They reported that what would interest him most was the possibility of creating a first-class school of engineering. Compton felt that there were only two in the country—the Massachusetts and California Institutes of Technology—and that developing one in St. Louis would depend in great measure on local support by the industries of greater St. Louis. Compton gave

---

d. *Author's note:* All of the correspondence between Arthur Holly Compton and Evarts Graham was conducted on a first-name basis, made possible by the mutual respect between the two, as well as the fraternal bond that develops between Princetonians. Every visit was marked by an invitation, extended also to their wives, to dinner at the home of either Graham or Compton.

them the impression that "the principle reason for his declining the offer about three weeks ago was because he felt that he did not wish to embarrass the university in any way by the fact that it would not be possible for him to serve immediately if he should accept." The issue that was raised was the possibility of Compton's appointment to Thomas Dewey's cabinet in the event that Dewey should win the upcoming presidential election, and whether Compton might be able to defer his Washington University appointment or possibly to serve in the cabinet while chancellor. Graham reminded him that David Houston had remained as chancellor even as he served in President Wilson's cabinet. In his long report to Wallace on the visit, Graham wrote: "On the whole I feel that the outlook for our getting Dr. Compton here is considerably better than it was on the occasion of his recent visit. I feel much more encouraged. ... the assurance of support for his pet scheme of a first class engineering school here would I think be the greatest possible inducement to him to come."[30] During the visit, Compton had remarked to Graham: "I think it is a very fine thing, for Mr. Wallace to send two members of the faculty to come here and see me, [it] shows a spirit of confidence in the faculty by the Trustees which is too often absent in universities. I am enormously pleased at this attitude of the Board of Washington University."[30]

The correspondence continued with Compton, who was expressing interest and promising that he "would try to find a basis for a firm answer to the acceptance of the Chancellorship by early October [1944]." He also expressed a desire to return to St. Louis within the month. He refused an offer to make use of the chancellor's residence, for fear it would imply a commitment.[31] Graham continued the encouragement: "What we want more than anything else is, if possible, a favorable decision. We would much prefer to have you take whatever time may be necessary to make up your mind without any feeling of pressure or harassment."[32]

The winter of 1944 to 1945 saw the great military effort in Europe, and correspondence about the chancellorship that had dwindled for a few months was renewed in February by Graham: "We are wondering if you have been able to come to any decision about your acceptance of the Chancellorship of Washington University. We don't want to hurry you. We hope you have decided to be with us after the War."[33] In March the pace quickened and Graham made a second visit to Chicago solely to discuss again the possibility of a Compton appointment. Five weeks later he wrote to Compton:

> I would like to say that those of us who are in the know are thrilled with the prospect that you may come here. ... Washington University has never had a Chancellor of broad vision and of courage with perhaps the possible exception of the first Chancellor. ... you could come here and set the place on fire, not only the University but the City of St. Louis as well. ... I am sure you will agree that it is personalities that

count more than anything else. You of course know that President Harper created the great University of Chicago out of an unknown and practically defunct little Baptist College ... also that Pasadena was completely unknown to the scientific world until CalTech was created. ... In spite of everything, the rumor has slipped out somewhere that the Chancellorship has been offered to you. Everyone who has mentioned the subject to me has expressed tremendous enthusiasm about it in the hope that you will find it possible to accept.[34]

By April, Compton had decided that St. Louis and Washington University offered the opportunities he desired; uranium from Oak Ridge, Tennessee, and plutonium from Hanford, Washington, had begun to move to the bomb assembly site at Los Alamos, New Mexico. Once this issue was resolved, Compton announced his acceptance of the chancellorship, on April 20, 1945.

Never before had the university fixed its sights on a chancellor of greater renown, and there was "remarkable agreement that Compton [stood] at the divide between the old Washington University and the new and [this appointment] set in motion the transformation of Washington University from a St. Louis streetcar college to a national research university of international standing."[1] Evarts Graham's friendship, determination, and unfailing energy were major features in Compton's decision. During Graham's memorial service, Chancellor E.A.H. Shepley credited Graham ·with Compton's recruitment, saying that while Graham's report would not so indicate, he was largely responsible for the success of the mission, the consequence of which is the preeminent stature of Washington University today.[35]

However, Graham's role in selecting chancellors was not yet finished. In April 1953 Compton resigned as chancellor. Mr. William M. Akin, president of the Laclede Steel Company, was named to lead a search committee with a faculty advisory group of five professors and deans chaired by Evarts Graham. The committee's initial choice was W. Barry Wood, who, after several months of indecision, elected to become vice-president of medicine at his alma mater, Johns Hopkins. The committee then looked to Arthur S. Fleming, president of Ohio Wesleyan, who later became United States secretary of health, education, and welfare. Graham's advisory group deferred to faculty pressures after Thomas H. Elliot, professor of political science, wrote on behalf of the faculty senate that Ethan A.H. Shepley, chairman of the Washington University Board of Trustees and acting chancellor, should be the only candidate. Following a short conversation between Akin and Graham, Akins' committee closed its search.

Graham's ability to make a decision and lead his advisory group provided Washington University with yet another great chancellor, one who would guide it through the unfinished scientific developments envisioned by Compton.[1] During his prestigious 8 years (1953 to 1961, the Einsenhower/McCarthy period), Shepley was unflinching in defense of academic freedom. He championed a far-sighted development plan, proved to be an able fund-raiser, and expanded the university's student body from a local to a national base. His chancellorship was as significant for Washington University as Compton's had been a decade earlier.

DEALING WITH MINORITY GROUPS

Evarts Graham's St. Louis years saw profound changes in the social fabric of America, particularly in regard to the status of minority groups. None of the individuals who have commented on Graham's social, religious, or political beliefs have touched upon his views toward minorities. A critical and close inspection is probably impossible now, but from his writings, a few of his actions, and the comments of his contemporaries, a superficial view about his feelings may be obtained.

The plight of minority groups was not an over-riding cause for Graham, although it was always of concern. His compassion for patients was far more intense, and it was always personal, gentle, and considerate; this compassion was a fiercely held personal principle that came with the obligation to serve those under his care.

His attitudes toward the excluded groups within Americana show him more as a willing participant than a leader in the emerging movements for rights and privileges. Medicine and medical education were white male prerogatives, and women, Blacks, and Jews were excluded by covert and outspoken quotas.[36] Graham, who was raised with the attitudes and beliefs held by the white Anglo-Saxon majority, was always cognizant of the cultural/social changes that were occurring between and after the two World Wars, and, although never an aggressive champion for change, he was sensitive and generally supportive. His lifestyle and writings reflect an advocacy for these social and cultural trends.

Women

Graham's attitudes toward women in science and medicine were ahead of those of his contemporary medical world. His wife was a successful, independent, scientific researcher, working within the budding feminist movement, where she was visible on social and political fronts (see chapter 19). Helen was undoubtedly a major influence on Graham's attitude toward women's issues, although his mother had also been a leader in her day (see chapter 2). Helen went her own way with tacit and an unwavering support from Evarts, and, although their professional lives were rarely intermingled, their social and cultural lives were deeply so. She was a partner in his efforts and he in hers.

During his years on the fellowship board in the 1920s, Graham was very supportive of female applicants for Rockefeller Fellowships. In his recommendations he seemed to appreciate that women could and would make significant contributions in many fields of science, and his reports appear to be less critical of females than they are of some of the males. Through Helen, he was supportive of female medical students at Washington University, but in a school that admitted five or eight women into each class of 86, he acquiesced to practices that were current rather than adopting a proactive stance to admit more women. Females were never admitted to his internship or residency programs[e].

Black People

Recognition of the role of Blacks in American society and the civil rights issues that became so prominent in the aftermath of World War II were issues barely raised during Graham's early years in St. Louis. However, he was always sympathetic toward the plight of Blacks, particularly the limited availability of educational opportunities. During the McCarthy frenzy of the 1950s, Graham became concerned about communism and made the comment, "Things are pretty good throughout the United States for most people.... I just don't understand how anyone in the United States could really become a communist," then, pausing, "except maybe a black man."[37]

On the national scene, Graham was a strong supporter of more medical schools and increased educational as well as social opportunities for black physicians. As late as 1950, the American Medical Association excluded Blacks from membership, as did 25 of the 79 medical schools, and, in the year before his retirement, Graham actively worked toward their admission to the American Medical Association and the American College of Surgeons.[38] In St. Louis he supported efforts to upgrade City Hospital No. 2—the Homer Phillips Hospital for Negroes (City Hospital No. 1 was for Whites). As chief surgical consultant to the Homer Phillips Hospital, he delegated the responsibility of overseeing the surgical service to Robert Elman, and he welcomed Homer Phillips residents to his staff conferences at Barnes.[39] In 1950 his efforts at the hospital were recognized by its award of meritorious service. On that occasion, an editorial in the *Journal of the National Medical Association* paid him a special tribute: "Among those who have championed our cause, none has done so more consistently, effectively or with more unassuming modesty...his battles on behalf of Negro surgeons several years ago are just becoming generally known.... He was one of the few pioneers...courageous and stalwart. He stood firm without fear of consequences. Finally justice won.... all Negro surgeons owe a lasting debt to Evarts Graham who fought for their rights."[40] At Barnes Hospital Graham approved the creation of a separate ward for black patients, but there is no record of an effort to secure integration of the races throughout the hospital or a voiced objection to the concept of separate blood banks. He never appointed a black intern or resident.

---

e. *Author's Note:* In those decades, few women would dare choose a surgical career, and there were no applicants.

Jewish People

Even though Graham's years in St. Louis were years in which Jews were becoming an active, visible, and increasingly important group in the surgical world, anti-Semitism was certainly not unknown in that world. Correspondence to and from Graham's colleagues consistently showed an awareness of ethnic origin. On occasion, Jewishness or non-Jewishness became the defining point in characterizing someone, and comments by Graham showed that, by his Midwest standards, he felt east-coast Jews had undesirable traits. Phrases such as, "I have no doubt that he is of the chosen race…"[41] are infrequently scattered through his letters: to Dean Lewis, "Contrary to what his name might indicate, he is not of the 'chosen race'";[42] to Dallas Phemister, "Although he is Jewish he is entirely white and has none of their objectionable characteristics";[43] to Harvey Cushing, in recommending an applicant for a residency, "He is not a Hebrew";[44] in a reference for Ed Lehman, "In case you might suspect that he is Jewish, I can assure you that he is not";[45] in 1930 to Elliott Cutler, regarding a surgeon who was requesting a staff appointment at Western Reserve, "He is, I think, an excellent man but he is an Episcopalian Jew if you know what that means; that he is of Jewish origin but belongs to the Episcopal Church";[46] and, in regard to a candidate for a fellowship on his chest service, "We may have two Jews on the Chest Service during the year beginning July 1, 1941. I doubt if we can take on a third."[47]

Graham was well aware of discrimination against Jews on the east coast as well as in the Midwest, and, in a frank discussion, he encouraged I.Y. Olch, a Jew, and one of Graham's favorite staff members, to move to California; he then supported the move with departmental funds, until he was called to task by Dean Shaffer. Olch recalled the conversation: "Being a Jew the opportunities in academic surgery in this country at that time were extremely limited. There were no places and [Graham] said [to me] that you can stay here as long as you want or go into private practice…. You may rise as a full-time Director of Surgery in [one of the] Jewish hospitals around the country…. [he] said it was coming some day and of course it has come about…. he was that sort of guy."[48] Two years later, in an internal memorandum concerning I.Y. Olch, Graham wrote, "The fact that he is Jewish made it somewhat more difficult for him to get a practice here than I thought it would be for him in Los Angeles."[49]

Graham was aware of unspoken quotas for Jewish students in many medical schools,[1] and he knew that after rejection by US schools, Jewish students frequently went to England, Scotland, or Ireland for their medical education.[50] The issue was of such importance on the east coast that, as late as 1950, Governor Nelson Rockefeller promoted a State University of New York (SUNY) with several medical schools that would provide educational opportunities to excluded Jewish students of greater New York City. Dr. Dan H. Funkenstein, an ex–Barnes resident, shortly after attempting to open his practice of surgery in Jacksonville, Florida, wrote to Graham asking for advice: "If I pursue a purely academic career I could never get very far due to prejudice.... I feel that you represent the most liberal point of view of American medicine and can understand my problem...."[51]

Graham's thoughts on the more global nature of anti-Semitism are expressed in three pieces of his correspondence. He wrote to Rabbi Isserman of Temple Israel on the occasion of the temple's gift of baptistery doors for the new St. Louis Christ Church Cathedral in honor of Bishop Scarlett: "[The gift is] one of the finest things that has happened in St. Louis for a very long time. What a magnificent symbol it is of an attempt by people of different religious thought and training to understand each other. It is a symbol which I hope will be enduring.... I consider myself fortunate to know both of you."[52] In 1945, in regard to membership in the Circle of the Round Table to which Dr. Edward Doisy was admitted and Dr. Joseph Erlanger was not (both were Nobel prize winners—Doisy in 1943 and Erlanger in 1944), he wrote: "I would like to ask that Erlanger's name be added to the list of candidates. I hope that he has not been excluded because he happens to be Jewish. I am afraid I should lose interest in the Round Table if such a narrow point of view were to be adopted."[53] In 1956, after receiving a complimentary copy of the newly founded *Hebrew Medical Journal*, with the request that it be advertised in the *Journal of Thoracic Surgery*, Graham wrote to the editor of the new journal: "It seems to me that the result of such a publication really is only to isolate the Jews from the rest of the community more than they are already. To me that is a great misfortune. I would prefer to see more intermingling and less isolation. Supposedly we are all citizens on equal standing in a great nation.... I am not in favor of carrying a notice [of your new journal] in the *Journal of Thoracic Surgery*."[54]

Graham was sensitive to the position of Jews as a separate people, but, as the last three anecdotes illustrate, he worked to minimize the distinction. He was a product of his times, yet he was generous, understanding, and foresightful. His use of terms seems to be descriptive, not derogatory. His basic crusade was for the betterment of surgery. The betterment of minorities was an issue beyond him, and, if any prejudice could be said to exist, it was manifest by a failure to aggressively recruit minorities, rather than by an overt discrimination.

Chapter 14

INTRAMURAL ACTIVITIES: PART 2

EDITORIAL ENTERPRISES

Graham's editorial obligations began less than 6 months after his arrival in St. Louis. By then he was the author of 24 publications that stemmed from his Chicago years and his 2 years with the army. He became involved with several surgical publications and maintained many of these associations throughout his life.

Archives of Surgery

In 1919 the American Medical Association (AMA) decided to publish *Archives of Surgery* to accompany the Archives series in other specialties. Its purpose was to "express ideas in the growing field of surgical education and provide an opportunity for the publication of original research in subjects that laid the foundation for surgical progress."[1] The mission statement was designed to counter the opposition of Lewis S. Pilcher, editor of the *Annals of Surgery*, and Franklin H. Martin, editor of *Surgery, Gynecology and Obstetrics*, both of whom complained that the *Archives* would encroach upon their turf of clinical surgery.

The first issue, July 1920, was prepared by an editorial board of six men[a], and headed by Dean Lewis of Johns Hopkins, who dominated the board until his illness

---

a. *Archives of Surgery* editorial board: Dean Lewis (of Chicago), Evarts Graham (of St. Louis), Hugh Cabot (of Ann Arbor), Thomas Cullen (of Baltimore), William Darrach (of New York City), William J. May (of Rochester).

in 1929 led to the appointment of Waltman Walters of Rochester, Minnesota.[1-3] Graham served until 1945, reviewing manuscripts, making suggestions, and attending board meetings once a year. His reviews for the *Archives* were not only rather desultory but uncritical and of uncertain help to the editor, for example: "I do not consider that Dr. Behan's article is worthy of very serious consideration. Dr. Deaver's article is, of course, of some interest. I should think it might be used if you are short of material but yet I would not feel like recommending it for publication."[4] Graham was never a major editorial voice behind the journal, although he used American Medical Association publications—*Journal of the American Medical Association* and the *Archives of Surgery*—in which to publish more than 50 of his works.

Graham's leaving of this board was not without controversy, which he engendered. In 1942 Waltman Walters was called to active duty with the navy, and he asked Lester Dragstedt of Chicago to serve as the board's temporary chairman. At the same time, Olin West, acting on behalf of the trustees of the AMA appointed Frederick Coller of Michigan, not on the board at the time, to be acting chairman. West's action surprised Dragstedt and outraged Graham, who wrote to his friend Lester:

> I was shocked. ... I think you have been handled outrageously by Olin West. ... Certainly unless the members of the Editorial Board are a group of rubber stamps they ought to have something to say about the selection of the Chairman of the Board. ... I can hardly imagine that Fred Coller would accept the position. ... I have been thinking for a long time that I ought to resign from the Editorial Board of the *Archives*. ... I think that no one should hold a position so long that he wears out his welcome. I did try to resign once and was asked to stay on. I believe however that I shall take this occasion to notify Olin West that I do not care to continue as a member of the Board.[5]

Dradstedt was likewise offended by the action and wrote to Olin West to complain about not having been notified before another acting chairman was designated, that it was a sharp practice, foreign to his own code. He promptly resigned.[6] Graham, eager to continue the contest of wills, also wrote to West:

> I can hardly let this episode go by without voicing a protest against the apparent discourtesy which you have shown to Lester Dragstedt and to the rest of the Editorial Board. ... It would seem to me, furthermore, that your action in this matter, without consulting the other members of the Board, can only mean that you regard us as rubber stamps. For these reasons I feel that I do not care to continue my membership on the Board and I am offering you my resignation with

this letter.... in view of my failure to receive any notification from you about what has happened during more than two weeks... I am led to believe that you are not planning to discuss this important question with the members of the Board.[7]

West returned a long apologetic letter,[8] to which Graham responded: "It would seem to me that under the circumstances the only dignified position which I can take in this matter is to insist on your acceptance of my resignation.... It has been my intention all along to retire from the Board when Dr. Walters returns from the War, my retirement might just as well come now as later."[9] To Dragstedt, he stated: "I feel that the Board must take a dignified position in regard to this matter and the only position to take is to resign."[10] Another letter of apology came from AMA representatives, Coller's name was withdrawn, and Dragstedt served until 1945 when Walters returned. It is not clear as to where the authority lay to choose an interim chairman—with the AMA, who owned the *Archives*, or with its editorial board. Graham, however, was willing to make it an issue, and he prevailed.

Graham attempted to resign a third time and wrote to Waltman Walters: "I sent my resignation to Dr. Olin West about a year ago.... one reason for my desire to resign is that I haven't done enough work for the *Archives* in the last few years to qualify as a member. That, likewise, is a source of embarrassment to me."[11] Receiving no reaction to this letter, Graham wrote again to Olin West, to resign from the editorial board: "I think already I have been on much too long.... I believe that once before I resigned to you, I also sent a resignation to Waltman Walters and neither one of them seem to have taken. I hope this one will."[12] With his resignation accepted, Graham ceased to publish in the *Archives of Surgery*. He wrote only once more for AMA publications—his landmark paper with Wynder on smoking and lung cancer appeared in the *Journal of the American Medical Association*.

Annals of Surgery

Evarts Graham became a member of the 12-man editorial board for the *Annals of Surgery* in 1935. The *Annals*, founded in 1885, is the oldest surgical journal in the United States, and for its first 50 years, it was under the sole editorial management of Dr. Lewis Stephen Pilcher. At his retirement, the J.B. Lippincott Company elected to replace him with an editorial board chaired by John Gibbon of Philadelphia.[13] As a member of this board, Graham was not expected to do more than review articles for the journal and make comments as to advisability for publication. Frequently delinquent, he received constant reminders to return manuscripts with his comments. After 5 years, unenthusiastic with this role, he requested and received a leave of absence effective May 1, 1940.[14] Graham had little further contact with this board, and in July 1947 he was officially transferred from the editorial board to the advisory board, a position he held until his death.[15]

Year Book of Surgery

The two editorial obligations carried by Graham that gave him the greatest pleasure were the *Journal of Thoracic Surgery* and the *Year Book of General Surgery*. The latter provided an opportunity to express unedited personal opinions to an extent not given elsewhere. The Year Books were a Chicago effort, and the Surgery volume was started in 1901; John B. Murphy, its editor, was succeeded in 1916 by Albert Ochsner, one of Graham's mentors at the Chicago Presbyterian Hospital. Upon Ochsner's death in 1926, Mr. Cloyd J. Head, the owner, invited Graham to become editor of the *Year Book of Surgery* and proposed that the obligations of editorship would be supported by Dr. Louis J. Mitchell, who would select and abstract reprints of appropriate articles. The editor was expected to add occasional editorial comments, make revisions to the text, and select additional articles that he wished to appear in the book. Routine copy editing and proofreading was to be done in the Chicago office.[16] After accepting the offer, Graham asked if it was customary to make compensation to the editor, for he had a full-time professorial position and was not engaged in private practice, and, for those reasons, would not derive financial profit from any prestige that might accrue to the editor of the publication.[17] His concerns were heard; in addition to paying the expenses of Mitchell's office, the Year Books agreed to pay Graham an annual honorarium of $300,[18] and plans were made to send him the initial set of abstracts.[19] Graham received five or six batches of reprints every year, each containing 60 to 80 articles, from which he returned his list of those that he felt should be abstracted; Heinz Haffner, a junior faculty member, was enlisted to help in making these selections. Graham established a close working relationship, first with Louis Mitchell, and then with his successor, Ms. Frances Wetherhold.

The initial volume with Graham as editor contained a short personal introduction, in which Graham acknowledged his debt to A.J. Ochsner, "feeling that his ripened clinical judgement and editorial comments could not be approached by one so much younger."[20] He wrote an introductory editorial for every issue until 1957. Over the years his comments varied in length. Some were short, merely highlighting references to several of the abstracts in an effort to guide the reader to those he felt warranted special consideration; some were lengthy and expressed Graham's philosophy.

Graham accepted the liberty of editorial comment to such an extent that, for the 1953 issue, he wrote an introduction entitled "Should Surgeons Be Honest?" It was a lengthy discussion of fee splitting, its definition, and its practice, and his condemnation of it.[21] At this juncture he happened to be chairman of the board of regents of the American College of Surgeons, and he was actively involved in attempts to move the college to a firm stand on the issue. The editorial staff reluctantly concluded that the editorial should not be published, for, although they agreed with the principles, they felt the subject matter was outside the sphere of the *Year Book*, and they requested that Graham write a new editorial. The editorial staff wished the book to present an annual review of the science of surgery, enlivened by the editor's personal comments; they had never planned for it to discuss medical ethics or the interaction of medicine and government.[22] Graham's surgical philosophy was, however, expressed that year in an editorial dealing with his ideas about surgical education.

Graham's thoughts on cancer, with some musings on its therapy, were contained in his introduction to the 1956–1957 volume—his last—which contained an abstract of an article by N.E. McKinnon on cancer mortality and the failure of control through case-finding programs.[23] McKinnon had concluded: "Case finding and control programs have not accomplished and cannot today accomplish the purpose for which they were established.... they do not represent a sound investment from the point of view from the money involved—or, it might be added, public trust, interest or co-operation—and they do not spell progress for public health."[23] Graham selected this abstract to discuss in one of his most lengthy introductions, and, in it, he asked himself and his readers: "have we been mistaken for about three quarters of a century in some of our basic concepts of the treatment of cancer? Is it possible that we could have been as wrong as many recent articles would imply?... now... comes McKinnon... who tells [us] that 'aggressive programs over the past twenty-five to thirty years for the control of cancer mortality, and more particularly that of breast cancer, have failed to make an impression on the latter recorded mortality.'"[24] After referencing a few articles not contained in this particular volume, Graham continued:

> It is distressing to find the mortality increasing in spite of the fact that undoubtedly there have been in recent years more excellent surgeons available in those countries than ever before who have the knowledge and equipment to give their patient the best that surgery can offer....
> I have limited my remarks here to cancer of the breast because that condition has perhaps been as well studied as any other cancer and there has been an excellent opportunity for many years to observe the effects of surgical and other forms of treatment but where does all this discussion leave us? I confess I do not know.[24]

In addition to the freedom of editorial comment in introductions, Graham enjoyed the privilege of adding a few lines after an occasional abstract that caught his attention, which sometimes got him into trouble. In the 1936 edition, Professor B. Schiassi of Bologna, Italy, claimed that cholecystotomy with simple removal of gallstones (cholecystendesis) was preferable to cholecystectomy, and that, in 314 patients, he had had 100 percent successful results.[25] Graham dismissed the observation:

> I have been wondering what the author of this article had to drink. Those of us who remove the gallbladder will now have to lie awake at night in a torment of worry about the dreadful things which will

happen to our patients. The operation of cholecystendesis (the name of which was given by Courvoisier) consists of opening the gallbladder, removing any contained stones, closing the opening and allowing the organ to drop back into the abdomen. It became obsolete because the results were not satisfactory. The author's statement that cholecysten- desis gives 100 per cent. of successful results becomes significant when it is recalled that he lives in Bologna.—Ed.[26]

The editorial staff of the *Year Book* enjoyed it; the *Cincinnati Journal of Medicine* even went so far as to chuckle over it in print. The Year Books received three requests from Bologna for a copy of the book—one from a bookstore, the other two from editors of surgical journals. The edition was soon out of print, and copies were never sent to Italy.[27] However, some copies must have arrived, for, within a few months, Charles Mayo wrote to Graham that he had received a letter from a prominent Italian surgeon, V. Putti, to the effect that Schiassi was severely offend- ed.[28] Graham wrote long letters to Mayo, Putti, and Schiassi, pleading that he had written the comment on a very hot day that summer, that a vacation had been in the offing, and that he had not seen the printer's proof. He heaped fulsome praise upon the university and city of Bologna, and closed by begging Schiassi's pardon, assuring him that "no personal offense was intended and certainly [he] did not mean to cast a slur upon [the] famous University or city."[29,30] Schiassi was not mol- lified, and he wrote Graham a three-page letter in French: "I regret the heat was able to influence your brain [so]...that you could not grasp...my discourse....When you read my affirmation of 100% you are so surprised that the word 'baloney' comes to you?...With this humor you make an insinuation...doubting my statis- tics....Do not think, M. le Docteur, that I have any rancour towards you....only I beg you to accept some advice: watch yourself, in the future, on hot days...."[31] The vice president of Year Book Publishers wrote to Graham: "Even if you were able to translate these jokes it might not soothe them altogether and I don't know that they will like it any better to know that you were just kidding....We stand ready to do anything we can to help. If worse comes to worst let me support you on the field of honor."[32] With the apology to Professors Putti and Schiassi the issue was closed,[33] and in a personal memorandum[b] for his own files Graham wrote, "Thus ended l'Affaire Schiassi with all the baloney, spaghetti, garlic, etc. pertaining thereto."[34]

---

b. In a seven-page memorandum entitled "L'Affaire Schiassi," Graham recorded the details surround- ing his editorial comment on the Schiassi article, and the resulting correspondence with Mayo, Putti, Schiassi, and the *Year Book* editors. This is similar to his memorandum "L'Affaire Fuller," which doc- umented his dealings with Colonel Fuller while at Camp Sheridan (see chapter 4). Both are detailed personal notes intended to be kept in his own files for his record and possibly posterity. A copy was probably sent to Simon of the Year Book Publishers, but no letter of transmittal has been found.

Graham's comments that followed the abstracts sometimes presented facts, sometimes praised, and sometimes admonished. A sample was collected in a small "Red Book" given to those who attended Graham's retirement dinner in November 1951. The "Red Book" contained 35 of the choicest remarks Graham had made during his 26 years as editor. Included with the Bologna comment were the following:[35]

> Truth is beauty, even when it concerns a hemorrhoid. (1950)

> These mortality and survival figures certainly do not indicate that the Nazi philosophy improves surgery. (1939)

> There is always a danger in generalizing too much. (1928)

> In regard to the case reported here it is difficult to avoid comment on the employment of two teams to avoid fatigue of the surgeon. In a large personal experience with this operation the Editor has never found this necessary. However if a surgeon's union is ever formed with a compulsory four or five hour day, it may be necessary for operating teams to work in shifts to prevent the surgeon from drawing overtime pay. Who can tell? (1948)

> The report of 100% efficiency for any therapeutic procedure usually indicates either an insufficient number of observations or inadequate observations. (1926)

> Ten cases hardly constitute a satisfactory test of the dangers of the methods. (1945)

The comments had been selected by Frances Wetherhold, with whom Graham had worked closely, and to whom he had extended a personal invitation to attend the dinner. Upon leaving the *Year Book* staff in 1955, Graham became a strong supporter of her application for a position in the Phoenix Museum of Indian Artefacts.

Involvement with the *Year Book* was Graham's most gratifying editorial experience, and he continued the involvement until his final illness.

Journal of Thoracic Surgery

The *Journal of Thoracic Surgery* was Evarts Graham's own publishing pride and joy and, with an occasional change of associate editors, he remained as editor-in-chief from its inception in 1931 until his death in 1957[c]. It was the official organ of the American Association for Thoracic Surgery (AATS), which grew out of the New York Society for Thoracic Surgery.

---

c. The Graham archives in the Becker Medical Library contain three separate notations to the effect that all of the files on the *Journal of Thoracic Surgery* have been moved to a destination unknown. Thoughts or ideas contained in his correspondence, either with publishers or authors, are unavailable.

The first meeting of the AATS, held in the office of Dr. Willy Meyer on February 20, 1917, was an attempt to create a national society that would be an association *for* thoracic surgery, not one *of* thoracic surgeons; it was to be a multidisciplinary effort. The 42 names submitted as prospects included surgeons, anatomists, physiologists, researchers, anesthetists, pathologists, internists, tuberculosis specialists, radiologists, and endoscopists. All were invited to a second meeting on June 17, 1917, held at the Waldorf Astoria Hotel, but, due to wartime travel restrictions, only five invitees from outside New York City were able to attend. Lung abscess, bronchiectasis, empyema, and chest wall tumors were the topics of interest, and many wondered if the field were so narrow that the society would fail because discussions would soon become repetitive. At a meeting held on June 10, 1918, at the Congress Hotel in Chicago, there were 65 members, six original papers, and a series of case reports. As years passed, the membership list grew longer, the scope wider, and interest gradually increased. In paying tribute to the leaders of the association, Graham labeled Willy Meyer, Howard Lilienthal, and Rudolph Matas "the triumvirate that kept the Association alive."[36]

Publication of material presented during the meetings of the early years was not obligatory, and each author was at liberty to select a journal of his own choosing. In 1922 Dean Lewis agreed to a yearly special edition of the *Archives of Surgery*. In 1931, with Evarts Graham as editor, Mosby's *Journal of Thoracic Surgery* became the official organ of the association; in 1959 it was renamed the *Journal of Thoracic and Cardiovascular Surgery*.

This journal did not provide Graham the liberty to express his personal views, as was permitted in the *Year Book of General Surgery*, and his only editorial opinion was expressed in a two-page introduction to volume I. Graham wrote: "Specially welcome are articles dealing not only with the purely clinical aspects of this field but also with reports of carefully conducted experimental investigations in the realms of physiology, bacteriology, pathology, etc., which may have a bearing on the clinical problems concerned."[36] However, the *Journal* does contain many of his thoughts on the clinical problems of thoracic surgery, through publications that began with a four-part discussion of bronchiectasis; thirteen more original articles were written before he finished publishing 20 years later. The *Journal* published all of the papers and discussions delivered at the annual meeting of the AATS. Graham was a frequent discussant; one to six discussions by Graham appeared in the *Journal* every year from 1931 to 1950, and through reading these discussions, it is possible to understand his views on almost every aspect of the expanding realm of thoracic surgery.

In 1950 the *Journal* began to publish two volumes each year, and in 1951, the year of his retirement at Washington University, Graham ceased to publish any of his own thoughts or to discuss the ideas of others. He disappeared from the *Journal's* author list. After his death, Emile Holman was elected editor, with Graham's protégés—Brian Blades and Thomas Burford—associate editors. Graham's *Journal* had become one of national stature.

Surgery

Surgery was founded by Mosby and Company, which had offices in mid-town St. Louis. Its first issue in January 1937 listed Graham as a member of its advisory board, but out of deference to his friend Owen Wangensteen of Minneapolis and co-editor of *Surgery*, he published only twice in the journal, lectures that he had given at the Mayo Clinic and at the University of Minnesota. He had little interest in *Surgery*, and his contributions were strictly titular; Graham's name appeared on the letterhead until he died.

In reviewing articles for *Surgery*, Graham was brief and cryptic, expressing his likes or dislikes with one or two sentences: "It is a fairly good text book presentation but you do whatever you think best" or "The article by Drs. Schindler and Gnazi is worth publishing for [I] know the authors to be careful and competent."[37]

MISCELLANY

Offers of Other Chairs

Invitations to leave St. Louis arrived on Graham's desk throughout his professional life. The first was a joint request from Cornell and the Rockefeller Institute that came 3 months after he had accepted the Washington University offer.[38] It was easily rejected.

Three years after the cholecystography success, Graham was approached in regard to his interest in returning to Chicago to become chairman of surgery at the University of Illinois, a position held by Dean Lewis who was preparing for his move to Johns Hopkins.[39] Graham waited 2 months before deciding not to return, citing his preference for a full-time position and his loyalty to the young men around him.[40]

Two years later, acting on behalf of the University of Minnesota, W.J. Mayo approached Graham regarding the chairmanship position in Minneapolis. Graham responded in a lengthy letter beginning:

> It is always pleasant to know that you think well of me.... In fact, I regarded that invitation as almost the highest honor that has come to me because it apparently represents your selection.... I could use very well the large increase in income which you have assured me, but money is only a means to enabling one to do good work.... I have always felt that surgery is a good deal like music. There is a place in the world for many different kinds of musicians; some desire to be great artists appearing before large audiences and incidentally making a large income. My own ambitions however have rather been directed toward [being] the composer who creates the things that the artist

plays. I would rather be a Beethoven than a Caruso. I really do not see how I could accomplish that ambition if I were confronted with the necessity of having a large surgical practice in order to make a living.[41]

In 1927 Graham was invited to become dean and professor of surgery at the University of California Medical School in Berkley, to which he responded by saying he was honored to be considered by one of the greatest universities of the country, but he had decided to stay in St. Louis. He again cited a fondness for his staff and how difficult it would be for him to sever his association with them.[42]

Mid-December 1927 saw the first offer from Harvard. Supported by Harvey Cushing, and spearheaded by Nathaniel Allison and David Edsall, both prior Washington University colleagues, Graham was offered the position of surgical chief at the Boston City Hospital. The offer was accompanied by the promise of a building for the Department of Surgery similar to the Thorndyke Memorial Laboratory that served the Department of Medicine. There was also a promise that political interference would not occur.[43,44] These overtures were followed by a letter of encouragement from Walter B. Cannon, who wrote: "I am sure you should give the offer very careful consideration and I hope the attractions here may prove so great that you will come to us and we shall have the advantage of your inspiration and services."[45] Without even a visit to Boston, Graham took only 2 weeks to refuse the offer. In a long letter to David Edsall, he detailed several reasons, one of which was that he could not become enthusiastic about a municipal institution, for he had seen excellent programs completely wrecked by a few years of a bad politics. Graham stated, "The opportunity which this invitation presents is so attractive to me that it has been only after considerable effort and after a good many precordial pains that I have arrived at my decision."[46] Several letters of regret came from Boston, with a particularly sympathetic letter from Harvey Cushing, who suggested that a person with a strong research tendency might very well get wholly out of his stride making a change of this kind.[47]

Less than a year later, Graham heard from yet another ex–Washington University faculty member, G. Canby Robinson, then dean at Cornell, who was overseeing the affiliation between Cornell Medical School and the New York Hospital. The invitation was supported by a letter from Abraham Flexner, to whom Graham replied: "I am trying to make up my mind about whether to stay here or go to the new Cornell enterprise in New York. The latter interests me very much because it seems to me that it would be an interesting experiment to see just what one could do with all of the money at hand that he could possibly wish for. ... I am sorry that I cannot have a talk with you about this whole matter because I should very much like to get your own point of view."[48] More than 2 months passed before Graham finally wrote to Robinson: "I have stood the strain just as long as I can bear. ... I have never before had such an important decision to make and I suppose that I shall never again have one of equal difficulty." He felt it was his duty to stay in St. Louis and expressed his appreciation of Robinson's "many kindnesses and courtesies" in connection with the proposition. He also apologized for having delayed so long in giving his final decision."[49]

At Cushing's retirement 2 years later, Graham was again approached by Harvard, this time for Cushing's position at the Peter Bent Brigham Hospital. The hospital trustees voted their approval on April 9, 1931, with assurance that there would be similar approval of the Medical School selection committee, headed by Walter B. Cannon. Henry Christian, the Brigham chief of medicine, wrote to Graham: "There has been a unanimous vote to the effect that in case you were nominated by the authorities in the Harvard Medical School they [the Brigham Trustees] would welcome it and be glad to have you as Surgeon-in-Chief."[50] The vote was a bit unusual in as much as the trustees of the hospital had not had a formal nomination from the university; it was an expression of their strong desire to have Graham as chief of surgery. In less than 3 weeks, Graham responded to Christian:

> I have been more or less in a stew about the whole matter ever since I received your letter. After very careful consideration however I feel that it would be unwise for me to transplant myself to your hospital [although it is] one of the highest honors that can come to anybody in surgery in America. ... Finally I may say that not only do I feel my inadequacy to fill Dr. Cushing's place but also I have some misgivings about being able to do the kind of work in which I am most interested and to develop the department such as I should like to have if one of my considerations must of necessity be the making of a living by practice. I feel that this consideration comes in a particularly strong way in a proposed transplantation to your hospital because it would mean that I would be forced to enter into some degree of competition from a practice standpoint with the very men whose wholehearted support and co-operation I should need.[51]

Once again, Graham did not make a visit to Boston to talk to someone or to view the scene—he knew that Boston was not for him.

Almost 10 years later, another offer—one far more difficult for him to refuse—came from Johns Hopkins University, 8 months following the retirement of Dean Lewis. A telephone call from Isaiah Bowman, president of Johns Hopkins, was followed up with a letter, indicating: "The Trustees authorized me to say that they will appoint you to the Chair if you will indicate your willingness to come. Their authorization was given by unanimous vote. Unanimous also was the vote of the Advisory Board of the School of Medicine and of the special committee which I appointed to make the recommendation to the Advisory Board. We have not offered the position to any other person since the retirement of Dean Lewis last March nor do we desire to consider any other name." Bowman outlined the financial commitments of the school: "$45,000 per year for the maintenance of the department, a surgical clinic with 150 hospital beds, a salary of $15,000 per annum with a possible increase of ten or fifteen thousand dollars." He continued, "It is no exaggeration to say that no-one whom we have ever invited to accept a Chair of the University has been invited with greater cordiality and with equal unanimity of opinion."[52] All formal correspondence regarding the position was carried out between Bowman and Graham, with letters of encouragement coming from Lewis Weed, chairman of the selection committee and Graham's colleague on the National Research Council; Winford Smith, the hospital superintendent; and Alan Chesney, the dean. On Graham's visit to Baltimore on January 9 to 12, 1940, he was accommodated at the Hotel Belvedere. The high point of the visit was an informal dinner at the Maryland Club on January 10 with 14 members of the faculty.[53] A formal invitation from Bowman 3 days later detailed the offer in its entirety.[54]

Graham began to receive unsolicited opinions as soon as the possibility of a move to Baltimore became known. Warren Cole wrote a long letter encouraging him to accept the position,[55] to which Graham responded: "I am more deeply rooted here than you were. . . . I should be very unhappy if the institution should gradually disintegrate because of the unsatisfactory hospital relationship. As far as I am personally concerned a new deal and a comparatively fresh start would be welcome to me in many respects. . . . I have found myself becoming more and more of a hack without the opportunity to do anything constructive."[56] Letters encouraging him to stay poured in from St. Louisians, including a cluster from St. Louis businessmen, many of whom were his personal acquaintances. In an effort to induce him to remain in St. Louis, members of the Round Table and the Serious Thinkers group[d] collected a sum of money (an estimated $150,000) for a "Graham fund," to be used partly for his retirement income and partly as discretionary funds for research in his surgical laboratories.

---

d. Graham achieved access to the power brokers of St. Louis through contacts in the Serious Thinkers group and the St. Louis Round Table, two groups that opened the intellectual and social/mercantile doors of St. Louis for him. Serious Thinkers was a small informal group of intellectuals, collected by Bishop William Scarlett of the Episcopal diocese, consisting of less than a dozen labor leaders, clergymen, physicians, managers, and officers of industry. They met at irregular intervals in each others' homes for a free-wheeling discussion of policies, events, and social forces that faced St. Louis and the rest of mankind. There was no formal membership roster, and the only requirement for inclusion was intellectuality and vision. This was undoubtedly Graham's most stimulating and exciting extracurricular contact.

The St. Louis Round Table, which dates from 1882, is an all-male organization of 185 members. It meets several times a year for dinner, at which formal attire is worn, and an address or paper is always presented. The roster of past speakers includes Franklin D. Roosevelt, David Rockefeller,

Bowman had asked for a decision that could be presented to a full meeting of the board of trustees on February 5, and on February 1 Graham finally responded: "I regard the invitation as one of the greatest honors which could come to anyone. I have decided that in view of all the circumstances involved it would be better for me to remain in St. Louis. I was strongly tempted to accept your invitation.... the financial features were most generous.... your kindly offer to extend facilities to Mrs. Graham was much appreciated."[57]

For Graham, one bothersome feature of the invitation was the St. Louis publicity given to it. During Graham's January visit to Baltimore, he was telephoned by the *St. Louis Post-Dispatch*, and upon his return reporters were frequently requesting his comments. News of the invitation was rather common knowledge, and Graham was afraid that some newspaper notice would appear after his decision to remain in St. Louis became known. He hoped there would be no publicity.[57] When Weed asked for a statement of his travel expenses, so that he might be reimbursed, Graham responded: "I would much prefer not to do that.... couldn't we compromise by your making an estimate about what it cost me and giving the money to some needy medical student. Perhaps you don't have any needy medical students but we do. If this suggestion seems too absurd then don't pay any attention to it."[58] Graham received letters of disappointment from several members of the Johns Hopkins faculty. Nathan Womack recalled his discussion with Graham about the Johns Hopkins position: "To begin with, Hopkins must have as a Chairman of the Department of Surgery a Johns Hopkins man. You see that the previous man just couldn't turn the job."[59]

After refusing the position, Graham called Mont Reid, chairman of surgery in Cincinnati and Halsted's favorite resident: "I think we ought to recommend someone. What do you think of Alfred Blalock?" The two soon met with Bowman in Chicago to propose Blalock. Bowman then flew to Nashville, offered the position to Blalock without his committee's approval and without discussing the offer with Barney Brooks, Vanderbilt's chairman. This oversight created a rift between Brooks and Blalock that never completely healed.[59]

In September 1947 Graham and Blalock visited England and Europe on a joint speaking and operating tour, and upon return Graham wrote to Bowman:

George H. Bush, and Mikhail Gorbachev. Evarts Graham attended his first meeting in November 1929, and, although never an officer, he gave the evening speech on two occasions—November 1930, on "Rambles in the South Seas," and January 1934, on "The Trick of Stability." With its roster of the industrial and social elite of St. Louis, The Round Table provided Graham an entrance to St. Louis's financial, monied, and corporate leaders, and it was here that his association with Edward Mallinckrodt flourished. Members of this group volunteered money for financial incentives that helped to persuade Graham to refuse the Johns Hopkins offer and to remain in St. Louis.

There has never been anything quite like Al Blalock's triumphal tour of Europe....I wish you could have been with me in London last month to have seen the acclaim which Alfred Blalock received. I could not help recalling some of the conversation...when he was being considered for his present post....I have always been confident that he would go far in surgery....I was tremendously proud of him and I could not help getting a great deal of satisfaction out of the thought that my confidence had not been misplaced.[60]

Bowman was so pleased that he sent a copy of Graham's letter to the 25 members of the board of trustees and then wrote to Graham: "I shall never forget the help that you gave me in a time of crisis."[61,62]

The final offer to move came once again from a Washington University ex-colleague, David M. Rioch, a neurologist who had been one of the founders of Washington University's Department of Neurology and Psychiatry. In the fall of 1951, following his retirement, Graham met with Rioch to discuss the possibility of becoming professor of surgery at the Army Graduate Medical School in Washington, DC. It was an easy refusal for Graham, who wrote to Rioch: "Everybody here [in St. Louis] has been very kind and I have been offered some jobs which an old man like myself can probably carry out so I think I shall stay here instead of moving to Washington....I could not face with pleasure a load of teaching and administrative work."[63]

Graham's training and his research, coupled with educational and clinical successes, made him an international figure and a very attractive catch to many institutions. The commitment to St. Louis that he made upon his arrival only became deeper by the repeated invitations. Despite his written comments, it is difficult to determine whether he seriously considered any of the offers, particularly since he did not make any visits, except to Johns Hopkins, whose chairmanship was probably the most prestigious surgical position in the United States. His friendship with Isaiah Bowman undoubtedly influenced him to make that visit. However, Graham realized that at Barnes Hospital and Washington University he possessed all that he had planned for or desired to do, and his overgracious refusals and maneuverings were likely more for show than for substance.

St. Louis had become Graham's home; he was a significant factor in the "building of the temple," and he knew where he belonged.

The Unattained Nobel Prize

The Nobel Prize Committee received three proposals on behalf of Evarts Graham. The first, prepared in 1927 by Dean William McKim Marriott, focused on the clinical aspects of Graham's cholecystography success. Graham prepared a lengthy description outlining the investigative process and the resulting clinical benefits, but failed to emphasize the intellectual concept of designing a tracer molecule and following it to its target. Graham was a practical man, not a philosopher, and was unable to appreciate the generic rather than the specific value of his effort.[64]

The second nomination was made in the fall of 1950 by Warren Cole of Chicago and Charles Johnston of Detroit. It centered around Graham's work on the physiology of the chest and mediastinum, and his pioneering efforts in thoracic surgery; Graham's monograph on empyema[65] was its central theme. Warren Cole even suggested that it might "be necessary to link his name up with Al Blalock, dividing the prize between these two, on the basis that they have revolutionized surgery of the thorax."[66]

The third nomination, made in 1956, was prepared by Dr. Wolfgang Denk of Vienna, Austria, a surgeon who had been a fellow on Graham's chest service during the summer and fall of 1948, and who was now the holder of Billroth's chair. The thrust of Denk's proposal was the Gilmore pneumonectomy of 1933, the subsequent development of thoracic surgery, and the worldwide acclaim that culminated in Graham's receipt of the Lister Medal.[67] Graham complied with Denk's request for supporting information but concluded: "I shall not be surprised, however, if the Nobel Committee has the opinion that my work does not deserve one of their prizes."[68] He was correct.

In viewing his own efforts, either regarding cholecystography or the pneumonectomy, Graham was always concerned with their practical, clinical aspects and seemed unable to identify or confront the theoretic concepts that lay behind them. Pneumonectomy had been coming, whether performed by Graham or Rienhoff. Cholecystography also would have arrived somehow, but its clinical success and the resulting human benefits are considerable, and Graham received well-deserved honors for them. However, the adding of an element (iodine) with a desired property (x-ray density) to a carrier (phthalein) that would take it to a desired location (the gallbladder) is a concept of monumental importance, which now has been extended to intracellular and molecular levels. Graham was either too modest or, for some other reason, failed to grasp the significance or magnitude of his idea of attaching something to a molecule that would be carried elsewhere to perform a specific task.

The author remembers when he and two other medical students were asked by Robert Moore, in an exercise that stemmed from our small History of Medicine group, to interview Dr. Graham with regard to "creativity." We left the 30-minute interview with Dr. Graham no wiser than when we came. Graham described what he had done in a matter-of-fact way, identifying details as though just anyone could have done the same thing, without any reflection on thoughtfulness, ideas, or intellectual activity. To Graham, the practical clinical benefits were the important and desired end. Likewise, none of his proposers to the Nobel Committee were able to discern the intellectual centerpiece of a cholecystography contribution that, if appropriately presented, might well have placed Evarts Graham on the list of Nobel laureates.

The Deer Project

During his 5 retirement years, Evarts Graham pursued two personal research interests. Although Carl Moyer had become the official director of research, Graham was a father figure who still sponsored and supported young men in the research laboratories.

Graham's major research effort was his smoking laboratory, overseen by Adele Croninger and supported by continuous written contact with Ernst Wynder in New York City (see chapter 18), but wound healing was another topic that captured his imagination, specifically as it pertained to the growth of bone. This had been a recurring theme during his membership on the National Research Council Committees on Surgery and on Growth, and it was of interest to him because of its biologic secrets as well as its clinical overtones. Graham turned to the study of the male white-tail deer, which grows a new set of antlers each year. Antlers are bone, identical to the animal's bony skeleton and unlike the horns of cattle or goats that are a product of skin elements (as are nails, hoofs, and hair). Antlers arise each June from two small pink buds on the forehead and grow rapidly. They are covered in a soft pinkish membrane (velvet) that is shed in late August or early September, leaving a bony rack for the fall rutting season, which is then shed during January or February. Regrowth is an annual occurrence, and a larger, more complicated rack develops with each succeeding year.

Work on the project began in the summer of 1952 with the help of Graham's old friend Harold Ickes, ex-secretary of the US Department of the Interior, who arranged for a National Forest Ranger to obtain and kill a young buck that was still in the velvet. The author was sent to Higgins Lake, Michigan, obtained the antlers, and returned with them in a chilled container. Chemical analyses of the velvet and the bone were unrewarding; there were no microscopic histologic studies.

Graham's next effort, encouraged by Carl Moyer, was the construction of a stall that would capture and hold a deer, *if* it could be enticed in. A runway with stall was prepared on the roof of the North Building in the dog holding area, and a young buck was obtained. Graham hoped to entice the animal into the stall daily and to draw blood from the large paranasal vein during the antler growing season. Analyses for calcium, phosphorus, alkaline phosphatase, and whatever else was available in 1953 and 1954 were planned, but Graham's almost daily visits with apples, carrots, lettuce, or other fruits and vegetables failed to entice the deer into the stall a second time. The first and only entry was followed by such kicking and bucking that the stall was destroyed, and, although a second and stronger stall was built, the animal never entered. The only result of this effort was visible frustration, almost anger, whenever Graham was questioned or kidded about it. He had planned to ask for government research funds, but the lack of sufficient data and an adequate research plan precluded a formal proposal. One day the deer disappeared, and, although its disposal was officially unknown, it was always suspected that it ended up on Carl Moyer's dinner table.

For his third attempt, Graham enlisted the help of friend and patient William Danforth, who was chairman of the board of Ralston Purina. The company produced feed for many varieties of domesticated animals—mice to horses—and maintained an experimental animal farm west of St. Louis for its feeding and breeding experiments. Mr. Danforth agreed to build a deer-holding area with a pen that would be made available to Graham so he could conduct whatever experiments he wished during the antler growing season. Pens were completed by January 1955, and deer were obtained from the Shaw's Garden herd,[69–71] but there is no record of any further activity on the project. Graham's hopes to describe, explain, and then control the growth of bone were never realized—they still are not.

Chapter 15

EXTRAMURAL ACTIVITIES: PART 1

TO ENGLAND WITH EDSALL
(1922)

In mid-1921 Abraham Flexner began to prepare for a survey of European schools, and he turned to Graham, among others, for opinions regarding the nature of an ideal department of surgery.[1] Graham responded with an eight-page document detailing his thoughts on the proper place of surgery in the modern medical school, the teaching of surgery, and equipment and costs. He stressed his belief that a Department of Surgery should include all of the surgical specialties, but it was "not necessary...and not desirable that one man should do the actual work in all of these fields."[2] Graham felt it should be the function of the department to train expert surgeons of the future through a graduated system of training that requires an adequate number of surgical beds. He asserted that a central laboratory is needed for diagnostic tests, but that surgical pathology should be kept within the Department of Surgery. Graham discussed the mix of full-time and part-time men and deplored the situation in which "younger men get into the habit of treating the condition rather than the patient, thus losing sight of much of the psychological and humanitarian aspect of the practice of medicine."[2] He also noted, "It should never become necessary for the full-time members to earn money for the support of the department."[2]

The thoroughness and thoughtfulness in this response was such that within 4 months, Graham received another call from the Rockefeller Foundation. Its Division of Medical Education was interested in how the schools of Great Britain used the dispensary and the clinical clerk system in surgical teaching, and they were preparing to send a commission to study the British approach. Richard Pearce, director of the Division of Medical Education, recruited Graham, by stating: "We are agreed that you would be the most suitable person to study this question on its surgical side—that is, the methods of the so-called surgical dressers in English hospitals, their importance in education and also the utilization of the surgical dispensary."[3] At 39 Graham, then a member of the cultural nouveau riche of the New World, was being asked to pass judgment on an old established European educational system that harked back to the year 1500 and Henry VIII. He indicated his willingness to share the project with David Edsall[a], previously of Washington University, and in 1921 dean at Harvard. Pearce prepared an outline suggesting things that might be observed: departmental administration, teaching methods, facilities, research, and general impressions of full-time teaching.[4] Graham arranged to sail with Edsall from Montreal on September 23 on the Canadian Pacific steamer *Metagama*, bound for Glasgow, Scotland. It was planned that none of the schools to be visited would be given prior notice.

The visit lasted for approximately 10 weeks. Graham gave special time and attention to the University College Hospital, St. Bartholomew's, and St. Thomas's in London, and to the University of Edinburgh in Scotland. Casual visits were made to the Universities of Glasgow and Leeds and to Guys Hospital in London. Graham developed close and special friendships with Sir Harold Stiles of Edinburgh, Professor E.P. Cathcart of the Institute of Physiology in Glasgow, and Sir George Newman, chief medical officer of the Ministry of Health and Board of Education in London. Upon his return to New York on December 18, Graham visited George Vincent, president of the Rockefeller Foundation, to make a verbal report on the trip. He had returned from his first foray into the world of

---

a. David Linn Edsall (1869 to 1945) was born in Hamburg, New Jersey. He received his bachelor of arts degree from Princeton, and in 1893 obtained a doctor of medicine degree from the University of Pennsylvania. After a period of private practice, he became professor of therapeutics and pharmacology at the University of Pennsylvania, doing research on human environmental diseases, before spending 1 year in St. Louis as professor of preventive medicine and the program planner for overall development of the new Medical School. Brookings was greatly influenced and captivated by the grandeur of Edsall's vision for rebuilding the school. Impatient with the rate of progress in St. Louis, Edsall left for Boston to become dean of the Medical School and Public Health School from 1915 to 1935. His greatest achievements were the rebuilding and reconstruction of the Harvard Medical School and the development of the Harvard School of Public Health. As a trustee of the Rockefeller Foundation, he recommended the foundation shift its support to the development of psychiatry. At 6 feet 4 inches tall, Edsall was a large man with a deep voice. He had a deliberate and dignified manner, with patience, candor, intellectual honesty, and a sound judgment. Edsall liked people, dealt easily with patients and colleagues, and found recreation in mountain climbing and hiking. After developing cardiac insufficiency, he spent his last 2 years as an invalid in Cambridge, Massachusetts. He is buried near his summer home in Greensboro, Vermont.

international surgery, having acquired many friends and admirers, and a base upon which he would expand his contacts across middle Europe in the coming years. With a sheaf of notes and fresh memories, he arrived in St. Louis in time for Christmas with his family.

Three weeks later Graham wrote to George Vincent, attempting to clarify some of the thoughts that he had expressed verbally: "I am sorry if I gave the idea that the British medical situation is all black. I do not think so at all. I think there are certain things which are done better in England than with us, but, in general I do feel that their medical schools are certainly much inferior to our best schools here. I certainly shall be very careful to avoid any language of any kind which might disturb the *entente cordiale*. I have not yet completed my report."[5] A letter also went to E.P. Cathcart in Glasgow: "I have not yet completed the report on my trip. . . . I was struck everywhere with the fact that there was a tendency on the part of the British surgeons to ignore physiology. I was astonished to find this tendency because, of course, everybody knows that you British physiologists are the most brilliant in the world. I cannot understand why your influence has not permeated the clinicians more than it has."[6]

The report was not soon in coming. In fact, 10 months passed before it was finally sent to the Rockefeller Foundation. In an explanatory letter to Pearce, Graham wrote that he seldom had anything more difficult to write. He wished to be as complimentary as possible to the British surgeons, but in spite of a desire to select praiseworthy points, he found very little about which he could become enthusiastic. He wrote the report five times before putting it aside for a few months to become a little more mellow in his point of view. "I think that has occurred [but] the report in its present form may seem much too severe to you. . . . I do not know what would be the best plan about publishing such a report as this. I shall leave that entirely to you except that if there is to be any general sort of publication I would appreciate it if I could be notified in advance because I might find that I can still make the report a little less severe."[7] In another letter to Pearce, he continued: "Possibly I was too brutal in the frankness with which I discussed the situation but conversations with…C.H. Mayo and Crile lead me to think that my criticisms were none too severe."[8] Pearce responded with the suggestion that Graham send a copy of the report to Newman and Stiles, asking for comments and criticisms on what could be considered an unfinished document. This was not done.

As finally submitted, the 35-page document began with Graham's observation that, in the London schools, clinical teaching was much more casual and unstructured than it was in American schools, and was in contrast to the schools in Scotland, where there was closer supervision over medical student instruction. Graham ascribed this to the orientation of the Scottish schools that had been founded as an integral part of a university, developing with university traditions; in London the medical schools had grown up in hospitals in which there had developed an apprentice system of clinical education—of having students walk the wards with their preceptors.[9]

Graham contrasted the American and German custom of having a single surgical department head with the English custom of having several firms within a single institution. He criticized the firm system, in which the chiefs obtained appointment by seniority, and there was no assurance that a young man would be rewarded for work of an exceptional character.[9]

Another striking difference in the English schools was the absence of the surgical specialization that was beginning to appear in many American schools. Graham commented that there were practically no surgeons in Great Britain who limit their work to neurologic or genitourinary surgery, although, at Edinburgh, several of the younger men had been encouraged to devote special attention to orthopedic surgery. He felt that, everywhere else, the idea of specialty surgery seemed practically in its infancy.[9]

Graham commented that the pathologic museums used for teaching purposes were excellent, but he stated, "The equipment for laboratory work, including that of the x-ray, is far below that … found in the best American schools." He also mentioned that notes made by the dressers and even the permanent records of the hospitals were inferior to the records in American hospitals; he thought they would be of no value for a detailed study, and it was rare to find a published systematic study of a group of cases. He singled out the record keeping of Sir Harold Stiles of Edinburgh and Professor Gask at St. Bartholomew's as being exceptions.[9]

Graham made note of the emphasis on gross anatomy and the absence of an effort in microscopic anatomy. He felt it was difficult to understand the strong emphasis on anatomy and the lack of emphasis on physiologic aspects: "In spite of the fact that the British physiologists lead the world, they seem to have had little influence on the surgeons….the questions of 'how' and 'why' are seldom asked. There is little if any surgical research being done in Great Britain which is experimental and which is likely to contribute any new knowledge to the question of function." After deploring the absence of blood transfusions, he criticized the laboratory examinations: "Laboratory methods in diagnosis are used in a minority of cases and the interpretation of a blood count is often a doubtful matter to many of those conducting the teaching of surgery. … The x-ray work is distinctly inferior to the best in America and the x-ray is not used to the same extent." He concluded, "There seems to exist among the surgeons a feeling that laboratory examinations [e.g. blood counts] are unnecessary. … it is hard to understand how they can emphasize so strongly the anatomical features of a lesion and yet completely ignore the condition of so important a part of the body as the blood."[9]

Graham was especially critical of the spirit of inquiry on the part of the surgical staffs: "Students are not stimulated to read current literature, and comparatively few do. … one sees students everywhere reading text books but seldom any of the medical periodicals. . . . the effect of this must be to give to the students the impression that surgery is static, that most of the problems have been settled and that little progress is to be hoped for in the future." There was a lengthy disparaging discussion of the registrar system, in which each prospective surgeon becomes associated with an active practicing surgeon and begins a long wait for a senior position as the head of a firm or service: "It is evident therefore that there is in general no provision for the reward of superior merit at a time in life when this would accomplish the most both for the man of exceptional ability and for the institution with which he is connected. . . . In the absence of the prospect of the reward there is a corresponding absence of incentive."[9]

Graham discussed the absence of educational requirements and noted: "Distinction in consulting practice, long experience of hospital posts and a 'good bedside manner' are valuable attributes but they do not necessarily make a man a teacher and leader of others. . . . The claims of a consulting practice outside the hospital and not the duty of teaching become paramount." Graham felt that teachers must be trained: "That was the conviction in Germany and America and that was the reason why the formal clinical teaching in both countries excelled."[9]

The hospital structure also received critical remarks:

> In private practice the general standards of British surgery are not equal to those in America. This is recognized by many of the leading British surgeons who candidly deplore the fact that usually the patient who is in the fee paying class cannot get service so good as the pauper. The reason for this is that the private practice of surgery is carried out almost entirely either in the patient's home or in nursing homes. Hospitals almost invariably have no accommodation for patients who can pay fees for the service rendered them. There are no hospitals in Great Britain like most of the hospitals in America, institutions where both rich and poor may be served with equal skills. The nursing homes are usually remodeled private dwellings operated for profit by a nurse or group of nurses who provide the nursing care for the patient. The equipment in most of these homes is a half century behind modern ideas of the practice of surgery. Either no laboratories or poorly equipped laboratories are available. No x-ray work at all can be done in most of them. There is no resident staff. . . . There must be many preventable tragedies which occur in these nursing homes. No records, in the modern sense, can be kept. . . . snap diagnoses must be the rule. . . . is it any wonder then that it pervades the whole outlook of the British surgeon in his teaching as well as in his private practice? What must be the attitude of the student towards the necessity of the careful study of his patient when most of his teachers are engaged in

this kind of practice?... Would it not be better from every standpoint that hospitals should provide facilities for the care of private patients on an extensive scale. The service to the public would be enormously improved, the hospitals would gain more revenue from the people who have been served, and a large amount of teaching material would be added to the equipment of the teaching hospitals.... American Hospitals find an advantage in having the interns and residents come in contact with others than the paupers.[9]

Graham praised the unofficial regulating influence of the Royal College of Surgeons and noted, "The nefarious practice of fee splitting, a curse of American surgery, is all but unknown in Great Britain." He additionally remarked, "The British Surgeon is at his best when confronted with the problem of the diagnosis and operative relief of a purely anatomical lesion. He shows himself in a less favorable light when confronted with a physiological problem... and tends to disregard functional defects. He is less of a philosopher and more of a craftsman."[9]

Graham closed his report by stating that many of the aspects of the teaching of surgery in Great Britain that he had mentioned unfavorably were clearly recognized by the British themselves. The spirit of introspective criticism that had swept over the American medical schools a decade ago, in response to Abraham Flexner's report, was now beginning to show itself in Great Britain: "The recent establishment of clinical units in five of the London schools under the direction of younger men is bound to have a profound influence in correcting many of the deficiencies which exist now."[9]

The visit to England gave Graham an unique opportunity to view surgical education, surgical research, and the interacting influences of hospital and medical school structure. The obligation to put it into writing required that it be crisp and clear, and several of the ideas he expressed in this report may be seen in actions he took throughout the remainder of his career: the Surgical Forum, full-time appointments, research attitudes, the constant input of young men with ideas, and concerns over standards of practice and ethical behavior.

Graham was apprehensive about his criticisms and, in a letter acknowledging receipt of a copy of Edsall's report, he wrote that he had attempted to soften some of his criticisms: "I was afraid that perhaps my report was a little offensive and that consequently they might not like it very well. I suppose that sometime I shall want to go back to England on a trip and I should not care to receive a cold shoulder everywhere because of the criticisms I have made."[10] A week later he wrote to Edsall again: "I am wondering how our two reports would be received over there if published. I am afraid that perhaps I was a little too severe in my criticisms but yet the remarks which I made represented my sincere convictions."[11] The issue was averted as the reports of both Graham and Edsall became confidential documents within the Rockefeller Foundation.

Four years later Graham was contacted by Barney Brooks, who was planning a trip to Europe. In a lengthy letter regarding whom Brooks might visit, Graham wrote: "I can supply you with letters to most anybody in England whom you would care to see because I have met nearly all of the surgeons of prominence....If your experience is anything like mine you will feel that you haven't learned very much about surgery from your trip to Europe because after all there is not very much that they can teach us and in most respects our work is far ahead of theirs, particularly from the standpoint of diagnosis and the development of new ideas."[12] He provided Brooks with 10 letters of reference to surgeons of England, Scotland, and France, and, upon returning, Brooks reported, "I have seen only one thing in Europe that I am convinced as to its real value."[13]

THE NATIONAL RESEARCH COUNCIL
(1928–1954)

Introduction to the Council

Requests for Evarts Graham's opinions, advice, and ideas began to occur shortly after his arrival in St. Louis, and it was not long before he became continuously involved with several societies of which he was a member and for which he was willing to devote unstinting time (see chapter 12). However, there were demands from many other sources. Graham was pleased with this attention; he considered it a duty as well as an honor, and he eagerly complied with almost all of the requests made of him. It seems as though he were almost incapable of turning down such requests.

The first major and perhaps one of the most significant requests came from the Rockefeller Foundation, through Abraham Flexner, in the spring of 1921. Washington University, in many ways, was a "Rockefeller" medical school, and Graham, then 38 years old and in St. Louis less than 2 years, was invited to dinner at the Harvard Club in New York City to advise the General Education Board as to how it may best spend its resources in order "to permit the best medical schools to supply properly trained teachers and investigators to meet the present needs of medical schools, research institutions and public health agencies during the period in which ...reorganization or improvement [will] create an emergency need that cannot be adequately met...."[14] The foundation prepared a seven-point agenda for the evening's discussion to address the upcoming need to provide preclinical and clinical teachers in sufficient numbers. It concluded: "The provision of fellowships may conceivably be a remedial factor....under what terms should they be given and what should be the mechanism for their distribution?"[15]

Upon returning to St. Louis, Graham wrote a lengthy letter to Flexner expressing the opinion that Rockefeller money would be better spent in long-term support of young faculty members rather than in fellowships for trainees: "I cannot help feeling that one of the most important considerations is...economic....As I said at the conference the other night, it is not so much a question of providing a living for a young man just out of school for a period of two or three years as it is the question of providing for him later." He proceeded to discuss economic issues and the disparity of incomes created when the clinical medical faculty was equated with mathematics, geography, and English faculties, and how disparate this income was from those generated in clinical practice. Feeling that salary arrangements, not fellowships, should be supported, he concluded, "If fellowships were to be awarded they should be awarded to men on their proven capability as determined by a central agency, not to institutions to award fellowship support by and within that institution."[16] The agenda for the April dinner in New York reads as though the foundation had already concluded that fellowships for trainees were the solution to the foreseen problem, and was only asking for opinions about difficulties that might arise. The following year the Rockefeller Foundation embarked upon a major program of scholar support, using the National Research Council (NRC) as its scholar selection and payment agency. The benefit that Graham received from his participation at the April dinner turned out to be an introduction to the NRC. In 1925 Evarts Graham began a 23-year stint with the Division of Medical Sciences of the National Research Council, serving first on its Medical Fellowship Board, then as chairman of the Committee on Surgery, and finally as a member of the Committee on Growth.

Medical Fellowship Board

Rather than establish an agency within itself to supervise the scholar program, the foundation turned to the National Research Council, an organization established in 1916 by the National Academy of Sciences, as its operational agency. With the cooperation of national scientific and technical societies, the NRC carried a roster of prominent scientists from many disciplines who, representing the scientific thinking of the day, became available for many of the NRC functions. The Medical Fellowship Board was established to identify promising scholars and to distribute funds from societies or foundations in accordance with directives of the donor. The Rockefeller Foundation now embarked upon a fellowship program to provide academic scientists to the medical schools of the United States, chiefly in the basic but also in the clinical sciences, using the Division of Medical Sciences of the NRC to advertise, interview candidates, and select Rockefeller Scholars. A panel of interviewers from across the country was recruited, and applicants were required to visit an interviewer at his or her home office for a 2-hour session, after which a report was sent to the council office. The Rockefeller Foundation pledged $50,000 per year to the NRC to support fellowships in medicine, not for those already established but for recent graduates "who planned to specialize in one of the preclinical sciences or to approach clinical medicine and surgery through temporary identification with one of the sciences."[17,18]

Graham was appointed to the fellowship board on July 1, 1925, to succeed his long-time colleague Dean Lewis of Johns Hopkins.[19] Graham interviewed between six and 10 candidates each year, and all were required to visit him in St. Louis for a 2-hour interview, after which he prepared a three- to five-page report outlining the individual's aspirations and qualifications, and Graham's impression of worthiness. Rockefeller Scholars became a highly visible group, and the scholarship was a special distinction.

Two years following his appointment, Graham became chairman of the Medical Fellowship Board[b],[20] and he was placed on the executive committee of the Division of Medical Sciences.[21] As the only surgical member of the division, Graham was asked if he had thoughts of any research projects in which the division (and, through it, the council) might be interested. The council wished to act not only in an advisory capacity but in the promotion of research, especially that of a cooperative and coordinated type in which several investigators or groups of investigators would take part.[22] There is no record that Graham provided any ideas that developed into research projects.

Graham's role in the selection of scholars provided him with an opportunity to survey the academic talent of the 1920s and 1930s. At its biannual meetings in Washington, DC, the fellowship board usually reviewed approximately 50 applications and initially approved seven to 10. Later, with more extensive Rockefeller support, 10 to 15 scholarships were awarded at each meeting. Graham remained faithful to this obligation and attended all of the meetings during his term on the fellowship board. [23]

Not all of Graham's activities in Washington were related to the National Research Council. In the fall of 1925, he began to correspond with the postal service in regard to pictures that appeared on postage stamps. Working through Vernon Kellogg, the permanent secretary of the National Research Council, he contacted the assistant postmaster general to inform him that the United States had never given official recognition to anyone who had really accomplished anything outside of the fields of business, politics, and war. Graham was sure that the postal service had never realized the fact, and he did not let the matter die. Four months later he again pressed Kellogg, noting that, "This whole idea was the suggestion of my eight year old son and I am anxious of course for him to get as much inspiration out of it as possible."[24]

Kellogg suggested the names of William Gorgas and Walter Reed in the field of medicine,[25] to which Graham responded: "I am very much pleased with the progress which you have made in the matter of stamps. I am sure also that my boy will get a great thrill out of your letters when I take them home to him this evening.

---

b. Members of Medical Fellowship Board: Evarts A. Graham (for surgery), Walter B. Cannon (for physiology), Eugene L. Opie (for pathology), Francis G. Blake (for medicine), Ludvig Hektoen (ex officio).

I really think that this apparently small matter will have a great deal of good influence in this country.... in regard to suggestions about representatives from medicine it would seem to me that perhaps it would be unwise and unfortunate to choose as the only two selections from medicine men who were in the Army." He then suggested the names of Crawford Long, the discoverer of ether anesthesia; William Beaumont, a gastric physiologist; Oliver Wendell Holmes, for his work on puerperal sepsis; and Willard Gibbs, a physiologist.[26] Further correspondence occurred during the subsequent few months, and, eventually, commemorative stamps honoring the social, cultural, and intellectual elite of the United States became an accepted feature of American philately. It is impossible to gauge the influence of the Graham-Kellogg correspondence.

Mid-1940 saw a rapid and major expansion of the NRC Division of Medical Sciences. The Committee on Surgery was one of several formed to act in an advisory capacity to the surgeons general of the army and the navy.[27] On July 1, 1940, the day following his termination as a member of the fellowship committee, Graham was appointed chairman of the surgery committee, an appointment he held for 5 years.[28]

Committee on Surgery

The challenges of the war in Europe brought a major expansion of all divisions of the National Research Council, with Lewis H. Weed succeeding Ludvig Hektoen as head of the Division of Medical Sciences. At the request of the surgeons general of the army and the navy departments and the United States Public Health Service, the NRC constructed nine civilian advisory committees, the largest of which was the Committee on Surgery, chaired by Evarts Graham.[27,28]

At its first meeting on June 15, 1940, the nine-man Committee on Surgery[c] formed 13 subcommittees[d]. The Subcommittee on Thoracic Surgery consisted of Graham as chairman, and his longstanding colleagues A. Bigger, E.D. Churchill, and Leo Eloesser. Graham was also a member of the Subcommittee on Surgical Specialties, chaired by Fred Coller, and chairman of the Subcommittee on Hospital and Surgical Supplies, which was held within the Committee on Drugs and Medical Supplies. This position automatically made him a member of the main committee.[29] On July 1, 1943, he once again became a

---

c. Members of the Committee on Surgery: E.A. Graham (chairman), Irvin Abell, Donald C. Balfour, George E. Bennett, Warren H. Cole (secretary), Charles G. Mixter, Howard C. Naffziger, Alton Ochsner (vice-chairman), A.O. Whipple.

d. Subcommittees and respective chairmen of the Committee on Surgery: Surgical infections, Frank L. Meleney; shock, Alfred Blalock; anesthesia, Ralph M. Waters; radiology, A.C. Christie; wound healing, A.O. Whipple; thoracic surgery, E.A. Graham; orthopedics, George E. Bennett; urology, Herman Kretschmer; ophthalmology, Harry S. Gradle; neurosurgery, Howard G. Naffziger; faciomaxillary surgery, Robert H. Ivy; otolaryngology, Harris P. Mosher; vascular injuries, John Homans.

member of the executive committee of the Division of Medical Sciences, and he served until June 30, 1946.[30]

The activities of the Committee on Surgery included organizing refresher courses given at six designated medical schools with six topics of instruction. War manuals were created in seven subspecialties to give instruction in wound management and the care of injured soldiers. The committee reviewed lists of surgical instruments and, at the request of the American Red Cross, revised its first aid handbook. Each specialty subcommittee prepared a list of all known specialists in its category in the United States. The committee received requests for grant-in-aid financial support for research projects and, in addition, created and directed research projects that members of the committee and its subcommittees suggested.[31] The congress gave money directly to the NRC to fund meetings, travel, honoraria, and these research projects, rather than using the military budgets to underwrite NRC expenses. When the Office of Scientific Research and Development (OSRD) was organized, its own medical research council reviewed all NRC decisions. Although the army subsidized postgraduate specialty courses given throughout the country, Ada Hanvey at Evarts Graham's desk did much of the paperwork, and many of the specific research contracts by the Committee on Surgery were typed in the St. Louis office.[32,33]

The largest research project approved by the Committee on Surgery was the one on management of war wounds—contaminated wounds and burns. Under the supervision of Frank L. Meleny, the Subcommittee on Surgical Infections planned to establish nine units throughout the country to study the prevention of infection in contaminated soft tissue wounds, compound fractures, and burns. This became the most contentious project sponsored by the Committee on Surgery, and Evarts Graham, and later A.O. Whipple, allocated to it hours of special attention.

The scope of topics considered by the Subcommittee on Thoracic Surgery chaired by Evarts Graham was extensive. In addition to preparing a manual on its subject, the listing and grading of civilian thoracic surgeons, and the making of recommendations concerning instruments, it attempted to arouse interest in the development of protective body armor—later known as bullet-proof vests. A recommendation was referred to the ordnance department of the army, which failed to respond or even to acknowledge the suggestion. In response to the inaction on the part of the government, in some desperation, Graham wrote to Lewis Weed[e]: "[There are] two or three things that have been worrying me a good deal.... Isn't

---

e. Lewis H. Weed (1886 to 1952), born in Cleveland, Ohio, received a bachelor of arts degree from Yale, and a doctor of medicine degree from Johns Hopkins in 1912. After 2 years at the Harvard Surgical Research Laboratory, he began 33 years with the anatomy faculty at Johns Hopkins. During World War I, he was an army captain, teaching neurosurgical techniques to army doctors. From 1923 to 1929, he served as dean of the medical faculty of the Johns Hopkins School of Medicine; then, until 1946, he served as director. Never married, much of his time and activities were spent on affairs of a

there some way of getting some money from the Government to enable the Committee ... to start its research program?"[34] He proposed that they bypass ordinary channels and go directly to both President Roosevelt and Surgeon General Admiral McIntire (the president's personal physician) and continued to complain:

> Another thing is that I don't know what happens to recommendations which our committees make.... at the meeting of the Sub-Committee on Thoracic Surgery we discussed the advisability of having the soldiers wear chest protectors to minimize the chance of thoracic wounds. Such a protector obviously would have to be light and probably made of metal. Because it would be of metal it would probably be necessary to have the co-operation of the Ordnance Department.... It might be well to have somebody in the Ordnance Department thinking about what sort of material, if a metal, would be the best to use. I am uncertain about the procedure.[34]

Nothing came of this until later years, later wars, and the development of tough plastic materials such as Kevlar.

Preparations for military conflict increased at a rapid pace between mid-1940 and the US entrance into the war in December 1941. Many of the NRC obligations were carried out by Graham from both St. Louis and Washington, DC. Graham visited Washington, DC, every 8 weeks before war was declared, every 6 weeks in 1942, and almost that frequently in 1943 and early 1944—and always traveled by train! The preparedness activities, manuals, research projects, and recommendations were all underway or completed by the time of the storming of Normandy, and NRC demands on Graham were sharply reduced by mid-1944. The various subcommittees each prepared their manuals, and a compound volume was available by July 1941.[35] The "Chest Manual" was large and contained a number of serious errors, and it was a disappointment to Eloesser, its editor.[36] Graham, too, was greatly disappointed, and wrote: "I don't feel, however, like continuing the struggle which I started because it takes so much time. Besides, I am afraid that I am licked

---

national nature that came from Washington, DC. With Baltimore as his home, Weed had easy access to Washington. In 1930 Weed was appointed trustee of the Institute for Advanced Study at Princeton, and, in 1935, trustee of the Carnegie Institute. His 14-year connection with the National Research Council began in 1935 with membership on its fellowship board and then chairmanship of its Division of Medical Sciences. For 6 years, 1941 to 1947, he sat as chairman of the Committee on Medical Research of the OSRD; this was followed by 2 years as chairman of the Medical Advisory Committee for the American Red Cross.

Weed acquired a vast number of friends in the academic and medical establishment. He was awarded nine honorary degrees and membership in the Order of the British Empire. He retired to Reading, Pennsylvania, and is buried in the family plot in Cleveland, Ohio.

already, and therefore there is not much use of beginning a new fight."[37] Graham took a paternalistic view of the manuals. He had suggested a committee should be set up that would deal with all aspects of surgery, and manuals covering special fields should be prepared. The size and comprehensiveness soon became an issue, that is, whether they would have front-line availability or be prepared for the larger institutions of the rear echelons. In response to Fulton's proposal that there be two types of manuals, Graham wrote: "Isn't your plan a good deal like the old idea of having in the barn door a large hole for the big cat and a little hole for the kittens?"[38] Graham believed in a small publication that would be lightweight and available to every military medical officer, printed on very thin paper, possibly rice paper, with flexible covers—pocket manuals, not textbooks. He buttressed his argument: "In the last war a man by the name of Ford wrote a book on medical military administration. I think that fully twenty thousand medical officers would have been glad to buy the book because it was very useful. ... I bought one and could not take it overseas with me ... because it weighed about five pounds."[38] The manuals were finally written, published, and sent overseas, and were available only in major military installations.

Recommendations made by subcommittees on the selection of instruments created problems, which landed on Graham's desk. Graham became disturbed about the instruments being recommended for the army since many were obsolete, and the question arose as to whether the Sklar Manufacturing Company was successfully unloading a lot of their obsolete instruments.[39]

The courses of instruction carried out under the supervision of the NRC led to concerns from all members of the Committee on Surgery as to the quality of the officers sent for the educational experience. The committees worried about the tendency of the army to send officers to courses other than those sponsored by the NRC; one such course was a thoracic surgery course sponsored by the Mayo Clinic, and Graham became distressed to hear reports periodically about the training of medical officers by Dr. Balfour at the Mayo Clinic. He felt: "The Army ought either to cooperate with us and our recommendations or they ought to tell us frankly they are not going to cooperate with us and thereby save us a lot of work. ... I must say that the action of somebody in the Surgeon General's office gives me a pain in the neck. I don't know who the person is."[40]

By the end of the first 12 months of the program, Graham felt the situation had reached a crisis[41] and, in frustration, wrote to Fred Coller:

> In the group for chest surgery there were several country doctors who didn't know what it was all about. There was really only one good man. ... of the ten men sent here for maxillofacial surgery, seven were dentists, two were obstetricians and one was a small town general practitioner. The group sent here for thoracic surgery included a

number of general practitioners in small towns and a proctologist. I telephoned Larkey...and told him that I would not be willing to go on with the course....he seemed to be very much disturbed but his disturbance was nothing compared to mine....I feel that all of the courses should be abandoned unless the Army can assure us that men of suitable caliber and training will be selected to take the courses.... when we planned these courses originally, I certainly had no idea that we would be confronted with such tripe.[42]

The courses were continued during the fighting in North Africa and Italy, and abandoned by D-day in June 1944.

The research component recommended by the NRC was next subjected to a review, which was performed by the Committee on Medical Research (CMR) of the Office of Scientific Research and Development that President Roosevelt had created, with Vannevar Bush as its director.[43] The OSRD Committee on Medical Research, with Lewis Weed now its chairman, approved or nullified all actions of the Committee on Surgery, and Graham "was astonished that the OSRD Committee on Medical Research went to 'top surgeons of the Army and Navy' for advice as to whether or not the work should be considered important to National Defense after it had been approved by the Committee on Surgery." He stated, "The main point which troubles me is that a recommendation of the Committee on Surgery has been censored by an anonymous group...who, I feel certain, are not in so good a position to predict the importance of the work as the members of the Committee on Surgery. If this policy is continued it seems to me that the Committee on Surgery may as well be disbanded."[44]

Graham was particularly upset that the proposal by Robert Elman of his Barnes Hospital staff had been rejected by the CMR after it had been approved by his Committee on Surgery; Weed placated him by explaining that when Elman's proposal came before CMR, the army and navy representatives desired a direct opinion from the ranking surgeons in the army and navy. The opinions were favorable to Elman's undertaking, but both services felt the work did not seem to them to come under the heading of a project directly related to the national defense. Weed then reminded Graham: "Under no circumstances would I construe the action taken by the Committee on Medical Research as being in any way a reflection upon the Committee on Surgery....many matters will be settled solely on the basis of military necessity....we must of course look forward to disappointments of this nature, particulary with war becoming more and more a threat to our shore and outlying possessions."[45]

Money for support of research contracts was slow in coming, and, characteristically, Graham decided to exert his influence through the office of Mr. Harold Ickes, Roosevelt's secretary of the US Department of the Interior. He visited Ickes in October 1940 to ask if Ickes could help in any way to obtain government money for the medical needs of the defense program. Four months later Graham wrote to Ickes:

> Well here it is the eighth of March and we are still waiting. Not so much as a cent in cold cash has reached us! I know of course that this matter does not concern your department and that you interested yourself in it ... only out of the kindness of your heart but isn't there just some way of hurrying the money? It was about the first of June that the request of the President of the National Research Council for funds was first made. Is it necessary that a delay of ten months should occur before we could even get started on our necessary program? Realizing your personal influence with the President I am taking advantage of our long friendship to ask if you know of any way by which we can overcome the inertia, the red tape or whatever it is that is blocking all the medical and health work. ... if we could have started some of this work last June we would now have the answers to many of these problems. ... I hope therefore that you yourself can see the urgency of helping us to get started on this important work. Actually the $250,000 which was said to have been allocated for all medical and health purposes is so triflingly insignificant that it is hardly worth considering but yet it is better than nothing. It is the equivalent of 25 men killed in the war to whose families the government might have to pay the sum of $10,000 of insurance to each one. With our various research problems which we have in mind we expect to be able to save thousands of lives. Multiply each one of these by the ten thousand dollars of government life insurance and you can get some idea of the practical worth of our program. I am sorry to bother you again with all of this but we are so desperate that I felt like turning to you again.[46]

Within 20 days the NRC received its first government checks, accompanied by a comment from Lewis Weed to Graham: "Unfortunately the type of hard-headed medicine which you and I believe in does not appeal to many of the new dealers; projects for the extension of medical service to the underprivileged seem much more likely to receive funds than do medical research undertakings which are directly related to Army and Navy needs. There is a marked social factor in the treatment of medicine by the federal government. ... I am sure that we may need utmost publicity if matters are not improved by Executive order."[47] Graham responded:

> You state in your letter that we must go on in spite of everything and see to it that the advice the Surgeons General need is forthcoming. I am

afraid that I only half agree with that statement. We are not doing our full job if we do not take measures to see that our work is accomplished. I am not in favor of having the most important representatives of the medical profession in the country made to sit quietly in the corner and to have their perfectly justifiable recommendations completely ignored and squelched.... it is time now to start the fireworks.[48]

Graham wrote again to his friend Harold Ickes: "I feel certain there must be a radical change in the scheme of organization made very soon. The morale of many who have been giving up a great deal of time and paying a lot of money out of their own pockets without any prospect of compensation or any thought of compensation, is slipping rapidly."[49] On Wednesday, July 16, the four members of the Committee on Medical Research within the Office of Scientific Research and Development were appointed—A. Newton Richards, Alphonse R. Dochez, A. Baird Hastings, and Lewis H. Weed—and with the support of Vannevar Bush, this committee greatly facilitated the flow of funds for research performed under auspices of the NRC.[50]

The Committee on Surgery authorized a large number of research projects including studies on gas gangrene, available sera, pain inhibitors, burn management, features of contaminated wounds, the nature of concussion injuries both in and out of water, and the general systemic response to infections, wounding, and blood loss. The largest, and possibly the most important, of these projects was the one concerned with the immediate local management of gunshot and shell fragment wounds, and the subsequent systemic response to infection, should it occur. This study swept Graham into the most controversial aspect of his chairmanship of the Committee on Surgery.

During World War I, the US Armed Forces developed and standardized the treatment of war wounds with the use of Carrel tubes to infuse Dakin's hypochlorite solution into the wound. Clinical observations led to the conclusion that wound infections were markedly reduced with Carrel-Dakin wound management. Between the wars, no one in civilian practice employed this treatment, for there were no such wounds, and the Carrel-Dakin principles and practices were abandoned. During the Spanish Civil War, Joséf Trueta and Hiram Winnett Orr treated compound fractures of the extremities with immobilization, dressings, and plaster of Paris casts over the dressings. The use of maggots to débride wound margins was common. The Trueta-Orr management was enthusiastically adopted by the military forces of Great Britain, particularly after the evacuation of Dunkirk, even though, by this time, sulfanilamide, sulfathiazole, and sulfadiazine had appeared on the horizon. At the attack on Pearl Harbor, wound management consisted of powdered sulfanilamide poured directly into the local wound, and the surgeons at Pearl Harbor were convinced that this markedly reduced the incidence of wound infection.

The Subcommittee on Surgical Infections, with Frank L. Meleney as its chairman, undertook a study of initial wound management, to make up-to-date recommendations to the surgeons general. This study received the largest grant given by the Committee on Surgery and covered not only the central study, but several smaller projects related to wound infections; it ran into trouble almost from the outset. The first plan to study the war wounds of British casualties was rejected as being unfeasible for several reasons, chiefly logistical. Eight hospitals in the United States were then selected to study the treatment of 2000 wounds, half of which were to be treated with the local sulfanilamide/sulfadiazine and, as controls, half without. Resistance came immediately from Pearl Harbor observers that it was wrong to withhold from these patients the benefit of the sulfanilamide drugs. A second problem arose following Meleney's initial report, which stated that he could find no evidence that either sulfonamide or equal parts of sulfonamide and sulfadiazine had reduced the incidence of local infection in soft tissue wounds or compound fractures.[51] A third area of controversy arose due to the personality and temperament of Frank Meleney, who responded poorly to those who took exception to his findings.

Meleny's first challenger was I.S. Ravdin, commanding officer of the 20th General Hospital in Burma, who challenged Meleney's studies on the incidence of local infection by stating emphatically: "Sulfonamides—locally and orally—do help to prevent major infection and after all that is all that counts. Some of our enemies don't use them and our most seriously infected wounds are seen in them." In his letter Ravdin took Graham to task. He was amazed that Evarts Graham had stated that no one could possibly believe that sulfonamides might minimize the necessity for surgical asepsis. He closed: "But I can say with considerable assurity that to neglect to use sulfonamides locally or orally, or preferably by both routes in war wounds still in my opinion makes the individual guilty of a very serious error.[52]

After 18 months investigators' discontent with Meleney swept Graham and Weed into the turmoil, and Graham wrote to Weed: "I must say that I have a good many misgivings. Evidently the whole problem of the study of wound infections is in about as bad a mess as it can be. Part of the difficulty undoubtedly is Meleney's personality, but … there has certainly been no cooperation from the Army."[53] Graham thought the difficulties pertaining to Meleney's personality could be ironed out rather easily, and he suggested merging the Subcommittee on Infected Wounds with the Subcommittee on Burns, and placing A.O. Whipple as chairman of the combined committee. He went further:

> Now I come to a question which concerns my own relation to the work. During the last few months I have felt more and more that I, as Chairman of the Committee on Surgery, am perhaps not in step with the rest of the work that is going on under the auspices of the National Research Council. I do not wish to be a drag or a handicap. …

Recently however I seem to have come into such sharp disagreement with some of the policies that have been established by the Army that I have decided it would probably be the best thing for everybody to have me resign from my position and permit you to appoint somebody else.... my feelings will not be hurt in the slightest degree if you think that someone else as Chairman of the Committee on Surgery would be more co-operative and therefore more helpful to you.[53]

Next, Graham conveyed his decision to amalgamate the two committees to Meleney: "I don't know really what all the basis is for the criticism of you. Of course you are as familiar as I that there is a sort of rebellion in your own committee against the continuation of the projects along the same lines."[54] Seven months later, in reviewing the status of the Committee on Surgery, he wrote to Lewis Weed that he had been thinking for some time it might be a good idea to have a new chairman of the Committee on Surgery, and, if Weed agreed, he would be only too glad to resign.[55] A month later, he repeated the sentiment: "I hope you will feel that whenever the time comes that you would like to have someone else there as Chairman of the Committee on Surgery you will let me know about it so that I can get out of the way. I assure you there will be no hard feelings."[56] To this letter, Weed responded: "Your resignation as Chairman of the Committee on Surgery just at this moment would add appreciably to my burdens and I am therefore delighted to have you agree to stay on.... I do not believe that as much of the work of your committee is futile as you seem to feel.... besides all this, I have a feeling that the Committee on Surgery under your jurisdiction will not do absurd things and I take great satisfaction in having you as leader of the group."[57] Graham's reasons for repeatedly offering to resign are unclear as to whether he truly desired to be rid of the contention or that he desired approbation for his efforts. The author believes it to be the latter.

The issue of untreated controls in the wound infection study continued to plague the study, and, despite all the controversy Graham stood staunchly behind Meleney and his results: "I think you handle the situation very well.... I see that Ravdin is still using the obsolete method of clinical judgement in talking about the effects of the sulfonamides in the prevention of infection.... I know what grief you have had in doing this monumental work.... I want you to know that I recognize the significance of the work you have done and that I congratulate you on it."[58] Following the final report from Meleney's committee, Graham wrote to Whipple:

I have always felt that the local use of the sulfonamides in wounds would be only a passing phase which would disappear in time and I think the situation is very analogous to the enthusiastic advocacy of the use of Dakins [sic] solution in the last war.... I have complete frustration at the almost unanimous opinion ... that clinical impressions in this study would be of greater value than a statistical study using controls. ... experience and time is bound to show that the general conclusions of the Meleney report are sound.[59]

Whipple responded: "It is obvious that a good many of the men, Churchill included, feel that the observations that are being made at the front are of far greater importance to the Armed Forces than anything that has been done by the projects of the NRC, ... especially the recent report of Churchill[60] [that] they are corroborating the findings of our committee as published by Meleney—against whom much of the criticism is leveled. ... I am sure that the greater part of the study carried out by the sub-committee will be increasingly corroborated by the military surgeons, but I doubt if they will ever give you credit for it."[61]

By early 1944 Graham began to think about post-war training for returning veterans, and, at Rankin's request from the surgeon general's office, he wrote to Weed about the advisability of having the Committee on Surgery of the National Research Council discuss plans for men whose training had been interrupted: "Do you think this would be a suitable question for our committee to discuss? It is certainly not a research matter. ... I feel that this is something which very definitely should be kept out of the hands of the Army because I fear the consequences if the Army has anything to do with it. I am particularly interested therefore in the fact that Fred Rankin has made the suggestion to me of having the Committee on Surgery try to arrange some plan."[62] The project was immediately shelved, with the feeling that the NRC was not the forum for such activity.

Graham's last correspondence from Weed was a letter received in mid-1946, terminating the appointment of NRC committee members on June 30, 1946, "based upon the completion of war duties and the indefinite character of future demands." Weed wrote to Graham, "The sincere appreciation and gratitude of the National Research Council is due you in full measure."[63]

This was the end of an intense and concentrated effort, filled with frustration and exasperation, yet coupled with a sense of accomplishment. It was an effort to which Graham had given his full measure of devotion.

Committee on Growth

Dissolution of the Committee on Surgery did not end Graham's contacts with the National Research Council. In July 1951 he became a member of the Committee on Growth, held within the Division of Medical Sciences, whose chairman was now M.C. Winternitz. The main activity of the growth committee was the review of applications for research funds and scholarships in accord with conditions imposed by donors. The list of donors included the American Cancer Society. In a task that was no longer of great interest, Graham reviewed these applications and returned them to R. Keith Cannan, the committee chairman. He failed to attend the meeting of January 1952, was present in January 1953, and absent in January 1954.[64] By 1954 he was involved in his laboratory research on smoking, cigarette tars, and the development of cancer, and the review effort became onerous. He wrote:

> I feel that under all the circumstances which exist I ought to resign from the Committee.... There is another reason that may be important in my resignation and that is from time to time I am the recipient of a grant for cancer research from the American Cancer Society. It seems to me that it is somewhat improper for me to continue to serve on the Committee on Growth which is acting for the American Cancer Society when I am interested in cancer research myself and am conducting some with the assistance of grants from that society.... It is just impossible for me to do justice to the work of the Committee. As things have gone I am very sorry that I ever agreed to serve....[65]

Grahams final thoughts regarding the committee were presented 1 year later when he was invited to a meeting of the Division of Medical Sciences for a general discussion of policies of the National Research Council. Unable to attend the meeting, he nevertheless felt impelled to convey his ideas:

> I have long felt that there is far too much emphasis on project research. After all it seems to me that when a man gains a reputation for being an outstanding scientist who is productive in his general field he should be allowed to have such funds as he wishes to have in reasonable amounts without the necessity of stating exactly what his research plan is. I think it is almost insulting that such a person must have his program reviewed by our committee, many [members] of whom are not at all of the same stature scientifically as the man who makes the request for funds.... Can one not therefore place a certain amount of confidence in the individual that the alloted funds will be well spent? In the case of young unknown men, of course the situation is different.... I feel also that the scientific work encouraged by the National Research Council would get along better with less auditing of accounts.... [The investigator] should be allowed the greatest possible freedom of action, he should even be allowed in the middle of the year, if he cared to do so, to change the whole program of his research. If he cannot be trusted to spend the money wisely then nobody can be trusted and nothing is to be gained by forcing him to adhere to a program which perhaps he drew up in his mind a year or so ago.... Another harmful effect of the present system of awarding research

grants is that there is overemphasis on practical values.... In almost every field of activity in this country we are essentially a practical people and we tend to support and to be much more interested in applied science than in theoretical science.[66]

At that time Graham and Croninger were busy with the smoking machine, and their studies relied heavily upon American Cancer Society funds (see chapter 18). Not only was there a conflict of interest in his position of being simultaneously both reviewer and the one reviewed, more importantly, he was frustrated that his projects and his research were being reviewed by those whom he thought were less knowledgeable than he. During his less-than-inspired participation with the Committee on Growth, he refused to be appointed to the Subcommittee on Thoracic Surgery, chaired by Brian Blades, that had not been called to meet for over a year.[67]

In his 69th year, Graham finally found it possible to refuse an offer from the National Research Council. This was his last hurrah to an agency that had claimed his attention, his efforts, his loyalty, and his devotion for more than a third of his life.

ONTO THE NATIONAL SCENE

The American Foundation
(1937–1939)

The world of national and medical politics first touched Graham in April 1933 by way of a letter from the American Foundation for Studies in Government, asking for his opinion about recognition of the Soviet Union by the United States.[68] In replying, Graham admitted that his information was inadequate to form a good opinion, yet his inclination was: "There is no good reason why we should not recognize the present Russian government. Certainly the Russians have a right to have any sort of government which they desire." He noted the many trade advantages to the United States if recognition were granted, and that he could not see any possibility of harm, but commented: "Although there is a certain amount of enthusiasm expressed for some of the public health programs, the conditions of ordinary practice are very bad and the opportunities for any real scientific research are practically non-existent." He could not see that interference by the government with medical research or with the ordinary practice of medicine should constitute an argument against recognizing the official Russian government.[69]

Graham's next involvement with the American Foundation occurred 3 years later. The foundation began to gather opinions from 2200 health professionals across the United States—doctors, dentists, nurses, physiotherapists—and in July 1936 Graham became a member of its medial advisory committee.[70] The foundation's cross-country survey of physicians had asked for their views on trends in education, the organization of the practice of medicine, and possible solutions to problems that the respondents envisaged. A preliminary report was made public on April 1, 1937, with Graham's name on the list of 23 advisors. Although the report covered many features of American medicine, its particular emphasis was placed on the attitudes of American physicians in regard to the public health policy of the American government.[71] The final two-volume report, entitled *American Medicine: Expert Testimony Out of Court*,[72] was ready by early October 1937. A copy sent to the American Medical Association before its official release on November 7 resulted in a pre-emptive blistering editorial in the *Journal of the American Medical Association*, condemning the report for its features of "socialized medicine."[73] The news media gave the document considerable editorial attention and noted that a veritable "Who's Who" in medicine had written the foundation's report. The thesis that the health of the people is a direct concern of the government was one of its main principles, and the suggestion that medical care be coordinated by a federal Department of Health was a central issue. The American Foundation report had been created to encourage discussion about trends in American medicine, and so it did. Excerpts were published in many newspapers across the country.[74–77]

The Committee of Physicians
(1937–1940)

As an outgrowth of the American Foundation effort, a group of 14 physicians constituted themselves a "Committee of Physicians for the Presentation of Certain Principles and Proposals in the Provision of Medical Care," later called the Committee of Physicians. Russell Cecil of Cornell University in New York was its chairman, and John P. Peters of Yale in New Haven was its dedicated secretary and driving force[f].

The committee designed four principles and nine proposals ("P&P"), with its basic principle being the need for a national public health policy. The expansive proposals concluded that health insurance alone did not offer a satisfactory solution to the needs for personal health care.[80] *Principles and Proposals* was published on November 7, 1937, with Graham as one of its 430 signatories. Its publication was followed by an effort by Dr. E.S. Kilgore and a group from San Francisco to withdraw their support for the P&P document and present their own declaration of convictions. When requested to participate,[81–83] Graham responded:

> I cannot see anything to be gained by having a number of Declarations of Convictions circulated throughout the country. ... I can also write a new set of declarations which would differ from all of the

---

f. Russell Cecil and John Peters were academic figures of great respect and renown: Cecil for his classic *Textbook of Medicine*,[78] and Peters for his *Quantitative Clinical Chemistry*,[79] coauthored with chemist Donald D. Van Slyke, which brought the biochemical laboratory to hospital wards.

others with which I am familiar and which would perhaps more nearly suit my ideas but I think that only confusion instead of clarity would result from it. It seems to me that the really important thing is for the medical profession to take the initiative rather than to have the government take it. It is almost certain that in the near future the government will take some initiative. The important thing, therefore, to my mind is that the government should recognize that any plans which are made should be made by qualified experts which of course includes the medical profession and moreover that any changes should be gradual rather than sudden.[84]

Although 32 of the original 430 withdrew, by February 1938 support had risen to 771 signatories. A National Health Conference in Washington, DC, was called for July 18 to 20, 1938. There were 171 delegates, of whom 53 were physicians, including representatives from the Committee of Physicians. The conference closed with the recognition of the necessity for cooperation between the medical profession and the government in the provision of medical care of the highest quality to all citizens.[85–87]

The Washington conference was followed by a congressional proposal to construct hospitals in small towns across the United States. Graham was vigorous in opposition, and wrote to Peters: "I cannot help feeling that there is much to fear in the erection of a large number of small hospitals throughout the country under government auspices. Such hospitals cannot possibly be efficient. As a surgeon I shudder to think of the sort of surgery to which the unsuspecting public will be subjected in such places."[88] After a lengthy response from Peters,[89] Graham again voiced his opinion:

> The matter of educating the doctor is one of such great importance, in my opinion, that it demands a very prominent place in the consideration in the care of the sick on a large scale. It seems to me that government funds could very properly be devoted to the assistance of our medical schools and of those hospitals which have already behind them a record of educational activities. . . . so far as surgery is concerned I do not see how a sixty bed hospital can be properly staffed and equipped to carry on the education of the surgeon. I fear . . . that those beds which are occupied in the smaller rural hospitals will be filled with patients who will be often victims of so-called surgeons who will be not only incompetent but who will perform needless operations merely because of the fee involved. I feel a fair amount of familiarity with what I am talking about because I was a small town surgeon for two years before the War. I learned much in that experience about the practice of medicine which I did not suppose could

possibly happen....I am also somewhat familiar with what has been going on for a good many years in our Veterans hospitals. Although doubtless there are exceptions I would say that most of the work with which I am familiar is nothing to brag about. Besides that, they cannot be regarded as competent places for the training of young men and despite a record of nearly twenty years of existence with many thousands of patients under absolute control, I do not know of a single bit of research that has come from any of them that is of any value whatsoever.[90]

As World War II approached, the fervor of the Committee of Physicians diminished, and other interests gained priority.[91,92] The opening session of congress in 1940 received the Hill-Burton proposal to erect community hospitals with federal funds; it was finally signed into law by Truman in 1946. Other features of government involvement with health policy were set aside as congress became preoccupied with events in Europe and Asia.

The American Foundation and the Committee of Physicians had provided Graham with his first incursions into the field of national politics, preparing him for membership on the Truman Commission a decade later.

Chapter 16

EXTRAMURAL ACTIVITIES: PART 2

COMBAT ON THE HOME FRONT
(1940–1950)

A Personal Crusade

Graham's first venture into events leading up to the second World War was with the Medical Bureau to Aid Spanish Democracy. As one of five St. Louisians on its national committee, his efforts to influence US policy existed only in the writing of letters. To President Roosevelt he insisted that the embargo on arms sales to Spain be lifted,[1] and in a lengthy letter to his friend Harold Ickes, secretary of the Department of the Interior, he pleaded for the blocking of Hitler and Mussolini by permitting the legitimate sale of arms to the government of Spain.[2] Following a warm reply from Ickes, he wrote: "You must be gratified to find out how unpopular you are with Hitler. I think it is a fine compliment."[3]

Graham's next pre-war involvement began in October 1940 with his appointment as regional chairman for the New York Medical and Surgical Supply Committee, a group that obtained medical supplies and surgical equipment for shipment to British emergency hospitals and field units. Graham was joined in this effort by Lawrence T. Post and Horace W. Soper of St. Louis,[4] but his involvement was more titular than active, for he was becoming uncomfortable with the recruiting policies of selective service, and the army and the navy. He turned his attention to the many problems he saw on the home front.

Graham's adversaries during World War II were not so much Hitler and Mussolini as they were individuals and organizations within the United States—

particularly Maj. Gen. Lewis B. Hershey, director of selective service, and the two surgeons general of the army and the navy, John C. Magee and Ross T. McIntire. Graham became one of the most visible and vocal opponents of the recruitment and manpower utilization policies of these three officers, despite the time and effort he spent with the National Research Council in support of the war effort and as civilian consultant in surgery to the surgeon general of the army. His personal opposition was voiced in professional journals, the lay press, public speaking forums, and voluminous personal correspondence. His formal opposition was voiced through two organizations—the American Medical Association (AMA) Committee on Post-War Planning, and the American College of Surgeons (ACS) Special Committee on the Drafting of Doctors.

Actions that were anathemas to him included:

1. The draft. First, selective service did not exempt premedical students, with the consequence that medical schools were left to enroll women, physically unfit males, or elders. Second, medical students were being drafted or forced to enroll in the army's ASTP (Army Specialist Training Program) or the navy's V12 (Navy College Training Program), and then called to active duty at the end of an inadequate internship.

2. Educational constraints. Medical schools were forced to reduce their curricula from 4 to 3 years and to reduce the resident house officers to one-half the number enrolled in 1940. After a 9-month rotating internship, one-third of the interns were permitted 9 months of residency training, and one-half of those could have 9 more months before being called to active duty. This became known as the "nine-nine-nine program."

3. Doctor to patient ratios. The armed forces had decided they required a ratio of 6.5 physicians per 1000 troops (one physician per 154 men), whereas the home front was left with a ratio of one physician per 1293 civilians. By late 1944 approximately 40 percent of American physicians were in the armed forces; the remainder were left to care for the entire civilian population of the United States.

4. Military assignment policies. Both services assigned physicians according to rank and size of the command, without regard to the medical needs of the servicemen or the special competence required of the medical officers. Only gradually did the armed forces begin to assign medical officers by capability in a medical specialty, regardless of rank.

5. Post-war planning. As the war wound down, it became apparent that unsavory induction measures would be retained following cessation of hostilities, and that a large military occupation force would require a continuous inflow of medical officers.

Practicing physicians were exempt from the draft, and in the 2 or 3 months after the attack on Pearl Harbor, doctors were not volunteering in the numbers hoped for by the medical departments of either the army or the navy; by early 1942 the military was threatened with a shortage. On April 3, 1943, the War Manpower Commission ordered teaching hospitals to reduce their number of residents, and planned to bring all ASTP and V12 medical students to active duty immediately after internship. Five months later the Procurement and Assignment Service decreed that the internship would be reduced to 9 months; it had to be rotating in character, with only 2 or possibly 3 months in surgery. These orders initiated the nine-nine-nine program.[5]

Vigorous opposition was not forthcoming from academic medical centers or established medical organizations, even though it was recognized that the United States would live with much larger armed forces in post-war years, and the prospect of an inadequate number of doctors was apparent to every planner. It was also recognized that when hostilities ceased and veterans returned, their relocation and re-education would become a serious problem since many had had an inadequate internship; a large demand for specialty residencies would occur.[6] Graham was quite bitter about the nine-nine-nine arrangement and was almost equally so at the failure of organized medicine to urge a less Draconian arrangement. He knew that no one who supported the nine-nine-nine program regarded it as ideal, but felt it was much better than the alternatives: "As a matter of fact officers in the Surgeon General's office ... stated they saw no reason why any man ... should be granted more than one year's training."[7,8] He discussed the matter at length with Robert Hutchins of the University of Chicago, a man whom he regarded as one of the most courageous of the university presidents, but Hutchins told him that he should not expect very much in the way of concerted action from university and college presidents.[9]

By April 1941 Graham decided to call public attention to the disruption of medical education created by selective service policies, and, at a sectional meeting of the American College of Surgeons held in Minneapolis, he stated that without complete deferment there would likely be an acute shortage of doctors. He noted that already 10 percent of American physicians had been called into service, postulated that the figure might be 30 percent before the year was out, and stated that if an equal percentage of medical students were forced to terminate their medical training, it would be a serious menace to civilian health after the national emergency was over.[10]

Graham made a more aggressive attack in 1944 with an editorial in *Surgery, Gynecology and Obstetrics* (*SGO*) entitled "What Kind of Medical Officers Do the Armed Services Want?"[11] He opened the editorial by reciting compliments from Army Surgeon General Norman T. Kirk that praised the remarkable results achieved by medical officers in the field. Graham then proceeded to explain that they were the product of the resident plan of graduate instruction that required many years before it became established on a sufficiently firm basis to influence the practice of surgery in this country. He decried the fact that laymen who have no adequate understanding of medical education dictated what may be given in a pre-medical course, shortened medical school years, and practically destroyed the resident system of training:

> Many medical officers will now enter the Army to serve in battalion aid stations and in other places demanding a knowledge of surgery whose maximum graduate hospital experience has been nine months of a rotating intern service with perhaps only two months in surgery. Is this the kind of medical officers the Armed Forces want? Pity the wounded if it is. ... let us imagine a group of surgeons with the authority to prescribe the education of line officers, be they Army or Navy. Would they wreck West Point and Annapolis? Would they reduce their faculties by 40 or 50% at the same time that they increase the number of the students? Would they reduce the period of training of artillery officers or submarine commanders to an amount which could not possibly make them efficient? It seems unlikely that they would. Yet if they were to exercise an interference with the training of line officers analogous to what the War and Navy Departments have done to the West Points of Medicine, that is exactly what they would do.[11]

Graham continued:

> We were told the Army needed 6.5 medical officers for each 1,000 men ... an excessively high ratio of one medical officer for every 154 men. ... this means that 68,250 medical officers were to be needed for the Armed Forces [leaving] one doctor for each 1293 civilians. ... Apparently only numbers count because of the baneful influence of the magic ratio of 6.5 per thousand, 'better have a lot of poor medical officers than a smaller number of good ones' seems to be the philosophy of the laymen running the War and Navy Departments. ... the fallacy of that reasoning is 'shall we send our men into battle with civil war muskets if the supply of modern arms is deficient'? ... Is it necessary that this large number of medical officers be provided or is not this demand for so many medical officers an unjustifiable extravagance for which there is no demonstrated need? ... The nine-nine-nine plan will not train surgeons and will not provide competent surgical officers. ... that plan should be scrapped. In its place a reasonable program for the training of medical officers should be substituted.[11]

Graham closed by recalling the wisdom of Aesop: "'The hen that laid a golden egg every day was killed by its owners in order to get all the gold at once, but alas no gold was found inside its body and the source of the daily golden egg was destroyed'. Is there no parallel here?"[11]

Graham received many letters, particularly from medical officers overseas, praising him for the article, and he sent a reprint to Alan Gregg of the Rockefeller Foundation, with the laconic comment, "The Secretary of War [Stimson] didn't like it much and wrote me a letter which constituted a rather weak defense of the Army's attitude."[12] Surgeon General Kirk wrote Graham a personal letter: "[The] advances…made in military surgery…are outstanding. It is most gratifying to see the grand job our young surgeons who have been so excellently trained here at home are doing in these theaters."[13] Graham responded: "Certainly the wrecking of the plan of training of these surgical officers will necessarily result in cutting down the supply of young men capable of doing such a grand job, but this is something which, I suppose, you do not feel like expressing yourself on very forcibly."[14] Within 3 days, Graham received his answer: "Right now we have a war to win and battle casualties and sick to care for and the people who have been trained in the past are doing a splendid job and training their junior officer assistants.…The only trouble is we don't have enough of either."[15]

Graham's frustrations were again visible in a letter to Fred Rankin of the surgeon general's office: "I am glad to see on the letterhead of your letter to me the very intriguing slogan 'Save. U.S. Army Conservation Program'. I am wondering what in hell the Army is trying to conserve? The letters from you are about the only ones I get from Army officers which do not carry with them carbon copies. Since the carbon copies are on good quality tissue paper I can think of only one possible use for them. Maybe the Army would not consider such use a waste of paper."[16] This correspondence merely contributed to Graham's desire to seek the ear of Secretary of War Stimson or President Roosevelt himself.

Turning his attention to a broader audience, Graham selected the *Saturday Evening Post*, the most widely read periodical of the time, as the vehicle through which he would bring his concerns to the public. In January 1945 the *Post* published his 5000-word editorial entitled "Have the Armed Services Crippled Medical Education?";[17] it was a major expansion of his *SGO* article. He opened with praise for the medical officers: "Much has been said of the lack of adequate preparation of the United States for war when the Japanese bombs crashed on Pearl Harbor on that never-to-be-forgotten morning in December, 1941. In at least one respect, however, we were very well prepared. We had the largest group of the most splendidly educated medical specialists in our whole history. Thousands…were at once ready for mobilization and use by the Armed Forces." He quoted Surgeon General Kirk's praise that in some army hospitals, the rate of salvage of those who reached the hospital had almost reached 100 percent; in addition, "serious epidemics of disease which have usually ravaged armies in time of war have been non-existent in the United States Army." Graham then continued:

> To those who have been engaged in medical education, this excellent performance has been no surprise; indeed it has been only what was expected. What will surprise many people … is the fact that the Army and Navy adopted policies which have already effectively prevented our medical schools and hospitals from continuing the supply of trained doctors. … The saving of lives is surgery—surgery—surgery. … the whole set up was so well planned [that] we had keenly intelligent personnel and the spirit to carry it through.[17]

At that point Graham turned to the achievements of residency programs and the salutary effects of the certifying boards:

> One might suppose that a plan that has been demonstrated to be effective in the preparation of medical officers would be allowed to continue in order to supply replacements of the same caliber. But instead it has been scrapped by the War and Navy Departments. Paradoxical as it seems, the program which probably supplied the best prepared officers in any group of the civilian population to enter immediately into wartime activities has been destroyed, although we are constantly told that the end of the War is by no means in sight. … The undergraduates are receiving fairly good instruction although not nearly so good as in prewar days but the most serious consequences of the disturbance caused by the War are in the period of graduate training.[17]

Graham described the circumstances that led to the nine-nine-nine plan:

> The thought seems not to have occurred to the Army and the Navy Departments that in the greatest emergency ever faced by this country teaching hospitals have been doing a magnificent job in giving them splendidly trained young medical specialists. … Then [could] you believe that the Army in need of well-trained surgeons would destroy the only plan producing them that has been found to work efficiently. Yet that is what has happened. … The general responsibility of those responsible for this policy seem to be 'better have a lot of poorly trained medical officers than fewer well trained ones'. If medical officers were merely so much cannon fodder perhaps this idea would not be so bad but it becomes tragic when one contemplates the harm that the half trained medical officer can do when placed in a

position requiring expert judgement. ... In defense of their policy which wrecks the plan of educating medical specialists the Army and Navy have stated that the War has made it necessary to interrupt the program of civilian training in all fields. ... We can get along for a period of time as we always do during wartime without new bridges, new roads, new buildings but there is no moratorium on sickness and death. In fact, during times of national calamities such as war there is likely to be an actual increase in the need for medical services for the home front. ... One should not wonder at or be too critical of our own Armed Forces for being over prepared to meet unexpected emergencies ... yet there must be some limit beyond which they cannot go even in total war without danger of destroying the nation whose defense they are undertaking. ... The health of the home front is one feature the importance of which cannot be minimized. It is now jeopardized by the virtual destruction of graduate medical education, a course which not only fails to benefit the Armed Services but threatens the future supply of competent doctors. ... The new officers the Armed Services are receiving now are only half trained and are necessarily inferior professionally to those received in the early part of the War. ... The future of American medicine requires a realistic approach to the needs of the Army and the Navy as well as the home front for doctors—and not slap dash doctors—but doctors trained in the thorough manner which is given to American civilian and military medicine a leading position in the world.[17]

Graham received hundreds of letters commending him for this article, but one third-year medical student made an uncomplimentary response, for he disliked the implication that Graham had condemned a whole generation of doctors who were prevented from having satisfactory training. Graham felt that the article had been very well received, but remarked that he had "not however heard from any of the brass hats in Washington."[18] To Alton Ochsner, he wrote: "I had a good deal of fun writing the article because as you know I never run away from a good fight. I felt that this was a particular [one], I wish I could feel sure that the article would accomplish something. I don't believe I am going to win this fight."[19] "I think the expression that the Army is eating up the seed corn is excellent,"[20] Graham wrote to Ralph Major.

A complimentary letter was received from Harold Dodds, president of Princeton University: "I was greatly pleased to find that you were the author and to know that a valued and distinguished alumnus of Princeton has spoken with such clear tones against one of the major scandals of the War. Please accept my congratulations, you are one of the few men of the country that has spoke with unquestioned authority and who has not become so publicly involved in earlier squabbles as to reduce your influence."[21] Graham responded that it was hard to predict how serious the results might be if the present program were allowed to continue much longer, and that, although the enemy may be defeated in a military sense, the war may be lost in a cultural sense: "It seems to me that the time has come for those who are responsible for education in this country to demand in whatever way seems best that the military people desist from their plans of completely wrecking our whole plan of education upon which our democracy and our American way of life are based."[22]

One letter arrived from William Dock of Brooklyn, New York, who wrote to condemn Rankin and Morgan in the surgeon general's office, and equally so, the medical school deans, who were willing to take in 40 percent more tuition each year. Dock felt: "The medical profession has constructed a very awkward bed for itself, … its leaders played possum in 1942." He claimed that the error would not be corrected until the profession accepted full responsibility for its passive stupidity in 1940 to 1942, and stated: "On you rests the heaviest responsibility, as is always true of men in positions of authority and prestige. … We were put in our place by Deans and fellow professors, not by the Services."[23] Graham responded to Dock: "The Secretary of War wrote me a note explaining to me that I was all wrong. … I have tried to get two large national organizations to exert pressure on the War Department but I have not been able to get anybody to act. Consequently I took the fight alone."[24]

Graham was informed that he would soon appear before the Senate Committee on Military Affairs, and he eagerly awaited a formal invitation to tell how the army and navy had ruined medical education. He hoped the trip would accomplish something and not belong to the category of wasted time and futile effort.[25] Graham shortly received a letter from Senator Hill, who told him the committee had been busy on other matters. Graham felt Hill was losing interest because of rapid developments in Germany,[26] and the invitation never came.

Graham's final censure of the military occurred in June 1945, 7 years after his ebullient and enthusiastic speech to the incoming class of September 1938[27](see chapter 11). In the commencement address, Graham told the new graduates:

> The old order has changed to a degree which you neophytes in the profession cannot fully appreciate. You have been caught in the maelstrom of these changes as they affect medical education. … Gradually the spreading ulcer of Naziism has destroyed European culture and medical science has gone down with it. A generation ago Germany and Austria were the leaders in medical research and the German Universities had so profound an influence on American education that many of our institutions strove to imitate them. … now many of those famous German Universities are only smoking ruins. … all former centers of important medical research, medical science and education

have been seriously curtailed if not completely wiped out.... Medicine like other sciences is international and all contributors make up its component parts.... almost without our realization the whole plan of specialized medical education has been virtually destroyed in this country, three thousand miles away from Germany [and] even worse is the fact that beginning with 1946 practically no able-bodied young man will be allowed to start the study of medicine in this country.[28]

He continued by discussing the reduction in the number of students who would enter medical school in 1946, 1947, and 1948, and he recognized that for many years after the war ended, the army and the navy would require large numbers of physicians. He was amazed that the army and the navy, who considered the supply of medical officers so necessary that this class had been financed by the government to complete their studies, could then support the policies of selective service with the cutting off of the supply of future medical officers at its source. He asked:

Does this make sense to you? It does not to me.... The temptation is great to blame our present plight in medicine on the military men, the so-called brass hats, who have taken over the running of our government and the control of our everyday activities ... with apparently only one purpose in mind, namely to win the war. No demonstrable effort has been made by them to salvage from the wreckage of war the priceless things which make up the culture of our country, the American way of life in its best sense.... we have an older generation that plunged the world into two devastating wars. It is hard to imagine that you could do worse than we have done.... remember that not only are you doctors of medicine but you are also citizens of a great democracy and ... the course which our government follows in the next few years may decide the fate of the world for centuries and will determine whether we shall have a rebirth of those attributes of our culture which have been destroyed or whether we shall enter another dark age.[28]

Two weeks before this graduation ceremony, victory in Europe had been accomplished. Military eyes were now turning to the Pacific, but an early surrender by Japan was not envisaged on that June morning. Plans had been drawn for Operation Olympic, a landing of the American Sixth Army on the island of Kyushu in November, to be followed by Operation Coronet, a landing of the First, Eighth, and Tenth Armies on the Tokyo Plain on March 1, 1946. These actions would require the movement of a million men across 3000 miles of the Pacific Ocean within a few short months, and it was expected that army, navy, and marine casualties could possibly exceed those seen in Europe.[29] The resolve of the US public to continue a fight so bloody and so far from home was uncertain and untested. However, the blood letting was spared by the dropping of bombs on Hiroshima and Nagasaki.

Combat Via the American Medical Association and the American College of Surgeons

In 1943 an opportunity to use the strengths of organized medicine for political action was afforded to Graham by the support of the American Medical Association, the American College of Surgeons, and the American College of Physicians (ACP). In April, Admiral Ross McIntire, surgeon general of the navy, spoke of the problems that would confront the medical profession in post-war years: the medical services of the army, navy, and Public Health Service would be substantially larger than ever before in peace time; returning medical officers would pose problems in postgraduate training; and the American medical profession would carry responsibilities for medical and health problems of many unfortunate countries.[30]

This warning led the trustees of the American Medical Association to create the Committee on Post-War Medical Services (CPMS), consisting of eight members from the AMA and five each from the ACP and the ACS, to consider these and other problems.[31] Roger I. Lee of the AMA was named chairman. Evarts Graham became an ACS representative[a].

The first meeting of CPMS took place in Chicago on June 5, 1943, and held a wide-ranging discussion that included shortened programs of medical education, reduction in the length of the internship, and the fact that medical schools would have soldier and sailor students. The meeting closed with a listing of six pressing problems. A few months later, the committee debated a lengthy anonymous letter to Chairman Roger Lee from an internist who had visited many of the posts and stations in Europe. The author claimed: "Many of the physicians in military service for two or three years were concerned about the fact that holding 'sick call' was not enough to keep them up to date and [they] visualized themselves among the 20,000 doctors who had never practiced or who will have to go back to a medical practice without any professional rehabilitation. … a feeling of hopelessness had developed."[32] Graham acknowledged that he, too, had received similar letters and that two sorts of opportunities should be offered to the veterans: one, a series of "brush-up" courses of perhaps 3 months' duration; the other, an effort to enlarge residency staffs in the teaching hospitals to double their ordinary size in order for men to receive sound training in the specialties. He announced that Barnes Hospital was planning to do both.[33]

---

a. ACS members of CPMS: Irvin Abell, Arthur W. Allen, Fredrick A. Coller, Evarts A. Graham, James M. Mason.

By early 1945 the policies and regulations of the army, the navy, and selective service would seriously reduce the numbers and quality of students admitted to medical schools that fall, and they would reduce enrollments further in 1946. The army, navy, and Veterans Administration estimated that 30,000 doctors would be required in addition to those available before the war. At its May 1945 meeting, Graham was appointed to membership on the CPMS Sub-Committee on Enrollment of Medical Students.

A bill (S-637) to defer premedical and medical students was introduced into the Senate by Allen J. Ellender, D. Louisiana, and its support became a matter of high priority to the CPMS.[34] After its introduction in late February, the Ellender Bill did not receive a favorable hearing in the Senate Committee on Military Affairs, and CPMS knew it was unlikely to receive favorable action by the Senate. Morris Fishbein, editor of the *Journal of the American Medical Association*, wrote that every possible means should be taken to acquaint the public—not merely the medical profession—with the seriousness and urgency of the matter;[35] perhaps he thought Graham's article in the *Saturday Evening Post*[17] had not been widely read.

Graham's interest in Ellender's Bill led him to write directly to the White House to ask for an interview with President Harry Truman in order to express the concerns of the medical educational world.[36] He was granted a meeting with the president on May 21, 1945. Truman had been president for barely 6 weeks, and was facing painful and distressing decisions regarding the number of casualties that could be expected from an invasion of the Japanese homeland. His thoughts may not have been focused on the problem of medical student education.[29] Fred C. Zaffe, Harvey Stone, Victor Johnson, and Evarts Graham met with Truman for approximately 45 minutes to present the case that adequate numbers of physicians must be provided for the improvement of the health of the nation, as well as for the support of expanded military commitments. They noted that, in the past year, virtually no able-bodied males had been permitted to commence a 2-year college premedical course because the selective service system would not defer them, and that women, physically disqualified males, and men over the draft age would supply scarcely 1200 to 1500 medical students, about 25 percent of the desired numbers. They held that their proposed adjustments were dictated by the necessity to preserve the health of the nation.[37] No action resulted from their meeting with President Truman.[38]

The director of selective service, General Hershey, believed that the number of returning veterans would be sufficient to adequately fill the enrollment needs of the medical schools, despite the fact that, at Hershey's request, a special committee headed by Frank Lahey had surveyed the number of veterans in premedical studies and reported to General Hershey that the supply would constitute only about 4 to 5 percent of incoming medical students.[39] After hostilities in the Pacific ended,

Graham ceased to attend CPMS meetings, and turned to the American College of Surgeons, hoping for some action. In February 1947 the CPMS was renamed the Joint Committee for Consideration of Medical Services.

At the beginning of the Korean conflict in 1950, Congress was considering a bill sponsored by the AMA that would draft one specific group of citizens—the doctors. The ACS Committee on Graduate Training, under the direction of Frederick Coller, then established a subcommittee, headed by Evarts Graham[b], that presented a statement about the upcoming Doctor Draft Bill to the board of regents in October 1950. It offered to help the United States Government provide an adequate supply of medical officers for the various services. It also expressed concerns about some aspects of the problem: the subcommittee felt that "undoubtedly... the most effective means of conserving medical officers and eliminating wastage would be the complete unification of the Medical Services for the Armed Forces." It was of "paramount importance that the Government should not remove from civil practice more doctors than were actually needed for the military emergency [since] highly educated physicians and surgeons are too valuable to be carelessly wasted." The statement encouraged the use of civilian consultants and civilian hospitals, and emphasized: "the withdrawal from the teaching hospitals of *unnecessarily* large numbers of young doctors who are in the midst of their graduate training should be scrupulously avoided." The committee stated emphatically: "The teaching hospitals should be regarded in the same light as 'essential industry' and nothing should be allowed to impair or wreck their educational function.... it is hoped that the mistakes of World War II in this respect will be avoided."[40]

This document was "pure Graham"; it embodied many of his personal feelings and, in reading between the lines, it is quite apparent that the ACS was piqued that the AMA had decided to act alone in proposing the Doctor Draft. The ACS statement was sent to 12 US Government officials, including the president; to all major newspapers of the United States; and to the editor of the *Journal of the American Medical Association* (but not to AMA officers). How much influence the statement carried is impossible to determine, although it must have been well known to Frank Berry, a member of the ACS and a close personal acquaintance of Graham.

Doctor Draft legislation was approved in 1951, and within it were portions that came to be known as the "Berry Plan"; the needs for specialized services by the armed forces would be identified, and, through a lottery, medical students and interns would be deferred for postgraduate residency training; then, as the military needed them, they would be called to active duty at the completion of their training. The Doctor Draft was continued for 20 more years, until 1973, and the Berry Plan accomplished much that the nine-nine-nine program could never do.

---

b. Members of the ACS subcommittee: Evarts A. Graham (chairman), B. Noland Carter, Loyal Davis, Paul B. Magnuson, Philip D. Wilson.

STUDYING MEDICAL DEPARTMENTS OF THE MILITARY

The Army
(1942–1943)

As United States activities in World War II intensified, Lt. Gen. Brehon B. Somervell, commanding officer of the service of supply, desired to review the practices and readiness of his medical department. He prevailed upon Secretary of War Henry Stimson to convene a committee to study the medical department of the army; Graham accepted an appointment to the committee, composed of six civilians and two army physicians, and chaired by Lt. Col. Stanford H. Wadhams (Medical Corps [retired]).[41]

Part of Somervell's motivation was the fact that, 6 months earlier, the office of the surgeon general of the army had been moved from the staff of Chief of Staff Gen. George C. Marshall to Somervell's staff in the service of supply. Concerns were raised that Surgeon General Maj. Gen. John C. Magee was now hampered because of a lack of access to both the chief of staff and the secretary of war. It was not clearly stated, but was highly suspect, that the investigation was undertaken as an effort on the part of Lieutenant General Somervell to remove General Magee from his position as army surgeon general. Magee was soon succeeded by Maj. Gen. Norman T. Kirk.

The army arrangement was in sharp contrast to that of the navy, wherein the surgeon general, Ross T. McIntire, was a member of the staff of Admiral-in-Chief Ernest King. McIntire also happened to be President Roosevelt's personal physician, and he accompanied the president on every major trip outside Washington, DC. The army shuffle placed physicians in the position of being considered as supplies, not unlike tanks, guns, food, and clothing.

Stimson's committee, with Mr. Corrington Gill as executive secretary, was charged to review 10 assigned topics. Its first meeting was held in Washington, DC, on September 25, 1942, and by November 24 its work was completed. The committee heard almost 100 presentations and visited three military installations during these 6 weeks. During the month of October, Graham spent 12 days at committee meetings; four more meetings were held in November prior to the final meeting.

The committee's report contained 17 major findings and 98 detailed recommendations, one of which was that an overall body be empowered to coordinate the procurement of physicians in such a manner that both civilian and military needs would be met. It also included a recommendation that the medical services of the army air forces be brought under the authority of the surgeon general of the army. Attention was paid to the office of the surgeon general of the army, for the committee believed that, within the service of supply, the office was administratively placed at too low a level within the war department; they recommended it be returned to the staff of the chief of staff. At the very least, if the chief surgeon remained within the service of supply, he should have a rank commensurate with his position and responsibility.[42]

The committee made a lengthy recommendation regarding qualifications for surgeon general of the army, and they went so far as to suggest that the surgeon general need not necessarily come from within the ranks—a remarkably unmilitary recommendation: "In the selection of the next Surgeon General a careful balancing of the value of military medical experience in its widest sense against the qualities so needed in this post must be made. On the one hand would be found the weight of military training while on the other hand would be the broad abilities found in civilian medical leaders. It is essential that the best man for the post be found either in the regular medical department or, if necessary, in the civilian medical profession."[42] The document was considered confidential with restricted distribution, and only three copies of the three-volume report were printed. None were sent to commission members.

Graham's lack of love for the military was not improved upon by this experience, and he was angered that the members of the committee were not going to receive copies of the completed report. Suspecting that Executive Secretary Gill was behind this decision, he decided to go directly to Secretary of War Stimson. On February 4, 1943, Graham made a special trip to Washington, DC, and, accompanied by Dr. Lewis H. Weed of Johns Hopkins, spent 45 minutes with the secretary of war. Graham reported that Stimson was "horrified to learn that members of the committee had been denied the privilege of having copies of the final report." Graham added: "The most disconcerting event of the interview was that Mr. Stimson told us he had not up to that time read the report. . . . We told him some of the most important recommendations. He seemed to be only mildly interested. . . . as a matter of fact, I think he dropped off to sleep once or twice during our interview." Graham ended his notes on the encounter by indicating that he would "be very glad to participate in any attempt to elevate the Medical Department of the Army to a place commensurate with its importance."[43] The committee's ideas about improving the position of the surgeon general and the medical department within the war department administrative structure received short shrift from both Lieutenant General Somervell and Secretary Stimson; on February 16 Stimson announced there would be no army organizational change with respect to the status of the army surgeon general.[44]

The sense of discouragement and disillusion that had occurred with membership on this small commission remained with Graham for a long time. Nine years later Col. Calvin A. Goddard, in writing this portion of the medical history of World War II, contacted Graham and requested that he proofread chapter 5 of the *Administration of the Medical Department*, which described the activities of Wadham's committee. Graham reflected on those years:

> I think all of us on that Committee felt that it was a very frustrating experience. Soon after our deliberations began, we got a very distinct

impression that we had been appointed by General Somervell as stooges to get General Magee. I may say also that we were not at all satisfied with the work of Mr. Corrington Gill, who was appointed as the Executive of the Committee.... I think perhaps the Committee might have continued its deliberations longer if it had been more satisfied with Mr. Gill and had been more convinced that its work was worthwhile. Most of us were very busy men, who were already carrying extra loads because of the War effort. To undertake an additional heavy load such as the work of this Committee would have been a pleasure, however, if we could have felt convinced that our work was really appreciated and that it would be regarded as important by those in a position of authority. When we began to realize that we were merely stooges for Somervell in what apparently was a personal quarrel with Magee, we naturally lost interest. The climax of our disgust came when we were not allowed to see the final report which had been prepared by Mr. Gill.[45]

In his response Goddard deeply regretted that Graham had found the experience of the Committee to study the Medical Department so frustrating: "I trust that you have learned that 'time heals all wounds.'"[46] It took a long time—perhaps the healing never occurred.

The Navy
(1947–1950)

Graham's disenchantment with his service as a commissioner for the army was not sufficient to deter him from further participation in national military affairs. In December 1947 he accepted an appointment as honorary consultant to the medical department of the navy.[47] There were 43 members on this commission, and duties were not burdensome, but the termination was equally as distasteful and, in some ways, as offensive to Graham as it had been with the army committee. He attended the first meeting on December 5, 1947. No meetings were scheduled during 1948 and 1949. During the meeting of January 28 to 29, 1950, Graham became ill with gastroenteritis and was hospitalized for 16 hours at the US Naval Hospital in Bethesda, Maryland.

The final meeting of the commission was planned for Friday, June 9, 1950, and on May 13 Graham received a letter from Chairman Frank Lahey of Boston to the effect that he was resigning. He gave as a reason his feeling that the members were being asked to support the navy in opposing unification and cooperation with the army, air, and Public Health Medical Services. Lahey stated, "I find it distasteful to look toward a conference in Washington, the principal aim of which is to reinforce the Surgeon General of the Navy and his colleagues in their determination to hinder the development of a more satisfactory medical program for our military personnel."[48]

Graham closed his involvement with the committee by avoiding its June meeting, stating: "It conflicts with our commencement.... I feel very much as you do about the whole thing.... Today I received from Bortz [a commission member] a copy of a letter which he has just written to Jim Paullin [another commission member] telling him that he does not approve of the idea of having the Navy use us as a bunch of stooges to rubber stamp their proposals.... I do hope that something may be done to change the attitude of the Navy so that they will work more harmoniously with the other services.[49,50]

The commission was dissolved, and Graham's appointment was formally terminated as of December 31, 1950.[51] It had been another unrewarding experience, with nothing accomplished.

Chapter 17

EXTRAMURAL ACTIVITIES: PART 3

THE TRUMAN COMMISSION
(1951–1952)

National Health Insurance had been included in Franklin Roosevelt's "New Deal," but it was Harry Truman who gave it unreserved and unwavering support. In 1943 Senators Wagner of New York, Murray of Montana, and Dingell of Michigan introduced a bill proposing that National Health Insurance be included within the Social Security Act, and the US surgeon general become its administrator. The bill specified that all classes of society would be included and that it would be universal and comprehensive.

The American Medical Association (AMA) felt the plan would turn doctors into slaves, and it hired a public relations firm, Whitaker and Baxter, to oppose it. The Wagner-Murray-Dingell Bill became a lightning rod that polarized medical reformers and conservatives through the remaining Roosevelt years and the entire Truman administration. During these years Evarts Graham was not deeply involved in the national politics of health care, for his governmental responsibilities were with the National Research Council; however, he did have his opinions.

Graham presented his thoughts about the bill in February 1946 at a meeting sponsored by the St. Louis Committee of House Physicians for the Study of Medical Care, headed by Dr. Richard Peters, a surgical intern at Barnes Hospital and son of John P. Peters[a] of Yale. Graham asserted that there should be little opposition to four parts of the projected program, but he took exception to the proposal that the surgeon general of the Public Health Service be its director, feeling that such an arrangement embodied the danger of medical dictatorship. He acknowledged the vehement opposition by organized medicine but also recognized that there was much room for improvement in the present quality of medical care in the United States. He favored a pilot plan that could work out the problems. After a 4- or 5-year trial, the plan could be revised and then applied generally. He suggested the trial occur in a small area, possibly the District of Columbia, which was already under the direct control of the federal government.[1] In 1946, with a Republican-controlled Congress, the National Health Insurance Bill was set aside, until Truman's 1948 surprise upset over Thomas Dewey.

Graham took a second opportunity to make known his opinion in 1949, following a $25 assessment by the AMA to oppose the expected coming of National Health Insurance legislation. In a protest to the projected use of the levy, he wrote to the speaker of the House of Delegates of the Missouri State Medical Association:

> I may say at the start that I am as much opposed to state medicine as anyone else. . . . as you doubtless know the AMA for years has fumbled the ball from the standpoint of its public relations on the question of socialized medicine. . . . I am only one of many who feel that the most certain way to get state medicine here is to have the AMA continue to pursue the same tactics it has pursued over the past ten years. . . . there is a very great danger of having Congress take the bit in its teeth and go ahead with legislation which we as doctors know would be very unwise. . . . I think a group could be organized to go into a very serious study of this problem. . . . perhaps state medicine may come eventually but it will certainly come sooner than it needs to come unless organized medicine and particularly the AMA changes very drastically its present attitude. . . . I would hope very much that the Missouri State Medical Association might be one of the first to make such a protest. That is the reason for this letter.[2]

Truman was determined that changes in health care were in order, and, 3 months after the end of World War II, he called upon Congress to enact a four-part program: (1) to provide for the expansion of hospitals (this was done); (2) to increase support for public health and maternal and child services (this was done);

---

a. Evarts Graham was ever conscious of those who became friends and supporters during his early years, and he repaid his obligations by accepting the sons of several of these men into his surgical internship and residency program; Richard Peters, son of J.P. Peters of the Committee of Physicians; Paul Keller and John Moncrief, sons of Colonels Keller and Moncrief of the surgeon general's office in World War I; Harrison Shoulders Jr., son of a president of the AMA; and D. Elliott O'Reilly, son of Archer O'Reilly, an orthopedist member of the early Barnes Hospital cadre.

(3) to give more federal aid to medical research and education (this was done); and (4) to create a single health insurance system that would be universal, comprehensive, and include all classes of society. The Wagner-Murray-Dingell Bill was part four of this effort.[3] Truman wished to ensure the right to adequate medical care and pressed his program with even greater energy after his re-election, giving Federal Security Administrator Oscar R. Ewing the duty of shepherding the proposals over the legislative hurdles.

By 1950 post-war reconstruction was well under way, and returning veterans were being cared for when new demands were suddenly placed upon the president. On June 25, 1950, North Korea invaded South Korea, and within 48 hours Truman had authorized US assistance to South Korea and had obtained the United Nations' support. The United States was once again involved in an armed conflict; this one would last until a truce was declared in July 1953. The peace treaty is still elusive. Once again, health needs of the military needed to be balanced against those of civilians.

On December 29, 1951, Truman established the President's Commission on the Health Needs of the Nation. He asked its 15 members[b], which included Evarts Graham, to study the following: "current and prospective supply of physicians;… the adequacy of the supply in terms of the present demands for service; and the ability of educational institutions… to provide such additional trained persons as may be required." The commission was to study the facts and present recommendations for safeguarding and improving the health of the nation. Truman wanted it to investigate such major health problems as "insuring an adequate supply of physicians, dentists, nurses and allied personnel; developing local public health units throughout the nation; making more hospitals and hospital beds available where needed; stepping up the tempo of fundamental medical research; meeting the needs of the chronically ill and aged; and providing adequate diagnostic, rehabilitative, and other health services to all income groups." He also requested that it look at the ability of local public health units to meet demands posed by civil defense requirements, and to examine problems created by the shift of thousands of workers to defense production areas, requiring a relocation of doctors and other

---

b. Members of the Truman commission: Paul B. Magnuson (chairman), medical director of Veterans Administration; Evarts A. Graham, Washington University; Joseph Hinsey, dean, Cornell University Medical School; Russell V. Lee, AMA delegate, Palo Alto Clinic; Gunnar Gunderson, AMA trustee (refused to serve); Marian W. Sheahan, director, National Nursing Committee; Ernest G. Sloman, president, American Association of Dental Schools; Walter Reuther, president, United Automobile Workers; A.J. Hayes, president, International Association of Machinists; Clarence Poe, editor, *Progressive Farmer*; Charles S. Johnson, president, Fisk University; Lowell Reed, vice president, Johns Hopkins; Chester Barnard, president, Rockefeller Foundation; Elizabeth S. Magee, general secretary, National Consumers League; Dean R. Clark, director, Massachusetts General Hospital.

professionals. The president gave the commission 1 year to complete its studies and to make its report.[4,5]

Truman had been urging the adoption of a national health insurance program without success since 1945; finally, his plan, now known as the Ewing Plan after its chief advocate and designer, was undergoing legislative scrutiny. In creating the commission, Truman noted that he had asked others to come forward with ideas of their own but that counter proposals had not been forthcoming, and he stated that "the Commission was to present its recommendations for safeguarding and improving the health of the nation." It was a broad mandate.[4]

Truman named Dr. Paul B. Magnuson[c], an orthopedic surgeon from Chicago, as its chairman. Formerly chief medical director of the Veterans Administration, Magnuson had been an outspoken critic of both Truman's plan and the "do-nothing" Republican Congress. Announcement of the formation of this commission brought a critical denunciation in the *Journal of the American Medical Association* by Gunderson[6] and a long defense by Howard Rusk in the *New York Times*.[7]

The commission planned to meet in Washington, DC, for 2 days every 3 or 4 weeks during the entire year of 1950, with its first meeting scheduled for February 12. Graham attended all but two meetings. During the first 2 months, meetings were concerned with organization and agenda. From April through October, they

---

c. Paul B. Magnuson, born in St. Paul, Minnesota in 1884, received his doctor of medicine degree from the University of Pennsylvania in 1908 and entered the practice of surgery in Chicago in association with John B. Murphy. From his office near the stockyards, he obtained extensive experience in the management of trauma, and, during World War I, as a captain in the army, he was first posted in the office of the surgeon general and later posted at the debarkation station on Ellis Island. Following World War I, he returned to his orthopedic practice in Chicago. He was active in many societies and was president of several.

Magnuson became aware of deficiencies in the Veterans Administration (VA) hospital system and, shortly after the attack on Pearl Harbor, proposed to the VA administrator that new hospitals would be needed when the war was over. He suggested that the new hospitals be located near medical schools and that an arrangement to use VA facilities for the training of residents be consummated. At the time, his proposal was rejected, but Paul Hawley eventually made it possible.

As World War II began to wind down, it was anticipated that 100,000 veteran casualties would return to the United States to be cared for by a VA system that had aging facilities and barely 100 doctors. General Omar Bradley became the post-war head of the VA, and Paul Hawley its chief medical director. The two prevailed upon Magnuson to return to Washington, DC, to promulgate his plan, thereby creating the Deans Committee VA Hospitals and freeing VA physicians from the shackles of civil service. Upon the departure of Hawley, Magnuson became the VA medical director. Following work on the Truman commission, Magnuson underwent a hemilaryngectomy, which only slightly diminished his pace. His interests turned to the raising of funds for the development of the Rehabilitation Institute of Chicago.

There was never room for doubt about where Magnuson stood on an issue. He had deep convictions, was scrupulously honest, expressed his views bluntly, and clung to his ideals. Magnuson died in 1968.

became study panels, which presented public hearings and engaged in data collection. During the last 2 months, the commission was occupied with writing the report. Eighteen study panels, each to hear from 10 to 12 experts on its topic, were designed, and from April through August, these panels met in the commission headquarters, an ancient, once fashionable residence at 901 16th Street Northwest. Evarts Graham was paired with A.J. Hayes, president of the International Association of Machinists, for two of the panels. On Wednesday, April 9, with Graham as chairman, the panel spent the day discussing specialization in the practice of medicine. On Tuesday, May 27, with Hayes as chairman, 10 invited experts discussed industrial health.

In addition to presentations by experts, held in Washington, DC, there were public hearings in eight major cities, each with a member of the commission presiding. At the hearing held in St. Louis on September 15, Graham was the local commissioner and Mr. Donald Danforth, president of the Ralston Purina Company and past president of the St. Louis Community Chest (now the United Way), was local chairman. Graham secured participation of state and local medical, labor, farm, consumer, health, and government organizations throughout the Midwest, and a full day of hearings was held in the auditorium of the North Building of the Medical School.

Presentations were limited to 10 minutes each, and the major health problems addressed that day were (1) shortages in health personnel; (2) the adequacy of local public health units; (3) the status and adequacy of medical research; (4) the degree to which hospitals and clinics meet existing needs; (5) the extent to which people were able to afford adequate medical care, with particular reference to health insurance plans; and (6) the adequacy of federal, state, and local health programs, with emphasis on the desirable level of such expenditures. Copies of the oral presentations and submitted memoranda were forwarded to Washington, DC, for inclusion in the final report.[8,9]

By the end of September, all of the statistics and material from the study sessions and public hearings had been collected, and an outline of the factual and descriptive material for the report, with most chapters in draft form, was ready for discussion. Two meetings in October and one in November gave the commissioners the opportunity to refine what had been prepared and to make suggestions. On returning from the November meeting, Graham wrote to Lester Breslow, author of the report:

> I would like to have you put into the final copy of the report in its proper place the following statement with my signature attached to it: "I favor a federal department of health with cabinet status. The Government is already concerned with health in a big way and we are recommending an increase of its activities. Whether or not the new department should include at the start the medical services of the

Armed Forces and the Veterans Administration and whether or not [Social] Security should be combined with it are matters of detail"....
in my opinion, however, the health activities are sufficiently great to justify a department devoted solely to that.... I think it is essential that we make some recommendations on this very important subject ...and there will be much disappointment if we fail to carry one....
Again there are some small points of presentation on other matters which I think might be changed to improve the material from the standpoint of its English.... on page two, line sixteen the word "either" should be omitted in my opinion. There are other minor revisions and corrections which should be made.[10]

The final five-volume report was entitled *Building America's Health*.[11] Volume 1 was small, containing only the findings and recommendations of the commission, with all of the detailed analyses left for the other four volumes. Work was complete by early December and, at the final meeting of the commission on Thursday, December 18, at 11:30 am, volume 1 was presented to President Truman. The other four volumes were completed by April 1953. In his telegram of invitation to this meeting, Magnuson said: "I am prouder of this Commission's work than of anything else in my lifetime.... in the chapter on government organization for health it recommends that the Congress establish a Department of Health and Security."[12]

The final report recommended a cooperative federal-state program to assist in the financing of personal health services in addition to public health activities. This plan proposed that a health authority be established in every state that wished to participate, and each state would then prepare its own plan for the development and distribution of health services to all residents of that state, using public or private agencies, or a combination. State plans developed in cooperation with local or regional authorities would be linked to the planned federal expansion of health financing to provide more comprehensive, more efficient, and more economical services to all. State plans were expected to conform to certain federal minimal standards and be submitted to the federal health agency for approval. The "principal of prepayment would be accepted as the most feasible method for financing the cost of medical care."[11]

The latter months of the commission's work brought it under increasingly harsh attack from the AMA; in Milwaukee on September 15, Graham counterattacked, labeling the AMA's public relations policies as destructive and the worst imaginable, and stating: "The AMA hierarchy condemned the Commission without any knowledge of what it planned to do or without any idea of what it would find out. ...if that isn't un-American I don't know what is. The hierarchy of the AMA is like an ostrich with its head in the sand. It simply doesn't know what is going on.... some intelligent layman had accused the medical profession of becoming a trade union.... in the case of the AMA I believe there is some basis for that charge."[13]

After the study was released, Graham voiced his support through the newspapers: "There are many millions who now get no medical care at all because they cannot afford it and are not eligible for the free federal care given to [veterans]." He continued: "Doctors face something far less desirable at the hands of Congress unless they get behind some plan like the one proposed today. It would provide prepaid medical care through federal payments to states with partial subsidy of persons with low incomes [and] a compulsory scheme of national health insurance is a strong likelihood because of a consistently increasing demand for government subsidy in medicine."[14] The commission's report proposed state managed, federally aided, prepaid medical service for everyone. Three months later the AMA, in a major editorial on the commission's report, recommended it be filed away in the archives marked "Creeping Socialism."[15]

Contacts with Hayes, Reuther, and other members of the commission left their mark on Graham. He became particularly close to Russell Lee and Paul Magnuson, and wrote to Lee: "The report wouldn't have been so good if it hadn't been for your inspired help. You provided much of the leadership which was necessary. I was sorry all the time that I could not devote more of my own time to the Commission: in fact I am always unhappy when I accept a job and am not able to do as much on it as the job really requires. I tried a couple of times to resign because my conscience did hurt me some but Paul Magnuson would never listen to me.... I developed a first class friendship with you."[16] Lee proposed a follow-up committee to sell the report to the people of the nation. Graham opposed it and wrote to Magnuson: "I don't see any good reason why we should try to jam these recommendations down the throats of anybody. I think if the recommendations are any good they will probably be adopted... and I cannot feel that it is our job to attempt to force our recommendations on the public. It is that sort of thing which I dislike in the whole philosophy of the AMA."[17] Graham turned down an opportunity to meet with a committee of the National Health Council on March 18 to 20 in New York City, giving to Russell Lee the same reason that he had given to Magnuson.

Graham's commitment to the purposes and recommendations of the commission continued throughout the next year, and, before the end of 1953, he prepared a 3500-word editorial explaining the commission, its purposes, its conclusions, the possible consequences, and its overarching precepts. His discourse, "The Right to Health: A New Concept," covered a full-page in the *St. Louis Post-Dispatch*, and, as his major statement, Graham wrote:

> The concept that every member of society has an inherent right to health is so new that it has been given practically no consideration until very recent times. There is by no means any general agreement among those few who have discussed the question.... That [it] can now be talked about is due to an almost miraculous progress which

has occurred in medicine since Jefferson's memorable document was written. ... The concept of a right to health implies of course that a citizen will be defended against disease as he might be defended against a foreign enemy. The idea is especially applicable to infectious diseases [and] the entire medical profession has enthusiastically supported government action in the control of infectious diseases. It is unthinkable that there would be any serious opposition to the [public health] program as a whole. ... The concept that every citizen has a right to have good health implies that he also has a right to have food, clothing, shelter and safe working conditions.

This [concept] culminated in the plan for compulsory complete federal health insurance ... [and] theoretically every citizen would be entitled to be in as good a state of heath as possible. It would be his inherent right to have that health. ... The repercussions aroused by the controversy over the legislation for compulsory health insurance have not ... died down. It is still difficult to have a discussion of this subject among groups of the medical profession without causing emotional outbursts. Similarly, it is difficult to have a quiet discussion of any further expansion of tax supported medicine. ... The defeat of the legislation ... [for] compulsory federal health insurance and the expressed opposition to the plan ... seem to indicate ... that the majority of the people are not yet ready to look with favor upon the idea. ... another apparently logical conclusion to draw would be that the country is not yet ready to concede the inherent right to health.[18]

In his editorial Graham noted that the life expectancy had increased from 47 to 68 years, chiefly by decreased infant mortality rather than a lengthening of life beyond the biblical three score years and ten. He followed: "The question can be raised would it be of advantage to try to lengthen life indefinitely, would it be desirable, if possible, to increase the life expectancy much beyond the present 68 years? Suppose it were lengthened to 78 or 88 years the complications presented to society would be enormous." He returned to the work of the Truman commission and noted that two basic principles had been agreed upon: an access to health care for everyone and that the preservation of health is a basic human right. He even praised the Republican Congress for creating a Department of Health with cabinet status, and remarked that the United States was about the last civilized nation to have a federal Department of Health.

Graham then returned to the insurance aspect of health care:

Some form of prepaid insurance seems to be the best safeguard against [personal] financial disaster. The Commission therefore recommended that the principle of prepaid health services be accepted as the most feasible method of financing the costs of medical care.... In order to get away from some of the criticism directed at the plan of compulsory federal insurance, a new and different proposal was made. This was to establish a co-operative federal/state program, under [which] a single state health authority would be set up in each participating state [with] an overall state plan for assisting the development and distribution of personal health services.[18]

Graham next turned to the nation's obligation to educate, emphasizing:

The most important element in the whole health picture is the physician. Nothing should ever be permitted to happen that would lower the quality of his education.... medicine in all respects is dynamic and refuses to go along unchanged.... one needs only to examine the record of the first half of this century.... There will be more and more aid from government, both federal and state, in improving and maintaining the health of the people ... [and] it is to be hoped that the medical profession will co-operate to ensure that such aid will be wisely used.[18]

The article had been prepared at the request of Tom Sherman, editor of the *St. Louis Post-Dispatch* and a close acquaintance to Graham, who had asked Graham to make a statement on the present situation in medicine.[19] Graham prepared his editorial in longhand, and after two revisions it arrived in Sherman's office on July 30.[20] A galley proof that modified his text was delivered in person by Sherman a few days later, and Graham was deeply offended with the revisions. He wrote to Sherman:

I have done a lot of thinking. As a result I have decided that you can take the enclosed article as it is written or not at all. I cannot agree to your rewriting it. You can hardly imagine my astonishment when I saw the mangled corpse of the article that you presented to me. I tried hard to sit on my temper so that you wouldn't see how disturbed I was and so that I could have time to mull over the whole thing before I might express my feelings. When you originally asked me to write the article you did not state that you reserve the privilege of rewriting it. If you had done so I would have declined to do the job.... I hardly recognize the product.... what you did was to take away my own style, clumsy as it was, and the flavor that I put into it. It became a Thomas Sherman article that carried my name at the top. I have never been interested in ghost writing any more than in ghost surgery. I cannot

agree to a let down in that respect now. Anyway, isn't an author entitled to write a signed article in his own way?[21]

Two days later Sherman capitulated, "Since you have decided we must publish the article as is we will of course do so."[22]

One month after the editorial appeared, President Eisenhower delivered his first State of the Union address. Graham applauded it in a press release, pointing out that a number of the recommendations presented by Eisenhower paralleled provisions advocated by the Truman commission: "As a member of the former Commission I must say I feel very much flattered that the new Administration thinks so well of our recommendations." He then proceeded to express his opinion as to what the federal government should do—"go much further than this and extend aid to medical schools in general." Graham added that this was a controversial matter, conceding that some medical schools, fearing possible government interference, would prefer not to accept federal aid, but he believed "aid to medical schools administered with wisdom must be a part of any overall federal health program."[23]

However, national health insurance was not yet to be. The commission was two decades ahead of its time. Twelve years later coverage limited to the elderly was achieved. Initially proposed in 1958, the Medicare Act that was signed into law by President Johnson in 1965 (title 18 of the Social Security Act) provided assistance through a totally federal program to everyone over 65, regardless of income or status. A parallel bill contained the Medicaid Act (title 19 of the Social Security Act), which provided funds for those ill and needy under 65 in an arrangement whereby federal funds matched those of state programs, a financing method carried over from proposals made by the Truman commission. The Truman commission had recommended Cabinet status for health, and in 1953 President Eisenhower established a Department of Health, Education and Welfare, with Oveta Culp Hobby as its first secretary.

Evarts Graham's own thoughts on a universal, comprehensive, national health policy were never spelled out in great detail. In the late 1940s the Veterans Administration was the prototype by which Graham felt the federal government would care for its citizens, and the health care given to the veteran segment of the US public disenchanted him. The rigidity of its organization was troublesome, and it appears as though his view of any federal involvement in personal (as opposed to public) health care was the VA model. He thought it would be cumbersome, bureaucratic, inefficient, and monolithic.

Graham was, however, committed to the idea that government, in its many tiers, should play a major role in ensuring that all of the citizens of his country received health care. He felt comfortable with the general concept that each state could establish its own rules, with guidelines, taxes, and benefits to care for the citizens of that state, and that the federal government would provide supportive funding for state-initiated programs (not too dissimilar to the Medicaid formula). This viewpoint was contained in the Truman commission report, and he stressed it in his 1953 *St. Louis Post-Dispatch* editorial. His anti–Veterans Administration feelings became evident in his support for the recommendations of the second Hoover commission.

THE HOOVER COMMISSION
(1953–1954)

Ink was barely dry on the fifth volume of the Truman commission report, and the political acrimony that it occasioned was reaching a feverish pitch, when Graham received another invitation to participate on a federal commission. In 1947 President Truman had asked ex-President Herbert Hoover to head a commission to review the organization and activities of the executive branch of the government, and more than 72 percent of its recommendations had been adopted. Shortly after taking office, Dwight Eisenhower reconstituted the commission and asked it to review the executive structure of his government, with particular reference to the roles of public versus private enterprise. Herbert Hoover was appointed to head a commission composed of 12 members supplemented by 137 special advisors, 544 clerks, researchers, accountants, and consultants, and divided into 14 task forces. In inviting Evarts Graham to be a member of the Task Force on Federal Medical Services, Hoover wrote: "One of the most important of our problems is the medical services of the federal government. Under authority from the Commission, I am again organizing a task force to examine and make recommendations on this subject.... You can make a most important contribution in advancing the solution of a very difficult and grave problem in our government." The general thrust was that of "eliminating non-essential services, functions and activities which are competitive with private enterprise."[24]

The Task Force on Federal Medical Services contained many of Graham's friends and associates from previous years[d], and, at its first meeting in Washington, DC, on November 11, 1953,[25] it appointed a special five-man Committee on Planning that met in the American College of Surgeons headquarters in Chicago on December 3.[26] The Committee divided the Medical Task Force into four divisions, to cover (1) the armed forces, (2) the Veterans Administration, (3) the Public Health Service, and (4) overall planning for military and civilian medical services

---

d. Composition of Task Force on Federal Medical Services: Herbert Hoover, Chauncey McCormick (chairman), Francis J. Braceland, Otto Brandhorst, Edward D. Churchill, Edwin L. Crosby, Michael DeBakey, Evarts A. Graham, Alan Gregg, Paul R. Hawley, Hugh Leavell, Theodore G. Klumpp, Basil C. McLean, Walter B. Martin, James R. Miller, Dwight Wilbur, and Milton Winternitz, and John B. Hollister, and Sidney A. Mitchell (staff).

in time of war. All reports were to be completed by April 1, 1954, a deadline not met until November.[27] Graham was assigned to Division No. 2—the medical services of the Veterans Administration—and, during the next 11 months, attended eight meetings in Washington, DC.

For the commission's final meeting on November 5 and 6, 1954, all the detail work had been completed, and the report was finished three weeks later.[28] Its Medical Task Force made 29 recommendations regarding the Veterans Administration and its hospitals. These included the establishment of a federal advisory committee on health, elimination of selective service, closure of many Veterans Administration hospitals, and restriction of new construction to sites in or adjacent to medical schools. The task force suggested that veterans be required to establish the nature of their service-connected disabilities, and to verify financial need for care of non-service-connected disabilities. It recommended an end to the care of merchant seamen and to dependents of men then in the armed services. It proposed that a federal advisory committee be established to review government research.[29,30]

Graham concurred with all of the recommendations and wrote to its recording secretary T.G. Klumpp to indicate: "I thoroughly approve of what you have done. ... These figures which the staff has made up are perfectly satisfactory to me. I am glad to know that on one more occasion I agree fully with Benjamin Franklin[e]."[31]

Graham's dissatisfaction with the Veterans Administration, which was expressed in this document, had also been expressed in 1951 at the time of his retirement dinner. It is apparent he believed the Veterans Administration would become the template upon which government medicine or a national health program would be designed, for he asked:

> What will be the state of affairs when the seventeen million living veterans persuade Congress ... to have the Government give free hospital care in Veterans hospitals to all the members of their families? Multiply seventeen by say four, an average family, and you will have sixty-eight million people getting free hospital service ... [and] if we have universal military training with each young man acquiring the status of the veteran it is apparent to anybody that most of the population of the country will have free hospital service paid by the Government and probably in the Veterans hospitals unless something is done to stop it. This will be truly government medicine whether it is called

e. The Franklin quotation to which Graham referred, from Franklin's 1787 speech entitled *Disapproving and Accepting the Constitution*, follows: "On the whole, Sir, I cannot help expressing a wish that every member of the Convention who may still have objections to it would, with me, on this occasion doubt a little of his infallibility, and to make manifest our unanimity, put his name to this instrument."

"socialized" or not. If and when that time comes many of the splendid institutions like those in our medical center will have to close their doors.[32]

Following submission of the commission's report, R.E. Blake, chairman of the Missouri Committee on the Hoover Commission Findings, asked if Graham would be willing to tour the state and publicize the substance of the report. Blake wished to launch a program of public education on the recommendations.[33] Graham refused the invitation and gave the following as his reason:

> I was very much annoyed to see when our report was printed … [it contained] a … statement by Commissioner Chet Holifield[f]. This appeared at the end of our report as a separate section. … the general effect of this separate statement will be to negate our most important recommendations. … in the last paragraph of his statement Mr. Holifield takes it upon himself to recommend that the government provide "an adequate medical insurance system for the whole population". Our task force is not in favor of making such a recommendation, at least not at this time. … I mistrust most Congressmen and I suspect that this fellow is keeping his eye on the voters and is not particularly interested in supporting any measure which he thinks might be unpopular. I am thinking particularly of the recommendations which we made about the Veterans Administration. … Under the circumstances I do not feel that I can go out to make speeches urging people to support the recommendations of the Hoover Commission when the only ones which I helped to write and about which I have special knowledge have been handicapped at the start by the criticism of a Congressman who cannot possibly know as much about the subject as I know, or as the other members of the Task Force know. What would you do under the circumstances?[34]

Graham did, however, give personal support to one of the very significant recommendations of the Hoover commission. Less than a year later, Theodore G. Klumpp, president of Winthrop-Stearns Pharmaceutical Company, prevailed upon Senator Lister Hill to initiate a bill that would create a national library and

---

f. The political orientation of the commission was distinctly conservative in regard to government involvement in affairs that might be carried on by private enterprise. Without success, Representative Chet Holifield of California continually challenged the commission's authority to recommend changes in government policy and function.[28] His supplementary memorandum regarding national health insurance was contrary to opinions expressed in the report prepared by the members of the medical task force.

museum of health; by January 1956 a draft bill (Senate No. 3430) had been submitted. Graham wrote to the Senate Committee on Labor and Public Welfare: "The Library is really an emergency matter.... I don't think a museum is nearly so important.... The Library is so important that there can be little doubt that important research is being held up because of the lack of a really first class library in Washington.... Probably you have read the report of our Medical Task Force of the Hoover Commission on that subject."[35]

Graham made recommendations in regard to the bill, suggesting that there be a substitution of the word "accomplishment" for the word "participation," stating "the sentence would then read, 'three members of the board shall be doctors of medicine distinguished for their active accomplishment in medical research' etc." He also took this opportunity to nominate Dr. Alan Gregg of the Rockefeller Foundation for chancellor, under the assumption that the library would be approved by Congress.[35] He followed this letter with one to Senator Lister Hill: "I am particularly pleased that the whole question fell into your hands since of course I have known for many years of your great interest in medical affairs. Actually I have met you on two or three occasions and we have exchanged letters.... I like your Bill and I hope very much that Congress will act on it favorably."[36]

The bill received approval and, for the past half century, the National Library of Medicine has fulfilled the dreams of those members of the Hoover commission who supported it and of those members of Congress who made it possible.

STEVENSON/KEFAUVER AND NUCLEAR TESTING (1955–1956)

Graham's formal participation in federal electoral politics began during his visit to the 1956 Democratic National Convention in Chicago. Admiration for Harry Truman, coupled with distaste for Dwight Eisenhower, led him to become an active supporter of Adlai Stevenson's second attempt to win the presidency.

On October 1, barely 6 weeks before the election, Graham joined with Dr. Paul Magnuson, a surgeon of Chicago, Dr. Carl Meyer, an internist and president of the Chicago Medical Society, and Dr. Benjamin Spock, a pediatrician at Case/Western University in Cleveland, as the founding nucleus of the National Committee of Physicians and Surgeons for Stevenson. Invitations were sent to approximately 1500 doctors; 441 replied and 429 showed support by accepting appointment to the committee.[37,38] Twelve days later Magnuson withdrew, and John H. Gibbon Jr. of Philadelphia replaced him. Magnuson's resignation gave Graham a cause for concern, and he expressed his "fear that some doctors will think he withdrew because of the proposed National Health Program[g] that Mr. Stevenson had discussed a couple of times in his public speeches.... doctors are very jittery about government interference in the practice of medicine."[40] Graham wrote to Stevenson's office about the health program, reminding the candidate that if he were not familiar with the report and recommendations of the Truman commission, he should certainly become acquainted with them.

The thrust of Graham's efforts was less related to a national health care program than to health issues resulting from atomic testing. The four founding national chairmen (Graham, Meyer, Spock, and Gibbon) prepared a five-item questionnaire that they sent to the White House to ask whether advisors to the National Security Council had discussed any recommendation regarding an end to hydrogen bomb (H-bomb) testing. To their questions that had been devised to confront the Eisenhower administration, they received a reply denying that any discussions of H-bomb tests had occurred.[41] Everell Harriman, governor of New York, then entered the fray. The New York State Department of Health reported that it had detected a "remarkably high" level of radioactivity in milk, and Stevenson charged the Eisenhower administration with having concealed the fact that radioactive strontium was contaminating the US milk supply.

As the result of a lengthy letter he had just received from Evarts Graham, Stevenson established his formal position on H-bomb testing in a speech given in Cleveland, Ohio, on the afternoon of November 2.[42] In his letter to Stevenson, Graham had disputed Eisenhower's position: "The Administration has officially dismissed the danger to human life from Strontium 90 fallout from continued tests of hydrogen weapons as negligible. This conclusion cannot be supported by the known facts." Graham charged:

> 1.) The [Atomic Energy Commission (AEC)] findings on fallout of radioactive Strontium have been released in two articles by AEC Commissioner Libby including one that children being born will absorb from milk and carry in their lifetime a burden of Strontium 90 2.) The International Commission on Radiological Protection has warned that when an entire population is exposed, the danger levels must be

---

g. Adlai E. Stevenson's National Health Program:[39]

> I believe access to medical care is a basic human right and that government should participate only in what cannot or will not be done privately.
>
> I believe the pursuit of medical knowledge and the practice of medicine must rest on a private relationship between the patient and the doctor—not on socialized medicine.
>
> In this context, I propose a National Health Program to include:
>
> Educational aid for medical researchers.
> A Federal loan and scholarship program for medical education.
> A program of comprehensive private health insurance—available and attainable to everyone: *voluntary*, not socialized.
> Federal aid to construct needed hospital and other medical institution facilities.

reduced at least ten times and 3.) The British Medical Council has warned that even a revised estimate may be inadequate in view of the known sensitivity of growing children to radiation.... the present burden of Strontium 90 comprises a public health problem of serious magnitude.... the Administration has persistently denied the existence of any serious problem but it is clear that as long ago as 1954 the AEC was aware of and worried about the danger, albeit in secret, and that after the explosion of an H-bomb on March 1, 1954, the "fallout from this bomb caused a sharp rise in the Strontium 90 content of American milk between March and August 1954".[43]

Graham added that the government had considered instituting purification procedures for milk, and concluded by stating: "It is clear from these facts that the Administration has considered the dangers from Strontium 90 in our food serious and worthy of urgent attention. For two years until the problem was made public by non-government sources, the Administration kept these facts from the American public. The continued insistence by the Administration that all is well can only be viewed as an attempt to misinform the public."[43]

Graham appended seven references to his letter, and, quoting the Eisenhower White Paper of October 20, he challenged the administration's denial of health hazards that "the continuance of the present rate of H-bomb testing...by the most sober and responsible scientific judgement...does not imperil the health of humanity."[43]

Stevenson's statements that arose from Graham's letter were fairly short, but parts were almost stated verbatim, and 2 days later the entire text of Graham's letter was published in the *New York Times*.[44] Graham became frequently quoted, not only in the *New York Times* but in other major newspapers, and the *St. Louis Post-Dispatch* carried a column about Graham's views every fourth or fifth day for the 6 weeks leading up to the election.

Graham was sufficiently upset about the testing of the hydrogen bomb with its strontium 90 fallout that, with Arthur Holly Compton as his cochairman, he formed a St. Louis Committee of Volunteers for the Election of Stevenson, and the two recruited 24 Washington University scientists to issue a statement favoring the halting of H-bomb testing, claiming that fallout might affect children yet unborn.[38] Graham took to the speaking circuit, and, at a televised public meeting on October 23, he presented a statement supporting Stevenson's plea for an international agreement to stop H-bomb testing, a plea that was severely criticized by President Eisenhower on the grounds that such a suggestion was out of order, for it was a military problem, not a concern of the public. Graham retorted: "We...share with many others the opinion that this subject is one of the most important that has ever faced humanity....generations yet unborn could suffer from the genetic effects of radioactive material entering the bodies of potential mothers and fathers now living."[44]

Although Stevenson was overwhelmingly defeated in the 1956 presidential election, the issue of nuclear fallout was far from over. Graham received a letter from the Stevenson-Kefauver Committee thanking him for his "invaluable support in connection with the Physicians and Surgeons Committee...as a member of the Doctors Committee and as co-chairman of the Volunteers of St. Louis."[45] The Washington University faculty members of the Graham-Compton St. Louis Committee of Volunteers then proceeded to gather 140 signatures on a petition that was sent to the Congressional Joint Committee of Atomic Energy. It read:

> Dear Sirs: We have been increasingly disturbed by the AEC data released in recent months which indicate a possibility that fallout from nuclear explosions may be approaching a level which constitutes a serious world wide threat to health. We are further concerned that the greatly divergent interpretations placed on these data in the recent campaign may have resulted in widespread confusion. It seems that public decisions of the greatest importance may turn in part on the significance of the AEC's findings. It is therefore of immediate importance that a responsible agency of the government review in public the complete findings of the AEC together with their most authoritative scientific interpretations. We strongly urge that the Joint Committee on Atomic Energy undertake open hearings on these matters at the earliest possible date.[46–48]

Within 3 days it was announced that on December 12 a public hearing would be held in St. Louis before Senator Hubert Humphrey's Sub-Committee on Reduction of Armaments. Graham's request that he be given time to present his case[49] was granted, and, in the Law School auditorium, he, along with seven others, made presentations to a subcommittee chaired by Senator Stuart Symington. Arthur Holly Compton, the Washington University chancellor and a Nobel laureate, made a strong statement favoring retention of the freedom to test tactical atomic weapons and ballistic missiles, for he felt the health hazards resulting from the tests had frequently been exaggerated. Graham's presentation stressed the need for popular education about the biologic effects of radioactivity. Graham realized the issue was far reaching:

> Even if nuclear bombs should never be used in warfare, atomic energy will be used in peaceful pursuits....More research...should be undertaken....how little is known for example about how cancers are produced by it!...My proposal to your Committee is that the curtain of secrecy that now conceals the activities and experimental results of the Atomic Energy Commission should be lifted, with the possible exception

of that part which may deal specifically with military weapons. . . . instead of secrecy, in my opinion there should be the widest possible publicity. . . . what is considered sometimes as insignificant amounts of radioactive material may become very significant by a process of concentration in plants and in animals that eat the plants.[50]

Graham introduced a New York study of strontium 90 in milk, emphasizing once again its concentration in cows milk produced by cows eating vegetation contaminated by fallout. He turned to the illustration of a rather famous muskrat found near a stream into which an "insignificant amount" of radioactive material had been dumped. The animal not only had a highly malignant cancer of one of its bones with secondary growths in its lungs and kidneys, but the radioactivity of its bones was 140 to 150 times greater than the water in the stream. "This experience illustrates very well how both the vegetation exposed to a small amount of radioactive material and an animal that eats it may, by concentration, acquire a dangerous amount of radioactivity from an original rather 'insignificant amount.'"[51] Symington was so intrigued, he asked Graham for the muskrat reference. Two days later, Graham wrote: "You asked me if I could send you the reference about the muskrat which has now become famous. It is as follows: Osteogenic sarcoma in a muskrat from an area of high environmental radio Strontium. Louis A. Krumholz and John H. Rust, A.M.A. Arch. Path. 57, 270–278 April 1954."[52]

This was Graham's final public statement on nuclear fallout, made less than 6 weeks before the diagnosis of his carcinoma of the lung. The Christmas holidays had been upcoming, and Graham had been experiencing increasingly troublesome malaise and cough. Graham's November letter to Stevenson had placed nuclear fallout as an issue in the Stevenson campaign, and from there it had been brought to public attention.

Graham had been one of the earliest to denounce nuclear testing, and, through Stevenson's political activities, a lengthy public debate had begun—a philosophic discourse whose truth would be revealed by the tragic reality of the accident at Chernobyl.

MISCELLANY

Finney-Howell Research Foundation
(1937–1941)

Graham's entrance into the world of cancer research began in 1937 as a consequence of the will of Dr. George Walker of Baltimore. Walker, a veteran of World War I and chief urologist for the American army, and without close family survivors, established the Finney-Howell Research Foundation and named three financial and 12 scientific trustees, among whom he specified Evarts Graham. Finney (a surgeon) and Howell (a physiologist) were outstanding members of the

Johns Hopkins faculty; the foundation was chartered in Baltimore with J.M.T. Finney, a wartime colleague of Evarts Graham, as its leading figure.[53]

The foundation was established to support "research work into the cause or causes and the treatment of cancer" by supporting fellowships in cancer research. It was directed to expend all of its income as well as the principal within a period of 10 years.[54] With a bare 10 days' notice, Finney called the first meeting,[55] an invitation to which Graham responded that he was unable to be present. He did, however, make a number of suggestions about the role of such a foundation, doubting very much if anything was to be gained by any ordinary pathologic studies, or by utilizing the fellowships for any further work in irradiation therapy. Graham suggested that three fields of work might be given particular emphasis, including carcinogenic substances, the influences of hormones, and aspects of growth other than the purely morphologic. Graham went so far as to make suggestions about men whom he considered would be appropriate sponsors of the researchers, and he noted, "one of the great difficulties will be to find the proper sort of men who should receive the fellowships." Mentioning his 15-year membership on the Medical Fellowship Board of the National Research Council, he commented: "I have therefore a very considerable knowledge of the difficulties of finding the proper kind of young men for this sort of work." He closed his letter with the suggestion that notices of meetings be sent out at least 2 months in advance.[56]

Although Graham had a distant interest in the foundation and reviewed applications for fellowships, his attendance at meetings was minimal. He attended the February 1939 meeting, missed October 1939 and February and October 1940, meetings, and finally resigned in March 1941. By this time 11 fellowships had been granted, and the secretary, Fischer, commented: "I fear nothing has turned up which would indicate the solution either of the cause or the possible treatment of cancer."[57]

American National Red Cross
(1941–1947)

Graham's involvement with the national office of the American Red Cross began when it was attempting to recruit physicians for Great Britain, approximately 1 year prior to the US entry into World War II. The British Red Cross had appealed to the American Red Cross (ARC), asking for 1000 young American doctors who might help relieve the acute doctor shortage in Britain; the US National Research Council (NRC) undertook to implement the request.[58] A three-man committee of the NRC—Evarts Graham, Morris Fishbein, and O.W. Perry Pepper—reviewed written applications of those who were interested. It was not a selection of individuals after interview. The effort lasted throughout 1941, and, from 250 applicants, only 70 physicians finally sailed for Britain.[59]

In early 1941 representatives from the army and the navy asked the NRC to review US facilities that might be available for the bleeding of donors and the collection of blood plasma for military use. The NRC then asked the Red Cross to establish 10 collection centers in various parts of the country; each would process approximately 2000 donors, with a goal of 200,000 cakes of dried plasma per month. The NRC was to set the standards and the ARC was to carry out the task. The St. Louis quota was 12,500 pints of blood. Because of his long association with the NRC fellowship board, Evarts Graham became the contact man for the St. Louis center. As a member of the NRC Blood Procurement Committee, headed by C.P. Rhoads, his function was to appoint the St. Louis director. He recruited Dr. Samuel Harbison, his most recent chief resident. Automatically, Graham became a member of the Red Cross executive committee, which supported the National Program for Blood and Blood Derivatives for civilians that was initiated in February 1947 and which, in January 1948, became the American Red Cross Civilian Blood Donor Service.[60–62]

At the war's termination, Graham accepted an appointment to the American National Red Cross Advisory Board on Health Services, chaired by Lewis H. Weed. He served as chairman of its Division of General Surgery,[63] and sat on its central advisory board, an appointment he accepted with the proviso that it not be time consuming.[64] From December 31, 1945, until his resignation on June 15, 1949, he chaired a committee composed of nine surgeons, all of whom had been closely associated with each other during the war years.

The committee's major effort was revision of the *Red Cross First Aid Text Book*, a task not particularly inspiring to Graham at a time when he was otherwise occupied. The most contentious feature of the book was the home treatment of minor scratches and small wounds. The issue that aroused the greatest discussion was whether to advise first aiders to apply an antiseptic to fresh wounds, for example, cuts, scratches, and bruises. Previous editions of the textbook had recommended the application of 2 percent iodine in alcohol, but under Graham's chairmanship the revised edition of 1945 recommended no antiseptic at all. It stated that only sterile gauze should be used and followed with an explanation of how the dressing should be applied.

The Red Cross officers resisted this recommendation and wrote to Graham: "The public feels much more comfortable to follow a recommendation of some sort about applying some antiseptic. The idea of the efficiency of a local antiseptic in the prevention of infection was so deeply ingrained in the public mind that it is very difficult to persuade people that such a practice may not only be useful but possibly be harmful."[65] Responding to this Graham, prepared a statement to be inserted in the revised text: "In previous editions of this text book it is recommended that the person administering first aid to a wound should apply a 2% alcoholic solution of iodine. This recommendation is omitted from the present edition because it has been found that the use of iodine by the laity in first aid treatment has often caused harm. The most modern surgical opinion is that since all antiseptic agents in the hands of non-medical people may do more harm than good it is better not to use them except under the advice and supervision of a physician. The use of an antiseptic therefore should be regarded as treatment by a physician rather than first aid care."[66,67] Graham's attitude obviously reflected his experiences with the contentious policy of using sulfanilamide powder in war wounds (see chapter 15).

Material of this nature was something that failed to arouse Graham's enthusiasm, and, during his 3½ years on this committee, he made only five trips to Washington, DC, rather than the expected 14 (four per year). Eighteen months before the completion of his term, he resigned, with the suggestion that Brian Blades of Washington, DC, become his replacement.[68]

American Hospital Association Commission on Hospital Care (1944–1946)

Graham's interest in post-war reconstruction added to his inability to decline invitations of a national nature and led him to membership on a commission of the American Hospital Association (AHA). This experience helped prepare him for a role in forming the Joint Commission on Accreditation of Hospitals (see chapter 12).

The AHA established a Commission on Hospital Care and charged it to make a 2-year study of the nation's hospital resources and to anticipate post-war needs. Funded by grants from the Commonwealth Fund, the W.K. Kellogg Foundation, and the National Foundation for Infantile Paralysis,[69] it was to pay special attention to the impending need for personnel and facilities to care for psychiatric cases. There was an estimate that more than 8,000,000 returning servicemen would need some type of help in personal adjustment and that 500,000 would need hospitalization.[70] The commission of 23 members, including five physicians, held its first meeting at the Barclay Hotel in Philadelphia on August 1, 1944.[71] Graham attended six of the eight meetings of this commission. Nine months after its formation, he was asked to become a member of its executive committee[72] and responded with hesitation: "I cannot face the prospect of any more jobs. If however the position would be one chiefly of asking me about my opinions on various matters which can be done largely by mail or telephone I should be very glad to accept the appointment. If the job requires trips to Philadelphia during the year I am afraid I shall have to decline your very kind invitation."[73]

Graham did accept the executive committee position, and he served through its final meeting. His contributions were chiefly concerned with the quality of surgical care in hospitals and the means whereby hospitals should, could, or might establish standards for the professional activities of their staffs. These were matters of concern to the American Board of Surgery and subsequently to the Joint Commission on Accreditation of Hospitals (see chapter 12). Graham made a special effort to introduce a topic that had become one of his particular interests:

The only thing which occurs to me as being too lightly considered is the question of the education of negro doctors and nurses.... you have shown the need of having more negro doctors and suggest the establishment of...[another] medical school for negroes. I am not at all sure that there is a need for another negro medical school. There are already several in existence in the country. The trouble...is they lack funds and they also lack proper hospital facilities for the training of both the young doctors and negro nurses.... I think it...unlikely that it would be necessary to establish another school which would probably struggle along trying to keep its head above water.... There are at present a fair number of very intelligent young negro doctors in the country interested in medical education.... they all feel greatly discouraged about the possibility of giving adequate medical education and hospital training to the negroes because of lack of facilities.[74]

A report was submitted to the trustees of the American Hospital Association following the commission's final meeting in September 1946. This was Graham's first move into the world of hospital standardization to improve the quality of hospital and surgical care; more was yet to come (see chapter 12).

The Memorial Hospital Review
(1946–1948)

Graham's thoughts about the educational potential of cancer hospitals, in particular, the Memorial Hospital for Cancer and Allied Diseases in New York City, began to form during his term as chairman of the American Board of Surgery. He was concerned about how well the experience of residents at Memorial served the interests of a good surgical education. In 1941 after Mont Reid had succeeded him as chairman of the board, Graham received a letter from Reid concerning inquiries made by Cornelius P. Rhoads regarding the board's position on the educational value of time spent by residents at Memorial Hospital. In response, Graham wrote: "I sympathize with Dr. Rhoads and the problem which he has, because it is a very real problem.... At the Memorial Hospital the men in training have practically no experience in acute emergency conditions of the abdomen or in any form of traumatic surgery. I do feel sure, however that if Dr. Rhoads would take into training only those men that had a very good experience in general surgery beforehand, he would find a more friendly attitude from both the American Board of Surgery and the American College of Surgeons."[75]

Shortly thereafter Graham became involved in a long-term relationship with Memorial Hospital that was almost foreordained. In March 1939, less than 2 years after Congress had created the National Cancer Institute (NCI), Graham, along with Ludvig Hektoen, Willard Rappleye, and Philip A. Shaffer, became members of its National Advisory Council.[76] On April 28, 1941, Graham was elected to membership in the National Academy of Sciences at its annual meeting in Washington, DC.[77]

By 1939 the Memorial Hospital had been rebuilt. A gift of $3 million plus land adjacent to the Rockefeller Institute permitted the erection of a 12-story building at East 67th and 68th Streets. It was a well-endowed private institution with a strong surgical staff limited to the treatment of patients with cancer. In 1945 Alfred P. Sloan Jr. of the General Motors Corporation gave the hospital $7 million to endow a Sloan-Kettering Institute for Research in Cancer, and the board of managers requested the National Academy of Sciences to assist in the planning of a comprehensive cancer program that would reflect the board's determination to make a cancer center that would render every possible service to mankind.[78]

After a satisfactory agreement had been reached between the National Academy of Sciences and Memorial Hospital, a panel of eight members[h], including Graham, was created.[79] Over the next 2 years, Graham made seven trips to New York City to review institutional material and to propose future developments for the hospital and the institute.

Graham and E.D. Churchill, as the only two surgeons on the panel, confined their efforts to the surgical features of the affiliation, leaving medicine, radiology, basic science, and medical therapeutics to the other members. The two prepared 16 pages of recommendations for the organization of a Section or Department of Surgery that opened with "a consideration of what the proper function of a specialized hospital, such as the Memorial Hospital, should be." They observed that, in the past, specialized hospitals had been built either to protect the public from contagion (eg, tuberculosis) or to provide treatment and custodial care for the mentally deranged. They wondered whether cancer, as a single entity, warranted similar treatment, and they questioned the justification for a special cancer hospital by asking:

1. Does it have better results of treatment?
2. Is more valuable research on cancer conducted in such a hospital?
3. Does it have a special educational function?

In addressing these issues Graham and Churchill wrote, "There is no convincing evidence at hand to indicate that the results obtained in the treatment of patients in a cancer hospital are any better than those in our best general hospitals."

---

h. Members of the Memorial study committee and their respective areas of specialty: W.T. Longcope (medicine), chairman; E.A. Graham (surgery); E.D. Churchill (surgery); A.R. Dochez (medicine); Basil C. McLean (hospital administration); Roger I. Lee (medicine); Carl F. Cori (physiology); Cecil J. Watson (medicine); Lewis H. Weed (National Research Council), ex officio.

They noted that the surgeons at Memorial Hospital were subspecialized by organ regions but felt that "such ultra-specialization in surgery must be regarded as an experimental phase which has not yet been proven." They wrote further: "Except in external cancer the clinical diagnosis of neoplasm demands a broad familiarity with all [other diseases] of the organ that may closely resemble it ... and this necessitates the conversion of a specialized clinic into a general diagnostic and therapeutic clinic in which patients with other ailments and cancer will be treated."[80]

The two felt that "the rationale of case finding programs in syphilis and tuberculosis for example cannot be transferred to cancer. ... Case finding in syphilis and tuberculosis strikes primarily at the incidence of these diseases in the community through prevention whereas case-finding in cancer is directed toward [lowering] mortality by more effective therapy. One is a problem of public health: the other a problem of individual survival." They closed the section by noting: "While pilot studies in the detection of cancer in the apparently well population are desirable, any extension on a mass basis is an impossible work load, not only for cancer specialists but very probably for the profession as a whole." In discussing the question as to whether research in such an institution is of value, they expressed doubt: "the best research results will be obtained by working exclusively with cancer patients [for] much fundamental work which we now recognize as having a bearing on the cancer problem was originally worked out with no particular reference to cancer. ... In the past there has been a field for statistical research concerning surgical results and this has been intensively pursued ... at the Memorial Hospital. The point has now been reached however which indicates that little more of great value will come from this type of research."[80]

Much of Graham and Churchill's presentation concerned the hospital's educational functions, for they felt the hospital had a "particular opportunity to give to [medical] students ... a broad view of the fundamental processes involved such as growth, the action of hormones and enzymes, the action of carcinogenic substances, the use of radioactive isotopes." In the teaching of students, they thought that special emphasis should be placed on the pathology of tumors and the medical and psychiatric problems presented by cancer patients. As to graduate education, they noted that residents and fellows constituted a group constantly subject to exploitation in the repetitive performance of routine procedures beyond the limit of their educational value, and that exploitation should be avoided as much as possible. The two continued their attack on the Memorial goal of training cancer specialists skilled in all intricate diagnostic techniques and competent to perform all of the necessary surgical operations. They felt it to be an impossible undertaking and that efforts to train such specialists should be discouraged. They recommended the period of surgical residency in the Memorial Hospital should be for only 1 or 2 years and that there should be "sufficient instruction in Pathology to make of each resident a fairly competent tumor pathologist."[80]

In the realm of lay education, the two foresaw only a limited field. Graham and Churchill felt it could be accomplished through the arrangement of exhibits, newspaper articles, lectures, and bulletins, but stated, "such a program will not be free from criticism from the medical profession as long as the hospital provides facilities for large, lucrative private practices by the members of its staff." In their opinion, the chief emphasis needed to be on cancer research, not on the treatment of patients, especially private patients. They recommended that the overwhelming proportion of surgical patients be reduced in order to permit admission of more medical patients.[80]

Graham and Churchill also suggested that "it would be preferable to have at least the most important members of the staff on a full time basis and probably with University appointments at Cornell, New York University or elsewhere." They closed with misgivings about any plan for the creation of more specialized hospitals restricted to the care of the cancer patient. Their conclusions showed their strong preference toward the integration of cancer research, and the care of the cancer patient within general hospitals.[80]

E. Coles Andrus, the National Research Council executive secretary, protested the inclusion of material about whether a cancer hospital achieves better results than a general hospital.[81] Graham responded:

> I find myself in some disagreement with you that it might be necessary for me to furnish documentary evidence to indicate that the results obtained in the treatment of patients in a cancer hospital are no better than those in our best general hospitals. I really think the burden of proof is on the cancer hospitals to show that.... I am not completely convinced that the statistics on operative mortality which you furnished me as coming from the Memorial Hospital are of very great value.... if you and the rest of the Committee think it would be better to omit the line of thought which I was presenting in my report, of which the troublesome sentence is a part, please change the report in any way that you wish. I must say, however that if my name is to be signed to it I must ask the favor of reading the final report before my name is affixed.... I have been willing to put in time because I have understood all along that my report would have considerable influence on the whole question of whether or not additional special cancer hospitals should be established.... I am still unconvinced that there is any good reason for multiplying Memorial Hospitals around the country [and] I am perfectly willing to modify my position to the extent of toning down the language somewhat but I should consider it a misfortune if the report should be worded in such a way that a possible misunderstanding might arise as to what our opinion really is

in regard to the very important matter of encouraging or discouraging the creation of more cancer hospitals.[82]

The final report, which was signed by Graham, contained a statement to which he took exception—that cancer is a general disease rather than a local one: "I cannot subscribe to that opinion. If that statement were correct then nobody would ever be permanently cured of his cancer by the surgical removal of the local growth.... I cannot let the opportunity pass without making a feeble protest against having the concept mentioned appear in a report compiled by people who know a good deal about cancer.... I think our recommendations are sound and I hope they will be adopted."[83]

The report with its several recommendations was submitted, and in March 1948 the committee disbanded.[84] Following this review, Graham's close friend and acquaintance Allen O. Whipple, professor emeritus at Columbia, became the surgical director at Memorial Hospital. Frequent personal contacts continued between the two until Graham's death.

Graham's last formal contact with the Memorial/Sloan-Kettering Institute was his appointment as a member of its board of scientific consultants, effective July 1, 1955, for a 3-year period.[85] Meetings of the board were held quarterly, and Graham attended every meeting, the last of which was held on December 5 and 6, 1956, barely 2 weeks before Graham developed the cough that foreshadowed his final illness.

Graham was never comfortable with the concept of a cancer hospital, but, although very critical of Memorial's surgical thrust, he never refused an opportunity to make some difference in its organization, and he never failed to discharge his obligations on its advisory boards.

Chapter 18

SMOKING AND LUNG CANCER

THE SETTING

Ernst Wynder, while a medical student, became a central figure in the events that established a causal relationship between cigarette smoking and lung cancer and entrapped Evarts Graham into a final research effort. Wynder's landmark report, coauthored with Evarts Graham, that appeared in the *Journal of the American Medical Association* in May 1950[1] was followed 4 months later by a similar report by Doll and Hill[a] in the *British Medical Journal*.[2] Their survey of the smoking patterns of lung cancer patients confirmed the findings of Wynder and Graham in almost every detail. The idea that smoking could cause lung cancer did not originate with Wynder and Graham or Doll and Hill, it was simply that Wynder and Graham made the first scientific confirmation that brought the issue to the world's attention. Wynder's work provided the substance, and Graham's prominence provided credibility and authority.

By 1950 it was known that bronchiogenic carcinoma had become the most frequent visceral cancer in men, an observation confirmed by autopsy statistics compiled by the American Cancer Society. As early as 1912, Adler had suggested that

---

a. Richard Doll, MD, MRCP, was a member of the statistical research unit of the Medical Research Council. A. Bradford Hill, PhD, DSc, was professor of medical statistics at the London School of Hygiene and Tropical Medicine, and honorary director of the statistical research unit of the Medical Research Council.

tobacco might play some role in this cancer, even as he apologized for a full book on such a rare disease. In seven subsequent publications, he expressed his convictions regarding the relationship between tobacco smoking and the increased incidence of cancer of the lung.[3,4]

In 1939 Franz Müller, working out of the Cologne Hospital Pathology Department, used a questionnaire survey to compare the smoking habits of 96 lung cancer cases to 86 healthy persons, and from this small case-control study, he concluded that tobacco consumption was responsible for primary carcinoma of the lungs.[5–7] Also in 1939, Ochsner[b] and DeBakey of New Orleans called attention to the similarity between the increased rate of cigarette sales with the increased incidence of bronchiogenic carcinoma, and they concluded that the increase in smoking with the universal custom of inhaling was probably the responsible factor.[8–10] In a later publication, they stated that every one of their patients, with the exception of two women, was an excessive smoker.[11] Ochsner's biography claims that "in the 1940's and 1950's he was the most prominent figure on the soap box, the speaker with the most authoritative voice,"[12] yet in Shimkin's *Contrary to Nature: a History of Cancer Treatment and Research*, Ochsner was not mentioned in the chapter on smoking and health. When asked about this oversight, Shimkin responded: "Alton Ochsner was a pioneer in suspecting the cigarette/lung cancer link, although he performed no critical test of his suspicion."[12] In 1987 C. Everett Koop, surgeon general of the United States Public Health Service, called Ochsner "one of the earliest and strongest foes of smoking.... He was very clear about the nature of the threat to health posed by cigarette smoking more than forty years ago."[12]

---

b. Born in Kimball, South Dakota, Edward William Alton Ochsner (1896 to 1981) obtained his bachelor's degree at the University of South Dakota (Phi Beta Kappa) before entering Washington University Medical School. After a surgical internship at Barnes Hospital, he combined work and study in Chicago under the direction of his uncle, A.J. Ochsner, with overseas trips to clinics in Zurich and Frankfurt. Ochsner became an instructor at Northwestern University and then assistant professor of surgery at Wisconsin, where he stayed for only 1 year before, at the age of 31, becoming professor of surgery at Tulane in New Orleans. Ochsner was interested in venous thrombosis and intra-abdominal abscesses. He and Owen Wangensteen were the founding coeditors of *Surgery*. Ochsner became a major crusader against smoking, taking a strong—almost virtuous—stand. As a director of National Airlines, he removed cigarettes from the airline's gratuities. He founded the Ochsner Clinic, and, although important in the Tulane medical environment, it never became the central clinical teaching unit that he had hoped. His students fondly remember his Saturday morning "bullpen" sessions.

Handsome and personable, Ochsner moved easily among his wealthy New Orleans neighbors. He was a persuasive fund-raiser, was active in many civic affairs, and in 1948 became Rex, King of Carnival, at the Mardi Gras festival. He was surgeon to many important world leaders and Hollywood stars, was president of many societies, and was particularly interested in the American Cancer Society. In January 1966 his wife, Isabel Ochsner, was diagnosed with cancer of the right lung. She died in April 1968 after 2 difficult years. Ochsner died at age 85 following open heart surgery to replace his aortic valve and bypass an occluded coronary artery.

Ochsner's impressions were considered inconclusive because no statistical study had been made on a series of cases large enough to be impressive. Although Ochsner's conclusion represented his firm conviction, it remained a personal opinion, and Müller's small epidemiologic study had become a war casualty. Nevertheless, the great increase in cigarette smoking following World War I was enough to initiate a search for incriminating evidence that the rising incidence of cancer of the bronchus might be related to the progressive and astonishing indulgence in cigarette smoking.

Evarts Graham was sceptical of Ochsner's theory about smoking and cancer, and Warren Cole, a medical school classmate of Ochsner, remembers sitting with Graham and Ochsner at a surgical meeting, when Ochsner said: "Dr. Graham I believe I have found a possible etiologic factor for cancer of the lung." Graham responded: "That would be quite a discovery Al, what is it?" When Ochsner replied, "Cigarette smoking," Graham flashed back, "How dumb and how stupid." Al defended himself: "But practically all of the fifty or more cases we have just reviewed have that history," to which Graham retorted: "But Al, you forget the importance of coincidence. So has the use of silk stockings increased."[12] In 1940 Graham wrote to Ochsner complimenting him on his observations regarding the possible effects of cigarette smoking on bronchogenic carcinoma: "My facetious remarks about the silk stockings should not be taken too seriously. On the other hand, I think there are still some things about bronchogenic carcinoma which are difficult to explain on the basis of cigarette smoking."[13] At least 10 years later, when the three surgeons were together again, Graham said: "Al, I am afraid I owe you an apology. ... You may or not recall a few years ago that you told me you thought cigarette smoking was the cause of cancer of the lung and I poo-pooed the idea. Well recently Wynder, an associate, and I completed a study of our patients with cancer of the lung and as you said, nearly all of them were heavy cigarette smokers." Ochsner replied: "Thanks Dr. Graham, yes, we have continued our studies and the evidence seems more convincing than ever." Since Graham seldom apologized to anyone for anything, Cole was struck by his doing so on this occasion.[12]

THE WYNDER STORY

Ernst Wynder[c] was born in Herford, Germany, in 1922, the son of Theresa and Alfred, a physician. In December 1938 father, mother, Ernst, and sister Lore emigrated to New Jersey. Ernst attended George Washington High School in New York City and during this time decided to become a physician like his father. Following

---

c. Dr. Wynder's early publications carried a byline of *Ernest* Wynder. In later publications he used the name *Ernst*. When asked why, he stated he thought it was really the correct way to spell his name.

his 1943 graduation with a bachelor of arts degree from New York University, he was stationed at Gettysburg, Pennsylvania, for 2 years as a member of the army psychological warfare group and as chief of a monitoring service that supplied material for the newspapers sent to Germany. Mustered out in 1945, he applied to several medical schools and entered Washington University in the fall of 1946.

Wynder soon became acquainted with E. Vincent Cowdry, chairman of anatomy, an international figure interested in human cancer and carcinogenesis. Early in his medical school days, Wynder began to work in Cowdry's research laboratory and voiced a desire to win the Borden Award for Research given to a medical student at completion of the fourth year, whereupon Cowdry insisted that he do some work in research. Later that year, while walking back to the Nu Sigma Nu fraternity house following the Borden Award ceremony, Wynder thought: "I am somewhat of a dreamer … and three years from now I want to get the Borden Award. … you are going to give a lecture and you surely will not read your speech. You get up there, you know your speech, turn off the light, face the audience and deliver your remarks."[14]

During these years E.V. Cowdry was painting methylcholanthrene and benzanthracene on the backs of mice to document the sequential development of epidermal carcinoma. Wynder was assigned this task under the tutelage of Alfred Lansing, a professor of anatomy. Extra time during Wynder's first 2 years in medical school was thus occupied; after school he would paint mice. In the summer between his freshman and sophomore years, Cowdry arranged for Wynder to work with Dr. C.C. Little at the Jackson Laboratory in Bar Harbor, Maine, to study the genetics of mouse cancer. During his sophomore course in pathology, Wynder developed an interest in the possible connection between smoking and lung cancer, and at its completion obtained a summer fellowship at New York University with Dr. Norton Nelson. With some questionnaires that he had prepared, Wynder walked across the street to the chest service and was given permission by its chief, Dr. Burns Amberson, to interview lung cancer cases and some respective controls.

Wynder was pleased. After interviewing 20 or so cases with controls, it became clear that some relationship must exist between smoking and lung cancer. Upon returning to St. Louis, he asked Cowdry to call Dr. Graham to see if Wynder could meet with him and explain his desire to continue interviewing cancer patients. Wynder did realize, however, that Graham had disparaged the relationship between smoking and lung cancer in lectures to students.

Graham received him graciously, but when Wynder indicated his wishes, Graham said he had two reservations about the correlation: "The first was that he rarely saw double primaries; after all, if smoking had such an important role maybe people ought to have more than one cancer." Secondly, "he had seen patients that had given up smoking a long time before they developed lung cancer." (The latency period of tobacco carcinogenesis had not been identified and probably had not even occurred to anyone.) Wynder was sent to see Thomas Burford, Graham's thoracic surgical associate, for a second opinion about the proposal. Burford was smoking at the time of the visit and told Wynder he was "wasting his time... for Burford knew with certainty there was no correlation." The following day, Wynder returned to Graham to learn that, even though Burford had supported Graham's opinion that there was no such relationship, Graham did express faith in the young medical student, and that, although he did not believe a smoking–lung cancer connection existed, Wynder was permitted to undertake the interviews. Forty-five years later, Wynder was still impressed with what a generous gesture this had been from a highly respected professor to a junior medical student. For the rest of the year, during his spare time, Wynder interviewed the lung cancer patients[d] on the Barnes Hospital wards.[14]

During the Christmas vacation of his third year, Wynder returned to New Jersey to spend several days in the Manhattan Cancer Society office with its medical director, Dr. Charles Cameron. In those days Cameron was a smoker and was quite certain that no correlation existed between smoking and lung cancer. Wynder presented his first 50 cases and, after seeing the results, Cameron told him: "That sounds pretty interesting. Why don't you go back to St. Louis and apply for a grant?"[14] Upon returning to St. Louis, Wynder spoke to Graham, who responded favorably; within a few weeks money was obtained through the Washington University American Cancer Society Institutional Research Grant INSTR-32[e].[14]

As a third year medical student, Ernst Wynder was now the coholder of a research grant of sufficient size to hire an interviewer; he chose Adele Croninger, a woman who had earned a master's degree in geology from Washington University with a thesis on the peach landscapes of northern Michigan. Wynder was impressed by the work that she had done on her thesis and felt that anyone who could take such beautiful pictures of peach landscapes was just the right kind of a person to do detailed interviews. Her hired her. Croninger continued to work on the smoking project after Wynder left for New York and after Graham's death. She moved from interviewing patients to running the smoking machine, caring for an animal laboratory, and finally closing out 12 years of the research effort.

---

d. The study design was remarkably similar to that of Müller, 10 years earlier, but it was much more powerful. Wynder studied 684 cases as opposed to Müller's 96. Wynder arrived at a similar epidemiologic conclusion—that heavy smoking was related to the development of lung cancer.

e. Washington University received American Cancer Society Institutional Research Grant INSTR-32 A-F, awarded to Evarts Graham between 1947 and 1956. Over these years the total amount awarded to Graham was $359,000. At Graham's death in 1957, E.V. Cowdry became the institutional coordinator.

The National Cancer Institute of the National Institutes of Health also supported the Graham-Wynder-Croninger efforts. Beginning in March 1951 and closing in September 1959, it awarded a total of $153,281 through account no. C-2640.

A National Cancer Conference of the American Cancer Society was scheduled for Memphis, Tennessee, in February 1949, and Graham wrote Alton Ochsner to alert him that Wynder had interested Cameron and others of the American Cancer Society, "They suggested he go to Memphis next week to give a preliminary report on his findings." Graham continued: "As a result of his combined figures he does have at least an interesting correlation. Just how much it means, I don't know.... It concerns the difference of opinion which you and I had several years ago.... It is possible that I may have to eat humble pie."[15] At Graham's urging, Wynder went to Memphis, prepared to present his material. The conference was fairly informal, and the word "Tobacco" appeared in the section under "Etiology." Wynder volunteered his material and later remarked: "I was just as ambitious then as I am now." He introduced himself to Dr. Walter Heston, the moderator, by saying: "In case tobacco as an etiologic agent comes up I will raise my hand." Wynder was the only person who volunteered to speak on the topic and suggested to Heston: "Since no one else raised their hand maybe you can give me ten minutes rather than the usual five." The response came: "No, five is it!"[14]

After presenting approximately 200 lung cancer cases with 200 controls, Wynder concluded there was a causative relationship between smoking and lung cancer. The moderator then asked if anyone would like to speak to Wynder's comments; there was no response from an audience that contained Alton Ochsner, Michael DeBakey, Evarts Graham, Brian Blades, and William Thomas Watson.[14] It seems that Evarts Graham, although Wynder's sponsor, was seemingly not sufficiently convinced to rise and speak in support of his young medical student. It surprised Wynder that Drs. Ochsner and DeBakey, who had been so vocal on the issue, failed to make supporting comments. Wynder recalled: "The following subject was pulmonary adenomatosis in sheep. The audience discussed that topic for half an hour. ...that was one of the most discouraging moments of my life.... Here I came up with what I thought was something very novel and got that kind of response."[14]

One year later, the spring of 1950, Wynder was preparing to graduate from medical school, and he placed a draft of the paper to be sent to the *Journal of the American Medical Association* on Graham's desk—without a byline. After a brief discussion, Graham said: "Wynder, since you did all the work, it should be Wynder and Graham." Dual authorship was thus established, and Graham, as coauthor, now was forced to accept responsibility for the results and the content of the paper.[1]

In May of that year, the $500 Borden Award for outstanding research was presented to Wynder—it was the award that had stimulated him while working with Cowdry. His survey and its results were submitted to the Borden Award Committee chaired by Dr. Oliver Lowry, professor of pharmacology. Dr. Carl Moore, the professor of medicine had his own protégé, Elmer Brown, submit a paper for the award; Brown was a man whom, according to Wynder, was one of the smartest students in the class. Four students were selected as finalists, and, the day prior to the presentation, Lowry met with the students to ask if they would like to know who won. Wynder said yes, because if he won he would have his father come from New Jersey. Lowry replied, "Tell your father to come."[16] At the conclusion of Wynder's presentation, Graham was enthusiastic, and claimed this to be one of the best pieces of research done at Washington University.

Dr. Lowry remembered the complicated and heated discussions surrounding the giving of that year's Borden Award to Wynder, for Wynder was brusque, straightforward, and relatively uncompromising in many of his ideas—not a particular favorite of many of the faculty of the Medical School. On several occasions Lowry reminded the selection committee that they were picking a winner based on quality of research and not on personal traits.[16]

Following the May 1950 publication of the Wynder-Graham survey, the press showed a great deal of interest; they gave Evarts Graham much of the credit because many thought a medical student could not possibly have borne the idea—it had to be that of the professor. Graham, however, consistently gave credit where the credit was due, and Wynder was wise enough to realize that the work would never have received such a response if someone as prominent as Graham had not been involved. Wynder ruminated, "As we look back over those first few years, the peers in general were not too supportive of the idea that smoking could cause lung cancer."[14]

THE SMOKING LABORATORY

After Wynder departed for his internship[f], Graham and Croninger undertook some laboratory experiments to explore the relationship between smoke, cigarette tars, and cancer. By this time, 10 studies had used alcohol, chloroform, or ether to obtain an extract from raw tobacco leaves that was then applied to the skin of experimental animals in an attempt to stimulate carcinogenesis. Sporadic carcinomas appeared and some papillomas were produced, but there was no study that used tobacco smoke rather than extracts from tobacco leaves. With Wynder participating from a distance, Graham and Croninger hunted for the link between tobacco, tobacco smoke, and cancer. Laboratory benches, facilities for small animals, and space for a smoking machine that would extract tars from cigarette smoke was found in the Wernse Laboratory for Cancer Research on the third floor of the North Building—where Wynder had painted mice 4 years earlier. Harking back to

---

f. Dr. Ernst Wynder left St. Louis in June 1950 to serve an internship at Georgetown University Hospital in Washington, DC, followed by a 3-year residency at the Memorial Hospital for Cancer and Allied Diseases in New York City. He became a member of its staff in 1964 and consultant epidemiologist from 1969 until his death in 1999. In 1993 Washington University presented him with an honorary degree. He established and held the position of director of the American Health Foundation in New York City.

Wynder's early experiences with Cowdry and Lansing, these tars were to be painted on the backs of mice, and microscopic sections showing changes in skin epithelium were made for review by Lauren Ackerman. Five publications from Graham, Wynder, and Croninger resulted from the effort.

The guiding principle of the experiment was to have a smoking apparatus that would create a situation similar to clinical smoking and collect the tars. A glass machine designed by Wynder was constructed in the adjacent machine shop. The final apparatus "smoked" 60 cigarettes at a time with intermittent puffing. The smoke was drawn into condensing flasks. Fifty cartons of cigarettes constituted a batch, and the tar-acetone compound was stored for future use. Measurements were made of the applied vacuum, the combustion temperature of the burning cigarette tip (average, 43.8°C), and the temperature of the smoke that was emitted (between 26°C and 60°C).

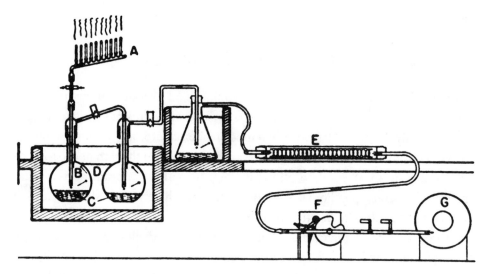

Schematic drawing of the smoking apparatus. A = smoking arm; B = condensing flask; C = tar; D = dry ice (95% ethanol); E = cotton filter; F = timer; G = vacuum. Adapted from Wynder EL et al.[17]

CAF_1 mice from the Jackson Memorial Laboratory in Bar Harbor, Maine, were the first experimental animals to be used. The mice were clipped or shaved, and the tar-acetone solution was applied three times per week. Excess amounts of the compound contained so much nicotine that a major systemic response, and even death, sometimes occurred, and, after 15 months of painting, as the animals aged, a denicotinized solution was used. At 24 months 60 percent of the animals had papillomas (a benign, precancerous [?] growth), and 40 percent had carcinomas, the first of which appeared by 12 months.[17] Transplantation of cancer from one animal to another occurred through 13 generations. The average time for appearance of the carcinomas was 71 weeks, roughly one-half of the animal's life span.[18] The development of cancer on the backs of mice was time consuming, but it was conclusive.

The second thrust of their research attempted to determine whether different mouse strains had different susceptibilities, and a small study contrasting Swiss and C57 mice was undertaken. Fifteen percent of the Swiss mice developed carcinomas at 24 months, as opposed to only 3 percent of the C57 mice.[19] Both strains developed fewer papillomas and carcinomas than were seen with the CAF_1 mice, but it was an unreliable comparison since there had been some modifications in the collection and storage of the tar.

The third project, a study of latency, involved two groups of mice. The first was painted for only 12 months, and carcinomas occurring after cessation of painting were observed. At 12 months 20 percent of the mice had developed papillomas and 4 percent, carcinomas. In the following year, in which the mice were not painted, 30 percent developed papillomas, and 20 percent developed carcinomas. The second group was painted for 24 months; the mice developed almost twice the incidence of papillomas and cancers that had been observed in the group painted for 12 months.[20]

The fourth study involved painting the ears of 65 albino New Zealand rabbits. At 18 months 100 percent had papillomas, and at 36 months 12 percent had developed carcinoma, some with regional metastases.[21]

The fifth project studied different types of tobacco, comparing cigars, pipes, and cigarettes without paper (tobacco leaves were used as wrappers). This study showed a higher degree of carcinogenesis from cigar and pipe tars than from cigarettes.

The above five research projects led Graham and Croninger to conclude that carcinogens were formed during the process of tobacco combustion, and that the amount depended on the temperature reached and the completeness of the combustion process.[22]

A study in collaboration with Drs. Cowdry and Suntzeff of the Department of Anatomy followed changes in the sebaceous glands of mouse skin, with the hope that this might produce a rapid assay for carcinogens. Comparisons were made between cigarette tars and known carcinogens such as methylcholanthrene, with noncarcinogenic substances used as controls. There was a significant agreement between the early destruction of sebaceous glands and later cancer formation.[23]

Other papers also appeared. A thorough review of industrial exposures as possible etiologic factors in the development of carcinoma of the lung led Graham and Wynder to conclude that city dusts and fumes could not account for the increasing incidence of lung cancer. There were a few occupations associated with increased lung cancer frequency, but decisive statistical evidence was not reached. The occupations of metal workers, painters, and those exposed to excessive fumes of oil, gasoline, varnish, and wood dust were of importance. This review re-inforced the idea that the greater the amount of tobacco smoke inhaled, the greater was the risk that primary carcinoma of the lungs would develop.[24]

At the 1954 National Cancer Conference, Graham discussed the occupations and habits of individuals with lung carcinoma and noted that among male and female smokers with bronchiogenic carcinoma, 96 percent had smoked for more than 20 years. He concluded:

> Comparatively few women have smoked for so long and long exposure seems necessary to produce the cancer.... perhaps if the present day young women smokers continue... in another decade or so bronchiogenic carcinoma may have a much higher incidence in females than it has now.... The "cigarette cancer" is almost always of the type commonly designated as epidermoid (squamous) and the type usually diagnosed as adenomacarcinoma seems to have little, if any, relation to cigarette smoking.[25]

Graham was now a convert.

In November 1954 Dr. William Rienhoff, a distinguished thoracic surgeon on the Johns Hopkins faculty, spoke to the Baltimore Rotary Club expressing his conviction that there was no connection between smoking and lung cancer. He stated that the whole furor had been started by two of his good friends, whose names he would not mention, but that they were simply fanatics. The talk was reported in the *Baltimore Sun*. Ochsner sent him a letter "wondering who the two friends were that he referred to."[26] To Graham he wrote: "I knew they could not be you or me, because we are not fanatical. I am at a loss to explain why Bill should take the stand he does, because he must know there is a definite relationship."[26] Four years earlier Graham had written to Rienhoff regarding the latter's scepticism of the smoking-cancer relationship: "There would be no need of your being upset even if you disagreed sharply with me. I don't mind a good fight, in fact I rather enjoy it. ... No matter what you said... our friendship will remain and I would not think any less of you for stating your frank disagreement with any conclusions of mine."[27]

GRAHAM, CAMERON, AND THE CANCER SOCIETY

Although the American Cancer Society supported Graham's research throughout most of these years, it threatened to withdraw its funding in early 1950 after a visit to St. Louis by Cuyler Hammond to review Graham's data. Feeling there must be an error because the association between smoking and lung cancer was so strong, Hammond led the American Cancer Society to conduct its own prospective study[g] that he believed would not confirm the Wynder-Graham observations.[28] Alton Ochsner, as president of the American Cancer Society during this period, was instrumental in developing the study by Drs. Hammond and Horn, which did confirm Wynder and Graham's conclusions.[29] In the forward to Ochsner's 1954 book *Smoking and Cancer*,[30] Graham noted: "Hammond has completely reversed himself from the position which he took in 1950 when he told me that our work here was no good and that if he had anything to do with it we would not get a nickel for any renewal of our work."[31] During the early years of his epidemiologic and then his laboratory studies, almost all of Graham's financial support came from the American Cancer Society; the National Cancer Institute gave some money during 1951 to 1959.

As Wynder was preparing to leave St. Louis in the summer of 1950, the initial 1948 to 1949 grant from the American Cancer Society was expiring, and Wynder applied for funds to permit Adele Croninger to cease interviewing patients and to move into the laboratory to carry out the planned smoking-machine experiments. The response was slow in coming, and Graham wrote to Ochsner to ask if he had heard anything from Cameron about their request for monies: "If the reason for the failure of Wynder's application for a grant is a personal dislike to Wynder by Cameron, do you think it would do any good if I would apply for a grant in my own name, leaving Wynder's name off it? I must do something immediately, otherwise we shall lose Miss Croninger. She is working without salary at all at the present time

---

g. The Graham-Wynder and Doll-Hill studies, as that of Müller, had examined the smoking habits of people who had developed lung cancer and compared them with controls who had not—a case-control study. The Hammond-Horn effort was a cohort study, in which proof of a causal relationship would be the incidence of carcinoma among smokers when compared to nonsmokers. Under American Cancer Society (ACS) auspices, they mounted a study using 22,000 ACS volunteers to perform repeated interviews of 200,000 men. Useable responses to questionnaires about smoking were collected from 190,134 white men between the ages of 50 and 69 during the period of January 1 to May 31, 1952. Ninety-nine percent (187,776) of responders were successfully traced, and 4854 were reported as having died. After 7 years the ACS statistics revealed a much higher incidence of lung cancer among smokers. The authors drew seven conclusions from this study, the final one being: "The findings just described do not merely indicate an association between cigarette smoking and death rates: it is a cause and effect relationship."[29]

because of her interest in the problem, but she cannot go on much longer."[32] Monies were forthcoming after Graham complained to Ochsner a second time:

> I cannot understand for the life of me why the American Cancer Society does not seize upon this great opportunity to devote resources to this problem.... I think that some of the two-for-a-nickel guys like Hammond, who have done everything they can to obstruct this work, should be shaken by the scruff of their necks.... I think you would be the guy to do it. You have great influence there and you are acquainted from the inside.... It will be difficult for me to think well of the American Cancer Society after my own experience with it.[33]

Funding from the American Cancer Society did continue but with an ever-increasing requirement for paperwork, and Graham became impatient with the complicated application requirements. He was particularly upset by the idea of peer review, and from his letters it is quite apparent that Graham was convinced he had no peers.

In 1954, in a two-page letter to Cameron following a discussion they had had at The Homestead in December 1953, Graham made a six-point proposal that included several personal thoughts:

> I think we are justified in asking that nobody should any longer hold the opinion that we are amateurs and that we should be expected to come begging for a handout.... I think we are as competent to know what leads of investigation in this field should be followed as any group who might pass judgement on a request for help from us....if the ACS would be interested in helping us financially but in a way which is perhaps new,... Would it be possible to obtain a grant of $75,000 or $100,000 under the following conditions: 1) We would not be obliged to submit a detailed program and.... 2) Not have to write to ask permission to transfer $100 from non-professional salaries to expendable supplies. 3) We could have a drawing account on the money, either from the ACS or the Treasurer of Washington University. 4) There would be no time limit on the expenditure but for auditing purposes we would keep an exact record of expenditures. 5) We would inform you in a general way of a program of study and be delighted to give annual progress reports. 6) All publications would carry the statement it had been funded from the ACS.[34]

In that letter Graham also complained about the Damon Runyon Fund; he had received no encouragement about its continuing support since the executive director had written, criticizing them "for announcing our experimental results…on the grounds that the tobacco industry might discontinue its contributions to the fund." Graham wrote about his experience with Flexner and the liberal funding that had come from the General Education Board, which was set up "to reward excellence by making it possible for the work and the particular workers to continue without the annoying experience of having to beg for frequent pittances with which to continue."[34] Not surprisingly, Cameron replied that he was aware of Graham's six-point position and then noted, "Scientists with long careers behind and before them accept the obligation of repeated requests.…the Society has never written a blank check for research and I predict it never will.…All of this adds up to saying that we may not be able to make a grant to you just as you have proposed but I think I can assure you that we will do everything reasonable to support you in a manner which will permit you to do the things you think important."[35]

Subsequent to another lung cancer conference, Graham wrote again to Cameron: "I appreciate greatly the talk with you and Mr. Spike on Sunday after the breakup of the meeting. I am now in the process of preparing a letter which I shall send to Mr. Spike making a plea for a continuation of our work.…Again also I wish you to know that I appreciate very much the effort which Mr. Spike took to arrange with Barry Commoner that an additional grant from the American Cancer Society for our work could be administered satisfactorily through Commoner's committee."[36] The Cancer Society funding continued until Graham's death.

THE C.C. LITTLE EDITORIAL

In 1956 the journal *Cancer Research* decided to publish a monthly guest editorial; the March issue contained an editorial written by C.C. Little entitled "Smoking and Lung Cancer," in which he expanded on the Hammond-Horn study. Little opened with the statement: "In June, 1954, when the first statistics indicating an association between cigarette smoking and the incidence of lung cancer were presented an extraordinarily, if not unique, situation resulted." Dr. Little then described carcinogens in the environment as a serious social obligation and one of national import. He was particularly critical of the "cause and effect" between tobacco and lung cancer, noting that the tobacco industry was deeply concerned and disturbed. The tobacco corporations had formed a Tobacco Industry Research Committee with a scientific advisory board[h], and Little praised the industry for its "industry-supported research effort."[37]

---

h. C.C. Little, director of the Roscoe B. Jackson Memorial Laboratory, also became chairman and scientific director of the scientific advisory board to the Tobacco Industry Research Committee.

Evarts Graham became so incensed after reading the editorial that he dispatched a blistering six-page letter to Dr. Harold P. Rusch, editor of *Cancer Research*:

> I could hardly believe my eyes when I discovered that Dr. Little believes that "the first statistics indicating an association between cigarette smoking and the incidence of lung cancer" were presented as recently as June 1954.... Must I remind him that as long ago as May 1950 Dr. Ernest Wynder and I published the first extensive statistics on this subject and prior to the 1954 publication of Hammond and Horn, to which probably Dr. Little refers, there were no less than eleven published series of statistics from various European countries as well as the United States.... We (Wynder, Graham and Croninger) have shown that cigarette smoke contains a carcinogenic factor.... the evidence already at hand for a causal relationship between heavy cigarette smoking and cancer of the lung is stronger than that for the efficacy of vaccination against smallpox, which is only statistical.[38]

Graham was highly critical of C.C. Little, who had accepted a commission by the tobacco industry and then proposed that he could be independent of tobacco industry influence.[38] The editorial was rejected by editor Rusch, who asked for a shorter version and wrote to Graham that personal attacks were out of place in a journal such as *Cancer Research*. Graham's shorter and more temperate version containing his complaints was published in the October 1956 issue with 20 references.[39] Dr. Little acknowledged his error in citing Hammond and Horn, but he added that he desired additional experimental evidence about the relationship between smoking and lung cancer.[40] Graham's exasperation was obvious when he responded:

> What stronger evidence is desired? Human experimentation is of course out of the question. Of how much value are the arguments that are being advanced in favour of occupational hazards as the explanation of the increase of lung cancer when the protagonists of that theory completely neglect the smoking habits of the workers involved?... It will be interesting to see if the Tobacco Industry Research Committee can produce any work that will refute the torrent of evidence from different parts of the world in favour of a definite etiological relationship between heavy cigarette smoking and cancer of the lung. Great Britain's Minister of Health... on March 5 tersely expressed to the House of Commons the opinion now generally held in that country. He said, "What has been shown is that there is a causal relationship between smoking and lung cancer—that we know."[39]

A few days later Graham wrote to A.B. Hill in London: "You may be surprised to know that Dr. C.C. Little was willing to become the chairman of that committee. It seems astonishing to me that a man of his eminence in the field of cancer and genetics would condescend to take a position like that."[41]

Graham summarized his challenge to the tobacco industry in a speech prepared for the University of Chicago Round Table that was presented by radio on March 30, 1954, from a podium shared with Charles Huggins of Chicago and John Joseph Bittner of Minneapolis. In closing, Graham stated:

> If the cigarette manufacturers of this country really wish to determine whether or not our results are true and significant they might follow the example set by their British colleagues. Recently the cigarette manufacturers in England raised among themselves a sum of money amounting to nearly three quarters of a million dollars. They gave this money to the British Research Council with a request that research be undertaken by that body to determine, in so far as possible, how much the smoking of cigarettes in England is responsible for the great increase in the incidence of cancer of the lung. The important point is that in England the money was turned over to a neutral scientific body which will not be biased in its results. In this country the manufacturers could raise a similar sum and turn it over to the National Research Council, the American Cancer Society or the American College of Surgeons and request that any one of those neutral organizations undertake research on the question.[42]

In 1954 Alton Ochsner published his major work *Smoking and Lung Cancer*,[30] with a foreword written by Graham who, in restating the smoking–lung cancer relationship, also proposed social action:

> The chief factor responsible for this outstanding increase has been the development of excessive cigarette smoking.... Unfortunately it has not been universally accepted and there are still many cigarette addicts among the medical profession. The obstinacy of many of them... compels one to conclude that it is their own addiction... which blinds them. They have eyes to see, but see not because of their inability or unwillingness to give up smoking.... All of this leads up to the question of what is going to be done about it.... are the radio and television networks to be permitted to continue carrying the advertising material of the cigarette industry? Isn't it time that the official guardian of the peoples health, the United States Public Health Service, at least make a statement of warning?[43]

Graham had become convinced and had entered the antismoking campaign with zeal. He was firm in his belief and proposed two measures that might have an effect: (1) eliminating airway advertising and (2) placing warning labels on tobacco merchandise. Both of these actions have materialized, but it took many years. In New York City, Wynder continued to publish on the industrial and public health issues of smoking.[44,45] The last paper jointly prepared by Graham, Wynder, and Croninger on the issue of smoking and carcinogenesis was published posthumously in 1958.[22]

Wynder and Graham's epidemiologic studies that showed an association between smoking and lung cancer were followed up by laboratory studies that demonstrated the carcinogenicity of cigarette tars. It is not only the primary publication but also the continued pursuit in the scientific laboratory to establish cause and effect that deserves so much credit. These efforts were barely completed before Evarts Graham succumbed to the disease he had been studying for these many years.

Chapter 19

HELEN TREDWAY GRAHAM: FAMILY, SCIENCE, AND CIVIC CONSCIENCE

The story of Evarts Graham would be incomplete without the story of Helen Tredway Graham, his wife of 41 years; she was a woman with a rare combination of intelligence, wit, and lady-like warmth, who probably had a keener mind than did Graham.[1] Helen was the perfect counterpart to her distinguished husband, and, as hostess to their many and varied acquaintances, she graced their reception rooms, provided stimulating conversation at the dining table, and was ever attentive to the needs of her guests—whether local, national, or international. Her life as a wife and mother was combined with her scientific life, in which she collaborated with some of the great names of neurophysiology and intracellular analytic chemistry. In addition, she was dedicated to and maintained an involvement with wide-ranging civic activities in the St. Louis community. As a role model for college-educated women, Helen was devoted to public welfare and was a forerunner in the women's liberation movement.

PARENTS

Helen Tredway was born on July 21, 1890, in Dubuque, Iowa, to Harry Ennis Tredway and Marion McConnell Tredway. Her paternal grandmother, Mrs. Alfred Tredway, had been born Elizabeth Skerritt Taft into a well-documented ancestral line that goes back to William Brewster of the *Mayflower* and includes many US political notables.

Harry Tredway, an executive in a prosperous hardware firm established by his father and brothers as the A. Tredway and Sons Hardware Company, was also president of the John Airnsdorf Iron Company and the Mentz Manufacturing Company. All three companies suffered severe financial difficulties during the 1930s, and Harry Tredway became an official in the Dubuque city government. He was a charter member and president of the Commercial Club, president of the Dubuque Golf Club, a member of the Elks, and president of the Dubuque Board of Education.

Marion McConnell was born in Jacksonville, Illinois, shortly before her parents moved to Chicago, where they became leaders in the city's literary and cultural life. After marriage to Harry Tredway she moved easily into her husband's life and became prominent in the social and civic affairs of Dubuque. An enthusiastic worker for the beautification of Dubuque, she was responsible for the development of many of the city's parks and other beauty spots, served as president of the Dubuque Women's Club, and was chairwoman of several civic committees of Dubuque and the State of Iowa.

Three girls were born to this marriage: Margaret, in August 1888, Helen, in July 1890, and Mary Leslie, in April 1899. After the 1940 death of Marion Tredway, Harry moved to Florissant, Missouri, to live with Helen and Evarts in their home on Old Jamestown Road until his demise in 1944.

EDUCATION

Helen Tredway, a child of this Midwestern, middle-class family, spent 8 years at the Lincoln Public School, entering at age 5. Her innate brightness and intelligence are obvious in the reports submitted to her parents during these years; of 80 test scores, 21 were scored as 100 percent, with only three below 90 percent. Her deportment was consistently recorded as excellent.[2]

Helen's teaching experiences began on the front porch of a nearby home, where she and sister Margaret held summer kindergarten for their younger sister, Mary Leslie, and some of the neighboring children. Helen was an avid reader during her grade- and high-school years and was never fond of childish games and dolls, but her reading interests did not preclude an active social life, and, during high school days, there was always one or more admirer in the vicinity. She became valedictorian of her class, obtained the highest score in the College Entrance Board Examinations that year, and was awarded a Western scholarship to Bryn Mawr College[a]. Here she spent 4 comfortable and pleasant years (1907 to 1911) working part-time as the dean's secretary, spending a fair amount of time in the science laboratories, and playing field hockey during athletic hours. Helen's sister Mary Leslie, in

---

a. Bryn Mawr College was established in 1885 in the suburbs of Philadelphia to provide and maintain an institution of advanced learning for women. It is one of three colleges founded by members of the Society of Friends (Quakers); the other two were Haverford, an all-male school, and Swarthmore, a coeducational school. Its buildings of grey stone collegiate Gothic architecture were

confirming the work load that Helen carried, added "all this doesn't mean she did nothing but study....I recall many accounts of Princeton football games, yellow chrysanthemums and weekends in Philadelphia and Atlantic City."[3]

An assiduous student, Helen's day was well organized as to whether to play hockey or study, and she attained a 91.62 grade in her undergraduate studies, the highest ever achieved by any Bryn Mawr student. As valedictorian of the class of 1911 she was awarded a $500 European scholarship that she postponed to spend 1 more year at Bryn Mawr to study for a master's degree.

At the Georg-August Universität in Göttingen, Helen chose laboratory and classroom studies in chemistry and became proficient in German. A Bryn Mawr classmate, Frances Shaffner, paid a brief visit and remembers being "introduced to [Helen's] fellow laboratory students, having them all click their heels and bow politely." They visited "a heavenly dance place called Marien Spring set in a pine grove where all the students sat at their separate tables drinking and singing until the orchestra broke into another dance. Helen was always being twirled and swung to the most lovely of all dances—a real European waltz." In addition to her studies, Helen learned to smoke and to drink beer; she came home a "roly poly," something she never again allowed to happen.[3]

After returning to the United States, Helen enrolled as the only female graduate student in the University of Chicago chemistry department headed by Julius Steigleitz. Her chemistry courses involved organic compounds whose odor permeated clothes and hair, and she and her mother designed neat, blue, denim dresses to be worn under a black, rubber, coachman's apron, and a blue denim hat to cover her hair. As she entered times and boiling points in her notebook, some of the men in the laboratory would cluster around, as though they had no work of their own to do; however, the man who caught her attention was Evarts Graham. She was determined to know the quiet, reserved, good-looking, young doctor who, claiming that he knew little about chemistry, had come, like the others, to see what was happening in her laboratory.

Helen and Graham designed a study of interest that followed up Graham's previous study of acids formed when chloroform was used as an anesthetic agent and during episodes of illness in patients with diabetes. Insulin had not been isolated, and diabetic ketoacidosis had yet to be defined. Graham concluded that glucose protected the liver from the hydrochloric acid derived from chloroform. The joint

---

populated by undergraduates, graduates, and "hearers." Chartered to confer bachelor, master, and doctorate degrees in liberal arts and sciences, it soon became so well endowed that European fellowships and scholarships could be awarded annually. As a member of the "Seven Sisters"—Smith, Wellesley, Mt. Holyoke, Barnard, Vassar, Radcliffe, and Bryn Mawr—it stood alongside the seven predominantly male-oriented Ivy League colleges—Harvard, Yale, Dartmouth, Princeton, Cornell, Columbia, and Brown.

experiment of Helen and Evarts was an attempt to determine if the protective action of carbohydrates could be reproduced in the laboratory, and they prepared tubes filled with gelatin that contained a litmus solution and sugars in varying amounts. Acid was layered over the top of the tube. As it diffused into the gelatin, the litmus changed color. They observed their tubes for 144 hours and reported diffusion in millimeters from the top. The pair tested eight different acids and used three different sugars with six different concentrations. They concluded that the diffusion of hydrogen ions into gelatin was retarded by the presence of sugar.[4] The results of this study were written up during days in Mason City, and the *Journal of the American Chemical Society* received their manuscript on April 1, 1918, the very day that Graham reported to Camp Lee, Virginia.

The academic year ended with Helen receiving highest honors in her doctorate studies and preparing for publication of her thesis, "The Thermal Decomposition of Symmetrical Diarylhydrazines,"[5] as a part of a continuing study by Drs. Steiglietz and George O. Curme on the breakdown of a complicated hydrazine molecule. After Curme left for Europe, Helen determined the degradation steps that led finally to toluidine and aniline, two very aromatic compounds. In a lengthy introduction to the final manuscript, Steiglietz acknowledged Helen's cotributions: "I take pleasure in using this opportunity of thanking my young collaborator, Mrs. Graham[b], to whose skill and perseverence the experimental part of this investigation is wholly due.—J.S."[5]

Helen received a doctor of philosophy degree in chemistry and physics from the University of Chicago at its September 3, 1915, convocation. Of the six women among the 34 recipients that year, four were in the science division: Helen in chemistry, two women in botany, and one in mathematics. During her next 2 years in Mason City, Helen continued some scientific work in the Park Hospital laboratory that had been prepared for Evarts, and analyzed some of the oils and fats found in the lining membranes of "strawberry gallbladder." Nothing came of these efforts.

In the spring of 1915, Helen and Evarts announced their engagement at a dinner with her Bryn Mawr colleague Frances Shaffner and his Chicago mentor Rollin Woodyatt. After a 9-month engagement, the two were married. It was to be a happy and productive life together—they were two people matched in intellect, interests, and a strong sense of community responsibility.[6] If discord ever existed, it was never made public. Evarts was ever attentive to Helen and supportive of her scientific and civic life. Separation was tempered with frequent letters and telephone calls, and there was never a hint of an extramarital attraction on the part of either. Their religious outlets were through the Ethical Society of St. Louis. Dr. James

---

b. Helen was single at the time of the study, and Steiglitz's "Mrs. Graham" reference acknowledges the delay in manuscript preparation and publication.

Hornback, the society leader, saw the couple as being "highly principled and secular humanists... religiously affiliated although not registered members, ones who would not accept revelations or supernatural beliefs and very responsible in civic affairs." Hornback described Evarts as "strong, silent and not talkative, refined, gentile and gentle."[7]

David Tredway Graham was born on June 20, 1917. He was intolerant of milk, and, in the days before baby foods could be purchased at the grocery store, Helen was required to spend an inordinate amount of time preparing a complicated formula. The Graham family now became touched by Tillie Hecht, a square-faced Iowa farm girl who helped with David's care and managed their apartment. They parted from Tillie upon leaving Mason City for military duty, but resumed contact 2 years later. When Evarts, Helen, and David moved to St. Louis, Tillie returned as the housekeeper, cook, and general manager of the household. Tillie was a woman of few words. She was very dedicated to Evarts and Helen and extremely fond of their boys. Helen was protective of Tillie. Not being much of a cook, herself, on Tillie's night off, Helen would prepare cheese and crackers to be eaten over the sink, so Tillie would not be offended by crumbs in the house.[8]

ARMY WIFE

When Evarts entered the army in January 1918, the three Grahams moved to Chicago to live with his parents for the months he spent teaching neurosurgery. Upon his appointment to Camp Lee, Virginia, Helen, in customary army fashion, followed her husband to Petersburg, 20 miles south of Richmond and adjacent to the camp. Her sister Margaret accompanied Helen on a rough train trip from Chicago. Both adults became car sick, and David was neglected. Evarts commuted from Petersburg to Camp Lee until his Baltimore assignment; the three then found a wartime apartment that had been carved out of a once-elegant old Baltimore residence. They obtained the daytime help of a girl named Maria, and Helen secured an appointment at Johns Hopkins as special assistant to J.J. Abel, with whom she worked for the remainder of the year.

At that time Abel was interested in compounds secreted by the pituitary gland, particularly histamine-like substances, and he gave Helen the task of making bovine pituitary extracts that would be tested either on the blood pressure of dogs or on the contraction of the guinea pig uterus. The effects of the extracts were compared to those of known solutions of histamine. Abel was so impressed with Helen that he commented to Lampson, his biographer: "I have seen a good many women in science and to tell the truth I have not felt that they were particularly well fitted for it but Dr. Graham is different. She has upset all of my ideas on the matter and she is as good if not better than any man whom I have ever had with me in the laboratory."[9]

Around Christmastime 1918, with a husband overseas and her housekeeper desiring to quit, Helen terminated her work in Baltimore and returned to Dubuque to live with her parents and await Evarts's homecoming. When he returned in April, the three Grahams relocated to Evanston for his period of duty at Fort Sheridan.

In St. Louis they bought their first home—a plain, square, brick, upper middle–class house at 4711 Westminster Place, six blocks from the Medical School. Helen was pleased with this house and meticulously cared for the yard and the garden—even to the extent of handpicking dandelions from the yard. Evarts walked to work every day, as did Helen 6 years later when she returned to scientific activity. In this house Helen established herself as a gracious hostess, bright and vivacious, with a warm personality and sense of humor. It was she who made people's visits enjoyable, being equally comfortable with the surgical greats of the day as with the young men who grew up with sons David and Evarts Jr. At one time, however, she confided to a friend that dinner parties for Evarts's associates were some of the most difficult times for her. As a team the Graham couple were popular in the community, Helen because of her intelligence, charm, wit, and gaiety, and Evarts because he was always bright, interesting, and challenging.

Helen became the significant figure in shaping the Grahams' social life. Evarts was serious-minded, practical, and pragmatic. He was always polite and bright, but was not a spontaneous conversationalist. His popularity in the social community was in large part due to Helen, who was easy to talk to. "She was small and attractive, and in both size and social grace was a contrast to her husband—they became a wonderful pair." One acquaintance said, "It was much easier to place Helen as a dinner partner than it was to find a person capable of making light social conversation with Evarts."[6]

Neither science or politics were places to have fun, and Helen was totally without humor when she talked about serious matters, scientific or civic. A modern woman she was a heavy cigarette smoker during student and early marriage years but abandoned the practice in the late 1920s, even though Evarts remained a heavy smoker until 1950. Always aware of the rules of polite society, when visitors came to her home, Helen made them go outdoors to smoke.[8,10]

FAMILY

During early married life, Helen was consumed with her family. Evarts Ambrose Jr., born February 4, 1921, grew up without the feeding problems of his elder brother David. Four years later Helen was pregnant again, and, on 1 June, 1925, a third son, John, was born after a difficult 18-hour labor, supervised by Dr. H. Schwarz, chairman of obstetrics and gynecology. The infant survived for 4 hours before dying of an intracranial hemorrhage. Evarts wrote to his colleague Sherwood Moore: "We are…much consoled in the fact that we would rather have him die this way than possibly to have him grow up as a mentally deficient and handicapped child."[11]

Helen shaped an intellectual home environment for her husband and children. She saw to it that their two very bright sons were raised in an inquiring atmosphere, and, at her dinner table, there was free exchange between boys and parents. It is doubtful that anyone challenged Evarts more than his two sons, for to them it became fun. On one occasion David told his father that chest surgery would become obsolete as soon as a drug better than streptomycin cured tuberculosis. Evarts and Helen took such arguments without rancor, whetting each other's intellect in a challenging atmosphere.[12]

David Tredway Graham, the first son, born in Mason City, received his primary and secondary schooling at the John Burroughs School in St. Louis. Following the tradition of his father and grandfather, he enrolled at Princeton to earn a bachelor's degree in 1938. After 2 years at Yale Medical School, he moved to St. Louis to complete his doctor of medicine degree at Washington University in 1943. Internship and residency years were interrupted by 2 years (1945 to 1947) in the army medical corps. In 1948 he began 3 years at Cornell as a medical research fellow, then returned to Washington University for 6 years as assistant professor of medicine, with a cross-appointment in the Department of Psychiatry. In 1957 David joined the Department of Medicine of the University of Wisconsin Medical School, where he served as assistant dean for admissions for 5 years, became chairman of medicine from 1971 to 1980, and then became professor emeritus in 1986. At that time he moved to Delaware as adjunct professor of psychology at the University of Delaware. David died in a nursing home in 1999 after a prolonged and debilitating illness due to Parkinson's disease.

In June 1941 David married Frances Kessler, who had earned a bachelor's degree from Pennsylvania State University and then, in 1942, a doctor of philosophy degree in psychology from Yale. She came with him to St. Louis as research associate in the Department of Psychiatry to serve for 2 years as acting director of the St. Louis Psychiatric Clinic. While David was at Cornell, she held an instructorship at Barnard College, and, upon returning to St. Louis, once again became a research associate in psychiatry. In Madison her first appointment was as research associate, from which she rose to become professor of psychiatry and pediatrics. During the last 6 of these years, she held the Hillside Endowed Research Professorship, and her work in the psychology of children was of such distinction that she was elected to membership in the National Academy of Sciences. David and Frances had three children: Norma (1944), Andrew (1945), and Mary (1952).[13]

Evarts Jr. was born at Barnes Hospital on February 4, 1921. He, too, attended the John Burroughs School, before going to Harvard College to graduate with a bachelor's degree in 1941 and following with 1 year as a reporter for the *St. Louis Post-Dispatch*. Drafted in 1942 as a private in the US Army, he was discharged 4 years later as first lieutenant in the army air corps. Three overseas years were spent mainly in London as an intelligence officer. After his discharge, Evarts Jr. returned to the *St. Louis Post-Dispatch* and remained with the paper for 40 years, becoming its managing editor from 1968 to 1979 and a contributing editor and columnist from Washington, DC, from 1979 to 1985. After the 1987 loss of his wife in Washington, DC, he returned to St. Louis to live at 4501 Lindell Boulevard in the west end of the city. He remained there until his death in 1996 from carcinoma of the prostate.

Perugina Adler, Evarts Jr.'s wife, was the daughter of a Bryn Mawr classmate of Helen. After 1 year at Scripps College in California, she transferred to and graduated from Radcliffe College in 1942. From 1945 to 1946, she was a civilian employee of the US Army in Germany. She then became a medical student at Washington University but dropped out after her second year. Two years after their June 1951 marriage, she obtained a bachelor's degree in occupational therapy from Washington University and began work as an occupational therapist and crafts instructor before their move to Washington, DC, where she died in 1987 after a lengthy illness. She and Evarts Jr. had three children: Stephen (1954), Helen (1957), and Sarah (1962).[14,15]

Helen Graham was interested in people who were "doers;" she felt that doing something in any sense made a person somebody important. Her semi-independence was declared in the way she used her name—Helen Tredway Graham or Helen Graham, never Helen T. Graham and almost never Mrs. Evarts Graham. She rarely went to meetings with Evarts and, by the time of his retirement, had heard him speak on only two occasions. Her dress was always neat, conservative, and tidy, but she cared little about style, merely that her clothes were clean and proper.[8]

An example of Helen's sense of self-worth can be seen in an occurrence during the inauguration of Arthur Holly Compton as chancellor of Washington University. Among 1200 people in the Gold Room of the Jefferson Hotel in St. Louis, Helen was seated next to Maj. Gen. Leslie Groves, director of the Manhattan Project that had developed the atomic bomb. She attempted to carry the conversation by saying, "I read the Smyth Report[c]," adding comments to the effect that from the material contained in the report, she had a general idea of the procedures used for the separation of uranium isotopes. Groves responded: "Oh you couldn't possibly understand that," to which she replied, "I am sorry, General Groves, but I have scientific training in Chemistry and Physics and I understand a great deal of what was in that report." Groves insisted, "You couldn't possibly have understood it." Subsequent to that interchange she had no use for the general and his pomposity.[15]

---

c. Helen was referring to Henry D. Smyth's *Atomic Energy for Military Purposes: The Official Report on the Development of the Atomic Bomb.*[16]

SCIENTIST, RESEARCHER, AND TEACHER

In July 1925, 1 month after the death of John, Helen returned to scientific activity, leaving David and Evarts Jr. to the care of Tillie. At the request of Dr. Herbert Gasser[d], she accepted a faculty appointment, and the Department of Pharmacology became her scientific home for 45 years—the rest of her life. Thirty years after the appointment, she achieved the rank of professor and in 1959 became professor emeritus.

During those early years, the Departments of Physiology and Pharmacology collaborated in research in neurophysiology. There were three outstanding individuals: Joseph Erlanger[e], chairman of physiology; Herbert Gasser, originally in the Department of Physiology then chairman of pharmacology; and George Bishop, professor of physiology then, later, ophthalmology and biophysics. Each would become an international figure.

An impediment to the early studies of nerve conduction was the damping effect of the heavy mechanical recording apparatus of the day, but in 1922 the Western Electric Company produced a satisfactory cathode ray oscilloscope, and Erlanger

---

d. Herbert Spencer Gasser (1888 to 1963), a native of Wisconsin, earned bachelor and master's degrees at its university. He attended 2 years of medical school at Wisconsin before he transferred to Johns Hopkins for 2 years leading to a doctor of medicine degree in 1915. Rejecting an instructorship in physiology at Johns Hopkins, Gasser returned to Wisconsin to spend 3 years in the Department of Pharmacology before receiving the surprise offer from Joseph Erlanger for an instructorship in physiology in St. Louis. This appointment led to his collaboration with Erlanger in a long period of research into circulation, secondary traumatic shock, and nerve transmission. Eli K. Marshall, the founding head of pharmacology, returned to Johns Hopkins, and in 1921 Gasser was appointed chairman of pharmacology. He left Washington University in 1931 for Cornell, then 4 years later became director of the Rockefeller Institute for Medical Research. For some years after leaving Washington University, Gasser continued to publish with Helen Graham and F.O. Schmitt. Phillip Shaffer then recruited a Czech immigrant, Carl F. Cori, from the University of Buffalo, to fill the vacancy occasioned by Gasser's departure for Cornell. Cori's father had been professor of biochemistry at the University of Prague, and Carl, with his fellow scientist and wife Gerti, became a Nobel laureate in 1947, 3 years after Gasser shared the prize with Erlanger.

e. Born in California, Joseph Erlanger (1874 to 1965) was the only one of seven siblings to go beyond the eighth grade. After receiving a bachelor's degree at Berkeley, he was drawn into medical studies at Johns Hopkins and graduated with a doctor of medicine degree in 1899. Following a Hopkins internship, Erlanger spent 6 years in Howell's physiology laboratory before being offered the chair of physiology at the University of Wisconsin, a position he held from 1906 to 1910. He was recruited by Robert Brookings to the newly reorganized Washington University faculty as one of its first three chairmen.

Erlanger's early research was confined to cardiac contractions, but, during World War I, he began to study the physiology of shock. In 1922 he and Gasser described the first biologic application of the cathode ray oscillograph, and the two began a long period of collaboration in neurophysiology. For years they paid particular reference to the electrical properties of nerve conduction, a special interest of Gasser's, and with the help of John Zimmer, the department's mechanic, and Gasser described its first biologic application.[17] In 1922 the first paper of the triumvirate described the action potentials of nerves as recorded by the scope.[18] Collaboration between the three continued until 1927, when Bishop became offended by Erlanger's efforts to prevent the publication of some work on electrical conduction in unmyelinated fibers that had been done by Peter Heinbecker of the Department of Surgery. By 1930 the conflict forced Bishop to move to the Department of Ophthalmology, where he began work on the optic nerve[f]. The move, negotiated by Dean McKim Marriott, had been supported by Evarts Graham and financed by Rockefeller money.[10]

Helen Tredway Graham arrived in the center of this vibrant and exciting neurophysiologic group, and, during her first 2 years, she studied muscles, gasses, lactic acid, narcosis, and anesthetics. After these early studies, she began a long-term collaboration with Gasser investigating peripheral nerves: first, the effects of some drugs; next, some characteristics of afterpotentials; and, finally, nerve conduction velocities.

During the next 15 years, Helen published 29 papers on nerve stimulation, the influence of nerve size, and the effects of drugs on nerve transmission. She was the first person to record spinal cord action potentials. Many of these studies were cooperative efforts with Gasser, with whom she continued to collaborate, and to whom she often wrote after he left for Cornell. Following Gasser's departure, Helen began work with Raphael Lorente-de-No, the research director of the Central Institute for the Deaf, and with James O'Leary, a clinical neurologist and electroencephalographer who had developed a laboratory that he shared with George Bishop.

The collaboration between Gasser and Erlanger produced the studies that resulted in their Nobel prize. By sharing the money with George Bishop, the two acknowledged his contributions, even though he had been excommunicated from their departments.[17,19] The proposal and documentation to the Nobel Committee had been made by none other than Evarts A. Graham.[16,18]

Erlanger constructed much of their equipment. After Gasser departed for Cornell, the two continued their correspondence and collaboration. Erlanger paid meticulous attention to detail and oversaw all equipment in his department. He read and approved every manuscript and presentation, took the liberty of making corrections as he saw fit, and controlled the daily luncheon meetings that were held with all levels of his staff and graduate students. Erlanger and Gasser shared the Nobel prize in 1944 for "discoveries regarding the highly differentiated function of nerve fibres." Evarts Graham had collected the supporting documents and submitted the nomination to the Nobel Committee.

f. As a 1938 to 1942 recipient of a National Youth Administration Award, the author's first assignment was to work with George Bishop interpreting oscillograph tracings that Bishop would make by stimulating the optic nerve of cats; subsequently, recordings from the colliculus and geniculate nuclei were taken. This work occurred at the beginning of evoked-response technology in the neurosciences.

In 1949 Dr. Oliver Lowry[g] became chairman of pharmacology, succeeding Carl Cori who moved to biochemistry. Helen Graham's interests then moved from the nervous system to intracellular chemistry, and she returned to histamine, her "old friend" from the Baltimore period with J.J. Abel. She and Lowry devised a method to measure intracellular histamine in mast cells,[20] and Lowry blamed himself for their failure to establish priority for that study because of his delay in its preparation for publication.[21] Helen proceeded to devise methods to measure histamine in body fluids and urine, producing nine publications, almost all jointly with Lowry. In 1968 her final publication was the measurement of histamine in human blood plasma.[22] As an independent investigator, she had discovered the histamine storage function of mast cells and blood basophils, and had developed highly sensitive methods for its measurement in all body fluids. At 79, the year before she died, her application for renewal of a National Institutes of Health grant to continue her histamine work was successful.

Following Evarts's death in 1957, Helen's research zeal dwindled, and activities in the civic arena increased. A special 65th birthday party, held at the Jefferson Hotel on June 24, 1959, celebrated her past achievements and her upcoming appointment as emeritus professor of pharmacology. In the 1950s Helen produced seven publications relating to histamine, but, during the decade of the 1960s, only three papers appeared, all in conjunction with Oliver Lowry. Her research efforts ended during 1966.

As a major contribution to the pharmacology curriculum in the early 1940s, Helen introduced statistical analysis of biochemical-pharmacologic data. She knew that all laboratory experiments ended with numeric data, and felt that medical

---

g. Born in Chicago, Oliver Howe Lowry (1910 to 1996) attended Northwestern University and obtained a bachelor of science degree in 1932. Five years at the University of Chicago leading to doctor of medicine and philosophy degrees in chemistry were followed by 6 years on the biochemistry faculty at Harvard. From 1942 to 1947, Lowry worked and studied at the Public Health Research Institute of New York, serving as chief of the division of physiology and nutrition during his final 3 years. In 1947 as Cori moved to biochemistry, Lowry was recruited to succeed Carl Cori in pharmacology. Chairman from 1947 to 1976, he remained active as emeritus distinguished professor until his death in 1996. He served as dean of the Medical School during the tumultuous years of 1955 to 1958.

Lowry is internationally known for research in microchemistry, starting with electrolytes and serum proteins at Harvard, vitamins and nutrition in New York, and intracellular metabolites and enzyme systems in St. Louis. He elected a career in pharmacology, believing that only the detailed biochemistry of individual cells of the brain could explain drug actions. His development of new ultramicro methods for intracellular metabolites and enzymes were of such fundamental importance that for many years he was the most cited individual in the I.S.I. Citations Index. A gentle, unassuming, and very personable man, he was a friend to almost everyone, demanding of his colleagues as much dedication as the encouragement and support he showed them. He was close to Helen Graham—very sustaining and attentive during the years following the death of Evarts—and always supported her work on histamine and mast cells. Lowry continued his laboratory work until 1994 to 1995 when his memory began to fail in an unusually rapid and devastating progression of Alzheimer's disease.

students had no appreciation of the significance of data with a fairly large spread. She began by examining the selectivity of questions in the pharmacology examinations, analyzing examinations given over the previous 3 years, and rating each question as to how well it ranked students when compared with their standing in pharmacology and their overall medical school standing. Carl Cori suggested that she publish the work, but Helen felt it not worthwhile, even though it did spark her interest in teaching students about how to interpret data from pharmacologic and medical experiments. Starting with the fact that "average," which students accepted as truth, told almost nothing about either reliability or variance, she prepared an "Introduction to Statistics" lecture that became a fixture. Beginning with one lecture on the topic, she expanded it to three per year, reviewing simple statistics and how they provide an estimate of data reliability. For several years medical students applied statistical analyses to data that came from their work in the pharmacology course. Helen lectured on the topic until the Department of Preventive Medicine recruited Barbara Nixon from the mathematics department on the main campus to take over the effort.[23]

Helen was a member of the American Association for the Advancement of Science, The American Chemical Society, the American Society for Pharmacology and Experimental Therapeutics, the American Physiological Society, and the Histamine Club, and was amused by being listed in American Men of Science for over 50 years.

HELEN'S MODERN HOME

In 1940 the Grahams sold their home on Westminster Place and for 3 years lived in a large grey, modern, limestone house at No. 10 Upper Ladue Road in a posh suburb of west St. Louis. A three-car garage was not out of proportion, and its large yard provided an opportunity for the two Grahams to indulge in their gardening interests. During these years Evarts and Helen purchased seven acres on Old Jamestown Road that ran along the bluffs overlooking the Missouri River, with Vilray Blair, a plastic surgeon, Alexis Hartman, chairman of pediatrics, and William Scarlett, bishop of the Episcopal diocese, as neighbors. Harris Armstrong, a leading St. Louis architect, designed a spacious house that showed the Frank Lloyd Wright influence—flat lines, open spaces, brick and wood interior, with uncluttered decor and no carpeting. It was both simple and elegant, and in 1943 Evarts, Helen, her father, Harry Tredway, Evarts Jr., and Tillie moved in[h].

Helen and Graham were very proud of the house and its view. Evarts was enchanted by the Missouri River, and, after reading *Across the Wide Missouri* by Bernard DeVoto, he wondered about how many things DeVoto had exaggerated or

---

h. Old Jamestown Road, 18 Jamestown Acres, Florissant, Missouri.

were not quite true. This house permitted Helen and Evarts to expand their interest in growing vegetables, flowers, and shrubs; they would take guests on a walk around the property to look at the plants. Evarts was interested in the esthetic effect of the garden, whereas Helen was more interested in the science of growing, whether it be trees, shrubs, flowers, or tomatoes, and she was proud of her compost pile, which she had decades before most people had heard of them. Also challenged by growing indoor plants, Helen developed a large collection of African violets and an enormous crown of thorns.[8] In an area especially designed for sewing, she taught the art to her granddaughters. She usually spent her Sundays with her grandchildren, always with suggestions of things to make or do. Helen developed a particular fondness for her grandson Steve and was devastated by his suicide in 1971.[24]

The Missouri River house was tailor-made for the dinners and receptions that had become a way of life, and Helen meticulously kept a card file of all visitors, the date of the visit, and the food she served.[25] She and Graham bought a small ride-on tractor, and after his death, the tractor remained Helen's connection to the land; her connection to St. Louis was a red Karman-Ghia that she drove until she moved into the city.

The first threat to Missouri bluff tranquility appeared in 1953 when the Laclede Gas Company planned to store natural gas in the limestone strata under the corner of Spinks Road and Old Jamestown Road, one-quarter of a mile underground and about a mile from the Graham home. In an effort to block the scheme, Drs. Graham and Dr. and Mrs. Alexis Hartman formed the Osage Gas Company, incorporated with $500 as capital, and an announced purpose to compete with Laclede. By using a special section of Missouri law, they went to court in early 1955. It was a contest of David-and-Goliath proportions, eagerly followed by newspaper coverage. In September 1955 a settlement was reached that approved the Laclede purchase of the Osage Gas Company for an undisclosed sum and permission to store its gas underground. Reasons for Graham's and Hartman's opposition, be it financial gain, property values, environmental concerns, or safety were never made clear. The actions, however, were typical of Evarts Graham.[26,27]

On January 27, 1955, while Evarts was in Princeton attending a National Institutes of Health subcommittee meeting on lung cancer, two burglars broke into the house and ransacked it for money. Using the cut telephone lines, they tied Helen and Tillie Hecht to the furniture, while Helen called out that their money was not in the house, that it was in the First National Bank and they should look there. The burglars took more than $2000 in cash (Tillie's savings of 3 years), clothing, jewelry, and a quantity of liquor before escaping in the Graham station wagon.[23] The entire episode lasted more than 2 hours. After the burglars departed the two women remained tied for about 20 minutes before Helen managed to work free and call for help on another telephone. In the succeeding months, Evarts made three appearances before the County Council to protest inadequate police protection. "Crooks know we have no protection" was his plea for an enlargement of the force. Nine deputy sheriffs were added, but the robbers were never caught.[28,29]

In the fall of 1966, Dr. Carl Harford suggested that Helen move into town and give up driving. Daughter-in-law Perugina was helpful in persuading Helen and Tillie to leave the Old Jamestown Road home, and she helped Helen obtain two two-bedroom apartments on the sixth floor of the Montclair apartment building at 18 South Kingshighway and convert them into one. The balcony overlooking Forest Park permitted Helen to continue her gardening. The Montclair was approximately five blocks from the Medical School, and Helen walked to work every day, climbing the two flights of stairs to her office in the pharmacology department. Mildred Trotter[i] was also an apartment dweller of the Montclair.

HELEN AND THE MEDICAL SCHOOL WOMEN

Following her acceptance of a position on the Washington University Faculty, Helen became one of a small network of faculty women. Foremost and most permanent was Mildred Trotter of the Department of Anatomy, whose office in the north wing of the basic science building faced Helen's office in the south wing. Margaret Smith, a pathologist, worked at some distance across Euclid Avenue. Zola Cooper, also a pathologist, had an office located at Barnard Hospital at Washington and Grand Avenue, and Helen's contacts with Zola were few and far between. Ethel Ronzoni, the wife of George Bishop, was a biochemist who worked two floors below Helen, and, although always friendly, the relationship was never warm, particularly after Bishop had been expelled from the Department of Physiology. Gerti

---

i. Born in Monaco, Pennsylvania, Mildred Trotter (1899 to 1991) received her bachelor of arts degree from Mount Holyoke in 1920 and a doctor of philosophy degree in anatomy from Washington University in 1924. She remained on the Washington University faculty throughout the rest of her life, becoming professor emeritus of anatomy in 1967.

Trotter devoted her scientific life to osteology as a student of Robert Terry and became the world's foremost female anthropologist. After World War II, she was special consultant to the US Public Health Services, and, as anthropologist to the Schofield Army Base in Hawaii and Fort McKinley in the Philippines, she assisted in the identification of remains of US soldiers.

Of medium stature, Trotter attracted everyone with her friendly demeanor and gentle smile. For half a century, medical students became her family. She dominated the course in gross anatomy and was particularly sensitive to the needs of the few female medical students. A quiet member of the activist group of women on the Washington University faculty, she became particularly close to Helen Graham. Her life revolved around an apartment on Kingshighway, five blocks north of the Medical School, and her teaching obligations. Trot, as she was known to her colleagues, left a very personal imprint on the many medical students who, in passing her way, came under her supportive and beneficial influence. In 1988 Trotter suffered a massive stroke, and she died in a nursing home 3 agonizing years later.

Cori, the wife of Carl and co-winner of a Nobel prize, arrived in the pharmacology department when Gasser left, and Helen's relations with Gerti were friendly and proper, but Gerti was so involved in her biochemical research there was little time for socializing, although they did share an interest in flowers, shrubs, and trees.[23]

It was Mildred Trotter with whom Helen Graham established the warmest, most friendly, and longest relationship. The Medical School enrolled between five and eight women in each class of 86, and the students were exposed to Mildred Trotter in anatomy and Ethel Ronzoni in biochemistry during their first year, then to Helen Graham in the pharmacology course of the second year. In befriending and looking after the female medical students, Helen and Millie established many lifelong friendships. Mildred Trotter was a single woman and, to a extent greater than Helen, was able to support and temporarily adopt many of the women students as her extended family, sharing social activities in addition to those that stemmed from her medical school office. Although the social side of Helen's contacts were less pronounced than were those of Mildred, her office door was always open. She was gracious, helpful, comforting, and very supportive to women who lived on an island of females in a sea of male medical students.

HELEN, LES GRANDES DAMES, AND CIVIC DUTIES

As Evarts was developing his contacts with members of the business and industrial community of St. Louis, Helen was moving into her world of notable and spirited women who dominated an era of public service. She established a network of friends[j] with interests in many of the political and social concerns of the day. They were bright and well-educated women, and, although they married men with money, they attained their positions by social alertness and hard-working faithfulness to their ideals. Helen was unique in this group because she possessed a professional scientific life in addition to these other attributes. Friendships opened her door to civic activities that began in early St. Louis years but became a dominant feature of her life following Evarts's death.

In 1923, as her first "out-of-home" involvement, Helen became a member of the American Association of University Women (AAUW), a membership she retained throughout her life. In her first year, she became unit fellowship chairman to increase registration, and, soon after, she became the section head to help raise a million-dollar endowment fund for AAUW fellowships. By 1928 she had achieved her goal and reported so at the National Meeting in Fort Worth, Texas, at which

---

j. Mesdames: Edna Gelhorn (Mrs. George), Marizin Senseney (Mrs. Eugene), Tess Loeb (Mrs. Virgil), Erma Stix (Mrs. Ernest), Louise McCarthy (Mrs. Ross), Terry Fisher (Mrs. Aaron), Justine Eiseman (Mrs. Fred), Aimée Schweig (Mrs. Martin).

time she became AAUW president. Several years later a fellowship was named in her honor, and in January 1963 Helen was one of 26 AAUW women cited for special recognition.

In 1932 Helen joined the League for Independent Political Action, and, although always describing herself as a political independent, she generally supported Democratic candidates. During the late 1930s and the war years, she was occupied with her home, Evarts's many activities, and her pharmacology research; there was limited civic action.

After Evarts's death, the many dinners, parties, and other obligations created by his professional life came to an end, and other activities immediately began to occupy her time. Evarts had been a member of a committee that selected the Metropolitan Board of Freeholders, and she spent 1958 to 1959 as the only woman on the nine-member board, helping to draft a metropolitan district plan for the consolidation of services in St. Louis and St. Louis County[k]. She represented the board at a public television hearing sponsored by the local radio-television station KETC. The plan was subsequently rejected by the voters of greater St. Louis.

Helen next became a member of the St. Louis County Civil Service Advisory Committee that proposed the Civil Service System ultimately adopted by the county council. In 1962 to 1963, she was a board member of the St. Louis–St. Louis County chapter of the White House Conference on Education, and followed this activity with a 3-year membership on the Higher Education Co-ordinating Council of Metropolitan St. Louis. By January 1967 her interests had expanded to include the St. Louis Civil Liberties Committee, and she and Mrs. Milton Landau attended its founding dinner, where she made painstaking notes of its procedures and plans and the development of its agenda. This ad hoc group was separate from the St. Louis chapter of the American Civil Liberties Union (ACLU) and was formed to press specifically for academic and scientific freedom. These were years following McCarthyism in the US Congress, and the St. Louis group was dissatisfied with what they perceived was a weak and ineffective stand taken by the national organization. Helen participated in a membership drive and solicited funds to make money available to the St. Louis Bail Fund. A decade earlier she had worked diligently to raise money for the support of Dr. Jeremiah Stammler, a faculty colleague who had been denounced by the House Committee on Un-American Activities.

In 1967 the Health and Welfare Council of Metropolitan St. Louis was composed of representatives from both sides of the Mississippi river—St. Louis and

---

k. In the State of Missouri, the cities of St. Louis and Kansas City are not in a county; they report directly to the state government. Surrounding St. Louis was St. Louis County, with approximately 92 large and small independent municipalities. In 1955 there was no metropolitan governance and no rationalization of services such as roads, police, water, sewage, and fire. Efforts to achieve consolidation that began in 1953, still continue 50 years later.

St. Louis County, Missouri; and St. Clair County, Illinois, which contained the city of East St. Louis. It became a central planning agency for voluntary and publicly supported health, welfare, and recreation services. Several subcommittees were developed, and Helen was named vice-chairman of the Committee on Air Pollution, a role that placed her on the council's executive committee. Her interest in air pollution had been sparked in 1956 when Evarts pressed Adlai Stevenson to make air pollution a part of his presidential campaign. Community leaders were desirous of having AAUW representation in their effort to emphasize a "hands across the river" approach to the inseparability of air pollution problems, and Helen's appointment to the council had come through her position as president of the Ferguson-Florissant chapter of AAUW. This council was a voluntary, bi-state approach to community education for clean air, and it sponsored observance of a National Clean Air Week with several events, meetings, and other activities. In addition to an organizing drive to encourage other branches of AAUW to support the cause, Helen organized an essay contest for grade 10 to 12 students, and, from 1967 to 1969, she raised funds, solicited judges, and provided the necessary advertising. Essays of 500 words or less were scored on a student's grasp of the air pollution problem and the originality of the presentation. A first prize of $50 was followed by six prizes of $10 each, and Helen collected $200 from the St. Louis Medical Society for the effort.

The Committee on Air Pollution disbanded 2 years after being formed; it was immediately succeeded by the St. Louis Regional Coalition for the Environment, which again had Helen as a founding member. This coalition of 156 individuals and 19 organizations was divided into five sections—air pollution, open space, solid waste, water pollution, and pesticides. Helen became interested in the first two of these areas and again represented the AAUW in the coalition's interest in solid waste pollution, particularly airborne waste. In March 1968 she testified before a state legislative committee on auto exhaust emissions, and in October 1969, while speaking before 200 angry citizens at a meeting of the coalition at Shaw's Garden, she encouraged the group to become more militant about cleaning up the air. She remained a member of the coalition's board of directors until her death.

Again as a representative of the AAUW, Helen served for 4 years on the Missouri Air Conservation Commission (1966 to 1970) and testified before a legislative subcommittee in 1970 to encourage national standards for air pollution. This action led to membership on the Open Space Council, an agency interested in parklands and air cleanliness in St. Louis and St. Louis County. Next, Helen became a director of the Committee for Environmental Information (CEI), a Missouri nonprofit corporation chaired by Barry Commoner and presided over by Margaret Mead. The CEI claimed 692 members, half of whom were in St. Louis, and published information about the air pollution situation in metropolitan St. Louis, as well as around the nation. In 1967, its 11th year of publishing the magazine *Environment*, Helen Graham was placed on its board of directors and became vice-president and life member of its science advisory board. After 3 years on this board, she refused the invitation for a second 3-year term.

In 1923 Helen joined the League of Women Voters, and in 1927 she became president of the St. Louis chapter. She gave financial support to the league, to the United Nations Association, and to the World Wildlife Fund. As a member of the St. Louis branch of the Women's International League for Peace and Freedom, she accepted the obligation of documenting the voting records of members of the Missouri Senate and General Assembly.

Helen's co-workers in these many civic activities praised her dedication, persistence, and modest willingness to work in any way necessary. They admired her intellect, judgment, incisive mind, intellectual honesty, and good humor,[30] and she showered affection and confidence on them.

HELEN, EVARTS, AND SHARED EDUCATIONAL ENTERPRISES

Concerns about education, both its quality and availability, were always of importance to the pair of Grahams. The two became active in the New School Association—later named the John Burroughs School Association—to found a day school on South Price Road in St. Louis County. Helen and Evarts were unanimously elected to the temporary board of the newly created John Burroughs School Association on November 17, 1922, and when the school opened in October 1923, both were members of its first board of trustees. Evarts became the board's second president, serving from 1931 to 1937. David and Evarts Jr. obtained primary and secondary school education at this institution, and the Graham family was an annual financial contributor.[31]

The Grahams were also involved with the Community School—an elementary school for the privileged—which was developed on progressive educational principles similar to those of the John Burroughs School. Helen and her colleagues traveled the United States to find quality faculty and staff for both schools, and in 1959, after Evarts death, Helen began a 6-year term as a member of the Community School Board of Trustees. In 1961 she helped create and then personally typed a report for the junior college district regarding the governance of public junior colleges. She followed this with a membership on the library committee of the Higher Education Co-ordinating Council, and later became its chairman.[29] In June 1946 Helen began a 6-year term as a member of the board of trustees of Bryn Mawr College, and in June 1960 she was one of 75 alumnae cited for their distinguished service to Bryn Mawr.[23]

FINALE

Shortly after climbing the two flights to her office on April 2, 1971, Helen felt ill. She became short of breath, developed pain in her chest, and was taken immediately to Barnes Hospital and placed under the care of Dr. Carl Moore. Her two sons stood guard at the door of her hospital room to dissuade the many who desired to pay a visit. Forty-eight hours later, Helen died from a heart attack.[23]

Following the precedent set by Evarts, she had signed a "gift of body" document (June 10, 1970), and after an autopsy confirmed the heart attack, the Missouri Anatomical Board gave her body to Washington University. She was placed in the anatomy department crematory on April 9, 1971, and her ashes were scattered on a university site. At various times Helen had stated to Mildred Trotter that since she had devoted so many years to teaching and research at Washington University, it was only fitting that her final contribution should be her body. A memorial service was held in the Graham Chapel 3 weeks later, with tributes and remembrances by Oliver Lowry and Mrs. Aaron (Terry) Fisher.[32-36] As with Evarts, there is no grave. Her personal propriety, stature, and position remained an inspiration to members of the Department of Pharmacology for many years.[32] Helen's independence, self-assurance, and sense of purpose and certainty were reflected in her children and her grandchildren.

Chapter 20

ILLNESS AND FINALE

DIABETES

Evarts Graham suffered from two major illnesses—diabetes mellitus and bronchiogenic carcinoma. His diabetes became manifest during a 1945 trip to Washington, DC, when he became ill. Graham was admitted to the Naval Hospital in Bethesda, Maryland, for 2 days and then returned to St. Louis. He consulted Barry Wood[a], his counterpart in medicine, who asked the medical chief resident, Dr. Robert Glaser, to analyze an unlabeled urine specimen. Glaser thought this rather unusual since staff in hospital laboratories, not chief residents, generally did such tasks. The urine specimen was positive for sugar, and 2 days later Wood confided in Glaser that it had come from Evarts Graham.[1]

Shortly after his return from Washington, DC, and his consultation with Barry Wood, Graham approached Dean Robert Moore to appraise him of his illness. He asked if it were appropriate for him to continue as chairman of the Department of Surgery—would Dr. Moore want an ill chairman? If not, Graham

---

a. Graham's dedication to the full-time Washington University faculty was so firm that he referred his patients only to full-time individuals; thus when the time came to select his own physicians, they could only be full-timers, for example, Richard Odell, Charles Eckert, Bill Daughaday, Edward Reinhard, Barry Wood, David Barr, and Tom Burford. Graham maintained an extremely close personal social relationship with Sam Grant, chief of the Grant Clinic and an interim professor of medicine, but when it came to personal care, Graham did not call upon his clinical confreres. It was a political statement he could not bring himself to make—he had a team to which he belonged and would not leave.

said he would be willing to resign on the basis of his health. Moore refused the proffered resignation.[2]

Prior to that episode, Graham's only illness requiring hospitalization was of a gastrointestinal nature, in November 1940. He was admitted with vertigo, cramps, and diarrhea, and placed under the care of Dr. David Barr, professor and chairman of medicine. He was discharged after 48 hours with the diagnosis of "acute gastroenteritis/non-specific."[3] A similar episode occurred in January 1949 during a 3-day visit to Washington, DC, as a consultant to the navy. Graham was hospitalized at the US Naval Hospital in Bethesda for 36 hours with abdominal cramps, which ended after an episode of diarrhea after he was discharged.[4] This hospitalization resulted in a disagreement about the hospital fee. Graham had refused the offer of professional courtesy by the navy, and insisted he be billed for care. Two days after returning home, he received a bill "for hospitalization and treatment from 26 January, 1949 to 29 January, 1949, a period of three (3) days at $9.75 per day. $29.25."[5] Graham picked up the error and immediately responded: "Yesterday I received the enclosed statement. Some mistake must have been made in the bookkeeping. I was admitted to your hospital on Friday, January 28 at about 6:45 p.m. I left the hospital on the morning of Saturday, January 29 at 10:00. The statement therefore is not correct that I was a patient in your hospital from January 26 to January 29. Will you please have this statement corrected and then send me a bill for the correct amount."[6] A corrected bill was sent, and payment was made.

Graham's diabetes was initially controlled by a moderate restriction of carbohydrates and a single daily injection of 45 units of PZI (protamine zinc insulin). By 1951, becoming impatient with dietary restrictions, Graham found he could eat more if he increased his insulin dosage to 60 units per day. Although he tested his urine daily, he made little or no attempt to control the details of diet. He particularly liked chocolate ice cream, and at lunch he always had a double helping for dessert, refusing to permit diabetes to restrain him from such enjoyment.[1] In order to eat what he liked, Graham gradually increased his intake of insulin from 45 to 60 units per day without adverse reactions, but in 1951, even when he ate a high-carbohydrate diet, he began to have occasional mild insulin reactions characterized by sweating and a jittery feeling that would awaken him at about 4:00 am. With restricted activity because of discomfort in his left knee, Graham took it upon himself to increase his insulin to 70 units daily.

In 1952 a painful left knee due to a suspected ligamentous tear led to a 3-day hospitalization. Compound F[b] was injected into the joint by the young orthopedic

---

b. Compound F was an isolate from bovine adrenal glands. The steroid hormones had not yet been identified and synthesized. Compound F contained large amounts of what was later known as hydrocortisone.

surgeon Richard Odell. During this admission for his knee problem, a chest radiograph revealed a compression fracture of the eighth thoracic vertebra but no abnormality in either lung field.

On February 1, 1956, because of skin infections of 6 weeks' duration, Graham was once again admitted to Barnes, this time as a patient of Dr. William Daughaday[c], the medical metabolic and endocrine expert. Then taking 55 units of NPH (neutral protamine Hagedorn) insulin daily and holding to a 2000-calorie diet, he had developed a large furuncle in the preauricular area on the right side of his face, and smaller ones on hands and posterior neck. Dr. Charles Eckert treated him with incision, drainage, and hot compresses to the furuncles in addition to 1,200,000 units of penicillin. A routine chest radiograph was obtained during this admission. Once again it showed the compression fracture of his spine, but now it was noted that the trachea was deviated to the right and "there was evidence of fibrosis (?) in the right upper lung field and fibrocalcific tuberculosis (?) in the left upper lung field."[3] It would be 1 year before the cause of these radiographic abnormalities was clarified.

CANCER

Diagnosis

Graham was an inveterate smoker. I.Y. Olch remembered that "he was smoking a cigarette all the time. The only time he never smoked was when he was asleep, when he was operating and when he was making ward rounds. . . . in the lab it was one cigarette after another. . . . In 1952 he was still smoking but by 1953 had quit." When asked by Olch, "'What gives?' Graham said he had finally decided to quit because people were ragging him so much about writing that paper on cancer of the lung and smoking he had to give it up."[7]

In the days preceding the 1956 Christmas holiday season, Graham developed a cough and experienced malaise and weakness. Initially thought to be influenza, it persisted into mid-January without remission. Consultation with Daughaday led to the performance of another chest radiograph. This time, the radiograph revealed a "mass in the left upper lobe extending outward, upward and posteriorly from the hilum and centrally to the mediastinum at the level of the aortic arch. . . . margins were . . . ill defined. All lobes of each lung were densely infiltrated with some

---

c. William Daughaday was born in 1918 in Chicago. He received his bachelor of arts degree, and then his doctor of medicine degree from Harvard in 1943. After an internship at Boston City Hospital, he became an assistant resident in medicine at Washington University, with interests in clinical chemistry. By 1951 he had been appointed director of the Diabetes and Endocrinology Research Center and Barnes Hospital Clinical Laboratories, a position he held until his retirement in 1987. He was a highly honored member of many US societies, including the National Academy of Medicine, and was recognized for his clinical investigations and research in metabolic diseases.

infiltrates being nodular in character. Mediastinum was abnormally wide." The diagnosis was "pulmonary carcinoma, primary in the left upper lobe with mediastinal metastases and disseminated pulmonary metastases."[3] Because the patient was Evarts Graham and because of the nature of the findings, an identity check was made on January 23 by a second conventional chest radiograph. Once again the diagnosis was pulmonary carcinoma.[3]

Daughaday brought the two sets of films to Graham's office and, in a short interview, broke the news that Graham had inoperable cancer of the lung. Following Daughaday's departure there was only silence in the office. After several minutes Ada Hanvey opened the door and asked if she could come in. Graham said, "I wish you would," whereupon, she asked, "Well, what does Dr. Daughaday have to say?" Graham replied, "Well it isn't good," picked up the radiographs, and, holding them to the window pane, said, "You see it is in both lungs…of course I have no future now." After being asked if there was anybody he would like to talk to, maybe Dr. Burford, Graham acquiesced, and Burford arrived shortly after being called. Before Hanvey made her exit from the office, Graham said again, "You see A.H. it's in both lungs." Hanvey did not know how to respond.[8]

Graham showed the films to his closest surgical associate, Thomas Burford, and asked Burford what he thought of them. The answer was quick in forthcoming, "This is bilateral carcinoma of the lung," whereupon Graham responded, "It is mine." To confirm the radiographic findings, Burford suggested a left scalene fat pad biopsy. On January 28 Graham was admitted to the hospital for the procedure, which was to be carried out under general anesthesia on the following day. The fat pad that was removed in fragments contained a 4 mm lymph node "almost completely replaced by undifferentiated squamous cell carcinoma. Other lymph nodes were not remarkable. s/Lauren Ackerman."[9,10]

Burford implored Ackerman to break the news to Graham: "Lauren you have to go and tell Dr. Graham. It's beyond me, I can't do it." Following this conversation, Ackerman entered Graham's room and said, "I have some bad news for you, the cytology is positive." Graham replied, "Lauren, are you sure? You have usually been right." He then paused before remarking, "You know, Lauren, that cancer must have been awfully mad at me to do this to me."[9,10]

Consultation regarding management was obtained with Dr. Edward H. Reinhard[d] and then later with Dr. Alfred Gellhorn[e]. Sixteen milligrams of nitrogen

---

d. Edward H. Reinhard (born 1913) received his doctor of medicine degree from Washington University in 1939, and, after an internship at New York Hospital, returned as a medical resident and remained on the Washington University medical faculty throughout his active years. With an interest in hematology, he was overshadowed by his chief, Carl V. Moore, but became the indispensable conscience of medical education for the department, conducting weekly medical/pathologic conferences that brought attendees from all over the city. Tall, lank, quiet, and unprepossessing, he was the quintessential internist, brilliant in all aspects of his specialty.

mustard were administered on February 1, and another 16 mg on February 2. Graham was discharged a day later with plans to repeat the chemotherapy in 4 weeks. Within 2 weeks he developed pain in the right hip; a radiograph taken on February 15 showed a destructive lesion involving the head of the femur and the right acetabulum. A repeat radiograph examination taken 1 week later showed progression of both lesions. Following betatron treatment to his hip, Graham developed spells of nausea and weakness. He was then receiving 45 units of NPH insulin daily. On the morning of February 26, while shaving, Graham became confused and weak, and had to be helped to bed. He was subsequently admitted to Barnes Hospital for the last time.

Correspondence

Three days following discharge from his scalene node biopsy, Graham began to write to friends and associates. One of his first letters was sent to Ernst Wynder:

February 6, 1957

Dear Ernie:

I suppose you have heard by this time from one source or another about the irony that fate has played on me. I think I told you a little while ago that I seem to have picked up a bad flu bug. After getting along without any particular progress for about six weeks, I decided to come in for an examination. It was found then that I had x-ray evidence of a bilateral involvement of bronchiogenic carcinoma.

An exploratory operation by Tom Burford revealed a spread to a gland in the scalenous fat pad. I am now on nitrogen mustard and rather uncomfortable because of the terrific jolt that that drug gives one.

I was very anxious for you to be one of the first ones to know about my illness because of my great interest in you and because of our long and happy cooperation in the enterprise of trying to defeat the enemy who seems to have got the best of me now.

You knew, of course, that I stopped smoking a little more than 5 years ago. Many other people know it also. Probably there will be a tendency for some to say that my case tends to negate the idea that

e. Alfred Gellhorn was born in 1913 in St. Louis, and after 3 years at Amherst received his doctor of medicine degree from Washington University in 1937. He spent 2 years as a surgical intern at Barnes Hospital before undertaking a gynecology residency at Passavant Hospital in Chicago and a medical residency at Columbia in New York City. He became dean of the University of Pennsylvania, then director of medical appointments for the New York Department of Health in Albany, before becoming director of cancer research at Columbia. Family friendships with the Grahams were present throughout his life. His mother, Edna, was one of the prominent St. Louis women who shared activist feminist interests with Helen Tredway Graham.

there is a causal connection between cigarette smoking and bronchio-genic carcinoma. By the way mine is a squamous cell cancer appar-ently like all the other smokers' lung cancers. I don't think anyone can bring up a very forcible argument against the idea of a causal connec-tion with smoking because after all I had smoked for about 50 years before stopping. It is true, however, that I never was a very heavy smoker and I seldom smoked more than 8 or 10 cigarettes per day.

This business, of course, has knocked me for a loop because I can no longer count on what the future may hold. My plan now, however, is to carry on as long as I can and as well as I can.

With best wishes,

Cordially yours,
s/Evarts A. Graham[11]

In a handwritten note in response to Charles Eckert's concern, he stated:

Of course the whole thing came as a great shock. When I was in the hospital last February under your care, the chest film showed nothing. In December I assumed that I had picked up a bad flu bug and that is why I had another exam. Also the fact that I hadn't smoked for little more than five years gave me some additional confidence that I did not have a malignant lesion. However, we have an article now in press that records some experiments in which we show that even as late as seven months after stopping the application of the tars to the skin, some mice will develop cancers. That period is probably equivalent to between five and ten years in the human. Moreover, I have smoked for 50 years and that is a pretty long time. Well I intend as much as pos-sible to take it all in my stride.[12]

On February 14 Graham wrote to Alton Ochsner: "Perhaps you have heard that I have recently been a patient in the Barnes Hospital because of a bilateral bron-chiogenic carcinoma which sneaked up on me like a thief in the night. I am taking nitrogen mustard and, as a result, feel like the devil. You know, I think, that I quit smoking more than five years ago, but the trouble was that I smoked for 50 years."[13] Ochsner replied, "It is a perfectly horrible thing to think that you have bronchio-genic carcinoma the condition for which you have done so much." He also indicat-ed his pleasure that Graham was trying nitrogen mustard.[14] To a letter of condolence from Owen Wangensteen, Graham responded that he was due to go into the hospital on March 1 for another bout of nitrogen mustard,[15] after which he telephoned Wangensteen and asked him to come from Minneapolis to St. Louis for a visit on Saturday morning, February 23. Wangensteen complied.

Graham's thoughts were not entirely self-centered and self-obsessed. In mid-February he received a letter from Dr. Laurence Farmer of New York asking for help in predicting the advances in surgery of the next quarter century.[16] Graham prepared a response to the Farmer request:

> Almost certainly within the next twenty-five years our knowledge of the exact processes involved in wound healing will be so developed that probably the period of time now expected of a non-infected wound to heal will be greatly shortened. I think this prophesy holds good, not only for wounds of the soft tissue but of bones as well.... This additional knowledge and understanding of the processes involved in the healing of wounds will also be concerned with all of those processes which we now group together under the heading of "growth". It is but an easy step apparently from growth to greater knowledge of neoplasms.... I therefore anticipate that with the assistance of large government grants really important and fundamental discoveries will be made on the chemotherapeutic control of cancer. I do not mean to imply that the job will be finished... but considerable progress should be made.... Just as some of the previously common surgical diseases have practically disappeared so I think that more of the infectious diseases which sometimes require surgical intervention will practically disappear. During my own surgical experience, for example, I have seen the common condition of post-pnemonic empyema, osteomyelitis, lung abscess, brain abscess, bronchiectasis...[17]

The letter was never completed for, at that juncture, Dr. James Gilmore walked into the office to give his condolences to his friend, physician, and acquaintance of 24 years.

Final Hospitalization

At the time of his final hospitalization on February 26, Graham was febrile (38.5°C), a condition for which he received penicillin and streptomycin. He experienced persistent shortness of breath and, 2 days later, some mental confusion and left-sided weakness. By March 1, quite short of breath, he was given 0.8 mg of digitalis and aminophyllin suppositories. In an oxygen tent with a *No Smoking* sign over the head of the bed, he remarked to Charles Underwood, one of his residents: "that is something everyone should read."[18] "The clinical chiefs took care of the 'old man' out of respect for his tremendous achievements. Dr. Carl Moore, Chairman of Medicine wrote the orders, Dr. Justin Cordonnier, Chairman of Urology put the catheter into his bladder, Dr. Carl Moyer, Chairman of Surgery started the intravenous lines.... Each day they patiently and lovingly took care of him.... the giants of medicine performed the 'art' of medicine on one of their own."[19] At Graham's request the intravenous administration of nitrogen mustard was carried out by a surgical rather than a medical resident, for he feared a venous thrombosis might break off and go to his lungs.[18] By March 2 Graham's fever was 40°C. He was unable to take oral feedings and became increasingly somnolent and occasionally unconscious. On March 4 he refused intravenous fluids, and, at 3:38 pm, Graham quietly expired. The death order was signed jointly by Drs. T.H. Burford and T.B. Ferguson.

Dr. Ferguson later wrote:

> The most striking thing in my memory of Dr. Graham concerns his last days. I had the sad responsibility, along with Doctor Burford, of caring for Dr. Graham from the time he was diagnosed as having hopeless carcinoma of the lung until the time of his death. I know little about Dr. Graham's religious background or his beliefs, but the impressive fact is that I have never encountered a man less afraid to die. From the day he was told that a positive diagnosis had been obtained at scalene node biopsy, until the end of his life, he was energetically looking toward the future: the future of the Chest Service, the future of the Surgical Department, the future of Washington University School of Medicine. He knew clearly that he had little time left and it was obvious to all around him that he spent his time getting his houses in order, never wasting a moment on reflection or self-pity. He knew that he would leave many jobs undone, but for a man such as Dr. Graham this did not seem to disturb him. For he seemed to know early in his career that there were not enough days in one lifetime to accomplish all he wanted to do.[20]

The duration of Graham's illness from the onset of symptoms to death was less than 2½ months, and from diagnosis to death was barely 6 weeks. Such rapid progression, even with carcinoma of the lung, is unusual. The rate of growth of carcinomas may be calculated from sequential radiographs that show the tumor, and this was done by John Spratt who recorded these as "doubling times[f]." Undifferentiated carcinoma of the lung has an average doubling time of 70 days. Measurements on Graham's chest radiographs showed a doubling time of 8 days[21]—the most rapid in Spratt's series.

---

f. *Doubling time* is a method that describes the rate of growth of cancers by using sequential radiographs. If two or more radiographs show a lesion, an estimate of volumes may be made. This is related to all of the radiographic examinations and plotted on a time scale. With simple calculations it is possible to estimate how many days are required for a tumor to double in size. The result is given in days. The time required to grow from 1 to 2 to 4 to 8 volumes is usually quite constant with any tumor in one individual, although doubling times vary from one individual to another.

AUTOPSY

The autopsy on Evarts Graham was begun at 4:45 pm on March 4 by Dr. Stanley Hartroft, professor of pathology, assisted by his chief resident, Dr. Walter Bauer, and witnessed by several members of the surgical faculty. At death Graham weighed 192 pounds. There were 11 primary and 27 accessory diagnoses, and the widespread character of the malignant process was quite apparent. Graham had a large mass in the upper lobe of the left lung, multiple carcinomatous nodules throughout both lungs, and involvement of peribronchial and mediastinal lymph nodes. Each adrenal gland contained two 4 to 6 mm tumor nodules, and there were several masses of cancer measuring up to 1 cm in diameter scattered throughout the liver. There was metastasic tumor in the right acetabulum and metastases to the cortex of each kidney. The renal glomeruli contained an accumulation of fibrin, with similar findings in the capillaries of the cortex of the brain[g]. Softening and degeneration of nerve fibers in the frontal cortical areas of the brain were present, and a 6 mm islet cell adenoma was found in the pancreas. There was a 3 cm enlargement of his aorta from the inferior mesenteric artery to its bifurcation. An occult carcinoma of the prostate was noted.

The death certificate was signed out as

> Myocardial Failure
> Due to: pulmonary insufficiency, 3 mos.
> Due to: widespread carcinoma of lungs
> Other: Primary bronchogenic carcinoma, left with spread.[3]

In his will, Graham left the bulk of his estate to his wife Helen, and rewarded his secretary, Ada Hanvey, with $5000.[22]

GRAHAM'S REMAINS

On the afternoon of death, in accordance with Graham's previously expressed wishes to have his body given to the Missouri Anatomical Board, his wife Helen

---

g. At the time of Graham's autopsy, the finding of fibrin thrombi in the renal glomeruli and the capillaries of the brain were merely interesting and careful observations. Twenty-five years later they were known to be characteristic of disseminated intravascular coagulation (DIC)—a state in which abnormalities of the clotting system associated with infections, malignancies, or injudicious use of chemotherapeutic agents lead to the formation of clots or fibrin thrombi throughout the capillary bed. The pattern is inconsistent, but it chiefly affects brain, lungs, heart, and kidneys. It is not a primary disease but a complication of many conditions associated with the widespread activation of thrombin. This is the most likely cause of Graham's extremely short terminal illness.

authorized its release in a "Gift of Body" document witnessed by Dr. Burford. In compliance with her wishes, his body was given by the Missouri Anatomical Board to Washington University, and received by Roy R. Peterson, professor of anatomy, on the morning of March 5. Three weeks later, on March 30, Dr. Mildred Trotter certified that Graham's body had been cremated in the crematory used by the anatomy department, and that his ashes were given by Dr. Trotter to her long-time friend Helen Graham.[23]

That evening Helen Graham, a new widow, cast Graham's ashes into his beloved Missouri River.[24] Even their two sons were not permitted to share in this final dedication[h]. Alone and in her loneliness, she parted from the man who had been her partner of 41 years, the man with whom she had enjoyed a lifetime of sharing—each in a different way, yet with common ideas, ideals, thoughts, and aspirations. Helen's final minutes with her husband were shared with no one; they were hers. There is no marker. There is no grave. His career was to be his monument. By her action in these moments of sorrow, Graham was transported *ad MARE et ad ASTRA*[i].

---

h. *Author's note*: In interviews by the author with Evarts Graham's two sons, neither offered any information about, and both denied any knowledge of, the disposition of their father's remains. Both knew there was no grave. The story relayed to the author in a letter from Shemuel Nissen in 1998 was told to Nissen by Helen Graham in 1957.

i. "To the sea and to the stars."

Chapter 21

EPILOGUE:
THE LIFE AS REMEMBERED

FORMAL REFLECTIONS

Final homage to Evarts Graham was paid on March 31, 3 weeks after he died. St. Louis was bathed in the coming of spring. One season had ended; another had begun. It was a time of renewal. Graham's life was memorialized in the Graham Chapel on the Hilltop Campus of Washington University; the grass was turning green, buds on the trees were beginning to swell, dogwood was barely showing pink, and forsythia was brilliant yellow. The starkness of winter still pervaded the bushes and trees, but a smell of something warm and soft came from the earth. The beauty of the day did homage to an almost transcendental life and helped to make the ceremony a definitive consecration.

The Graham Chapel, constructed in memory of Benjamin Brown Graham (no relation), that stands at the center of the Washington University Campus was inspired by St. George's Chapel in Windsor and Kings College Chapel in Cambridge. It is an example of Gothic revival architecture, with octagonal turrets and jagged pinnacles that point in one direction—skyward. Constructed in 1909, not only is it situated at the heart of the Washington University Campus, it is the center of its soul. Grandiose as well as classical, it helped usher in a period of Gothic construction at Duke, Yale, and other universities.[1] Washington University had been Graham's home for 38 years, and its final honoring of the man who had been so important to making it a great institution belonged in its spiritual home. It was a fitting venue, and many medical greats were among the more than 1000 people who came that day to acknowledge his distinguished career. The service was testimony to his accomplishments during the 50 years in which he had become a towering figure, not only at Washington University, but also within the surgery, medicine, medical education, and medical research of the United States and the Western World.[2]

Five speakers were chosen to present facets of Evarts Graham's life. Dr. Frank Berry[a], who opened the program on behalf of the medical services of the US Government, saw Graham as a doctor of medicine for all mankind, a master of surgery, one who ever sought and always taught the truth. He praised the rich heritage Graham had given to humanity through his own labors and through those whose privilege it had been to know him.

Dr. Joseph C. Hinsey[b] then spoke for the national academic medical world. He remembered Graham as one who had profoundly influenced the progress of surgery in his century, equalling or excelling the contributions of Halsted and Cushing. Hinsey saw him as one who had maintained a proper balance in an outstanding department, and who had contributed as much as anyone to the development of the residency system that had become commonplace. He remarked on Graham's strong social conscience, which led him out of the ivory tower to make contributions to the society in which he lived. Last, Hinsey acknowledged Graham's unusual powers of discrimination, which permitted him to separate real people from counterfeits.[2]

---

a. Frank Brown Berry (1892 to 1976), born in Dorchester, Massachusetts, obtained a doctor of medicine degree from Harvard in 1917. After a brief clinical experience at the Boston City and the newly opened Peter Bent Brigham Hospitals, he spent 1918 and 1919 in the United States Army. Graduate education included a residency in pathology at the Boston City Hospital, a residency in surgery at the Columbia-Presbyterian Hospital, and a residency and then visiting surgeon at Bellevue Hospital. Brown practiced general medicine in Providence, Rhode Island, for 2 years, and, from 1924 to 1954, he practiced surgery in New York City, finally becoming professor of clinical surgery at Columbia-Presbyterian. A colonel in the army medical corps from 1942 to 1946, he served as surgical consultant to the Seventh Army and remained in the army to retire as brigadier general in 1952. In 1954 President Eisenhower appointed him to the Department of Defense as assistant secretary for health and medical affairs, where he oversaw manpower, health, and medical affairs until 1963. A man of gentle mien and a devoted friend to all who knew him, he was a scholar who was able to translate *Theodoric* from the Latin.

Berry initiated the Dependents Medical Care Act of 1956, but he is remembered most importantly as the author of the "Berry Plan"—an arrangement developed with Harold W. Glattley and put in place in 1954 during the Korean War as an attempt to correct the inefficient and destructive draft and recruitment policies that had so decimated medical education during World War II. The program ceased with the 1973 abolition of the Doctor Draft. Graham maintained close personal ties to Frank Berry, and, after having opposed the universal draft of premedical students during World War II (see chapter 16) and the destructive nine-nine-nine policy of post–medical school training, he supported Berry's constructive efforts for drafting or deferment of premedic students, medical students, interns, and residents.

b. Joseph Clarence Hinsey was born in Autumwa, Iowa, in 1901 and was buried there in 1981. After graduating from Northwestern University with both a bachelor's and a master's degree, he served as

Graham's role at the Medical School was addressed by W. Barry Wood[c], ex-chairman of the Department of Medicine, who felt that Graham was one of the greatest men he had ever known, and that, in the Medical School, Graham was its most powerful and effective leader. In commenting on Graham's personal attributes, Wood observed that his most outstanding characteristic was positiveness, for never on any important question did Graham appear to be in doubt, and, although this gained him a certain number of enemies, it was his greatest strength. To Wood,

---

professor of zoology and biology, first at Northwestern and then at Western Reserve University. From 1924 to 1928, he was assistant professor of neuroanatomy at Washington University, obtaining a doctor of philosophy degree there in 1927. Hinsey then moved to Northwestern as a neuroanatomist for 3 years, and then to Stanford for 6 years. His final move to Cornell University was in 1936, first as professor of physiology and then, from 1939 to 1953, as its professor of anatomy. From 1942 until 1953, he was director of the New York Hospital–Cornell Medical Center, instrumental in designing the affiliation between university and hospital.

Hinsey was a towering figure on the national and international scenes of academic medicine in the 1940s to 1960s. He served with Graham as a member of President Truman's Committee on Health Needs of the Nation and as a trustee of the Sloan-Kettering Institute for almost 30 years. His most important and influential role was with the Association of American Medical Colleges as a member of its executive committee for 8 years and as its president in 1949. He was a man of immense personal talent and charm whose vision and insight into changes in medical education were felt by medical institutions throughout the United States.

c. W. Barry Wood Jr. (1910 to 1971), born in Milton, Massachusetts, showed talents as a star student and an athlete at the Milton Academy before matriculating at Harvard. There he was elected to Phi Beta Kappa, received his bachelor of arts degree summa cum laude, and was elected first marshall of his class. As an undergraduate, Wood worked with L.J. Henderson in the Fatigue Laboratory and published an honors thesis on the leukocyte response to exercise. His prowess as an athlete was equally impressive. He won 10 varsity letters: three each as center on the hockey team, shortstop or first baseman in baseball, and captain of the football team. He was the unanimous choice as All-American Quarterback in 1931. Wood's tenth letter was awarded for tennis.

Despite contrary advice from Boston Brahmin physicians, Wood attended medical school at Johns Hopkins. While there, he worked in the chemistry laboratory of W. Mansfield Clark investigating oxidation/reduction potentials. Although tempted by a career in biochemistry, he elected clinical medicine and completed a medical residency under Warfield T. Longcope. Fascinated by the pathogenesis of pneumococcal infection, he returned to Boston to study in the bacteriology laboratories of Hans Zinsser before returning to Hopkins for 2 years as an assistant in the Department of Medicine. At the age of 32, only 6 years after receiving his doctor of medicine degree, Wood was recruited by Dean Philip Shaffer and Evarts Graham to become the Busch Professor and chairman of the Department of Medicine at Washington University. During his 13 years in St. Louis, he not only attracted a group of superior house officers but also published 47 scientific papers on the host response to the pneumococcus. In 1955 he was appointed vice-president of the Medical Institutions at Johns Hopkins, then in March 1971, missing a life in research, he became chairman of the Department of Microbiology, a post he held until his untimely death.

Barry Wood constantly aimed for excellence in all things: research, teaching, administration, and sports. He knew neither hatred, jealousy, or ill-will; was reserved, unassuming, and retiring; and was gracious to high and low, making everyone feel important. Those who knew him at Washington University knew a superb clinician, a stimulating teacher, and a productive investigator. His legacy there was a strong department, a host of friends, good will, and good feelings.

Graham was uncompromising in both argument and action, and his courage was boundless; to Wood, the reputation of the Medical School was due more to Graham than to any other single member of the faculty.[2]

Wood was followed by Alfred Blalock[d], speaking on behalf of American surgery. Blalock noted that the death of Graham had removed the most widely known and most influential surgeon in the world, one who, like Billroth and Halsted, had developed a school of surgery. He commented that among surgery's most eminent men, some were noted for scientific attainments, some for ability in clinical surgery, some for attainments in stimulating students, and some for activities in important national organizations. Blalock concluded: "It was given to Dr. Evarts Graham to rank at or near the top in all of these attributes. I regard him as the most versatile surgeon this country has produced."[2]

Sir Russell Brock[e] closed on behalf of the international surgical world, calling Graham, without doubt, the most prominent figure in surgery in the first half of

---

d. Alfred Blalock (1899 to 1964) was born in Culloden, Georgia. Four years spent at the University of Georgia were followed by 4 at Johns Hopkins, with a medical degree earned in 1922. His subsequent years were unusual: Blalock was an intern in urology, an assistant resident in surgery, and extern in otolaryngology at the Johns Hopkins Hospital. In 1925, responding to an invitation by Tinsley Harrison, Blalock left for Vanderbilt University as chief resident in surgery. Although a large portion of his Vanderbilt years were spent in the research laboratory, his surgical expertise was sufficient that, by 1938, he was appointed professor of surgery. Two of these years at Vanderbilt were spent recovering from pulmonary tuberculosis in the Trudeau Sanatorium at Saranac Lake in Upstate New York. Blalock's laboratory experiments included studies of shock and the fluid dynamics accompanying a reduction in blood volume. In his studies of hypertension, he became proficient with vascular anastomoses and, at one period, was implanting the subclavian artery into the pulmonary artery to produce pulmonary hypertension. In 1941 he returned to Johns Hopkins as professor and chairman of the Department of Surgery, where Edward Park recognized that the subclavian-pulmonary anastamosis might answer Helen Taussig's quest to correct the physiologic abnormalities of the tetralogy of Fallot. This operation—the Blalock-Taussig operation—placed Blalock at the forefront of cardiac surgery.

A recipient of eight honorary degrees and the president of many prestigious surgical societies, Blalock possessed the important talents of patience, courage, and an ability to appoint, inspire, and stimulate promising young residents. A man of impeccable ethics and character, he followed Halsted, Cushing, and Graham as a member of the National Academy of Sciences. He was probably the American surgeon Graham most admired and respected. Influential in his appointment to Johns Hopkins, Graham was very laudatory about his subsequent accomplishments. The unusual nature of Blalock's educational experience and his outstanding surgical accomplishments were elements similar to those of Graham. Both were convinced that periods in the operating room were not as important as was contemplative creativity in the research laboratory. Blalock was the world's outstanding vascular surgeon of the early 1950s, with disciples and pupils heading departments of surgery around the world. Following a brief illness, Blalock died from a carcinoma originating in a ureteral stump that remained after a nephrectomy.

e. Russell Claude Brock, Lord Brock of Wimbledon (1903 to 1981), obtained his fellowship in surgery from Guy's Medical School. One year later, in 1929, as a Rockefeller Fellow, he arrived at

the twentieth century. Brock felt that Graham's surgical contributions and achievements; his influence on other surgeons; his character, distinguished presence, and ability to inspire affection, loyalty, and confidence made him a true leader of men. Brock noted, "The future of the world and of a country does not lie in leadership in the army or the navy...but in new ideas...and Graham was one of those men so gifted as to be able to give such new ideas to the whole world." He gave thanks for Graham's achievements; saluted his memory, his dignified presence, and fine manner; and ended by saying that Graham would be remembered with affection and respect. With all Graham's great attributes—his massive physique, his deep melodious voice, his slow careful speech, his warm humanity, his tolerant understanding, and his personal kindness—he still retained a modesty that contributed to the charm and respect in which he was universally held.[2]

The service was over. Everyone silently left the chapel; a few paid personal respects to his widow, Helen Graham. The sun shone as the Graham epoch finished, and all moved toward a new and different future, realizing that he had accomplished much upon which the next generation would build.

EXCERPTS FROM OBITUARIES

The many obituaries that appeared in medical journals, newspapers, and magazines (*Time Magazine* devoted a full page) testified to Graham's influence on the surgical and medical world of his day. Some were crisp, some flowery, and some personal; excerpts underscore the admiration of, respect for, and reverence in which the man was held:

A man of high integrity and deep convictions, he expected equal of others and did not hesitate to do battle with those who seemed to fall short. He was an unsparing critic of any deviation from a strict code of ethics. (C.F.W. Illingworth[3])

Graham was an enlightened and often militant liberal—a born crusader, emotionally and ethically...an unreformed Victorian....privilege and

---

Barnes Hospital to work with Evarts Graham, before returning to Guy's as Hunterian Professor of Surgery. He became president of many medical societies including, in 1968, the Medical Society of Great Britain. During the Blalock-Graham visit to England in 1947, he developed a personal friendship with Alfred Blalock in addition to reinforcing his friendship with Evarts Graham.

Lord Brock was reserved, had few intimate friends, and was the pioneer in thoracic surgery in the United Kingdom. He was disappointed not to be asked to operate upon King George VI. A firm and stern taskmaster, he expected the perfection from everyone that he demanded of himself. Brock was recognized as one of the world's outstanding thoracic surgeons. He was a surgical statesman— a spokesman for the highest aspirations of the surgical profession in England and internationally.

power implied stern responsibility. He knew no motive but interest—no criterion but success and it was inevitable that his rise to high position should foster a sense of *noblesse oblige* and that this should make men often falsely call him cold, autocratic and even ruthless. (T.H. Burford[4])

His true qualities were thoroughness, industry and an intense desire to know both sides of the question and to stand up for honest convictions. He had the durable qualities of honesty, fair mindedness and untainted ideals. (A.O. Whipple[5])

He had a feeling of tremendous responsibility that he in his position must fill. ... No situation was violent enough to disturb the simple values that Evarts Graham possessed. ... He had less interest in an idea than he did in experimental support for the idea. He was proud of the men who studied with him. (N.A. Womack and B.B. Blades[6])

He had that priceless, indefinable gift—a presence. His dignity, his near courtliness and his restrained but genuine warmth left no doubt in anyone's mind that here was the Professor. (T.H. Burford[7])

He was a man of great determination—once he reached a conclusion he was uncompromising in both argument and action. (B.B. Blades[8])

He was steadfast to his principles, open to new ideas, frank in his criticism and loyal to his friends. (E.L. Wynder[9])

At the time of his death he was widely recognized as the leading surgeon of his day. In every sense a surgical statesman and for many years the most influential voice in surgical meetings all over the world. (L.R. Dragstedt[10])

LOOKING THROUGH THE LETTERS

In an attempt to gain an overview of Graham's individual personality, I wrote to 38 people who knew him and who were still alive during the preparation of this book and asked them to give their views of Graham—not what he did, but what he was like as a person. I requested verbal impressions from 10 others. No two people saw Evarts Graham through identical eyes. Many anecdotes described what he did or said, not what he was like or who he was, perhaps because so few were permitted to know him intimately. Almost everyone saw a man of impressive physical stature, large but not fat, who was tall, straight, of imposing demeanour, and in command of the moment.

Even to intimate friends, Graham showed no trace of the mystical, romantic, or sentimental. In the Capitoline Museum, he paused before the statue *The Dying Gaul* and remarked to Carl Cori, "It is obvious that the man is dying of a traumatic pneumothorax."[7] Graham seemed incapable of being light-hearted about anything of a major scientific, political, or international matter, and he surrounded himself with people of great intellect. Although many saw him as a man with little time for humor, Evarts Jr. attempted to dispel this impression by recounting the time when a resident was given a 1-week leave for his honeymoon. At the end of the week, he sent a telegram: "It is wonderful here—can I stay another week?" Graham replied, "It is wonderful here too, come on home."[11] On noticing a woman standing in the Barnes corridor admiring his portrait, with the light bulb burned out, he wryly commented, "That is what happens at the end, they hang you up and turn out the light."[11]

Graham was simple and direct in both speech and written word; he used the English language as something that transmitted a thought, not as something of interest in itself. Even at the lunch table, he frequently dampened easy conversation by interjecting serious comments about grammar or the meaning of words into light-hearted discussions. I remember a 5-minute discourse on the difference between the St. Francis and the Sir Francis Drake hotels when we discussed an upcoming trip to San Francisco, and C. Rollins Hanlon wrote of a 15-minute etymologic harangue with a speaker at the lectern to discuss the difference between odiferous and odoriferous."[12]

There was little personal warmth between Graham and his house staff; actually, a silent fear lay beneath the great respect in which he was held. Despite the closeness of his formal working relationship with Tom Burford, at times, even Burford felt insecure; Graham depended upon Burford's professional skill but not necessarily upon his friendship. Graham acknowledged that he, like Barney Brooks, was cantankerous, frank, and tactless, and that a good argument was a favorite indoor sport. In his enjoyment of a spirited intellectual fight, he was a formidable adversary. His trait of confrontation arose several times during his career, and he freely acknowledged his refusal to tread lightly in such circumstances. As a citizen-soldier, Graham lacked the temperament to be successful in the military, for he was unable to adjust to formal authority and the chain of command.

On the American College of Surgeons Board of Regents, Graham was an aggressive, forceful, dictatorial chairman, never asking for advice; if a shy member of the board did not speak, Graham would never know his opinion. He treated many of the regents as he would medical students, sarcastically decrying their expressed opinions or attitudes. Loyal Davis was certain that Graham could not stand opposition.

Throughout all of this, Graham was devoted to his residents and his patients in his own way. He searched for excellence, was uncompromisingly honest, was unforgiving, and accepted no excuse for error. Yet he was tolerant in ways sometimes difficult to understand: Ernest Sachs was less than co-operative, Thomas Burford was a prima donna, Glover Copher a tenuous associate, J. Albert Key an unpredictable colleague, and J. Barrett Brown a selfish antagonist. Graham not only tolerated them, he supported their efforts and gained in stature because of their successes. His perspective was above and beyond the personal.

SUMMARY AND CLOSING

The closing pages of this book bring an opportunity for me, as author, to see Evarts Graham from a personal viewpoint and to take a final look. Since having lived with him in medical archives for the past 10 years, he has become an entirely different man than the one I saw upon admission to the Medical School, by which time he had already achieved international stature. In those years I knew him as someone who owned the halls of the Medical School and Barnes Hospital and who rarely spoke. Fifty years later I have had the rare opportunity to see him through the reams of paper he left behind. The experience has been a rare privilege, and to capture him in entirety has been a daunting task, for I still see the man I knew from 1938 to 1956.

Physically, I, as did everyone else, saw an imposing figure who gave directions and countenanced little difference of opinion. A man of forbidding presence and of purpose, he showed little concern for the personal feelings of others, except perhaps for his patients. For me, he extended many actions of support but no words to that effect, and I tended to avoid him for fear of condemnation. He had a remarkable intellect, an extraordinary determination, and a purpose in life, all of which were coupled with a comprehensive grasp of the surgical thought of his day. Graham was an intuitive activist with vision and the capacity to either persuade others to follow or, if necessary, to dominate or coerce. I never made up my mind in front of him for I knew I would do things his way; I always returned in a few days with my own decision. With faith in the right thing to do, Graham seemed never to be in doubt and possessed the courage to act on his beliefs. His was a pragmatic approach to getting something done, and he had an appetite for accomplishment.

I found Graham to be without humor, and it was difficult to make light conversation with him; a half-hour at the lunch table in Graham's company was a half-hour of agony. I knew him in his later life, not in his middle years, and by that time the many kudos he had received were incorporated into the power of his person. In seeing him through the intermediary of the archives, it is now possible for me to grasp the true greatness of the man and the magnitude of his accomplishments.

The surgical world was Graham's oyster, and the improvement of surgery through teaching, research, and education of the surgeon was the pearl he sought.

He was sensitive to implied slights and aggressively rose to challenges whenever and wherever he felt them. He was a force for change, and my surgical world became better because he had been a part of its making. Evarts Graham was indeed the "Surgical Spirit of St. Louis" and American surgery's "Man for All Seasons."

APPENDIX A:
CURRICULUM VITAE

Born	March 19, 1883, Chicago, Illinois
Died	March 4, 1957, St. Louis, Missouri
Married	January 29, 1916, to Helen Tredway
Children	David Tredway Graham, born 1917, Mason City, Iowa. Died 1999
	Evarts Ambrose Graham, born 1921, St. Louis, Missouri. Died 1996
	John, stillborn 1925

Education

Public schools and Lewis Institute, Chicago

A.B., Princeton University, 1904

M.D., Rush Medical College, Chicago, 1907

Intern, Presbyterian Hospital, Chicago, 1907 to 1908

Fellow in pathology and Nicholas Senn Fellow in surgery, Rush Medical College, 1908 to 1909

Assistant surgeon, Presbyterian Hospital, Chicago, 1909 to 1912

Special student in chemistry, University of Chicago, 1913 to 1914

Licensure and Certification

Licensure: Illinois, 1907; Iowa, 1915; Missouri, 1919

American Board of Surgery, 1937

American Board of Thoracic Surgery, 1948

Positions

Assistant and instructor in surgery, Rush Medical College, 1905 to 1915

Staff member, Otho S.A. Sprague Memorial Institute, laboratory of clinical research, Rush Medical College, Chicago, 1912 to 1915

Chief surgeon, Park Hospital, Mason City, Iowa, 1915 to 1917

Captain, medical corps, US Army, Chicago, 1918

Major, medical corps, US Army: member, Empyema Commission, Camp Lee, Virginia, and Johns Hopkins University, Baltimore, Maryland

Commanding Officer, Evacuation Hospital No. 34, France, 1918 to 1919

Bixby Professor of Surgery, Washington School of Medicine, and surgeon-in-chief Barnes Hospital and St. Louis Children's Hospital, 1919 to 1951

Bixby Professor Emeritus of Surgery and lecturer in surgery, Washington University School of Medicine, 1951 to 1957

Editorial Boards

Archives of Surgery, editorial board, 1920 to 1945

Year Book of General Surgery, editor, 1926 to 1957

Journal of Thoracic Surgery, editor, 1931 to 1957

Annals of Surgery, editorial board, 1935 to 1946; advisory board, 1947 to 1952; editorial and advisory board, 1953 to 1957

Honorary Degrees

LL.D.   Central College, 1927

Sc.D.   University of Cincinnati, 1927

M.S.   Yale University, 1928

Sc.D.   Princeton University, 1929

Sc.D.   Western Reserve University, 1931

Sc.D.   University of Pennsylvania, 1940

Sc.D.   University of Chicago, 1941

Sc.D.   McGill University, 1944

LL.D.   University of Glasgow, 1951

LL.D.   Johns Hopkins University, 1952

LL.D.   Washington University, 1952

LL.D.   University of Leeds, 1954

Sc.D.   Emory University, 1954

Sc.D.   New York University, 1955

Lectureships

Harvey Lectures, New York City, 1924 and 1934

Mütter Lecture, Philadelphia, 1924

McArthur Lecture, Chicago, 1926

Shattuck Lecture, Worcester, Massachusetts, 1928

Permanent Post-Graduate Committee Lectures, Melbourne, Australia, 1930

Alvarez Lecture, Atlantic City, 1930

Joyce Lecture, Portland, Oregon, 1931

Arthur Dean Bevan Lecture, Chicago, 1934

Caldwell Lecture, Chicago, 1934

Donald C. Balfour Lecture, Toronto, Canada, 1935

Judd Lecture, Minneapolis, 1937

Ernest E. Irons Lecture, Chicago, 1939

Arthur D. Hertzler Lecture, Kansas City, 1943

Lister Oration, London, England, 1947

Churchill Lecture, St. Louis, 1947

Roswell Park Memorial Lecture, Buffalo, 1949

James Ewing Memorial Lecture, New York City, 1950

Sykes Lecture, Detroit, 1951

Henry Jacob Beigelow Lecture, Boston, 1951

Dallas B. Phemister Memorial Lecture, Chicago, 1952

Annual Barney Brooks Lecture, Nashville, 1953

Nathanial Bedford Lecture, Pittsburgh, 1953

A. Murat Willis Oration, Richmond, 1953

Sir John Fraser Memorial Lecture, Edinburgh, Scotland, 1954

Jacob J. Singer Lecture, San Francisco, 1954

Rollin T. Woodyatt Memorial Lecture, Chicago, 1955

Roy D. McClure Lecture, Detroit, 1956

Awards, Medals, and Prizes

Samuel D. Gross Prize, Philadelphia Academy of Surgery, 1920

Gold Medal, Radiological Society of North America, 1925

Leonard Research Prize, American Roentgen Ray Society, 1925

Gold Medal, St. Louis Medical Society, and Certificate of Merit, 1927

Gold Medal, Southern Medical Association, 1932

John Scott Medal of the City of Philadelphia, 1937

Lister Medal for 1942, Royal College of Surgeons of England, awarded 1947

St. Louis Award, 1942

Charles Mickle Fellowship, University of Toronto, Canada, 1943

Roswell Park Medal, Buffalo Surgical Society, 1949

College Award Medal, American College of Chest Physicians, 1949

Mississippi Valley Medical Society Honor Award, 1949

Distinguished Service Medal, American Medical Association, 1950

Henry Jacob Bigelow Medal, Boston Surgical Society, 1951

American Cancer Society Annual Award, 1951

Homer G. Phillips Hospital Annual Award, 1951

Katharine Berkan Judd Award, Memorial Hospital, New York City, 1954

University of Chicago Alumni Medal, 1955

1955 Award, Alumni Association, St. Louis College of Pharmacy and Allied
   Sciences, 1956

Pittsburgh Surgical Society Award, 1956

Nu Sigma Nu Merit Degree Medal, 1956

Other Distinctions

Sent by Rockefeller Foundation to Great Britain to investigate teaching of
   surgery in British medical schools, 1922

National Research Council: Medical Fellowship Board, member, 1925 to 1939;
   Committee on Surgery, chairman, 1940 to 1946; Committee on Growth,
   Division of Medical Sciences, member, 1951 to 1954

National Board of Medical Examiners, member, 1924 to 1933

Peter Bent Brigham Hospital, Boston, temporary surgeon-in-chief, 1925

John Burroughs School, board of trustees, 1928 to 1938; president, 1930 to 1937

American Board of Surgery, founder member and first chairman, 1937 to 1941

St. Bartholomew's Hospital, London, temporary professor of surgery, 1939

Committee appointed by Secretary of War to study the Medical Department of the Army, member, 1942

Royal College of Surgeons of England, honorary fellow, 1943

Commission on Hospital Care, American Hospital Association, member, 1944 to 1945

Medical department of US Navy, honorary consultant, 1947 to 1950

Board of Thoracic Surgery, founder member, 1948

President's Commission on Health Needs of the Nation, member, 1952

National Committee on Lung Cancer, American Cancer Society, member, 1952 to 1957

Chevalier Légion d'Honneur, République Française, 1952

Medical Task Force Hoover Commission, member, 1953 to 1954

Royal College of Surgeons of Edinburgh, honorary fellow, 1954

Evarts A. Graham Oration with a medal to the orator, established by former students, 1955

Board of Scientific Consultants, Sloan-Kettering Institute for Cancer Research, member, 1955 to 1957

Los Alamos Medical Center, honorary medical staff, 1955 to 1957

Society Memberships and Offices

Alpha Omega Alpha

American Association for Thoracic Surgery, president, 1928

American College of Surgeons: president, 1940 to 1941; board of regents, member, 1941 to 1954; board of regents, chairman, 1951 to 1954; advisory council of board of regents, member, 1954 to 1957

American Medical Association, Section General and Abdominal Surgery, chairman, 1925

American Philosophical Society

American Society for Clinical Investigation

American Surgical Association, president, 1937

Central Surgical Association

Interstate Postgraduate Medical Association of North America, president, 1948

National Academy of Sciences

St. Louis Association of Surgeons, president, 1925

Société Internationale de Chirurgie, president XVI Congrès, Copenhagen, 1955

Society for Clinical Research

Society for Clinical Surgery
Society for Experimental Biology and Medicine
Southern Medical Association
Southern Surgical Association

Honorary Memberships

Des Moines Academy of Medicine, 1928
Kaiserlich Deutsche Akademie der Naturforscher, member, 1932
Chicago Surgical Society, 1933
Minneapolis Surgical Society, 1937
Association of Surgeons of Great Britain and Ireland, honorary fellow, 1938
Society of Thoracic Surgeons of Great Britain and Ireland, honorary member, 1938
Society of University Surgeons, 1939
Mississippi Valley Medical Society, 1939
Royal Society of Sciences, Uppsala, Sweden, honorary member, 1941
Sociedad Argentina de Cirujanos, honorary member, 1941
La Sociedad Medica del Hospital General de Mexico, honorary member, 1946
Société Belge de Chirurgie, honorary member, 1946
Académie de Chirurgie, France, honorary member, 1947
Greek Surgical Society, honorary member, 1947
Société de Chirurgie de Lyon, foreign honorary member, 1948
Southern Surgical Association, honorary member, 1949
St. Louis Medical Society, honorary member, 1949
Académie Royal de Médecine de Belgique, foreign honorary member, 1950
Royal Society of Medicine, England, honorary fellow, 1951
Wisconsin Surgical Association, honorary member, 1952
American College of Chest Physicians, fellow emeritus, 1952
Thoracic Society, Great Britain, honorary member, 1953
Boston Surgical Society, honorary member, 1953
American Society of the French Legion of Honor, member, 1954
Académie Nationale de Médecine, France, foreign correspondent, 1954
Buffalo Surgical Society, honorary fellow, 1954
Societas Chirurgica Danica, Denmark, honorary member, 1955
American Association for Thoracic Surgery, honorary member, 1955
Allen O. Whipple Surgical Society, honorary member, 1956

APPENDIX B:
PUBLICATIONS

1906

(With E.E. Irons) Generalized Blastomycosis. J. Infect. Dis. 3:666-682, 1906

1907

Latency of Carcinoma. Surg. Gyn. & Obst. 4:701-704,1907. Also: Tr. Chicago
   Path. Soc. 7:8-13, 1907

1908

On the Phagocytability of Pneumococci in the Sputum in Pneumonia. J. Infect.
   Dis. 5:273-278, 1908

1909

Olive-Oil for Postanesthetic Nausea. JAMA 53:2094-2095, 1909

1910

The Effect of Ether on Certain Processes of Immunity. JAMA 54:1043-1045, 1910

1911

The Influence of Ether and Ether Anesthesia on Bacteriolysis, Agglutination, and
   Phagocytosis. J. Infect. Dis. 8:147-175, 1911

1912

The Pathogenesis of the Hemorrhagic Diseases of the New-Born. J. Exper. Med.
   15:307-329, 1912.
(With R.T. Woodyatt) Alimentary Respiration: The Secretion of CO_2 by the
   Alimentary Mucosa and Its Relation to Eructations of Gas and Abnormal
   Inflation of the Stomach and Intestine. Tr. Chicago Path. Soc. 8:354-359, 1912

1913

Further Observations on the Relation of Fats to Anesthesia. Tr. Chicago Path.
   Soc. 9:49-51, 1913

1914

The Origin and Nature of Foetal Movements. Surg. Gyn. & Obst. 19:360-364, 1914

1915

The Resistance of Pups to Late Chloroform Poisoning in Its Relation to Liver Glycogen. J. Exper. Med. 21:185-191, 1915

Late Poisoning with Chloroform and Other Alkyl Halides in Relationship to the Halogen Acids Formed by Their Chemical Dissociation. J. Exper. Med. 22:48-75, 1915

1916

Late Chloroform Poisoning. Am. Year-Book of Anesthesia and Analgesia 1915. New York, Surgery Publishing Co., 1916, pp 136-151

1917

Spinal Puncture in Diabetes Insipidus. JAMA 69:1498-1500, 1917

Diabetes Insipidus as a Sequel to Gunshot Wound of the Head. Ann. Surg. 66:529-532, 1917

Toxic Factors of Some of the Common Anesthetic Substances. JAMA 69:1666-1668, 1917

Some Theoretical Considerations Concerning Chloroform. Am. J. Surg., Q. Suppl. Anesth., 31:34-38, 1917. Also: Dental Summary 37:506-514, 1917. J. Nat. Dent. Assoc. 4:733-739, 1917

1918

(With Helen Tredway Graham) Retardation by Sugars of Diffusion of Acids in Gels. J. Am. Chem. Soc. 40:1900-1917, 1918

Two Stage Prostatectomy. New York Med. J. 107:447-450, 1918

Acidosis in Surgery. J. Iowa Med. Soc. 8:130-136, 1918

An Unusual Skin Infection Due to Bacillus Mucosus Capsulatus Associated with a Bladder Drainage after prostatectomy. Surg. Gyn. & Obst. 26:394-395, 1918

Hepatitis; A Constant Accompaniment of Cholecystitis. Surg. Gyn. & Obst. 26:521-537, 1918

(With the Empyema Commission) Cases of Empyema at Camp Lee, Va., Preliminary Report. JAMA 71:366-373 and 443-448, 1918

(With Richard D. Bell) Open Pneumothorax: Its Relation to the Treatment of Empyema. Am. J. M. Sc. 156:839-871, 1918

1919

The Maximum Nonfatal Opening of the Chest Wall. JAMA 73:1934-1935, 1919

1920

Sodium Carbonate in Chloroform Poisoning. Arch. Int. Med. 25:575-583, 1920

Some Principles Involved in the Treatment of Empyema. Surg. Gyn. & Obst.
31:60-71, 1920

Importance of the Vital Capacity in Thoracic Surgery. JAMA 75:992-995, 1920

1921

Some Surgical Aspects of Asphyxia. Cinquième Congrès de la Société
Internationale de Chirurgie, 1920, Brussels, M.Hayez, 1921, pp. 425-459.
Also: Ann. Surg. 73:170-198, 1920

(With M.G. Peterman and Walter S. Priest, Jr.) The Association of Hepatitis with
Experimental Cholecystitis and its Bearing on the Pathogenesis of
Cholecystitis in the Human. Arch. Surg. 2:92-115, 1921.
Also: J. Missouri Med. Assn. 18:106-107, 1921

(With M.G. Peterman) Pathogenesis of Infections of the Biliary Tract. Tr. Am.
Surg. Assn. 39:126-138, 1921

Influence of Respiratory Movements on the Formation of Pleural Exudates.
JAMA 76:784-785, 1921

Resection of Clavicle in a Case of Tuberculosis of Sterno-Clavicular Joint, A Case
of War Surgery in Peace. J. Missouri Med. Assn. 18:104, 1921

Excision of Left Lower Lobe of Lung for Bronchiectasis.
J. Missouri Med. Assn. 18:180, 1921

1922

(With M.G. Peterman) Further Observations on the Lymphatic Origin of
Cholecystitis, Choledochitis and the Associated Pancreatitis. Arch. Surg.
4:23-50, 1922

Consideration of the Surgical Treatment of Bronchiectasis. South. Med. J.
15:639-644, 1922

(With Duff S. Allen) Intracardiac Surgery - A New Method. JAMA 79:1028-1030,
1922

Surgical Treatment of Syphilis of the Stomach. Ann. Surg. 76:449-456, 1922
Also: Tr. Am. Surg. Assn. 40:402-413, 1922

A Case of Familial Hemolytic Icterus Associated with Pulmonary Tuberculosis
and Old Tuberculosis of the Hip. Splenectomy. Cholecystectomy. Relief from
Jaundice. S. Clin. North America 2:1483-1491, 1922

Hernia of the Lung and Adenoma of the Thyroid. S. Clin. North America
2:1493-1500, 1922

A Case of Lung Abscess due to the Friedländer Bacillus. S. Clin. North America
2:1501-1514, 1922

(With J.J. Singer) The Newer Treatment of Bronchiectasis. J. Missouri Med. Assn.
19:390-393, 1923

Surgical Service. Report of the Barnes Hospital, Saint Louis, for 1920. Saint
  Louis, H.S. Collins Press, 1922, pp 48-53

1923

The Surgical Treatment of Bronchiectasis. Arch. Surg. 6:321-336, 1923

Principes qui Decoulent de la Chirurgie Intrathoracique. Presse Méd. 31:141-
  144, 1923

(With Vincil Rogers Deakin) Functional Liver Tests: An Experimental Study.
  Surg. Gyn. & Obst. 36:348-354, 1923

Recent Phases of Thoracic Surgery. JAMA 80:1825-1831, 1923

(With J.J. Singer) A Study of Thirty Four Cases of Abscess of the Lung. JAMA
  81:193-194, 1923

Pneumonectomy with the Cautery. JAMA 81:1010-1012, 1923

Lung Abscess. Surg. Gyn. & Obst. 36:719-721, 1923

Clinic on Cholecystitis at University of California Medical School, Feb. 9, 1923.
  California Acad. of Med. 1923

Clinic on Empyema at Leland Stanford Junior University School of Medicine,
  Feb. 10, 1923. California Acad. of Med. 1923

1924

A Reconsideration of the Question of the Effects of an Open Pneumothorax.
  Arch. Surg. 8:345-356, 1924

(With Warren H. Cole) Roentgenologic Examination of the Gallbladder. JAMA
  82:613-614, 1924

(With H. Deutsch) The Value of Sgambati's Reaction for Acute Peritonitis. Arch.
  Surg. 8:588-591, 1924

Principles Involved in the Treatment of Acute and Chronic Empyema. Surg. Gyn.
  & Obst. 38:466-470, 1924

(With Warren H. Cole and Glover H. Copher) Visualization of the Gallbladder
  by the Sodium Salt of Tetrabromophenolphthalein. JAMA 82:1777-1778, 1924

The Surgical Treatment of Empyema in the Acute and Chronic Stages. The
  Medical Department of the United States Army in the World War,
  Washington, D.C., Government Printing Office, 1924, 11, part 2, pp. 285-319

(With Warren H. Cole and Glover H. Copher) Roentgenological Visualization of
  the Gall-bladder by the Intravenous Injection of Tetrabromophenolphthalein.
  Ann. Surg. 80:473-477, 1924

The Possibilities of Thoracic Surgery. Ann. Clin. Med. 3:96-98, 1924

A Method for the Roentgenological Visualization of the Gall-bladder. Ann. Clin.
  Med. 3:99, 1924

Surgery of the Thorax. Abt, I.A.: Pediatrics. Philadelphia, W.B. Saunders
  Company, 1924, pp. 60-193

Alterations of Intrapleural Pressure and Their Significance (Harvey Lecture). Medicine 3:417-452, 1924. Also: Harvey Lect. 19:123-153, 1923-24

Considerations in the Diagnosis of Lesions of the Biliary Tract (Mütter Lecture) Tr. & Stud. Coll. Physicians Philadelphia 46:821-840, 1924

The Treatment of Chronic Non-Tuberculous Suppurations of the Lung. Tr. Nat. Tuberc. Assn. 20:147-149, 1924

1925

(With Warren H. Cole and Glover H. Copher) Cholecystography: An Experimental and Clinical Study. JAMA 84:14-16, 1925

Cautery Pneumonectomy for Chronic Suppuration of the Lung. Arch. Surg. 10:392-418, 1925

(With W.H. Cole and Glover H. Copher) The Roentgenological Visualization of the Gall Bladder by the Use of Intravenous Injections of Sodium Tetrabromophenolphthalein. Radiology 4:83-86, 1925

(With Warren H. Cole and Glover H. Copher) Cholecystography: The Use of Sodium Tetraiodophenolphthalein. JAMA 84:1175-1177, 1925

(With Warren H. Cole, Sherwood Moore and Glover H. Copher) Cholecysography: The Oral Administration of Sodium Tetraiodophenolphthalein. JAMA 85:953-955, 1925

Role of Surgery in the Treatment of Pulmonary Suppuration. JAMA 85:181-184, 1925

Some Fundamental Considerations in the Treatment of Empyema Thoracis (Samuel D. Gross Prize Essay). St. Louis, The C.V. Mosby Company, 1925, 110 pp

Physiology. Lilienthal, H.: Thoracic Surgery. Philadelphia, W.B. Saunders Company, 1925, pp 83-116

Acute Hemorrhagic Pancreatitis with Probably Recurrent Attacks Followed by Recovery After Operation During the Last Attack. S. Clin. North America 5:1387-1396, 1925

Cardiolysis for Chronic Mediastinopericarditis. S. Clin. North America 5:1396-1402, 1925

Cholelithiasis. Advantages of Cholecystography. S. Clin. North America 5:1402-1409, 1925

X-ray Diagnosis of Gallstones. On Cholecystographic Examination Shadows Found to be Outside of Gall-bladder. S. Clin. North America 5:1409-1411, 1925

What is Surgery? (Oration on Surgery, Southern Medical Association). South. Med. J. 18:864-867, 1925

(With Warren H. Cole and Glover H. Copher) Cholecystography: Its Development and Application (A Leonard Prize Paper). Am. J. Roentgenol. 14:487-495, 1925

Report of the Surgical Service. Report of the Barnes Hospital, St. Louis, for 1921-1922-1923. St. Louis, Advertisers Printing Co., 1925, pp 32-39

1926

(With Warren H. Cole, Glover H. Copher and Sherwood Moore) Simultaneous Cholecystography and Tests of Hepatic and Renal Functions by a Single New Substance, Sodium Phenoltetraiodophthalein: Preliminary Report. JAMA 86:467-468, 1926

Discussion on Vital Capacity in Intrathoracic Therapy. Arch. Surg. 12:280-284, 1926

(With J.J. Singer) Roentgen-Ray Study of Bronchiectasis. Am. J. Roentgenol. 15:54-58, 1926

(With J.J. Singer) The Treatment of Bilateral Lung Suppuration. Am. Rev. Tuberc. 13:225-239, 1926

Gall-bladder Diagnosis from the Standpoint of the Surgeon. Radiology 6:273-278, 1926

The Treatment of Abscess of the Lung. Ann. Clin. Med. 4:926-932, 1926

(With Warren H. Cole, Glover H. Copher and Sherwood Moore) Cholecystography: The Use of Phenoltetraiodophthalein. JAMA 86:1899, 1926

(With Glover H. Copher and Shuichi Kodama) The Filling and Emptying of the Gall Bladder. J. Exper. Med. 44:65-73, 1926

(With Warren H. Cole, Glover H. Copher and S. Kodama) Some New Phases of the Physiology of the Biliary Tract. Ann. Surg. 84:343-351, 1926

Some Recent Developments in Our Knowledge of the Biliary Tract. Brit. Med. Jour. 2:671-676, 1926

The Surgical Treatment of Pulmonary Suppuration in Children. JAMA 87:806-808, 1926

New Developments in Our Knowledge of the Gall Bladder (McArthur Lecture). Am. J. Med. Sci. 172:625-643, 1926

Editor, General Surgery. Practical Medicine Series 1926. Chicago, The Year Book Publishers, 1926

1927

Le Diagnostic des Cholécystites et le Mécanisme de Vidage de la Vésicule biliaire. Rev. Méd. Française 8:119-127, 1927

The Present Status of Cholecystography and Remarks on the Mechanism of Emptying of the Gall Bladder. Surg. Gyn. & Obst. 44:153-162, 1927

Report of the Surgical Department. Report of the Barnes Hospital, St. Louis, for 1924-1925. St. Louis, Advertisers Printing Co., 1927, pp 34-53

The Teaching of Clinical Work to the Undergraduate. JAMA 88:1379-1383, 1927

The Treatment of Pulmonary Suppuration. Ann. Surg. 86:174-181, 1927

(With Joseph W. Larimore) Diverticula and Duplicature of the Duodenum With Reference to the Importance of Cholecystitis in the Production of Symptoms. Surg. Gyn. & Obst. 45:257-265, 1927

Editor, General Surgery. Practical Medicine Series 1927. Chicago, The Year Book Publishers, 1927

Washington University School of Medicine, Department of Surgery. Methods and Problems of Medical Education, Eighth Series. New York, The Rockefeller Foundation, 1927, pp. 327-339

The Roentgenological Examination of the Gall Bladder. Canad. Med. Assn. J. 17:1019-1023, 1927

(With W.H. Cole) Simultaneous Cholecystography and Determination of Liver Function. Proc. Soc. Exper. Biol. & Med. 24:500-502, 1927

1928

The Bronchoscopic and Surgical Treatment of Pulmonary Suppuration. Am. Rev. Tuberc. 17:33-41, 1928

(With E.R. Wiese) Lipomas of the Mediastinum. Arch. Surg. 16:380-385, 1928

(With Warren Henry Cole, Glover H. Copher and Sherwood Moore) Diseases of the Gall Bladder and Bile Ducts. Philadelphia, Lea & Febiger, 1928, 477 pp.

Remarks on Carcinoma of the Lung. South. Med. J. 21:199-202, 1928

(With W.H. Cole and Glover H. Copher) Simultaneous Cholecystography and Determination of Hepatic Function. JAMA 90:1111-1113, 1928

Gall Bladder Cases. South. Med. J. 21:271-274, 1928

Report of the Surgical Service, 1926-1927. Report of the Barnes Hospital, St. Louis, for 1926-1927. St. Louis, Con. P. Curran Printing Co., 1928, pp. 34-48

Editor, General Surgery. Practical Medicine Series 1928. Chicago, The Year Book Publishers, 1928

Some Functional Tests and Their Significance. New England J. Med. 199:1-7, 1928

1929

Uses and Abuses of Cholecystography. South Med. J. 22:10-15, 1929

The Significance of Changed Intrathoracic Pressures. Arch. Surg. 18:181-189, 1929

Pulmonary Tuberculosis Combined with Carcinoma of Lung. J. Missouri Med. Assn. 26:70-73, 1929

Editor, General Surgery. Practical Medicine Series 1929. Chicago, The Year Book Publishers, 1929

The Surgical Treatment of Pulmonary Tuberculosis. J. Missouri Med. Assn. 26:583-586, 1929

Decompression of the Heart. Ann. Surg. 90:817-826, 1929

(With Duff S. Allen) Effects of Pressure on the Heart, with Reference to the Advisability of Decompression of Greatly Enlarged Hearts. Arch. Surg. 19:1663-1671, 1929

(With Duff S. Allen) Thoracoplasty and Phrenicectomy. Arch. Surg. 19:1545-1551, 1929

(With Robert Elman and Norman Arneson) Value of Blood Amylase Estimations in the Diagnosis of Pancreatic Disease. Arch. Surg. 19:943-967, 1929

(With Jacob J. Singer) Clinic Demonstrations. Arch. Surg. 19:1552-1570, 1929

The Application of Surgery to Pulmonary Tuberculosis. Proc. Ann. Meeting, Missouri Tuberc. Assn. Sept. 27, 1929

1930

Editor, Surgical Diagnosis by American Authors. Philadelphia, W.B. Saunders Company, 1930, 4 vols.

(With Franklin E. Walton and Robert M. Moore) The Nerve Pathways in the Vomiting of Peritonitis. Proc. Soc. Exper. Biol & Med. 27:712-714, 1929-1930

(With H.C. Ballon, H.M. Wilson, and J.J. Singer) Esophagus, Stomach and Heart Following Unilateral Phrenicectomy. Arch. Surg. 21:1291-1314, 1930

Editor, General Surgery. Practical Medicine Series 1930. Chicago, The Year Book Publishers, 1930

Physiological Aspects of the Lungs of Importance to the Surgeon. Lewis, D: Practice of Surgery. Hagerstown, Md., W.F. Prior Company, Inc., 1930, vol. 4, chap. 9, pp 1-26

Report of the Surgical Service. Report of the Barnes Hospital, St. Louis, for 1928-1929. pp.40-57

1931

(With N.A. Womack and W.B. Gnagi, Jr.) Adenoma of the Islands of Langerhans with Hypoglycemia. JAMA 97:831-836, 1931

The Story of the Development of Cholecystography (Alvarez Lecture). Am. J. Surg. 12:330-335, 1931. Also: Tr. Am. Gastro-Enterol. Assn. 1930, 24-29, 1931. J. Missouri Med. Assn. 28:434-438, 1931

(With Harry C. Ballon) Surgical Aspects of Cancer of the Esophagus. Ann. Otol. Rhin. & Laryng. 40:895-908, 1931

The Prevention of Carcinoma of the Gall-bladder. Ann. Surg. 93:317-322, 1931 (James Ewing Festschrift)

(With Franklin E. Walton and Robert M. Moore) The Nerve Pathways in the Vomiting of Peritonitis. Arch. Surg. 22:829-837, 1931

Observations on the Reaction of Bronchial Fistulae to Acute Infections of the Upper Respiratory Tract. Am. J. Surg. 14:382-383, 1931 (Matas Festschrift)

Lowering the Mortality After Operations on the Biliary Tract. Illinois Med. J. 60:196-202, 1931

Editor, General Surgery. Practical Medicine Series 1931. Chicago, The Year Book Publishers, 1931

1932

How Shall We Estimate the Operative Risk and Diminish the Mortality in Patients with Disease of the Biliary Tract? Proc. California Acad. Med. 2:1-13, 1931-32

(With Robert Elman) The Pathogenesis of the "Strawberry" Gallbladder. Arch. Surg. 24:14-22, 1932

(With Harry Ballon and J.J. Singer) Bronchiectasis. J. Thoracic Surg. 1:154-193, 296-326, 397-431, 502-561, 1932

Editor, General Surgery. Practical Medicine Series 1932. Chicago, The Year Book Publishers, Inc. 1932

(With Herbert A. Carlson, Harry C. Ballon and Hugh M. Wilson). Effect of Phrenicectomy Upon the Efficiency of Cough and Upon Elimination of Lipiodol from Lungs. Proc. Soc. Exper. Biol. & Med. 30:292-293, 1932-1933

1933

(With Nathan A. Womack) The Application of Surgery to the Hypoglycaemic State Due to Islet Tumors of the Pancreas and to Other Conditions (Bevan Lecture). Surg. Gyn. & Obst. 56:728-742, 1933

Estimating the Risk of Operations on the Biliary Tract by Testing the Excretory Function of the Liver. Radiology 21:191-194, 1933

(With Herbert A. Carlson, Harry C. Ballon and Hugh M. Wilson) The Effect of Phrenicectomy Upon Cough and Expectoration. J. Thoracic Surg. 2:573-584, 1932-1933

(With Maurice Berck) Principles versus Details in the Treatment of Acute Empyema. Ann. Surg. 98:520-527, 1933

Editor, The 1933 Year Book of General Surgery. Chicago, The Year Book Publishers, Incorporated, 1933

(With J.J. Singer) Successful Removal of an Entire Lung for Carcinoma of the Bronchus. JAMA 101:1371-1374, 1933

1934

The Diagnosis and Treatment of Primary Carcinoma of the Bronchus or Lung (Caldwell Lecture). Am. J. Roentgenol. 31:145-152, 1934

(With William Ehrlich and Harry C. Ballon) Superior Vena Caval Obstruction with a Consideration of the Possible Relief of Symptoms by Mediastinal Decompression. J. Thoracic Surg. 3:352-364, 1933-1934

(With Alexis F. Hartman) Subtotal Resection of the Pancreas for Hypoglycaemia. Surg. Gyn. & Obst. 59:474-479, 1934

In Memoriam - Dr. Carl Arthur Hedblom. J. Thoracic Surg. 3:553-558, 1933-1934

(With W. Arthur Mackey) A Consideration of the Stoneless Gall-bladder. JAMA 103:1497-1499, 1934

The Clinical Application of Some Recent Knowledge of the Biliary Tract (Harvey Lecture). Harvey Lect. 29:176-203, 1933-1934

Editor, The 1934 Year Book of General Surgery. Chicago, The Year Book Publishers, Incorporated, 1934

1935

(With J.J. Singer and Harry C. Ballon) Surgical Diseases of the Chest. Philadelphia, Lea & Febiger, 1935, 1070 pp.

(With Robert W. Bartlett and George Crile, Jr.) A Lymphatic Connection Between the Gall Bladder and Liver. Surg. Gyn. & Obst. 61:363-365, 1935

Editor, The 1935 Year Book of General Surgery. Chicago, The Year Book Publishers, Incorporated, 1935

1936

Primary Carcinoma of the Lung or Bronchus (Balfour Lecture). Ann. Surg. 103:1-12, 1936

(With Henry L. Cabitt and J.J. Singer) Bronchography Following Thoracoplasty for Tuberculosis. J. Thoracic Surg. 5:259-266, 1935-1936

The Islands of Langerhans (Hyperinsulinism). Christopher, F.: A Textbook of Surgery by American Authors. Philadelphia, W.B. Saunders Company, 1936, pp. 245-247

Report on the Committee to Study Further Problems of Postgraduate Surgical Education in General and the Qualifications for Specialization in General Surgery in Particular. Ann. Surg. 103:863-869, 1936

Training of the Thoracic Surgeon from the Standpoint of the General Surgeon. J. Thoracic Surg. 5:575-578, 1935-1936

(With J.J. Singer) Three Cases of Resection of Calcified Pulmonary Abscess (or Tuberculosis) Simulating Tumor. J. Thoracic Surg. 6:173-183, 1936-1937

Editor, The 1936 Year Book of General Surgery. Chicago, The Year Book Publishers, Incorporated, 1936

Foreword. Cole, W.H. and Elman, R.: Textbook of General Surgery. New York, D. Appleton-Century Company, Incorporated, 1936, pp. ix-x

Surgical Diseases of the Chest. ibid., pp. 788-855

1937

(With Wm. M. Tuttle and E.J. O'Brien) Studies on Tuberculin
Hypersensitiveness. J. Thoracic Surg. 6:544-560, 1936-1937

Samuel Gross Looks in on the American Surgical Association (Address of the
President). Ann. Surg. 106:481-491, 1937

Editor, The 1937 Year Book of General Surgery. Chicago, The Year Book
Publishers, Incorporated, 1937

1938

Graduate Training for Surgery from the Viewpoint of the American Board of
Surgery. Bull. Am. Coll. Surgeons 23:33-34, 1938

Some Accomplishments of Thoracic Surgery and its Present Problems (Judd
Lecture). Surgery 3:485-505, 1938

(With Nathan A. Womack) Mixed Tumors of the Lung; so-called Bronchial or
Pulmonary Adenoma. Arch. Path. 26:165-206, 1938 (Hektoen Festschrift)

Obiter Dicta About Hospitals and Medicine. Ladies' Auxillary of the Isabella
McCosh Infirmary at Princeton, New Jersey, June 18, 1938

Welcoming Address to Freshman Class September 21, 1938. Washington
University Medical Alumni Quarterly 2:25-36, 1938

Clinic on Bronchiectasis. S. Clin. North America 18:1189-1217, 1938

Editor, The 1938 Year Book of General Surgery. Chicago, The Year Book
Publishers, Incorporated, 1938

1939

(With Eugene M. Bricker) The Inhibitory Effect of Sulfanilamide on Wound
Healing. JAMA 112:2593-2594, 1939

Report on the American Board of Surgery. Ann. Surg. 110:1115-1117, 1939

Editor, The 1939 Year Book of General Surgery. Chicago, The Year Book
Publishers, Incorporated, 1939

(With Brian Blades) The Surgical Treatment of Intractable Pulmonary
Hemorrhage. Internat. Clinics, New Series 2,4:77-83, 1939

In Memoriam - John Lawrence Yates, 1873-1938. J. Thoracic Surg. 8:466-468,
1938-1939

The Islands of Langerhans (Hyperinsulinism). Christopher, F.: A Textbook of
Surgery by American Authors. ed. 2. Philadelphia, W.B. Saunders Company,
1939, pp. 269-271

1940

A Plea for the Earlier Recognition of Bronchiogenic Carcinoma. Frank Howard
Lahey Birthday Volume. Springfield, Illinois, Charles C. Thomas, 1940,
pp. 199-202

With How Little Lung Tissue is Life Compatible? Surgery 8:239-246, 1940 (Mayo Memorial Volume)

Aneurysm of the Ductus Arteriosus with a Consideration of its Importance to the Thoracic Surgeon. Arch. Surg. 41:324-333, 1940 (Dean Lewis Birthday Issue)

Editor, The 1940 Year Book of General Surgery. Chicago, The Year Book Publishers, Incorporated, 1940

1941

Foreword. J. Mount Sinai Hospital 7:243-244, 1940-1941 (Lilienthal Festschrift)

Two Centuries of Surgery (Address, Bicentennial Celebration, University of Pennsylvania). University of Pennsylvania, Bicentennial Conference, Studies In the History of Science. Philadelphia, University of Philadelphia Press, 1941, pp. 65-87

(With Nathan A. Womack) Epithelial Metaplasia in Congenital Cystic Disease of the Lung, Its Possible Relation to Carcinoma of the Bronchus. Am. J. Path. 17:645-654, 1941

The National Research Council Committee on Surgery. A Brief Statement of its Work. Surg. Gyn. & Obst. 72:541-542, 1941

(With Brian Blades) Pulmonary Abscess and Gangrene. Nelson Loose-Leaf Medicine, New York, Thomas Nelson & Sons, vol. 3, pp. 501-522C

(With Edward M. Kent) Experimental Observations on the Use of Drugs of the Sulfonamide Group in the Pleural Space. J. Thoracic Surg. 11:198-202, 1941-1942. Also: Medico-Surgical Tributes to Harold Brunn. Berkeley, California, University of California Press, 1942,   pp. 231-236

Editor, The 1941 Year Book of General Surgery. Chicago, The Year Book Publishers Incorporated, 1941

(With Thomas H. Burford) The Local Use of Sulfanilamide in the Pleural Cavity. J. Thoracic Surg. 11:203-209, 1941-1942

(With Brian Blades) Surgical Diseases of the Chest. Cole, W.H., Elman, R.: Textbook of General Surgery. ed. 3. New York, D. Appleton-Century Company, Incorporated, 1941, pp. 828-894

1942

American Surgery in a Changing World (Presidential Address, American College of Surgeons). Surg. Gyn. & Obst. 74:273-280, 1942

(With Nathan A. Womack) Developmental Abnormalities of the Lung and Bronchiogenic Carcinoma. Arch. Path. 34:301-318, 1942

(With Brian Blades) The Surgical Treatment of Bilateral Bronchiectasis. Surg. Gyn. & Obst. 75:457-464, 1942

(With C.B. Mueller) Influence of Hypophysectomy on the Epithelization of Wounds and on Fibroplasia. Arch. Surg. 45:534-541, 1942

Editor, The 1942 Year Book of General Surgery. Chicago, The Year Book Publishers, Incorporated, 1942

1943

Foreword. Crile, G., Jr., and Shively, F.L., Jr.: The Hospital Care of the Surgical Patient. Springfield, Illinois, Charles C. Thomas, Publisher, 1943, pp. vii-viii

Editor, The 1943 Year Book of General Surgery. Chicago, The Year Book Publishers, Incorporated, 1943

(With Jacques Bruneau) A Caution Against too Liberal Use of Citrated Blood in Transfusions. Arch. Surg. 47:319-325, 1943

(With S. Mackler) Aneurysm of the Ductus Botalli as a Surgical Problem. J. Thoracic Surg. 12:719-727, 1942-1943

1944

Indications for Total Pneumonectomy. Dis. Chest 10:87-94, 1944

The Modern Successful Treatment of Bronchiogenic Carcinoma. S. Clin. North America 24:1100-1107, 1944 (Barnard Hospital Number)

(With Edward M. Kent, Brian Blades and Anibal Roberto Valle) Intrathoracic Neurogenic Tumors. J. Thoracic Surg. 13:116-161, 1944

What Kind of Medical Officers do the Armed Services Want? Surg. Gyn. & Obst. 79:217-219, 1944

Editor, The 1944 Year Book of General Surgery. Chicago, The Year Book Publishers, Incorporated, 1944

(With Anibal Roberto Valle) Agenesis of the Lung. J. Thoracic Surg. 13:345-356, 1944

1945

Have the Armed Services Crippled Medical Education? The Saturday Evening Post, January 27, 1945, p. 34 ff.

(With Nathan A. Womack) The Problem of So-called Bronchial Adenoma. J. Thoracic Surg. 14:106-119, 1945

Medical Education: A War Casualty (Commencement Address, Washington University School of Medicine). Washington University Medical Alumni Quarterly 8:147-153, 1945

(With Nathan A. Womack) The Islands of Langerhans (Hypoglycemia). Christopher, F.: Textbook of Surgery by American Authors. ed. 4. Philadelphia, W.B. Saunders Company, 1945, pp. 303-306

Editor, The 1945 Year Book of General Surgery. Chicago, The Year Book Publishers, Incorporated, 1945

1946

Chest Tumors. J. Missouri Med. Assn. 43:837-839, 1946

Editor, The 1946 Year Book of General Surgery. Chicago, The Year Book
Publishers, Incorporated, 1946

1947

Ether and Humbug (Address, Ether Anesthesia Centenary). JAMA 133:97-100,
1947

Primary Carcinoma of the Lung. Modern Medicine 15:63-65, 1947 (Special
Cancer Issue)

Chest Surgery. "The Doctors Talk it Over." New York, Lederle Laboratories
Division American Cyanamid Co., 1947, vol.6, pp. 86-93

Some Aspects of Bronchiogenic Carcinoma (Lister Oration). Ann. Roy. Coll.
Surgeons England 1:248-264, 1947

Editor, The 1947 Year Book of General Surgery. Chicago, The Year Book
Publishers, Incorporated, 1947

1948

(With Thomas H. Burford and John H. Mayer) Middle Lobe Syndrome.
Postgrad. Med. 4:29-34, 1948

Editor, The 1948 Year Book of General Surgery. Chicago, The Year Book
Publishers, Incorporated, 1948

The Work of the Empyema Commission in World War I. North Carolina Med. J.
9:5-6, 1948

(With Thomas H. Burford) Surgical Diseases of the Chest. Cole, W.H., Elman, R.:
Textbook of General Surgery. ed. 5. New York, Appleton-Century-Crofts, Inc.,
1948, pp. 875-940

Malvern Bryan Clopton, 1875-1947. Tr. Am. Surg. Assn. 66:562-563, 1948

1949

Bronchiogenic Carcinoma. Surg. Gyn. & Obst. 88:129-131, 1949. Also: Wisconsin
Med. J. 48:232-234, 1949

(With Norman C. Delarue) Alveolar Cell Carcinoma of the Lung (Pulmonary
Adenomatosis, Jagziekte?). J. Thoracic Surg. 18:237-251, 1949

The First Total Pneumonectomy. Texas Cancer Bull. 2:2-4, 1949

Surgical Diseases of the Lung. Postgrad. Med. 6:299-302, 1949

Editor, The 1949 Year Book of General Surgery. Chicago, The Year Book
Publishers, Incorporated, 1949

1950

Primary Carcinoma of the Lung. Dis. Chest 18:1-11, 1950

Considerations of Bronchiogenic Carcinoma (Churcill Lecture). Ann. Surg. 132:176-188, 1950

Changing Concepts in Surgery (Presidential Address, Interstate Postgraduate Medical Association). Postgrad. Med. 7:154-156, 1950

(With R. Leonard Kemler) Studies on the Influence of Sex Hormones on Successful Heterologous Transplantation of Human Bronchiogenic Carcinoma. Cancer 3:735-738, 1950

(With Ernest L. Wynder) Tobacco Smoking as a Possible Etiologic Factor in Bronchiogenic Carcinoma. JAMA 143:329-336, 1950

Diagnosis and Treatment of Pulmonary Suppuration. Postgrad. Med. 7:202-205, 1950

The Problem of Bronchiogenic Carcinoma (Roswell Park Lecture). S. Clin. North America 30:1259-1277, 1950

Editor, The 1950 Year Book of General Surgery. Chicago, The Year Book Publishers, Incorporated, 1950

(With R.M. Peters, A. Roos, H. Black and T.H. Burford) Respiratory and Circulatory Studies after Pulmonectomy in Childhood. J. Thoracic Surg. 20:484-494, 1950

1951

Statement by the American College of Surgeons Concerning the Drafting of Doctors. Bull. Am. Coll. Surgeons 36:14-16, 1951

Primary Cancer of the Lung with Special Consideration of its Etiology (Ewing Lecture). Bull. New York Acad. Med. 27:261-276, 1951

(With Ernest L. Wynder) Etiologic Factors in Bronchiogenic Carcinoma with Specific Reference to Industrial Exposures. A. M. A. Arch. Indust. Hyg. 4: 221-235, 1951

Some Questions about Bronchiogenic Carcinoma (Bigelow Lecture). New England J. Med. 245:389-396, 1951

Editor, The 1951 Year Book of General Surgery. Chicago, The Year Book Publishers, Incorporated, 1951

(With Martin Bergmann) Pneumonectomy for Severe Irradiation Damage of the Lung. J. Thoracic Surg. 22:549-567, 1951

1952

(With Ernest L. Wynder and Adele B. Croninger) Cigarette Smoking and Cancer of the Lung (abstr.). Science 116:521-522, 1952

(With Thomas H. Burford) Surgical Diseases of the Chest. Cole, W.H., Elman, R.:
  Textbook of General Surgery. ed. 6. New York, Appleton-Century-Crofts, Inc.,
  1952, pp. 875-940

Remarks of Evarts A. Graham at the Dinner, November 30, 1951, Honoring Him
  on the Occasion of His Retirement as Bixby Professor of Surgery. Ann. Surg.
  136:12-17, 1952 (Graham Festschrift)

Editor, The 1952 Year Book of General Surgery. Chicago, The Year Book
  Publishers, Incorporated, 1952

1953

Statement Conveying American College of Surgeons' Hospital Program to the
  Joint Commission on Accreditation of Hospitals. Bull. Am. Coll. Surgeons
  38:116-118, 1953

(With Ernest L. Wynder and Adele B. Croninger) Experimental Production of
  Carcinoma with Cigarette Tar. Cancer Res. 13:855-864, 1953

Editor, The 1953 Year Book of General Surgery. 1953-1954 Year Book Series,
  Chicago, The Year Book Publishers, Incorporated, 1953

The Right to Health: A New Concept. St. Louis Post-Dispatch, Seventy-Fifth
  Anniversary Supplement, December 13, 1953, p. 30

1954

Introduction, Section on Lungs. Surgical Forum 1953, 4:233, 1954

(With F. Goldman) The Quality of Medical Care Provided at The Labor Health
  Institute, St. Louis, Missouri. Labor Health Institute, St. Louis, 1954, 11 pp.

Foreword. Birnbaum, G.L.: Anatomy of the Bronchovascular System. Chicago,
  The Year Book Publishers, Inc., 1954, pp. vii-viii

Etiologic Factors of Bronchiogenic Carcinoma. Proceedings of the Second
  National Cancer Conference, New York, The American Cancer Society, 1954,
  vol. 2, pp. 859-866

Remarks on the Aetiology of Bronchiogenic Carcinoma (From the Second Sir
  John Fraser Lecture). Lancet 1:1305-1308, 1954. Also: Bull. Am. Coll. Surgeons
  40:128-133, 1955

Foreword. Ochsner, A.: Smoking and Cancer. New York, Julian Messner, Inc.,
  1954, pp. vii-viii

Foreword. Forsee, J.H.: The Surgery of Pulmonary Tuberculosis. Philadelphia,
  Lea & Febiger, 1954, p.5

Editor, The Year Book of General Surgery. 1954-1955 Year Book Series, Chicago,
  The Year Book Publishers, Incorporated, 1954

1955

Foreword. Boyden, E.A.: Segmental Anatomy of the Lungs. New York, The
  Blakiston Division, McGraw-Hill Book Co., Inc., 1955, p. v

A Brief Discussion of the Etiology of Bronchiogenic Carcinoma (Singer Lecture). Dis. Chest 27:357-368, 1955

(With Ernest L. Wynder and Adele B. Croninger) Experimental Production of Carcinoma with Cigarette Tar. II. Tests with Different Mouse Strains. Cancer Res. 15:445-448, 1955

Editor, The Year Book of General Surgery. 1955-1956 Year Book Series, Chicago, The Year Book Publishers, Incorporated, 1955

1956

Cancer of the Lung: One Disease? American Cancer Society: Cancer of the Lung, Proceedings of the Scientific Session, Annual Meeting, 1953, New York, The American Cancer Society, Inc., 1956, pp. 205-207

International Society's Cophenhagen Session in Review. Bull. Am. Coll. Surgeons 41:47, 1956

Letter to the Editor. Cancer Res. 16:816-817, 1956

A Tribute to Rollin Turner Woodyatt. Quart. Bull. Northwestern Univ. M. School 30:286-289, 1956

Vilray Papin Blair, 1871-1955. Tr. Am. Surg. A. 74:491-494, 1956

Hommage à René Leriche 1879-1955. Lyon Chir. 52:8, 1956. (René Leriche Memorial Volume)

Editor, The Year Book of General Surgery. 1956-1957 Year Book Series, Chicago, The Year Book Publishers, Incorporated, 1956

1957

The Changing Character of Surgery and the Implications of Those Changes for this Society (Presidential Address, XVI Congress, International Surgical Society). Seizième Congrès de la Société Internationale de Chirurgie, 1955, Brussels, Imprimerie Médicale et Scientifique, 1957, pp. 260-269

A Brief Account of the Development of Thoracic Surgery and Some of its Consequences (Woodyatt Lecture). Surg. Gyn. & Obst. 104:241-250, 1957

(With Adele B. Croninger and Ernest L. Wynder) Experimental Production of Carcinoma with Cigarette Tar. III. Occurrence of Cancer After Prolonged Latent Period Following Application of Tar. Cancer 10:431-435, 1957

A Brief Account of the Surgery of a Half Century Ago and Some Personal Reminiscences. Med. Clin. North America 41:1061-1070, 1957

(With Adele B. Croninger and Ernest L. Wynder) Experimental Production of Carcinoma with Cigarette Tar. IV. Successful Experiments with Rabbits. Cancer Res. 17:1058-1066, 1957

(With V. Suntzeff, A.B. Croninger, E.L. Wynder and E.V. Cowdry) Use of Sebaceous-Gland Test of Primary Cigarette-Tar Fractions and of Certain Noncarcinogenic Polycyclic Hydrocarbons. Cancer 10:250-254, 1957

(With Thomas B. Ferguson) Physiologic Aspects of the Lungs of Importance to
the Surgeon. Lewis' Practice of Surgery. Hagerstown, Md., W.F. Prior
Company, Inc., 1957, vol. 4, chap. 9, pp. 1-22

(With Adele B. Croninger and Ernest L. Wynder) Experimental Production of
Carcinoma with Tobacco Products. V. Carcinoma Induction in Mice with
Cigar, Pipe, All-Tobacco Cigarette, and Base-Free Cigarette Tars (abstr.).
Cancer Research 18 1263-1271, 1958 (Posthumous)

APPENDIX C:
CHIEF SURGICAL RESIDENTS OF BARNES HOSPITAL– WASHINGTON UNIVERSITY (1914 TO 1954)

FRED MURPHY:
- 1914 to 1916—Omar T. Sevin
- 1916 to 1918—Barney Brooks
- 1918 to 1919—William T. Wilkening

EVARTS A. GRAHAM:
- 1919 to 1920—Edwin P. Lehman
- 1920 to 1922—Glover H. Copher
- 1922 to 1923—Bransford Adelsberger
- 1923 to 1924—Duff S. Allen
- 1925 to 1926—Warren H. Cole
- 1926 to 1927—Joe E. Gale
- 1927 to 1928—Nathan A. Womack
- 1928 to 1929—Nathan A. Womack
- 1929 to 1930—William Hamm
- 1930 to 1931—Franklin E. Walton
- 1931 to 1932—Franklin E. Walton
- 1932 to 1933—Kenneth Bell
- 1933 to 1934—Edwin Grove
- 1934 to 1935—James Pittman
- 1935 to 1936—James Pittman
- 1936 to 1937—Bradford Cannon
- 1937 to 1938—Eugene Bricker
- 1938 to 1939—George Sanders
- 1939 to 1940—Heinz Haffner
- 1940 to 1941—Samuel Harbison
- 1941 to 1942—Carl E. Lischer
- 1942 to 1943—Alfred M. Large
- 1943 to 1944—Charles Eckert
- 1944 to 1945—Gordon F. Moore, John T. Aiken
- 1945 to 1946—Gordon F. Moore

1946 to 1947—Yasuyuki Fukushima, John Modlin

1947 to 1948—Yasuyuki Fukushima, John Modlin

1948 to 1949—Robert Anschuetz, Russell Crider, Louis Knotts, Henry Schwarz II

1949 to 1950—Ben Eiseman, Paul Keller

1950 to 1951—Richard Lemmer, C. Barber Mueller

CARL MOYER:

1951 to 1952—Harvey Butcher, Mather Pfeiffenberger

1952 to 1953—Willard Walker, Merlin Kilbury, William F. Collins (neurosurgery), Marshall Conrad (Orthopedic surgery), Peter Randall (plastic surgery)

1953 to 1954—John A. Moncrief, Lawrence O'Neal, Harrison Shoulders

APPENDIX D:
LIST OF PROTÉGÉS WHO
BECAME DEPARTMENT
CHAIRMEN

Barney Brooks	Vanderbilt University
Edwin P. Lehman	University of Virginia
Warren H. Cole	University of Illinois
Nathan A. Womack	University of North Carolina
Brian Blades	George Washington University
Robert M. Moore	University of Texas
Samuel P. Harbison	University of Pittsburg
James Growden	University of Arkansas
Joseph W. Gale	University of Wisconsin
Ben Eiseman	University of Kentucky
Charles Eckert	Albany Medical College
C. Barber Mueller	State University of New York
Watts Webb	Tulane University
Charles Illingworth	University of Glasgow
W. Arthur Mackey	University of Glasgow
Ian Aird	British Postgraduate Medical School
Alfred Weiss	University of Strasbourg
Jacques Bruneau	University of Montreal
Seng Tongsprathroeth	Siriraj Medical School
Judson Chesterman	University of Sheffield

APPENDIX E: GRAHAM'S NOTE ON THE OPERATION ON JAMES GILMORE

An incision was made over the 6th rib; the rib was removed from the transverse process to the anterior axillary line. The bundle was excised. The pleura was opened and the upper lobe was found to be atelectatic. Several masses could be felt within it suggestive of infiltration with carcinoma. Although the apex of the lung was free from adhesions there were many other adhesions between the lung and the chest wall. There were particularly dense adhesions between the upper lobe and pericardium and also posteriorly between the upper lobe and the parietal pleura. The lower lobe was adherent everywhere to the chest wall. In the upper part of the upper lobe several firm nodules were felt which were suggestive of carcinomatous metastases. In attempting to separate the upper lobe from the lower lobe, it was found that the interlobar fissure was not fully developed. There were also some nodules in the upper part of the lower lobe which were suspicious of carcinomatous involvement. It was felt that not only would it be very difficult to remove the upper lobe alone but also that in doing so some of the cancer would be left behind. Consequently it was decided to remove the entire left lung. After separating the adhesions most of which required clamping and cutting followed by ligation, the pedicle was freed and a small catheter was tightly secured around it. It seemed preferable to use the soft pressure of the rubber catheter rather than a crushing clamp for this purpose, in order to preserve the blood supply as much as possible to the end of the stump of the bronchus. The idea behind this was to encourage healing of the bronchial stump as much as possible. Distal to the catheter two clamps were placed on the entire pedicle and an incision was made between them thereby cutting away the entire lung. After cutting away the lung the open stump of the bronchus was cauterized thoroughly with the actual cautery and then swabbed with 25% silver nitrate solution. The stump was then transfixed with a needle carrying a double thread of #2 Chromic catgut. This was tied securely around the whole pedicle. Another double ligature of #2 Chromic catgut was placed in a position slightly distal to the first ligature and finally a third ligature of the same sort was applied. The catheter was then removed and no bleeding from the stump occurred. The open end of the stump of the bronchus was slightly less than one inch from the bifurcation of the trachea. The aorta was plainly visible immediately posterior to the stump of the left bronchus. Because the entire lung had been removed there was no tissue available for covering over the stump of the bronchus. Two enlarged mediastinal glands which could be seen immediately below the bifurcation of the trachea were removed for microscopic examination. These however seemed soft and evidently did not contain any cancer. Because the patient's condition seemed excellent, and because it was felt desirable to obliterate the pleural space as much as possible, additional ribs were removed from the transverse processes to the anterior axillary line. The ribs removed were the 4th, 5th, 6th, 7th, 8th, 9th and 10th. Through a small stab wound a small catheter was inserted below the line of incision and carried into the pleural cavity just below the stump of the pedicle. This catheter fitted tightly so that no leakage of air at all occurred around it. The wound was then closed in layers and it was noted that the soft tissues collapsed readily into the pleural cavity. No attempt was made to suture the parietal pleura together. The sixth and seventh muscle bundles had been removed in order to give exposure but the rest of the muscle bundles were not cut away. The patient was given a blood transfusion in the Operating Room. He left the Operating Room with blood pressure and pulse the same as they had been at the beginning of the operation. The rubber catheter was connected with a longer rubber tube which was brought down to the level of some boric acid solution in a bottle in order to give air tight drainage.

APPENDIX F:
PETER DEAN OLCH

Born in St. Louis, Missouri, Peter Olch, the adopted son of I.Y. Olch, moved to Los Angeles at the age of 6. After graduating from Pomona College, he received a doctor of medicine degree from Johns Hopkins in 1955. An internship in surgery under Alfred Blalock was followed by 2 years at the National Cancer Institute, and then 2 years as surgical resident with Henry Harkins in Seattle, Washington. Deciding to switch to pathology, Olch returned to the National Cancer Institute for 4 more years and was certified in anatomic and clinical pathology. Finding this to be less than fulfilling, Olch became special assistant to the director of the National Library of Medicine for 1 year, and selected a life in the history of medicine. He then did 1 more year of study at Johns Hopkins before he returned to the National Library of Medicine as deputy chief of the history of medicine division, where he initiated its Oral History Program, with particular interest in twentieth century physicians. In 1982 Olch became an adjunct associate professor of medical history at the Uniformed Services University of the Health Sciences in Bethesda. In 1990, fascinated with the American West and Americana, he founded the Owl and Buffalo Books, featuring antiquarian books on medicine in the American Western tradition. Nearly a decade after his bout with diffuse cutaneous histiocytic lymphoma, Olch developed a facial Merkel cell carcinoma, which metastasized to his thoracic spine, partially paralyzing him before he succumbed to a pulmonary embolus.

Peter Olch was a large, always cheerful, outgoing man who easily became everyone's friend. He enjoyed people, was enamored of books, and loved the early American West so much that he began to dress in Levi trousers, leather fringed jackets, and bolo ties. One friend expressed pleasure that he was not studying Greek because he might then have come to work in a toga and sandals. Olch found his calling in medical history, only to be ravaged by a rapid spread of the carcinoma that cut short his life as a scholar. He deserved to write the Graham biography; it would have become his greatest work.

APPENDIX G:
ROBERT S. BROOKINGS

Born in Cecil County, northeastern Maryland, Robert Somers Brookings (1850 to 1932) was left fatherless at the age of 2. After remarrying, his mother moved to Baltimore, where Brookings continued irregular schooling until he was 16, completing grade eight. Despite this simple beginning, he was to become wealthy—a merchant, educator, philanthropist, and statesman. He would receive an honorary degree from each of Yale, Harvard, and the University of Missouri, and two from Washington University, one of which was doctor of medicine. Brookings was to be honored with the Distinguished Service Medal of the United States of America, the Legion of Honor from France, and the Commander of the Crown from Italy. He would become a trustee of the Carnegie Institute, a regent of the Smithsonian Institution, an advisor to the Army Industrial College, chairman of the board of the Brookings Institution in Washington, DC, and, from 1895 to 1928, president of the Corporation of Washington University in St. Louis.

There were seven major episodes in Brooking's productive career. The first began in 1866 when his brother Harry encouraged him to move to the frontier town of St. Louis to become a clerk and then a traveling salesman for Cupples and Marston, brokers of wooden ware and cordage. He spent 10 years traveling the territory that extended from Minneapolis to New Orleans and from St. Louis to San Francisco. In 4 years he was so successful that Cupples made him a partner. The two achieved a relationship in which Samuel Cupples became a friend, an advisor, an admirer, and almost a surrogate father, in place of the impoverished stepfather that Brookings had never really known. The wooden-ware company prospered, and by 1880, with Robert at the head of sales and brother Harry in charge of purchasing, the Cupples Company had been transformed from a regional to a national enterprise, with offices and warehouse depots in every major distributing center from New York City to San Francisco. The money rolled in.

In 1874 the opening of the Eads Bridge across the Mississippi River permitted eastern railroads to converge on St. Louis and to deliver goods to the many railroads that fanned out to the west. Each railroad had its own station and warehouse; therefore overland drayage was required. Brookings conceived of a union freight depot-warehouse complex that would receive, store, and trans-ship goods, avoid drayage, monopolize the east-west trade, and share in north-south river traffic. In 1882 he and Cupples began to acquire land in the area of Eighth and Spruce Streets near the western end of the Eads Bridge and the southern mouth of the tunnel that led railroads underground past St. Louis and then on to the west. Their

18 warehouses and railroad marshalling yards were collectively known as Cupples Station. More money rolled in.

An 1884 sojourn to Berlin with Nicholas Murray Butler, later president of Columbia University and Nobel laureate, enlarged his horizon, particularly for music and the arts. During his 10 years as a traveling salesman, Brookings had played the violin. It accompanied him to Berlin, where he played in front of Josef Joachim who expressed the feeling that Brookings would never make a concert violinist, an opinion to which Brookings acquiesced.

The trip to Europe awakened in Brookings the sense of an insufficient education, and, under the tutelage of Marshal Snow, dean of the City College of Washington University, he began to read literature, history, and economics. He took rooms in the home of an elderly lady named Sarah Beaumont Keim, daughter of Dr. William Beaumont, pioneer gastrophysiologist. As a cultivated woman and grand dame of St. Louis society, she became the authority that he needed to enter her world of beauty, color, texture, proportion, and sound, an experience that expanded his world of utilitarian mercantile values. She undertook the delicate task of directing him into the society to which his wealth permitted admission. He became a director of the Choral Society (precursor of the St. Louis Symphony) and president of the Mercantile Library.

At about this time, after consulting friend and mentor Samuel Cupples, Brookings decided that several (an estimated 5 to 8) million dollars was enough money, and that he should become a philanthropist. At the age of 45, he relinquished active management of both the Cupples Corporation and Cupples Station and joined his mentor as a member of the board of trustees of Washington University, a small school with its College Hall at Seventeenth Street and Washington Avenue in downtown St. Louis. It had begun in 1853 as a college without a religious denominational background, and without either the patrimony of a government or the munificence of a benefactor. When Brookings joined the board, the university claimed an enrollment of less than 200 students. Encroaching slums hemmed in the school. Brookings made plans to move it farther west.

By this time Brookings was moving in a circle composed of the industrial, financial, and social elite of St. Louis, several of whom were also members of the Washington University Corporation. William K. Bixby, of American Car and Foundry, Edward Mallinckrodt Sr., owner of a chemical plant, Robert McKittrick Jones, a financier, and Aldophus Busch, who had brewery interests, became his partners in the Washington University enterprise. As president of the corporation, Brookings enlisted their money as well as much of his own fortune to move the campus to a hill in western St. Louis overlooking Forest Park. It now enjoys a magnificent view of downtown St. Louis and the Arch that has become the city's symbol.

The 1909 visit of Abraham Flexner forced Brookings to turn his attention and philanthropy from developments on the hill to developments at the eastern edge of Forest Park—the Washington University Medical School campus. His association with Rockefeller and Flexner, as well as his many acquaintances in St. Louis, financed the growth and development of an ideal medical school that was planned to rank with Harvard and Johns Hopkins. Brookings and his colleagues shaped the external arrangements of the school, while Philip Shaffer's ideas and unwavering support shaped the internal administrative and faculty arrangements. A dozen years later, Evarts Graham gave international visibility to the enterprise and brought an aura of greatness to the school that Brookings had built.

World War I brought Brookings an invitation from President Wilson to go to Washington, DC, as one of a three-man War Industries Board headed by Bernard Baruch. Brookings became chairman of its Price Fixing Committee (price controls), something that was totally antagonistic to the open market and laissez faire aspect of his mercantile world. It changed him in many ways, among which was a recognition of the need for education in the service of government. By 1916 he was instrumental in forming an Institute for Government Research. Remaining in Washington after the war, in 1922 he organized an Institute of Economics to permit individuals to gain experience and instruction in applied economics and applied politics. His third effort was to establish the Graduate School of Economics and Government at Washington University, in which students would spend 2 years in St. Louis and 1 year at the institutes in Washington, DC. His Washington, DC, efforts were soon separated from Washington University, and the Robert Brookings Graduate School of Economics and Government was established in Washington, DC. In 1927 the two institutes and the graduate school were amalgamated as the Brookings Institution, with Robert Brookings as chairman of its board of trustees, its intellectual spirit, and its major financial contributor. It has become an institution that receives scholars from around the world who study the inter-relationships of economics and government, and it remains a major resource for the US Congress.

At 77 years of age, Brookings turned to his friend Isabel Vallé January, a woman whom he first met when she was a child of 8, almost 40 years prior, and persuaded her to marry him. He was a man of business, industry, and finance, and she was a woman of the spirit, of mysticism, gentleness, tenderness, and compassion. On June 19, 1927, he informed his housekeeper and cook, Etta Cayse, that he would be bringing a friend home for lunch the following day—the friend turned out to be Isabel, his bride of 24 hours.

Brookings continued to write about the obligations of government, the restructuring of society, the nature of the worker in an industrialized world, and the obligations of philanthropy. Isabel nursed him through periods of congestive heart failure and finally blindness, caring for him until he died at his home in Washington, DC, on November 15, 1932.

Under the guidance of a businessman who had climbed the ladder of success as an itinerant wooden-ware salesman to become a millionaire in the warehouse terminal business, Washington University was revitalized. The School of Medicine was prepared to become one of the leaders in American medical education, and the United States was given an institute of international renown. Brookings left behind an estate of less than $400,000, having given away more than 90 to 95 percent of his fortune and being sorry there was not more to give. His major gift, however, probably was not the gift of money but, rather, the gift of a creative intellectual spirit coupled with vision, ardor, executive powers, and consummate business talents. It was philanthropy at its finest.

REFERENCES

CHAPTER 2

1. Moncreiffe, Sir Iain of that Ilk. The Highland clans. Revised ed. New York: Clarkson N. Potter, Inc.; 1982.
2. American Historical Genealogy Society. Graham, E.A. 1927. St. Louis: Washington University School of Medicine—BML.
3. Oxford Universal Dictionary. 3rd ed. Oxford: Clarendon Press; 1955. p. 1668.
4. Fraser GM. People of the marches: hands across the border. In: Fraser GM, editor. The steel bonnets: the story of the Anglo-Scottish border reivers. London: Collins Harvill; 1989. p. 68.
5. Fraser GM. Malefactors of the name of Graham. In: Fraser GM, editor. The steel bonnets: the story of the Anglo-Scottish border reivers. London: Collins Harvill; 1989. p. 366–373.
6. Kell KT, Graham PJ. David Graham of Chester County, South Carolina and his descendents. Bethesda (MD): KT Kell and PJ Graham; 1990.
7. Records of the Office of the Adjuvant General United States Army, 1775–1917. Record Group 94.
8. Silver HM. Surgery in Bellevue Hospital fifty years ago. Med J Record 1924; 120:551–557.
9. Starr RJ. Harper's University: the beginnings. Chicago: University of Chicago Press; 1966. p. 17.
10. Bates ME to EA Graham [letter], 1950 Jul 18. St. Louis: Washington University School of Medicine—BML.
11. Herrick JB. Memories of eighty years. Chicago: University of Chicago Press; 1949. p. 237–238.
12. Dragstedt LR. Evarts Ambrose Graham Mar 19 1883–Mar 4 1957. Bibliographical memoirs XLVII. New York: New York Academy of Sciences; 1976. p. 221–231.
13. Graham EA to E Churchill [letter], 1951 Sep 4. St. Louis: Washington University School of Medicine—BML.
14. Blech G to EA Graham [letter], 1938 Jan 1. St. Louis: Washington University School of Medicine—BML.
15. Johnson CB. Sixty years in medical harness. New York: Medical Life Press; 1926. p. 325.
16. McMillan MH. Mrs. David W. Graham. Am J Nurs 1932;32:65–66.
17. The Presbyterian Hospital of the City of Chicago. Bulletin. 1948;40:6–8.
18. Levinson SA to EA Graham [letter], 1949 Jan 25. St. Louis: Washington University School of Medicine—BML.
19. Graham E Jr in conversation with CB Mueller, 1994 Mar 23. St. Louis: Washington University School of Medicine—BML.

The Bernard Becker Medical Library of the Washington University School of Medicine is designated by BML.

20. Graham EA to Editor, St. Louis Post-Dispatch [letter], 1945 Jul 19. St. Louis: Washington University School of Medicine—BML.

21. Graham EA to AC Deakins [letter], 1953 Nov 6. St. Louis: Washington University School of Medicine—BML.

22. Graham EA to GN Carman [letter], 1935 Mar 28. St. Louis: Washington University School of Medicine—BML.

23. Veysey LR. The emergence of the American university. Chicago: University of Chicago Press; 1970. p. 52, 242.

24. Churchill ED. Evarts Graham: early years and the hegira. Ann Surg 1952;136:3–17.

25. Wilson W to EA Graham [letter], 1903 Mar 17. St. Louis: Washington University School of Medicine—BML.

26. Irons EE. The story of Rush Medical College. Chicago: Rush Medical College; 1953. p. 34–36.

27. Bonner TN. Medicine in Chicago, 1850–1950. Madison: The American History Research Center; 1957.

28. McLean FC. University of Chicago, history and development of medicine in the Division of Biological Sciences. New York: The Rockefeller Foundation; 1931.

29. Meyer AB to PD Olch [letter], 1984 Mar 1. St. Louis: Washington University School of Medicine—BML.

30. Womack N in an interview with PD Olch, 1971 Dec 9. St. Louis: Washington University School of Medicine—BML.

31. Irons EE, Graham EA. Generalized blastomycosis. J Infect Dis 1906;3:666–682.

32. Graham EA. Latency of carcinoma. Surg Gynecol Obstet 1907;4:701–704.

33. Davis L. Fellowship of surgeons. History of the American College of Surgeons. Chicago: American College of Surgeons; 1973. p. 205.

34. Graham EA. On the phagocytability of pneumococci in the sputum of pneumonia. J Infect Dis 1908;5:273–278.

35. Graham EA. The effect of ether on certain processes of immunity. JAMA 1910;54:1043–1045.

36. Graham EA. The influence of ether and ether anesthesia on bacteriolysis, agglutination and phagocytosis. J Infect Dis 1911;8:147–175.

37. Graham EA. Olive oil for post anesthetic nausea. JAMA 1909;53:2094–2095.

38. Graham EA. Some theoretical considerations concerning chloroform. Anesthesia 1917;31:34–38.

39. Shedd DP, De Lacure MD. Nicholas Senn: outrider of modern head and neck oncology. Bull Am Coll Surg 1996;81:16–24.

40. Graham EA to ED Churchill [letter], 1951 Sep 4. St. Louis: Washington University School of Medicine—BML.

41. David VC to HN Harkins [letter], 1952 Apr 14. St. Louis: Washington University School of Medicine—BML.

42. Graham EA. A tribute to Rollin Turner Woodyatt. Northwestern University Medical School Quarterly Bulletin 1956;30:286–289.

43. Graham EA. The pathogenesis of the hemorrhagic diseases of the new-born. J Exp Med 1912;15:307–329.

44. Graham EA. Late poisoning with chloroform and other alkyl halides in relationship to the halogen acids formed by their chemical dissociation. J Exp Med 1915; 22:48–75.

45. Olch PD. Evarts A. Graham: pivotal figure in American surgery. Perspect Biol Med 1983;26:472–484.

Additional Reading

Hyde FE. The hospitals of the city of New York. The Sanitarian 1873;1:337–353.

Ludmerer KM. Learning to heal. New York: Basic Books Inc.; 1985. p. 193–198.

Macrory P. The seige of Derry. Oxford: Oxford University Press; 1988. p. 94.

New York University Alumni Catalogue. Vol. III. Medical Alumni 1842–1907. New York: New York University; 1908.

Starr RJ. Harper's University: the beginnings. A history of the University of Chicago. Chicago: University of Chicago Press; 1966. p. 142.

CHAPTER 3

1. Brenton HL in an interview with CF Starr, undated. St. Louis: Washington University School of Medicine—BML.

2. New Surgeon in Chief for Park Hospital. Dr. E.A. Graham is here. Mason City Morning Times 1915 Apr 30.

3. Minutes of Park Hospital Building Co., 1917 Mar 19. Mason City (IA): Park Hospital Building Company; 1917.

4. Minutes of Park Hospital Building Co., 1917 Sep 17. Mason City (IA): Park Hospital Building Company; 1917.

5. Long WE to EA Graham [letter], 1934 Apr 30. St. Louis: Washington University School of Medicine—BML.

6. Graham EA to E Childers [letter], 1952. St. Louis: Washington University School of Medicine—BML.

7. MacGregor JK to PD Olch, 1989 Jan 23. St. Louis: Washington University School of Medicine—BML.

8. Mason City. Now a medical center. Mason City Daily Globe Gazette 1916 May 24; Supplement.

9. Graham EA. Spinal puncture in diabetes insipidus. JAMA 1917;69:1498–1500.

10. Graham EA. Diabetes insipidus as sequel to a gunshot wound of the head. Ann Surg 1917;66:529–531.

11. Graham EA. Toxic factors of some of the common anesthetic substances JAMA 1917; 69:1666–1669.

12. Graham EA. Some theoretical considerations concerning chloroform. J Natl Dent Assoc 1917;4:738–739.

13. Forty physicians attend meeting of medical society. Mason City Morning Times 1916 Jan 26.

14. Cerro Gordo medics place ban on fee splitting. Mason City Morning Times 1916 Nov 29.

15. Speaking of operations. Mason City Morning Times 1916 Dec 2.

16. Medics have big meeting. Mason City Daily Globe Gazette 1916 Dec 29.

17. Dr. E.A. Graham to succeed Egloff on northern Iowa branch. Mason City Daily Globe Gazette 1917 July 31.

18. Change in North Iowa draft board. Mason City Daily Globe Gazette 1917 Oct 30.

19. Long WE to EA Graham [letter], 1919 Dec 10. St. Louis: Washington University School of Medicine—BML.

20. Morgan HW to EA Graham [letter], 1934 Mar 3. St. Louis: Washington University School of Medicine—BML.

21. Long WE to EA Graham [letter], 1934 Dec 24. St. Louis: Washington University School of Medicine—BML.

22. Houlahan JE to EA Graham [letter], 1938 Aug 2. St. Louis: Washington University School of Medicine—BML.

23. Graham EA to JE Houlahan [letter], 1938 Aug 8. St. Louis: Washington University School of Medicine—BML.

24. Graham EA. Acidosis in surgery. J Iowa Med Soc 1918;8:130–136.

25. Womack NA in an interview with PD Olch, 1971 Dec 9. Bethesda (MD): National Library of Medicine, Oral History Section 59. 1971 OH 59.

26. Graham EA to A Kanavel [letter], 1919 Nov 10. St. Louis: Washington University School of Medicine—BML.

27. Graham EA to NA Womack [letter], 1954 Mar 12. St. Louis: Washington University School of Medicine—BML.

CHAPTER 4

1. Billings F to F Badgley [letter], 1917 Nov 5. St. Louis: Washington University School of Medicine—BML.

2. Medical Department of the United States Army in the World War. Vol I. Washington: Government Printing Office; 1923. p. 437, 456–457.

3. Bayne-Jones S. The evolution of preventive medicine in the United States Army, 1607–1939. Office of the Surgeon General, Department of the Army. Washington: Government Printing Office; 1968. p. 133, 149–155.

4. MacCallum WG. The pathology of the pneumonia in the United States Army camps during the winter of 1917–18. Monograph No. 10. New York: Rockefeller Institute for Medical Research; 1919. p. 142–146.

5. Graham EA. The surgical treatment of empyema in the acute and chronic stages. Medical Department of the United States Army in the World War. Vol XI. Pt 2. Washington: Government Printing Office; 1924. p. 3, 285–318.

6. Graham EA. Summary of report on replies to questionnaire on empyema. In: Report of the Surgeon General. United States Army to the Secretary of War, 1918. Washington: Government Printing Office; 1918. p. 352–360.

7. Gorgas W to EA Graham [letter], 1918 Apr 23. St. Louis: Washington University School of Medicine—BML.

8. Empyema Commission. Cases of empyema at Camp Lee, Virginia. Preliminary report. JAMA 1918;71:366–373, 443–448.

9. Report of the Surgeon General. Washington: Government Printing Office; 1918. p. 330–331.

10. Report of the Surgeon General. Washington: Government Printing Office;1919. p. 1089.

11. Moynihan B. American addresses. Philadelphia: W.B. Saunders Co.; 1917. p. 128.

12. Duval P. Gunshot wounds and their treatment at the front. Surg Gynecol Obstet 1919;28:1–4.

13. Dunham EK to A Kanavel [letter], 1918 Jun 10. St. Louis: Washington University School of Medicine—BML.

14. Sullivan RP to WS Halsted [letter], 1918 Jun 29. St. Louis: Washington University School of Medicine—BML.

15. Halsted WS to Sullivan RP [letter], 1918 Jul 6. St. Louis: Washington University School of Medicine—BML.

16. Graham EA, Bell RD. Open pneumothorax: its relation to the treatment of empyema. Am J Med Sci 1918;156:839–871.

17. Graham EA to his parents [81 letters], 1918 Aug to 1919 May. St. Louis: Washington University School of Medicine—BML.

18. Graham EA. A brief history of Evacuation Hospital No. 34 [handwritten notes], undated. St. Louis: Washington University School of Medicine—BML.

19. Graham EA. L'affair Fuller [notes], undated, circa 1918–1919. St. Louis: Washington University School of Medicine—BML.

20. Coutes JB, Wiltse CM, editors. The Wadham's Committee investigation. In: Medical Department United States Army in World War II: organization and administration. Washington: Office of the Surgeon General, Department of the Army; 1963. p. 145–185.

21. Emerson H. Typhoid fever in the American Expeditionary Forces. J Mo State Med Assoc 1920;17:230–232.

22. Graham EA to H Emerson [letter], 1920 Jun 15. St. Louis: Washington University School of Medicine—BML.

23. MacCallum WG to EA Graham [letter], 1919 Apr 12. St. Louis: Washington University School of Medicine—BML.

24. Darnell FP to EA Graham [letter], 1919 Feb 26. St. Louis: Washington University School of Medicine—BML.

25. Graham EA to members of Evacuation Hospital No. 34 [letter], 1920 Mar 25. St. Louis: Washington University School of Medicine—BML.

26. Graham EA to EK Dunham [letter], 1919 Sep 20. St. Louis: Washington University School of Medicine—BML.

27. Graham EA. The maximum non-fatal opening of the chest wall. JAMA 1919;73:1934–1935.

28. Graham EA. Some principles involved in the treatment of empyema. Surg Gynecol Obstet 1920;31:60–71.

29. Graham EA. Importance of the vital capacity in thoracic surgery. JAMA 1920;75:992–995.

30. Graham EA. Influence of respiratory movements on the formation of pleural exudates. JAMA 1921;76:784–785.

31. Duval P. Les données actuelles de la chirurgie intrathoracic unilaterale en plève libre. Presse Med 1922;30:409.

32. Duval P. Les pleves communiquent-elles normalment chez le chien. Presse Med 1923;68:733.

33. Graham EA. Principes qui decoulent de la chirurgie intrathoracic. Presse Med 1923;31:141–144.

34. Graham EA. A reconsideration of the question of the effects of an open pneumothorax. Arch Surg 1924;8:345–356.

35. Graham EA. Principles involved in the treatment of acute and chronic empyema. Surg Gynecol Obstet 1924;38:466–470.

36. Graham EA. Alterations of intrapleural pressure and their significance. Medicine 1924;3:417–452.

37. Graham EA. Some fundamental considerations in the treatment of empyema thoracis. St. Louis: The C. V. Mosby Company; 1925.

38. Graham EA. The significance of changed intrathoracic pressures. Arch Surg 1929;18:181–189.

39. Graham EA, editor. Surgical diagnosis. Vol 3. Philadelphia: W.B. Saunders Co.; 1930. p. 9–13.

40. Graham EA, Berck M. Principles vs details in the treatment of acute empyema. Ann Surg 1933;98:520–527.

41. Graham EA. The work of the Empyema Commission in World War I. N C Med J 1948;9:5–6.

CHAPTER 5

1. Shaffer PS. Speech in honor of EA Graham celebrating twenty years as professor of surgery, 1939 Oct 12. [Unpublished.] St. Louis: Washington University School of Medicine—BML.

2. Dragstedt LR. Evarts Ambrose Graham: biographical memories. Washington (DC): National Academy of Sciences; 1976. Vol XLVIII.

3. Graham EA to FG Murphy [letter], 1919 Sep 20. St. Louis: Washington University School of Medicine—BML.

4. Olch PD. Section three [personal notes], undated. In the possession of CB Mueller.

5. Washington University Bulletin, 1910. St. Louis: Washington University School of Medicine—BML.

6. Ludmerer KM. Reform of medical education at Washington University. J Hist Med Allied Sci 1980;35:149–173.

7. Anderson P, Hunt M. Forerunners. The earliest history: McDowell's College and Popes College. Washington University School of Medicine. The Outlook 1991; Summer:18–22.

8. Brodman E. The great eccentric. Washington University Magazine 1980;51:6–11.

9. Morrow RE. Washington University in St. Louis. St. Louis: Missouri Historical Society Press; 1996.

10. Anderson P. Before Barnes: Washington University Hospital. Washington University School of Medicine. The Outlook 1982;Autumn:18–26.

11. Flexner A. Medical education in the United States and Canada. New York: Carnegie Foundation for the Advancement of Teaching; 1910.

12. Ludmerer KM. Learning to heal—the development of American medical education. New York: Basic Books Inc.; 1985.

13. Fleming D. The "full time" controversy. J Med Educ 1955;30:398–406.

14. MacCallum WG. William Stewart Halsted—surgeon. Baltimore: Johns Hopkins Press; 1930.

15. Memorandum of agreement between General Education Board and Washington University, 1916 Jun 5. St. Louis: Washington University School of Medicine—BML.

16. Brookings RS to A Flexner [letter], 1917 Apr 5. St. Louis: Washington University School of Medicine—BML.

17. Flexner A to RS Brookings [letter], 1917 Apr 10. St. Louis: Washington University School of Medicine—BML.

18. Shaffer PA. Memorandum to members of the executive, 1917 Mar 17. St. Louis: Washington University School of Medicine—BML.

19. Graham EA to JJ Morton [letter], 1927 Jan 17. St. Louis: Washington University School of Medicine—BML.

20. Graham EA to J Fraser [letter], 1943 Dec 16. St. Louis: Washington University School of Medicine—BML.

21. Hermann H. Brookings: a biography. New York: The MacMillan Company; 1936.

22. Anderson P. Dictionary of Missouri biography. St. Louis: University of Missouri Press; 1999. Robert Somers Brookings (January 22, 1850–November 15, 1932). p. 119-121.

23. King K. Three days to remember. Washington University School of Medicine. The Outlook 1990;Summer:8–13.

24. What's past is prologue: a history of Barnes Hospital. St. Louis: Barnes Hospital Department of Public Relations; undated. St. Louis: Washington University School of Medicine—BML.

25. Ludmerer KM. Washington University and the creation of the Teaching Hospital. JAMA 1991;266:1981–1983.

26. Washington University School of Medicine—fifty years (1899–1900 to 1949–1950) and the 100th anniversary of the birth of Robert S. Brookings [printed program], 1950 Feb 21. St. Louis: Washington University School of Medicine—BML.

27. Hunt M. Historic moments; the School of Medicine celebrates its centennial next year. Washington University School of Medicine. The Outlook 1990;Fall:17–23.

28. Hektoen L to EA Graham [letter], 1919 Jul 18. St. Louis: Washington University School of Medicine—BML.

29. Graham EA to his parents [81 letters], 1918 Aug to 1919 May. St. Louis: Washington University School of Medicine—BML.

30. Eiseman B to CB Mueller [letter], 1995 Nov 9. St. Louis: Washington University School of Medicine—BML.

31. Bradley F. History of Barnes Hospital. [Unpublished.] St. Louis: Washington University School of Medicine—BML.

32. Agreement between General Education Board and Washington University, 1914 Jan. St. Louis: Washington University School of Medicine—BML.

33. Graham EA. The surgical treatment of pulmonary suppuration in children. JAMA 1926;87:806–808.

34. Sachs E. 1917–18 annual report to Barnes Hospital. St. Louis: Washington University School of Medicine—BML.

35. Murphy F. Budget for the Department of Surgery 1917–18 and 1918–19. St. Louis: Washington University School of Medicine—BML.

36. Sachs E. Fifty years of neurosurgery: a personal story. New York: Vantage Press; 1958. p. 64.

37. Bradley F in an interview with P Olch, 1971 May 5. St. Louis: Washington University School of Medicine—BML.

38. Sachs E Jr to CB Mueller [letter], 1999 Jan 26. St. Louis: Washington University School of Medicine—BML.

39. Schwartz H in conversation with CB Mueller [unedited], 1991 Dec 6. St. Louis: Washington University School of Medicine—BML.

40. St. Louis Medical Society Award of Merit, 1927 Jun 8. St. Louis: Washington University School of Medicine—BML.

41. Gradwohl RBH. Editorial. Bull St. Louis Med Soc 1927;XXI(39):9.

42. Flexner A to EA Graham [letter], 1934 Feb 23. St. Louis: Washington University School of Medicine—BML.

43. Gradwohl RBH. Editorial. Bull St. Louis Med Soc 1927; XXII(11):135–136.

44. Ball JM to EA Graham[letter], 1928 Jul 20. St. Louis: Washington University School of Medicine—BML.

45. Graham EA to JM Ball [letter], 1928 Jul 23. St. Louis: Washington University School of Medicine—BML.

46. Marriott WM to FC Rand. Memorandum with attached historical summary of university clinics, 1931 Sep 29. St. Louis: Washington University School of Medicine—BML.

47. Code and Contract Board Appointed. Wkly Bull St. Louis Med Soc 1933;Oct 10:44–46.

48. Proposed declaration of agreement between the Code and Contract Board of the St. Louis Medical Society and the hospitals, 1934 Jan 10. St. Louis: Washington University School of Medicine—BML.

49. Graham EA. A response to the proposals made by the Code and Contract Board, 1934 Jan 19. St. Louis: Washington University School of Medicine—BML.

50. Proposed agreement between the St. Louis Medical Society and Washington University Clinics, undated. St. Louis: Washington University School of Medicine—BML.

51. Rutledge JH to G Copher [letter], 1935 Nov 1. St. Louis: Washington University School of Medicine—BML.

52. Graham EA to JC Morfit [letter], 1934 Feb 2. St. Louis: Washington University School of Medicine—BML.

53. Stieger EG to PA Shaffer [letter], 1936 Nov 18. St. Louis: Washington University School of Medicine—BML.

54. Minutes of Board of Managers of Washington University Clinics, 1944 Nov 13. St. Louis: Washington University School of Medicine—BML.

55. Council of Barnes Medical Society to EA Graham [letter], 1947 May 28. St. Louis: Washington University School of Medicine—BML.

56. Thompson JW to EA Graham [letter], 1949 Dec 13. St. Louis: Washington University School of Medicine—BML.

Additional Reading

Alexander E Jr. Ernest Sachs (1879–1958): the first secretary—the power behind the throne. Neurosurgery 1986;18:115–117.

Catalogue of Washington University Medical School, 1912 Jun. St. Louis: Washington University School of Medicine—BML.

Graham EA. Washington University School of Medicine Department of Surgery. In: Methods and problems of medical education. 8th series. New York: Rockefeller Foundation; 1927. p. 1–13.

Munger DB. Robert Brookings and the Flexner report. J Hist Med 1958;30:356–371.

CHAPTER 6

1. Connaughton D. Landing a muskie: the discovery of cholecystography. In: Warren Cole, M.D., and the ascent of scientific surgery. Chicago: Warren and Clara Cole Foundation; 1991. p. 73–84.

2. Abel JJ, Rowntree LG. On the pharmacological action of some phthaleins and their derivations with especial reference to their behaviour as purgatives. J Pharmacol Exp Ther 1910;I:231–264.

3. Rowntree LG, Hurwitz SH, Bloomfield A. Experimental and clinical study of the value of phenoltetrachlorophthalein as a test for liver function. Bull Johns Hopkins Hosp 1913;24:327–347.

4. Graham EA. The story of the development of cholecystography. Am J Surg 1931;12:330–335.

5. Rous P, McMaster PD. The concentrating activity of the gall bladder. J Exp Med 1921;34:47–73.

6. Cole WH. The story of cholecystography. Am J Surg 1960;99:206–222.

7. Boyden EA. The gallbladder in the cat. Anat Rec 1922–23;24:388–389.

8. Graham EA, Cole WH, Copher GH, Moore S. Diseases of the gallbladder and bile ducts. Philadelphia: Lea and Febiger; 1928.

9. Graham EA, Cole WH. Roentgenologic examination of the gallbladder. JAMA 1924;82:613–614.

10. Riedell H Jr in conversation with CB Mueller, 1993 Dec 9. St. Louis: Washington University School of Medicine—BML.

11. Cole WH. The development of cholecystography: the first fifty years. Am J Surg 1978;136:541–560.

12. Cole WH. The development of cholecystography. J Thorac Cardiovasc Surg 1984;88:827–833.

13. Sosman MD, Whitaker LR, Edson PJ. Clinical and experimental cholecystography. Am J Roentgenol 1925;14:495.

14. Cushing H to EA Graham [letter], 1924 Nov 14. St. Louis: Washington University School of Medicine—BML.

15. Whitaker LR, Milliken GA. Comparison of sodium tetra bromo phenolphthalein with sodium tetra iodo phenolphthalein in gallbladder radiography. Surg Gynecol Obstet 1925;40:17–23.

16. Graham EA to H Cushing [letter], 1924 Nov 24. St. Louis: Washington University School of Medicine—BML.

17. Graham EA, Cole WH, Copher GH. Cholecystography: an experimental and clinical study. JAMA 1925;84:14–16.

18. Graham EA to H Cushing [letter], 1925 Sep 12. St. Louis: Washington University School of Medicine—BML.

19. Cushing H to EA Graham [letter], 1925 Sep 16. St. Louis: Washington University School of Medicine—BML.

20. Graham EA to H Cushing [letter], 1925 Nov 12. St. Louis: Washington University School of Medicine—BML.

21. Kirklin BR. Cholecystography—a general appraisal. Arch Surg 1929;16:2246–2256.

22. Graham EA to D Lewis [letter], 1929 Jun 25. St. Louis: Washington University School of Medicine—BML.

23. Lewis D to EA Graham [letter], 1929 Oct 26. St. Louis: Washington University School of Medicine—BML.

24. Graham EA to D Lewis [letter],1929 Oct 29. St. Louis: Washington University School of Medicine—BML.

25. Graham EA to BR Kirklin [letter], 1929 Oct 29. St. Louis: Washington University School of Medicine—BML.

26. Graham EA to J Fulton [letter], 1946 Jan 7. St. Louis: Washington University School of Medicine—BML.

27. Fulton J to EA Graham [letter], 1946 Jan 11. St. Louis: Washington University School of Medicine—BML.

28. Graham EA to E Mallinckrodt [letter], 1925 Jun 1. St. Louis: Washington University School of Medicine—BML.

29. Mallinckrodt Chemical Works to EA Graham [letter], 1925 Jun 11. St. Louis: Washington University School of Medicine—BML.

30. Graham EA to W McKim Marriott [letter], 1927 Nov 23. St. Louis: Washington University School of Medicine—BML.

31. Graham EA to Schering Corporation [letter], 1944 Apr 24. St. Louis: Washington University School of Medicine—BML.

32. Scott W. Sherwood Moore, M.D. 1880–1963. Am J Roentgenol Radium Ther Nucl Med 1963;90:1305–1308.

33. Graham EA to W McKim Marriott [letter], 1927 Nov 14. St. Louis: Washington University School of Medicine—BML.

CHAPTER 7

1. Graham EA. The first total pneumonectomy. Tex Cancer Bull 1949;2:2–4.

2. Blades B. Fifty years of surgical progress 1905–1955. Surg Gynecol and Obstet 1955; Suppl:163–174.

3. Graham EA. Pneumectomy with the cautery. JAMA 1923;81:1010–1012.

4. Brunn H. Surgical principles underlying one stage lobectomy. Arch Surg 1929;18:490–515.

5. Shenstone NS, Janes RM. Experiences in pulmonary lobectomy. Can Med Assoc 1932;27:138–145.

6. Ochsner A. History of thoracic surgery. Surg Clin North Am 1966;46:1358–1377.

7. Carlson HA, Ballon H. The operability of carcinoma of the lung. J Thorac Surg 1933;2:323–348.

8. Guedel AE, Waters RM. New intratracheal catheter. Anesth Analg 1928;7:238.

9. Graham EA. Discussion of Archibald. J Thorac Surg 1935;4:369.

10. Nissen R. Exstirpation eines ganzen Lungenfluegels. Zentralbl Chir 1931;LVIII: 3003–3006.

11. Haight C. Total removal of left lung for bronchiectasis. Surg Gynecol Obstet 1934;58:768–780.

12. Patient record of James Gilmore, #89475, 1933. St. Louis: Barnes Hospital Archives and Records.

13. Gilmore J to CB Mueller [letter], 1996 July 17. St. Louis: Washington University School of Medicine—BML.

14. Blades B. Presidential address—a case report and miscellaneous comments. J Thorac Surg 1958;36:285–300.

15. Lamb H. Anesthesia. In: Graham EA, Singer JJ, Ballon HC. Surgical diseases of the chest. Philadelphia: Lea and Febiger; 1935. p. 37–40.

16. Graham EA, Singer, JJ. Successful removal of an entire lung for carcinoma of the bronchus. JAMA 1933;101:1371–1374.

17. Womack N. The pathology report on J.L. Gilmore—April 8, 1933. St. Louis: Washington University School of Medicine—BML.

18. Ackerman L. The pathology report on J.L. Gilmore—Nov. 11, 1948. St. Louis: Barnes Hospital Records and Archives.

19. Graham EA to HA Carlson [letter], 1933 Apr 12. St. Louis: Washington University School of Medicine—BML.

20. Lillienthal H. Pneumonectomy for sarcoma of lung in a tuberculosis patient. J Thorac Surg 1933;2:600–615.

21. Graham EA to W Adams [letter], 1934 Apr 11. St. Louis: Washington University School of Medicine—BML.

22. White JJ. Edward Archibald and Willian Reinhoff Jr.: fathers of the modern pneumonectomy—an historical footnote. Surgery 1970;68:397–402.

23. Graham EA to EJ Simmons [letter], 1937 Sep 15. St. Louis: Washington University School of Medicine—BML.

24. Olch IY in an interview with PD Olch, 1970 May 28. St. Louis: Washington University School of Medicine—BML.

25. Blades BB. Evarts Ambrose Graham: a benign paradox. Bull Am Coll Surg 1973;58:13–14.

26. Graham EA to RC Brock [letter], 1942 Jan 5. St. Louis: Washington University School of Medicine—BML.

27. Eastwood DW in conversation with CB Mueller, 1993 Mar 6. St. Louis: Washington University School of Medicine—BML.

28. Graham EA to JL Gilmore [letter], 1935 Apr 9. St. Louis: Washington University School of Medicine—BML.

29. Graham EA to JL Gilmore [letter], 1953 Apr 7. St. Louis: Washington University School of Medicine—BML.

30. Gilmore JL to EA Graham [letter], 1933 Jul 23. St. Louis: Washington University School of Medicine—BML.

31. Habbe JE to JL Gilmore [letter], 1934 Nov 8. St. Louis: Washington University School of Medicine—BML.

32. Gilmore JL to JE Habbe [letter], 1934 Nov 10. St. Louis: Washington University School of Medicine—BML.

33. Gilmore JL to EA Graham [letter], 1933 Oct 29. St. Louis: Washington University School of Medicine—BML.

34. Graham EA to JL Gilmore [letter], 1933 Nov 6. St. Louis: Washington University School of Medicine—BML.

35. Arbuckle MF to JL Gilmore [letter], 1934 Mar 13. St. Louis: Washington University School of Medicine—BML.

36. Arbuckle MF to JL Gilmore [letter], 1934 May 12. St. Louis: Washington University School of Medicine—BML.

37. Arbuckle MF to JL Gilmore [letter], 1934 Jun 20. St. Louis: Washington University School of Medicine—BML.

38. Graham EA to E Lehman [letter], 1951 Jul 11. St. Louis: Washington University School of Medicine—BML.

39. Graham EA to JL Gilmore [letter], 1951 Sep 27. St. Louis: Washington University School of Medicine—BML.

40. Nissen R. Development of total pneumonectomy. Am J Surg 1949;LXXVIII:816–830.

41. Reinhoff WF Jr. Pneumonectomy. A preliminary report of the operative technique in two successful cases. Bull Johns Hopkins Hosp 1933;53:390-393; JAMA 1934;102:876–877.

42. Homberger F to EA Graham [letter], 1951 Sep 26. St. Louis: Washington University School of Medicine—BML.

43. Graham EA to F Homberger [letter], 1951 Oct 2. St. Louis: Washington University School of Medicine—BML.

44. Vischer AL to EA Graham [letter], 1951 Oct 22.

45. Graham EA to F Homberger [letter], 1951 Oct 25. St. Louis: Washington University School of Medicine—BML.

46. Homberger F to EA Graham [letter], 1951 Oct 30. St. Louis: Washington University School of Medicine—BML.

47. Zimmerman LM, Vieth I. Great ideas in the history of surgery. Baltimore: Williams and Wilkins; 1961. p. 536–547.

48. Graham EA to G Crile [letter], 1926 Sep 23. St. Louis: Washington University School of Medicine—BML.

49. Graham EA to WB Peek [letter], 1926 Oct 2. St. Louis: Washington University School of Medicine—BML.

50. Graham EA. The first total pneumonectomy. Reprinted in: What's new. Milwaukee: Abbott Laboratories;Feb 1950. p. 3–5.

51. Alexander J to RM Wattrous [letter], 1950 Jun 26. St. Louis: Washington University School of Medicine—BML.

52. Graham EA to J Alexander [letter], 1950 Jul 3. St. Louis: Washington University School of Medicine—BML.

53. Graham EA to F Coller [letter], 1950 Jul 5. St. Louis: Washington University School of Medicine—BML.

54. The first pneumonectomy. Time Magazine 1950;55:57–58.

55. Graham EA to F Coller [letter], 1950 Jul 7. St. Louis: Washington University School of Medicine—BML.

56. Graham EA to Editor, Time Magazine [letter], 1950 Jul 9. St. Louis: Washington University School of Medicine—BML.

57. Coller F to EA Graham [letter], 1950 Aug 3. St. Louis: Washington University School of Medicine—BML.

58. Graham EA to F Coller [letter], 1950 Aug 25. St. Louis: Washington University School of Medicine—BML.

59. Longmire WP. Two great American surgeons, each with four aces. Pharos 1983;46:9–14.

60. Alexander J. Fifty years of thoracic surgery. Am J Surg 1941;LI:217–224.

61. Brewer LA III. Historical notes on lung cancer before and after Graham's successful pneumonectomy. Am J Surg 1982;143:650–659.

62. Lindskog G. A history of pulmonary resection. Yale J Biol Med 1957;30:187–200.

CHAPTER 8

1. Graham EA to GC Robinson [letter], 1919 Sep 26. St. Louis: Washington University School of Medicine—BML.

2. Graham EA to EP Lehman [letter], 1928 Jul 3. St. Louis: Washington University School of Medicine—BML.

3. Graham EA to RS Brookings [letter], 1923 Oct 16. St. Louis: Washington University School of Medicine—BML.

4. Flexner A to EA Graham [letter], 1921 Dec 7. St. Louis: Washington University School of Medicine—BML.

5. Graham EA to A Flexner [letter], 1921 Dec 12. St. Louis: Washington University School of Medicine—BML.

6. Allen DS, Graham EA. Intracardiac surgery—a new method. JAMA 1922; 19:1028–1030.

7. Connaughton D. Warren Cole and the ascent of scientific surgery. Warren & Clara Cole Foundation. Champaign (IL): University Of Illinois Press; 1991.

8. O'Neal LW, Brunt LM. I.Y. Olch, M.D., and parathyroidectomy. St. Louis Metropolitan Medicine 1999; April: 23.

9. Nathan Womack in an interview with PD Olch, 1971 Dec 9. St. Louis: Washington University School of Medicine—BML.

10. Graham EA to GC Robinson [letter], 1924 Dec 30. St. Louis: Washington University School of Medicine—BML.

11. Graham EA to B Brooks [letter], 1926 Oct 7. St. Louis: Washington University School of Medicine—BML.

12. Graham EA to CC Bass [letter], 1926 Dec 2. St. Louis: Washington University School of Medicine—BML.

13. Graham EA to MK Eggleston [letter], 1928 Feb 16. St. Louis: Washington University School of Medicine—BML.

14. Graham EA to GC Robinson [letter], 1929 Oct 25. St. Louis: Washington University School of Medicine—BML.

15. Graham EA to RM Pearce [letter], 1930 Jan 18. St. Louis: Washington University School of Medicine—BML.

16. Graham EA to H Cushing [letter], 1931 Feb 17. St. Louis: Washington University School of Medicine—BML.

17. Bricker E to CB Mueller [letter], 1992 Feb 11. St. Louis: Washington University School of Medicine—BML.

18. Copher G to EA Graham [letter], undated, circa 1943. St. Louis: Washington University School of Medicine—BML.

19. Graham EA to G Copher [letter], 1944 Jul 10. St. Louis: Washington University School of Medicine—BML.

20. Bradley F in an interview with PD Olch, 1971 May 5. St. Louis: Washington University School of Medicine—BML.

21. Graham EA to F Bradley [letter], 1948 Feb 27. St. Louis: Washington University School of Medicine—BML.

22. Graham EA to P Hawley [letter], 1954 Jan 11. St. Louis: Washington University School of Medicine—BML.

23. Graham EA to W Cole [letter], 1944 Jan 26. St. Louis: Washington University School of Medicine—BML.

24. Graham EA to F Bradley [letter], 1941 Jun 26. St. Louis: Washington University School of Medicine—BML.

25. Graham EA to RA Moore [letter], 1946 Jan 16. St. Louis: Washington University School of Medicine—BML.

26. Ackerman L. Cancer. St. Louis: Mosby; 1947.

27. Ackerman L, del Regato J. Surgical pathology. St. Louis: Mosby; 1953.

28. Ackerman L in conversation with CB Mueller, 1993 Jan 22. St. Louis: Washington University School of Medicine—BML.

29. Hanvey A in an interview with PD Olch, 1971 Jun 18. St. Louis: Washington University School of Medicine—BML.

30. Alderson H in conversation with CB Mueller, 1994 Feb 11. St. Louis: Washington University School of Medicine—BML.

CHAPTER 9

1. Sachs E. Report to Barnes Hospital Board of Trustees 1917–1918. St. Louis: Washington University School of Medicine—BML.

2. Graham EA. Report to Barnes Hospital Board of Trustees January 1921. St. Louis: Washington University School of Medicine—BML.

3. Graham EA to A Flexner [letter], 1923 Feb 26. St. Louis: Washington University School of Medicine—BML.

4. Graham EA to RC Buerki [letter], 1936 Sep 18. St. Louis: Washington University School of Medicine—BML.

5. Graham EA. Training of the thoracic surgeon from the standpoint of the general surgeon. J Thorac Surg 1935–36;5:575–578.

6. Graham EA, Hartman A. Subtotal resection of the pancreas for hypoglycaemia. Surg Gynecol Obstet 1934;59:474–479.

7. Graham EA to L Stark [letter], 1937 Mar 4. St. Louis: Washington University School of Medicine—BML.

8. Graham EA to M Lewis [letter], 1937 Mar 3. St. Louis: Washington University School of Medicine—BML.

9. Graham EA to T Parran [letter], 1938 Sep 22. St. Louis: Washington University School of Medicine—BML.

10. Graham EA. Open letter to members of the American Board of Surgery. 1935 Oct 4. St. Louis: Washington University School of Medicine—BML.

11. Graham EA. Relationship of surgical specialties to the Department of Surgery, undated. St. Louis: Washington University School of Medicine—BML.

12. Schwartz H in conversation with CB Mueller, 1991 Dec 6. St. Louis: Washington University School of Medicine—BML.

13. Zimmerman LM, Vieth I. Great ideas in the history of surgery. Baltimore: Williams and Wilkins; 1961.

14. Graham EA, Singer JJ, Ballon HC. Surgical diseases of the chest. Philadelphia: Lea and Febiger; 1935.

15. Graham EA. Annual report to Barnes Trustees 1926–27. St. Louis: Washington University School of Medicine—BML.

16. Marriott WM to B Quinn [letter], 1932 Apr 11. St. Louis: Washington University School of Medicine—BML.

17. Singer JJ, Graham EA, Burlingham LH. A service for chest diseases in a general hospital. The Modern Hospital 1932;39:1–4.

18. Graham EA. Memorandum of conversation between F Bradley and EA Graham, 1939 Jun 8. St. Louis: Washington University School of Medicine—BML.

19. Bradley F. History of Barnes Hospital. [Unpublished, circa 1945 to 1950.] St. Louis: Washington University School of Medicine—BML.

20. Graham EA to B Blades [letter], 1935 Jul 17. St. Louis: Washington University School of Medicine—BML.

21. Blades B to EA Graham [letter], 1946 Jan 12. St. Louis: Washington University School of Medicine—BML.

22. Graham EA to B Blades [letter], 1946 Jan 17. St. Louis: Washington University School of Medicine—BML.

23. Sachs E to R Sachs [letter] in Schwartz papers. St. Louis: Washington University School of Medicine—BML.

24. Cushing H to EA Graham [letter], 1922 Dec 23. St. Louis: Washington University School of Medicine—BML.

25. Sachs E to EA Graham [letter], 1933 Mar 6. St. Louis: Washington University School of Medicine—BML.

26. Olch IY in an interview with PD Olch, 1970 May 28. St. Louis: Washington University School of Medicine—BML.

27. Sachs E. Fifty years of neurosurgery—a personal story. New York: Vantage Press; 1958.

28. Graham EA to H Schwartz [letter], 1945 Jul 17. St. Louis: Washington University School of Medicine—BML.

29. Graham EA to E Sachs [letter], 1945 Jul 18. St. Louis: Washington University School of Medicine—BML.

30. Graham EA to H Schwartz [letter], 1945 Jul 25. St. Louis: Washington University School of Medicine—BML.

31. Graham EA to E Sachs [letter], 1946 Jan 14. St. Louis: Washington University School of Medicine—BML.

32. Sachs E Jr to EA Graham [letter], 1947 Mar 20. St. Louis: Washington University School of Medicine—BML.

33. Graham EA to E Sachs Jr [letter], 1947 Apr 3. St. Louis: Washington University School of Medicine—BML.

34. Schwartz H to E Sachs Jr [letter], 1947 Apr 4. St. Louis: Washington University School of Medicine—BML.

35. Graham EA to RA Moore [letter], 1949 May 9. St. Louis: Washington University School of Medicine—BML.

36. Furlow LT. Ernest Sachs, A.B., M.D., F.A.C.S., 1879–1958. Surg Neurol 1975; 3:173–175.

37. Ford EL to CB Mueller [letter], 1999 Jun 18. St. Louis: Washington University School of Medicine—BML.

38. Abbott LC. John Albert Key 1890–1955. J Bone Joint Surg 1956;38-A:453–456.

39. Ford EL. Department of orthopaedic surgery—resident directory, Washington University, June 1995. St. Louis: Washington University School of Medicine—BML.

40. Jurkiewiecz MK to CB Mueller [letter], 1999 Mar 23. St. Louis: Washington University School of Medicine—BML.

41. Royce R. Notes on the history of urology at the Washington University School of Medicine, 1996 Apr 7. [Unpublished.] St. Louis: Washington University School of Medicine—BML.

42. Graham EA. Description of GYN and surgery at Washington University, March 2, 1927. St. Louis: Washington University School of Medicine—BML.

43. Crossen HS to EA Graham [letter], 1921 Apr 23. St. Louis: Washington University School of Medicine—BML.

44. Graham EA to HS Crossen [letter], 1921 May 4. St. Louis: Washington University School of Medicine—BML.

45. Allen WP to PA Shaffer [letter], 1943 Nov 2. St. Louis: Washington University School of Medicine—BML.

CHAPTER 10

1. Graham EA. Report to the Barnes Trustees, 1920. St. Louis: Washington University School of Medicine—BML.

2. Gray GW. The control of pain. Harpers Magazine 1938; Nov: 635–646.

3. Bradley F. History of Barnes Hospital. [Unpublished.] St. Louis: Washington University School of Medicine—BML.

4. Eastwood D in conversation with CB Mueller, 1993 Mar 6. St. Louis: Washington University School of Medicine—BML.

5. Graham EA to H Beecher [letter], 1944 Oct 23. St. Louis: Washington University School of Medicine—BML.

6. Graham EA to S Martin [letter], 1945 Oct 1. St. Louis: Washington University School of Medicine—BML.

7. Graham EA to S Cullen [letter], 1950 Jun 23. St. Louis: Washington University School of Medicine—BML.

8. Lyons AS, Petrucelli RJ II. Medicine, an illustrated history. New York: Abradale Press, Harry N. Abrams Inc.; 1987.

9. Graham EA. Ether and humbug. JAMA 1947;133:97–100.

10. Means JH to EA Graham [letter], 1946 Nov 5. St. Louis: Washington University School of Medicine—BML.

11. Graham EA to M Fishbein [letter], 1946 Nov 18. St. Louis: Washington University School of Medicine—BML.

12. Fulton J to EA Graham [letter], 1946 Nov 4. St. Louis: Washington University School of Medicine—BML.

13. Graham EA to J Fulton [letter], 1946 Nov 8. St. Louis: Washington University School of Medicine—BML.

14. Graham EA to ED Churchill [letter], 1947 Jan 2. St. Louis: Washington University School of Medicine—BML.

15. Beecher H to CA Moyer [letter], 1946 Oct 20. St. Louis: Washington University School of Medicine—BML.

16. Graham EA to EA Rovenstine [letter], 1946 Oct 24. St. Louis: Washington University School of Medicine—BML.

17. Rovenstine EA to EA Graham [letter], 1946 Dec 3. St. Louis: Washington University School of Medicine—BML.

18. Graham EA to EA Rovenstine [letter], 1947 Feb 7. St. Louis: Washington University School of Medicine—BML.

19. Womack N to CA Moyer [letter], 1946 Nov 6. St. Louis: Washington University School of Medicine—BML.

20. Moyer CA to EA Graham [letter], 1946 Dec 5. St. Louis: Washington University School of Medicine—BML.

21. Moyer CA to EA Graham [letter], 1947 Jan 6. St. Louis: Washington University School of Medicine—BML.

22. Graham EA to CA Moyer [letter], 1947 Jan 10. St. Louis: Washington University School of Medicine—BML.

23. Moyer CA to EA Graham [letter], 1947 Jan 12. St. Louis: Washington University School of Medicine—BML.

24. Moyer CA to EA Graham [letter], 1947 Feb 24. St. Louis: Washington University School of Medicine—BML.

25. Graham EA to CA Moyer [letter], 1947 Apr 4. St. Louis: Washington University School of Medicine—BML.

26. Graham EA to CA Moyer [letter], 1947 Apr 24. St. Louis: Washington University School of Medicine—BML.

27. Beecher HK, Todd DP. Study of deaths associated with anesthesia and surgery (based on a study of 599,548 anesthesias in ten institutions 1948–1952 inclusive). Ann Surg 1954;140:2–34.

28. Moyer CA to EA Graham [letter],1947 May 6. St. Louis: Washington University School of Medicine—BML.

29. Graham EA to CA Moyer [letter], 1947 May 20. St. Louis: Washington University School of Medicine—BML.

30. Graham EA to CA Moyer [letter], 1947 Oct 8. St. Louis: Washington University School of Medicine—BML.

31. Moyer CA to EA Graham [letter], 1947 Oct 12. St. Louis: Washington University School of Medicine—BML.

32. Graham EA to CA Moyer [letter], 1947 Nov 28. St. Louis: Washington University School of Medicine—BML.

33. Graham EA to CA Moyer [letter], 1947 Dec 10. St. Louis: Washington University School of Medicine—BML.

34. O'Neal LW in conversation with CB Mueller, 1998 Oct 15. St. Louis: Washington University School of Medicine—BML.

35. Glaser R to CB Mueller [letter], 1991 May 21. St. Louis: Washington University School of Medicine—BML.

36. Brown S to CB Mueller [letter], 2000 July 21. St. Louis: Washington University School of Medicine—BML.

37. Washington University. Public announcement, 1948 Feb 3. St. Louis: Washington University School of Medicine—BML.

38. Burford TH to EA Graham [letter], 1950 May 6. St. Louis: Washington University School of Medicine—BML.

39. Eastwood DW to CB Mueller [letter], 1993 Mar 1. St. Louis: Washington University School of Medicine—BML.

40. Eastwood DW to CB Mueller [letter], 1993 Sep 16. St. Louis: Washington University School of Medicine—BML.

41. Eastwood DW to CB Mueller [letter], 1999 Jun 24. St. Louis: Washington University School of Medicine—BML.

42. Eastwood DW to CB Mueller [letter], 1999 Oct 1. St. Louis: Washington University School of Medicine—BML.

43. Davis L. Fellowship of surgeons. Chicago: American College of Surgeons; 1973.

44. Blalock A. Editorial. JAMA 1928;1:24.

45. Graham EA to H Beecher [letter], 1954 Jul 30. St. Louis: Washington University School of Medicine—BML.

46. Ravdin IS to EA Graham [letter], 1956 Apr 25. St. Louis: Washington University School of Medicine—BML.

47. Mousel LH to ER Cuniffe [letter], 1954 Feb 23. St. Louis: Washington University School of Medicine—BML.

48. Mousel LH to EA Graham [letter], 1955 Dec 3. St. Louis: Washington University School of Medicine—BML.

49. Graham EA to LH Mousel [letter], 1954 Dec 7. St. Louis: Washington University School of Medicine—BML.

50. Graham EA to P Hawley [letter], 1955 Mar 15. St. Louis: Washington University School of Medicine—BML.

51. Mousel LH to EA Graham [letter], 1955 Aug 16. St. Louis: Washington University School of Medicine—BML.

52. Graham EA to LH Mousel [letter], 1954 Aug 26. St. Louis: Washington University School of Medicine—BML.

53. Hawley P to EA Graham [letter], 1955 Mar 23. St. Louis: Washington University School of Medicine—BML.

54. Graham EA to FA Bradley [letter], 1955 Sep 20. St. Louis: Washington University School of Medicine—BML.

55. McQuillan F to FA Bradley [letter], undated, circa 1955 Sep 25. St. Louis: Washington University School of Medicine—BML.

56. Cluck JR to EA Graham [letter], 1955 Oct 3. St. Louis: Washington University School of Medicine—BML.

57. Graham EA to JR Cluck [letter], 1955 Oct 7. St. Louis: Washington University School of Medicine—BML.

CHAPTER 11

1. Graham EA. Report of the surgical service 1928–29. St. Louis: Washington University School of Medicine—BML.

2. Rutkow IM. Surgery, an illustrated history. St. Louis: Mosby Yearbook; 1993.

3. Rutkow IM. American surgery, an illustrated history. Philadelphia: Lippincott-Raven; 1998.

4. Halger K. The illustrated history of surgery. London: Harold Starke; 1988.

5. Davis L. Fellowship of surgeons. Chicago: American College of Surgeons; 1960.

6. IY Olch in an interview with JF Newsome [letter], undated, circa 1977. St. Louis: Washington University School of Medicine—BML.

7. Graham EA. The changing character of surgery and the implications of those changes for this society. Brussels: Imprimeri Médical et Scientific; 1957. p. 260–269.

8. Graham EA. Washington University School of Medicine Department of Surgery. In: Methods and problems of medical education. 8th series. New York: The Rockefeller Foundation; 1927. p. 327–339.

9. Womack NA in an interview with PD Olch, 1971 Dec 9. Bethesda (MD): National Library of Medicine, Oral History Section 59; St. Louis: Washington University School of Medicine—BML.

10. Graham EA to RN Pearce [letter], 1930 Jan 18. St. Louis: Washington University School of Medicine—BML.

11. Graham EA. Report of the surgical service to the board of trustees, 1927–28. St. Louis: Washington University School of Medicine—BML.

12. Lischer CE. Evarts A. Graham (1883–1957): surgeon and educator. Am J Surg 1977;133:733–736.

13. Graham EA. Welcoming address to freshmen class, Sept 21 1938. Washington University Medical Alumni Quarterly 1938;2:25–36.

14. Graham EA to E Cutler [letter], 1932 May 11. St. Louis: Washington University School of Medicine—BML.

15. Bradley F in an interview with PD Olch, 1971 May 5. Bethesda (MD): National Library of Medicine, Oral History Section 63; St. Louis: Washington University School of Medicine—BML.

CHAPTER 12

1. Davis LA. Fellowship of surgeons: a history of the American College of Surgeons. Chicago: American College of Surgeons; 1996.
2. Martin FH. The American College of Surgeons—the past, the present and the future. Surg Gynecol Obstet 1929;50:887–896.
3. Roberts JS, Coole JG, Redman RR. A history of the Joint Commission on Accreditation of Hospitals. JAMA 1987;258:936–940.
4. Graham EA. What is surgery? South Med J 1925;18:865–867.
5. Warren WD. Not for the profession…for the people. Ann Surg 1983;198:241–250.
6. Kanavel AA. Greetings from the president. The preliminary program for the St. Louis Clinical Congress. Bull Am Coll Surg 1932;XVI:5–24.
7. Martin FP to EA Graham [letter], 1933 Dec 4. St. Louis: Washington University School of Medicine—BML.
8. Graham EA to 20 selected surgeons [letter], 1933 Jul 14. St. Louis: Washington University School of Medicine—BML.
9. Graham EA to JMT Finney [letter], 1933 Oct 28. St. Louis: Washington University School of Medicine—BML.
10. Graham EA to ACS Board of Regents [letter], 1933 Oct 10. St. Louis: Washington University School of Medicine—BML.
11. Graham EA to 20 surgeons [letter], 1933 Oct 14. St. Louis: Washington University School of Medicine—BML.
12. Graham EA to FP Martin [letter], 1933 Dec 21. St. Louis: Washington University School of Medicine—BML.
13. Stephenson GW to PD Olch [letter], 1971 Aug 18. St. Louis: Washington University School of Medicine—BML.
14. Cutler E to EA Graham [letter], 1934 Jan 14. St. Louis: Washington University School of Medicine—BML.
15. Archibald EW. Higher degrees in the profession of surgery. Ann Surg 1935;102:481–495.
16. Cutler EC, Heuer GJ, Whipple AO. Symposium on surgical education. Ann Surg 1935;102:496–530.
17. National Board Bulletin 1928;5:2.
18. Bowles T to CB Mueller [letter], 1997 Mar 23. St. Louis: Washington University School of Medicine—BML.
19. Eckert C. Evarts A. Graham and the American Board of Surgery. J Thorac Cardiovasc Surg 1935;88:842–847.
20. Womack NA in a interview with PD Olch, 1971 May 27. Bethesda (MD): National Library of Medicine, Oral History Section 59; St. Louis: Washington University School of Medicine—BML.
21. Stephenson GW. The American College of Surgeons and graduate education in surgery. Bull Am Coll Surg 1971;56(Spec Issue):1–80.
22. Graham EA. Report of the subcommittee to study further problems of postgraduate surgical education in general and the qualifications for specialization in general surgery in particular. Ann Surg 1936;103:863–869.
23. Ravitch MA. A century of surgery. Philadelphia: J.B. Lippincott; 1981. p. 1542–1546.
24. Griffin W to CB Mueller [letter], 2000 Nov 27. St. Louis: Washington University School of Medicine—BML.

25. Rodman JS. History of the American Board of Surgery, 1937–1952. Philadelphia: J.B. Lippincott; 1956.

26. Advisory Board for Medical Specialties. Annual report and reference handbook, 1997. Chicago: ABMS; 1997.

27. Miller SH to CB Mueller [letter], 1998 Jan 13. St. Louis: Washington University School of Medicine—BML.

28. Ivy RH. Some circumstances leading to organization of the American Board of Plastic Surgery. Plast Reconstr Surg 1955;16:77–85.

29. Fox CG, Graham WP. The American Board of Plastic Surgery 1937–1987. Plast Reconstr Surg 1988;82:1-10.

30. Figi FA. History of the American Association of Plastic Surgeons. Plast Reconstr Surg 1950;5:54–57.

31. Blair V to EA Graham [letter], 1937 Apr 3. St. Louis: Washington University School of Medicine—BML.

32. Graham EA to VP Blair [letter], 1938 May 23. St. Louis: Washington University School of Medicine—BML.

33. Sloan H. The American Board of Thoracic Surgery—a 50 year perspective. [In preparation]

34. Graham EA. Training of the thoracic surgeon from the standpoint of the general surgeon. J Thorac Surg 1935–36;5:575–578.

35. Graham EA. Graduate training for surgery from the viewpoint of the American Board of Surgery. Bull Am Coll Surg 1938;23:33–34.

36. Rankin F. Graduate training for surgery from the viewpoint of the American Board of Surgery. Bull Am Coll Surg 1938;23:34–35.

37. Graham EA. Report on the American Board of Surgery. Ann Surg 1939; 110:1115–1117.

38. Stephenson GW. The college's role in hospital standardization. Bull Am Coll Surg 1981;66:17–26.

39. American College of Surgeons. Twenty-first annual hospital standardization report. The 1938 survey. Bull Am Coll Surg 1938;23:293–304.

40. Lull G. AMA secretary's letter, 1950 Oct 17. St. Louis: Washington University School of Medicine—BML.

41. Allen A to all fellows [letter], 1951 Jan 16. St. Louis: Washington University School of Medicine—BML.

42. Schlicke CP. American surgery's noblest experiment. Arch Surg 1973;106:379–385.

43. Statements conveying hospital program to commission. Bull Am Coll Surg 1953;38:116–121.

44. Minutes of the first meeting, corporation of the Joint Commission on Accreditation of Hospitals, 1951 Dec 15. Chicago: American Hospital Association.

45. Crosby EL. Bulletin of the Joint Commission on Accreditation of Hospitals, 1953 Mar. St. Louis: Washington University School of Medicine—BML.

46. Minutes of the Committee on General Practice, JCAH, 1953 Apr 18. St. Louis: Washington University School of Medicine—BML.

47. Graham EA to AJJ Rourke [letter], 1956 Jul 11. St. Louis: Washington University School of Medicine—BML.

48. Hawley P to EA Graham [letter], 1955 Dec 9. St. Louis: Washington University School of Medicine—BML.

49. Graham EA to P Hawley [letter], 1955 Dec 16. St. Louis: Washington University School of Medicine—BML.

50. American Medical Association. Fee splitting, report of the Judicial Council. JAMA 1952;150:1706.

51. Hawley P. Too much unnecessary surgery. U.S. News and World Report 1953;34:47.

52. Graham EA. Thoughts about the meeting of the trustees of the AMA with the regents committee [memorandum], 1953 Nov. St. Louis: Washington University School of Medicine—BML.

53. Hawley P to EA Graham [letter], 1954 Feb 22. St. Louis: Washington University School of Medicine—BML.

54. Wangensteen OH. The Society of University Surgeons and the need for a surgical forum. Surgery 1940;8:118–121.

55. Wangensteen OH. Reflections. Contemp Surg 1980;17:37–80.

56. Bull Am Coll Surg 1991;76:38.

57. Graham EA to all US members of ISS [letter],1949 May 19. St. Louis: Washington University School of Medicine—BML.

58. Graham EA. International Society's Copenhagen session in review. Bull Am Coll Surg 1956;41:47.

59. Graham EA to L Dejardin [letter], 1956 Apr 13. St. Louis: Washington University School of Medicine—BML.

60. Graham EA to O Wangensteen [letter], 1956 Aug 29. St. Louis: Washington University School of Medicine—BML.

61. Ravitch MA. A century of surgery. Philadelphia: J.B. Lippincott; 1981. p. 5.

62. Graham EA. Samuel Gross looks in on the American Surgical Association. Ann Surg 1937;106:481–491.

63. Davis L to PD Olch [letter], 1972 Mar 10. St. Louis: Washington University School of Medicine—BML.

64. Members in the news. Mo Med 1953;50:876.

65. Graham EA. Letters. Mo Med 1953;50:961.

66. Williams VT to EA Graham [letter], 1953 Nov 3. St. Louis: Washington University School of Medicine—BML.

67. Thorek M. Letters. Mo Med 1954;51:159–160.

68. Vedder BB to EA Graham [letter], 1954 Feb 22. St. Louis: Washington University School of Medicine—BML.

69. Graham EA to BB Vedder [letter], 1954 Feb 25. St. Louis: Washington University School of Medicine—BML.

70. Graham EA to BB Vedder [letter], 1954 Mar 12. St. Louis: Washington University School of Medicine—BML.

71. Graham EA to BB Vedder [letter], 1954 Mar 19. St. Louis: Washington University School of Medicine—BML.

72. Hawley P to EA Graham [letter], 1954 Mar 16. St. Louis: Washington University School of Medicine—BML.

73. Graham EA to P Hawley [letter], 1954 Mar 19. St. Louis: Washington University School of Medicine—BML.

74. Graham EA. Letters. Mo Med 1954;50:414–415.

75. Martin F to EA Graham [letter], 1935 Jan 16. St. Louis: Washington University School of Medicine—BML.

76. Stephenson GW. The formulation of college policy: clarification. Bull Am Coll Surg 1997; Oct: 45.
77. Graham EA to O Wangensteen [letter], 1954 Dec 21. St. Louis: Washington University School of Medicine—BML.
78. Bull Am Coll Surg 1954; January/February.
79. Davis L. A surgeon's odyssey. Garden City (NY): Doubleday and Company; 1973. p. 305–306.

CHAPTER 13

1. Morrow RE. Washington University in St. Louis, a history. St. Louis: Missouri Historical Society Press; 1996.
2. Throop GR to members of staff [letter], 1936 Oct 14. St. Louis: Washington University School of Medicine—BML.
3. Throop GR to EA Graham [letter], 1936 Oct 23. St. Louis: Washington University School of Medicine—BML.
4. Throop GR to EA Graham [letter], 1937 Feb 2. St. Louis: Washington University School of Medicine—BML.
5. Throop GR to EA Graham [letter], 1936 Oct 24. St. Louis: Washington University School of Medicine—BML.
6. Statement by the executive faculty concerning relations of the Medical School with the Barnes Hospital, adopted by the faculty 1937 May 12. St. Louis: Washington University School of Medicine—BML.
7. Shaffer PA to GR Throop [letter], 1937 May 17. St. Louis: Washington University School of Medicine—BML.
8. Graham EA to AH Compton [letter], 1945 Oct 25. St. Louis: Washington University School of Medicine—BML.
9. Compton AH to EA Graham [letter], 1945 Nov 6. St. Louis: Washington University School of Medicine—BML.
10. Alexander HL to PA Schaffer [letter], 1942 Jan 26. St. Louis: Washington University School of Medicine—BML.
11. Graham EA to FC Rand [letter], 1949 Dec 9. St. Louis: Washington University School of Medicine—BML.
12. Graham EA. Memorandum of conversations with Mr. Abraham Flexner about endowment funds for a surgical addition to Barnes Hospital, undated, circa 1928. St. Louis: Washington University School of Medicine—BML.
13. Bradley FR. History of Barnes Hospital. [Unpublished.] Circa 1950. St. Louis: Washington University School of Medicine—BML.
14. Graham EA. Report of the surgical service 1928–1929. St. Louis: Washington University School of Medicine—BML.
15. Graham EA. Memorandum of action of Barnes Hospital trustees concerning General Education Board funds, 1932 Dec 29. St. Louis: Washington University School of Medicine—BML.
16. Announcement of Rand/Johnson gift and General Education Board gift to the Department of Surgery at Barnes Hospital, undated. St. Louis: Washington University School of Medicine—BML.
17. Hanvey A. Memorandum dictated by EA Graham, 1937 Jul 2. St. Louis: Washington University School of Medicine—BML.

18. Graham EA to FC Rand [letter], 1937 Jun 29. St. Louis: Washington University School of Medicine—BML.

19. Throop GR to EA Graham [letter], 1936 Oct 24. St. Louis: Washington University School of Medicine—BML.

20. Graham EA to W Darrach [letter], 1937 Jul 23. St. Louis: Washington University School of Medicine—BML.

21. Schwartz H in conversation with CB Mueller, 1991 Dec 6. St. Louis: Washington University School of Medicine—BML.

22. Declaration of termination—trustees to Washington University corporation, 1938 Sep 30. St. Louis: Washington University School of Medicine—BML.

23. Rand FC to M Clopton [letter], 1938 Sep 30. St. Louis: Washington University School of Medicine—BML.

24. Clopton MB to FC Rand [letter], 1938 Oct 4. St. Louis: Washington University School of Medicine—BML.

25. Report on Department of Surgery to Barnes Hospital trustees, 1924 Oct 18. St. Louis: Washington University Archives.

26. Graham EA. Statements conveying hospital program to commission. Bull Am Coll Surg 1953;38:116–121.

27. Bradley F in an interview with PD Olch, 1971 May 5. St. Louis: Washington University School of Medicine—BML.

28. Compton AH to HB Wallace [letter], 1944 Jul 11. St. Louis: Washington University School of Medicine—BML.

29. Graham EA to AH Compton [letter], 1944 Jul 18. St. Louis: Washington University School of Medicine—BML.

30. Graham EA to HB Wallace [letter], 1944 Jul 31. St. Louis: Washington University School of Medicine—BML.

31. Compton AH to HB Wallace [letter], 1944 Aug 12. St. Louis: Washington University School of Medicine—BML.

32. Graham EA to AH Compton [letter], 1944 Aug 18. St. Louis: Washington University School of Medicine—BML.

33. Graham EA to AH Compton [letter], 1945 Feb 19. St. Louis: Washington University School of Medicine—BML.

34. Graham EA to AH Compton [letter], 1945 Mar 28. St. Louis: Washington University School of Medicine—BML.

35. Shepley EAH. Remarks made at Memorial Service for EA Graham [letter], 1957 Mar 31. St. Louis: Washington University School of Medicine—BML.

36. Ludmerer KM. Time to heal. New York: Oxford University Press, Inc.; 1999.

37. Hunter E in conversation with CB Mueller, 1992 May 7. St. Louis: Washington University School of Medicine—BML.

38. Howard University professor cites three steps for absorbing negroes in profession. St. Louis Post-Dispatch 1950 Apr 21.

39. Sinkler WH to EA Graham [letter], 1946 Jan 16. St. Louis: Washington University School of Medicine—BML.

40. Editorial. Dr. Evarts Graham. J Natl Med Assoc 1950;42:43–44.

41. Graham EA to TS Cullen [letter], 1921 Dec 15. St. Louis: Washington University School of Medicine—BML.

42. Graham EA to DD Lewis [letter], 1923 Jan 25. St. Louis: Washington University School of Medicine—BML.

43. Graham EA to DB Phemister [letter], 1925 Jan 13. St. Louis: Washington University School of Medicine—BML.

44. Graham EA to H Cushing [letter], 1928 Oct 10. St. Louis: Washington University School of Medicine—BML.

45. Graham EA to DJ Davis [letter], 1925 Jul 8. St. Louis: Washington University School of Medicine—BML.

46. Graham EA to E Cutler [letter], 1930 Apr 19. St. Louis: Washington University School of Medicine—BML.

47. Graham EA to JH Mulholland [letter], 1940 Nov 27. St. Louis: Washington University School of Medicine—BML.

48. Olch IY in an interview with PD Olch, 1970 May 28. St. Louis: Washington University School of Medicine—BML.

49. Graham EA. Internal memorandum 1937 Sep 10. St. Louis: Washington University School of Medicine—BML.

50. Graham EA to EP Cathcart [letter], 1933 Jul 18. St. Louis: Washington University School of Medicine—BML.

51. Funkenstein DH to EA Graham [letter], 1938 Dec 9. St. Louis: Washington University School of Medicine—BML.

52. Graham EA to Rabbi Isserman [letter], 1942 Dec 14. St. Louis: Washington University School of Medicine—BML.

53. Graham EA to G Spearl [letter], 1945 Jan 23. St. Louis: Washington University School of Medicine—BML.

54. Graham EA to M Einhorn [letter], 1956 Mar 15. St. Louis: Washington University School of Medicine—BML.

CHAPTER 14

1. Baue AE. 60 years of the *Archives of Surgery*, July 1920–July 1980 [editorial]. Arch Surg 1980;115:809–811.

2. Simmons GH to EA Graham [letter], 1919 Dec 18. St. Louis: Washington University School of Medicine—BML.

3. Baue AE. Seventy-five years of the *Archives of Surgery*, July 1920–1995 [editorial]. Arch Surg 1995;130:717–719.

4. Graham EA to DD Lewis [letter], 1920 Dec 7. St. Louis: Washington University School of Medicine—BML.

5. Graham EA to LR Dragstedt [letter], 1944 Apr 25. St. Louis: Washington University School of Medicine—BML.

6. Dragstedt LR to O West [letter], 1944 Apr 25. St. Louis: Washington University School of Medicine—BML.

7. Graham EA to O West [letter], 1944 Apr 25. St. Louis: Washington University School of Medicine—BML.

8. West O to EA Graham [letter], 1944 May 1. St. Louis: Washington University School of Medicine—BML.

9. Graham EA to O West [letter], 1944 May 11. St. Louis: Washington University School of Medicine—BML.

10. Graham EA to L Dragstedt [letter], 1944 May 18. St. Louis: Washington University School of Medicine—BML.

11. Graham EA to W Walters [letter], 1945 Apr 19. St. Louis: Washington University School of Medicine—BML.

12. Graham EA to O West [letter], 1945 Aug 24. St. Louis: Washington University School of Medicine—BML.

13. Editorial board. Ann Surg 1935;101: i, ii.

14. Lee WE to EA Graham [letter], 1940 May 7. St. Louis: Washington University School of Medicine—BML.

15. Gibbon JH Jr to EA Graham [letter], 1947 Jun 26. St. Louis: Washington University School of Medicine—BML.

16. Head CJ to EA Graham [letter], 1926 Mar 3. St. Louis: Washington University School of Medicine—BML.

17. Graham EA to CJ Head [letter], 1926 Mar 8. St. Louis: Washington University School of Medicine—BML.

18. Head CJ to EA Graham [letter], 1926 Mar 10. St. Louis: Washington University School of Medicine—BML.

19. Head CJ to EA Graham [letter], 1926 Mar 16. St. Louis: Washington University School of Medicine—BML.

20. Graham EA. Introduction. Year Book of General Surgery. Chicago: Year Books; 1927. p. 1

21. Graham EA. Should surgeons be honest? Year Book of General Surgery. [Unpublished.] 1953. St. Louis: Washington University School of Medicine—BML.

22. Wetherhold F to EA Graham [letter], 1953 Aug 26. St. Louis: Washington University School of Medicine—BML.

23. McKinnon NE. Limitations in diagnosis and treatment of breast and other cancers: a review. Can Med Assoc J 1955;73:614–624.

24. Graham EA. Introduction. Year Book of General Surgery. Chicago: Year Books; 1956–1957. p. 1–4.

25. Schiassi B. Cholecystendesis vs. cholecystectomy for biliary calculi. J Chir (Paris) 1934;43:8.

26. Graham EA. Editorial comment. Year Book of General Surgery. Chicago: Year Books; 1936. p. 590.

27. Simons HA to EA Graham [letter], 1935 May 14. St. Louis: Washington University School of Medicine—BML.

28. Mayo C to EA Graham [letter], 1935 Jun 24. St. Louis: Washington University School of Medicine—BML.

29. Graham EA to V Putti [letter], 1935 Jul 8. St. Louis: Washington University School of Medicine—BML.

30. Graham EA to B Schiassi [letter], 1935 Jul 8. St. Louis: Washington University School of Medicine—BML.

31. Schiassi B to EA Graham [letter], 1935 Aug 5. St. Louis: Washington University School of Medicine—BML.

32. Simons HA to EA Graham [letter], 1935 Jul 2. St. Louis: Washington University School of Medicine—BML.

33. Graham EA to HA Simons [letter], 1935 Jul 8. St. Louis: Washington University School of Medicine—BML.

34. Graham EA. L'Affair Schiassi. 1935. St. Louis: Washington University School of Medicine—BML.

35. It would seem…Evarts A. Graham. Chicago: Year Book Publishers; 1951.

36. Graham EA. Editor [foreword]. J Thorac Surg 1931;I:1–2.

37. Hanvey A to OW Wangensteen [letter], 1939 Jun 30. St. Louis: Washington University School of Medicine—BML.
38. Cole R to EA Graham [letter], 1919 Sep 17. St. Louis: Washington University School of Medicine—BML.
39. Davis DJ to EA Graham [letter], 1925 Mar 14. St. Louis: Washington University School of Medicine—BML.
40. Graham EA to DJ Davis [letter], 1925 May 12. St. Louis: Washington University School of Medicine—BML.
41. Graham EA to WJ Mayo [letter], 1925 Oct 15. St. Louis: Washington University School of Medicine—BML.
42. Graham EA to WW Campbell [letter], 1927 Mar 31. St. Louis: Washington University School of Medicine—BML.
43. Allison N to EA Graham [letter], 1927 Dec 6. St. Louis: Washington University School of Medicine—BML.
44. Cushing H to EA Graham [letter], 1927 Dec 13. St. Louis: Washington University School of Medicine—BML.
45. Cannon WB to EA Graham [letter], 1928 Jan 23. St. Louis: Washington University School of Medicine—BML.
46. Graham EA to D Edsall [letter], 1928 Feb 11. St. Louis: Washington University School of Medicine—BML.
47. Cushing H to EA Graham [letter], 1928 Feb 20. St. Louis: Washington University School of Medicine—BML.
48. Graham EA to A Flexner [letter], 1929 Mar 9. St. Louis: Washington University School of Medicine—BML.
49. Graham EA to GC Robinson [letter], 1929 May 11. St. Louis: Washington University School of Medicine—BML.
50. Christian HA to EA Graham [letter], 1931 Apr 10. St. Louis: Washington University School of Medicine—BML.
51. Graham EA to H Christian [letter], 1931 Apr 30. St. Louis: Washington University School of Medicine—BML.
52. Bowman I to EA Graham [letter], 1939 Dec 7. St. Louis: Washington University School of Medicine—BML.
53. Chesney AM to EA Graham [letter], 1940 Jan 2. St. Louis: Washington University School of Medicine—BML.
54. Bowman I to EA Graham [letter], 1940 Jan 15. St. Louis: Washington University School of Medicine—BML.
55. Cole W to EA Graham [letter], 1940 Jan 4. St. Louis: Washington University School of Medicine—BML.
56. Graham EA to W Cole [letter], 1940 Jan 8. St. Louis: Washington University School of Medicine—BML.
57. Graham EA to I Bowman [letter], 1940 Feb 1. St. Louis: Washington University School of Medicine—BML.
58. Graham EA to LH Weed [letter], 1940 Feb 10. St. Louis: Washington University School of Medicine—BML.
59. Womack NA in an interview with P Olch, 1971 Dec 9. St. Louis: Washington University School of Medicine—BML.
60. Graham EA to I Bowman [letter], 1947 Oct 30. St. Louis: Washington University School of Medicine—BML.

61. Bowman I to EA Graham [letter], 1947 Nov 3. St. Louis: Washington University School of Medicine—BML.

62. Longmire W. Alfred Blalock, his life and times. Los Angeles: Longmire; 1991. p. 8, 9.

63. Graham EA to DM Rioch [letter], 1951 Oct 1. St. Louis: Washington University School of Medicine—BML.

64. Graham EA to W McKim Marriott [letter], 1927 Nov 14. St. Louis: Washington University School of Medicine—BML.

65. Graham EA. Some fundamental considerations in the treatment of empyema thoracis. St. Louis: C. V. Mosby Co.; 1925.

66. Cole W to A Hanvey [letter], 1950 Nov 9. St. Louis: Washington University School of Medicine—BML.

67. Denk W to EA Graham [letter], 1956 Nov 16. St. Louis: Washington University School of Medicine—BML.

68. Graham EA to W Denk [letter], 1956 Nov 20. St. Louis: Washington University School of Medicine—BML.

69. Danforth WH to EA Graham [letter], 1954 Dec 14. St. Louis: Washington University School of Medicine—BML.

70. Graham EA to W Danforth [letter], 1954 Dec 17. St. Louis: Washington University School of Medicine—BML.

71. Danforth WH to EA Graham [letter], 1955 Jan 4. St. Louis: Washington University School of Medicine—BML.

CHAPTER 15

1. Flexner A to EA Graham [letter], 1921 Dec 7. St. Louis: Washington University School of Medicine—BML.

2. Graham EA to A Flexner [letter], 1921 Dec 21. St. Louis: Washington University School of Medicine—BML.

3. Pearce R to EA Graham [letter], 1922 Apr 24. St. Louis: Washington University School of Medicine—BML.

4. Pearce R to EA Graham [letter], 1922 Jun 16. St. Louis: Washington University School of Medicine—BML.

5. Graham EA to GE Vincent [letter], 1923 Jan 18. St. Louis: Washington University School of Medicine—BML.

6. Graham EA to EP Cathcart [letter], 1923 Jan 4. St. Louis: Washington University School of Medicine—BML.

7. Graham EA to RM Pearce [letter], 1923 Oct 16. St. Louis: Washington University School of Medicine—BML.

8. Graham EA to RM Pearce [letter], 1923 Nov 24. St. Louis: Washington University School of Medicine—BML.

9. Graham EA. A report of an investigation of the teaching of surgery in representative British medical schools, based on a visit to Great Britain in 1922 under the auspices of the Division of Medical Education of the Rockefeller Foundation. Rockefeller Archives Center, North Tarrytown, New York, Collection RF, Record Group 1.1, Series 401a, Box 16, Folder 217; St. Louis: Washington University School of Medicine—BML.

10. Graham EA to D Edsall [letter], 1924 Mar 18. St. Louis: Washington University School of Medicine—BML.

11. Graham EA to D Edsall [letter], 1924 Mar 25. St. Louis: Washington University School of Medicine—BML.

12. Graham EA to B Brooks [letter], 1927 Jun 23. St. Louis: Washington University School of Medicine—BML.

13. Brooks B to EA Graham [letter], 1927 Nov 12. St. Louis: Washington University School of Medicine—BML.

14. Flexner A to EA Graham [letter], 1921 Mar 22. St. Louis: Washington University School of Medicine—BML.

15. Agenda, General Education Board Meeting, 1921 Apr 4. St. Louis: Washington University School of Medicine—BML.

16. Graham EA to A Flexner [letter], 1921 Apr 20. St. Louis: Washington University School of Medicine—BML.

17. Announcement of fellowships in medicine by the National Research Council, 1925. St. Louis: Washington University School of Medicine—BML.

18. Kellogg V to GC Huber [letter], 1927 Feb 26. St. Louis: Washington University School of Medicine—BML.

19. Hektoen L to EA Graham [letter], 1925 May 26. St. Louis: Washington University School of Medicine—BML.

20. Hektoen L to EA Graham [letter], 1927 Jun 3. St. Louis: Washington University School of Medicine—BML.

21. Hektoen L to EA Graham [letter], 1927 Jun 30. St. Louis: Washington University School of Medicine—BML.

22. Hektoen L to EA Graham [letter], 1926 Oct 21. St. Louis: Washington University School of Medicine—BML.

23. Weed LH to AC Christie [letter], 1940 Jun 19. St. Louis: Washington University School of Medicine—BML.

24. Graham EA to V Kellogg [letter], 1925 Oct 1. St. Louis: Washington University School of Medicine—BML.

25. Kellogg V to EA Graham [letter], 1926 Mar 24. St. Louis: Washington University School of Medicine—BML.

26. Graham EA to V Kellogg [letter], 1926 Mar 29. St. Louis: Washington University School of Medicine—BML.

27. National Research Council. Organization and members 1941–1942. St. Louis: Washington University School of Medicine—BML.

28. Larkey SV. The National Research Council, Division of Medical Sciences. List of committees and sub-committees August 12, 1940. St. Louis: Washington University School of Medicine—BML.

29. National Research Council. Committee on Drugs and Medical Supplies. Medical division. Report on activities, March 16 1942 to January 27 1943. St. Louis: Washington University School of Medicine—BML.

30. Weed LH to EA Graham [letter], 1943 May 4. St. Louis: Washington University School of Medicine—BML.

31. National Research Council. Report of Committee on Surgery, undated, circa 1941 Jun. St. Louis: Washington University School of Medicine—BML.

32. Hanvey A in an interview with PD Olch, 1971 Jun 18. St. Louis: Washington University School of Medicine—BML.

33. Weed LH to EA Graham [letter], 1941 Mar 24. St. Louis: Washington University School of Medicine—BML.

34. Graham EA to LH Weed [letter], 1940 Aug 19. St. Louis: Washington University School of Medicine—BML.

35. Hillman CC to EA Graham [letter], 1941 Jul 26. St. Louis: Washington University School of Medicine—BML.

36. Eloesser L to EA Graham [letter], 1942 Dec 19. St. Louis: Washington University School of Medicine—BML.

37. Graham EA to L Eloesser [letter], 1942 Dec 31. St. Louis: Washington University School of Medicine—BML.

38. Graham EA to JF Fulton [letter], 1942 Jul 1. St. Louis: Washington University School of Medicine—BML.

39. Graham EA to M Fishbein [letter], 1942 Sep 1. St. Louis: Washington University School of Medicine—BML.

40. Graham EA to FA Coller [letter], 1942 Apr 20. St. Louis: Washington University School of Medicine—BML.

41. Graham EA to HC Naffziger [letter], 1943 Apr 9. St. Louis: Washington University School of Medicine—BML.

42. Graham EA to FA Coller [letter], 1943 Apr 16. St. Louis: Washington University School of Medicine—BML.

43. Stewart I. Organizing scientific research for war. The administrative history of the Office of Scientific Research and Development. Boston: Little, Brown and Co.; 1948.

44. Graham EA to LH Weed [letter], 1941 Dec 12. St. Louis: Washington University School of Medicine—BML.

45. Weed LH to EA Graham [letter], 1941 Dec 15. St. Louis: Washington University School of Medicine—BML.

46. Graham EA to HL Ickes [letter], 1941 Mar 4. St. Louis: Washington University School of Medicine—BML.

47. Weed LH to EA Graham [letter], 1941 Mar 24. St. Louis: Washington University School of Medicine—BML.

48. Graham EA to LH Weed [letter], 1941 Mar 14. St. Louis: Washington University School of Medicine—BML.

49. Graham EA to HL Ickes [letter], 1941 Apr 15. St. Louis: Washington University School of Medicine—BML.

50. Weed LH to EA Graham [letter], 1941 Jul 18. St. Louis: Washington University School of Medicine—BML.

51. Meleney FL. The study of the prevention of infection in contaminated accidental wounds, compound fractures and burns. Ann Surg 1943;118:171–186.

52. Ravdin IS to FL Meleney [letter], 1944 May 5. St. Louis: Washington University School of Medicine—BML.

53. Graham EA to LH Weed [letter], 1943 Sep 28. St. Louis: Washington University School of Medicine—BML.

54. Graham EA to F Meleney [letter], 1943 Oct 19. St. Louis: Washington University School of Medicine—BML.

55. Graham EA to LH Weed [letter], 1944 May 16. St. Louis: Washington University School of Medicine—BML.

56. Graham EA to LH Weed [letter], 1944 Jun 6. St. Louis: Washington University School of Medicine—BML.

57. Weed LH to EA Graham [letter], 1944 Jun 10. St. Louis: Washington University School of Medicine—BML.

58. Graham EA to FL Meleney [letter], 1944 Jul 19. St. Louis: Washington University School of Medicine—BML.

59. Graham EA to AO Whipple [letter], 1944 Aug 14. St. Louis: Washington University School of Medicine—BML.

60. Churchill ED. The surgical management of the wounded in the Mediterranean Theater at the time of the fall of Rome. Ann Surg 1944;120:268–278.

61. Whipple AO to EA Graham [letter], 1944 Nov 10. St. Louis: Washington University School of Medicine—BML.

62. Graham EA to LH Weed [letter], 1944 Jan 14. St. Louis: Washington University School of Medicine—BML.

63. Weed LH to EA Graham [letter], 1946 Jun 30. St. Louis: Washington University School of Medicine—BML.

64. National Research Council. Index of Committee on Growth, Sections and Panels, undated, circa 1951 to 1952. St. Louis: Washington University School of Medicine—BML.

65. Graham EA to OM Ray [letter], 1954 Mar 30. St. Louis: Washington University School of Medicine—BML.

66. Graham EA to RK Cannan [letter], 1955 Apr 22. St. Louis: Washington University School of Medicine—BML.

67. Winternitz MC to EA Graham [letter], 1952 Jun 2. St. Louis: Washington University School of Medicine—BML.

68. Lape EE to EA Graham [letter], 1933 Apr 17. St. Louis: Washington University School of Medicine—BML.

69. Graham EA to EE Lape [letter], 1933 Apr 25. St. Louis: Washington University School of Medicine—BML.

70. Schnabel TG to EA Graham [letter], 1936 Jul 16. St. Louis: Washington University School of Medicine—BML.

71. Lape EE to EA Graham [letter], 1937 Mar 3. St. Louis: Washington University School of Medicine—BML.

72. American medicine: expert testimony out of court. New York: American Foundation Studies in Government; 1937.

73. The American Foundation proposals for medical care [editorial]. JAMA 1937; 109:1280–1281.

74. Problems of American medicine; doctors give views. St. Louis Post-Dispatch 1937 Apr 1.

75. Doctors and the public. New York Times 1937 Apr 4. p. 9.

76. National policy on health asked by 430 doctors. New York Times 1937 Nov 7. p. 1.

77. Medicine and government. New York Herald Tribune 1937 Nov 8.

78. Russell C. Textbook of medicine. Philadelphia: W.B. Saunders; 1933.

79. Peters J, Van Slyke DD. Quantitative clinical chemistry. Baltimore: Williams and Wilkins Company; 1931.

80. Committee of Physicians. Principles and proposals, issued by Office of Secretary, 1937 Nov 7. St. Louis: Washington University School of Medicine—BML.

81. Kilgore ES to EA Graham [letter], 1937 Nov 11. St. Louis: Washington University School of Medicine—BML.

82. Kilgore ES to EA Graham [letter], 1937 Nov 12. St. Louis: Washington University School of Medicine—BML.

83. Kilgore ES to EA Graham [letter], 1937 Nov 16. St. Louis: Washington University School of Medicine—BML.

84. Graham EA to ES Kilgore [letter], 1937 Nov 23. St. Louis: Washington University School of Medicine—BML.

85. Committee of Physicians, secretary to committee members [letter], 1938 Mar 2. St. Louis: Washington University School of Medicine—BML.

86. Peters JP for Committee of Physicians to all signatories [letter], 1938 Jul 14. St. Louis: Washington University School of Medicine—BML.

87. Peters JP. Report of the National Health Conference; 1938 Jul 18–20; Washington (DC). Committee Of Physicians Bulletin, 1938 Aug 8. St. Louis: Washington University School of Medicine—BML.

88. Graham EA to JP Peters [letter], 1938 Aug 6. St. Louis: Washington University School of Medicine—BML.

89. Peters JP to EA Graham [letter], 1938 Aug 10. St. Louis: Washington University School of Medicine—BML.

90. Graham EA to JP Peters [letter], 1938 Aug 12. St. Louis: Washington University School of Medicine—BML.

91. Peters JP. Aims of the committee. Committee Of Physicians Bulletin 1940 Mar 4. St. Louis: Washington University School of Medicine—BML.

92. Peters JP. The story of the principles and proposals for the improvement of medical care. Committee Of Physicians Bulletin, undated. St. Louis: Washington University School of Medicine—BML.

CHAPTER 16

1. Graham EA to FD Roosevelt [letter], 1939 Jan 25. St. Louis: Washington University School of Medicine—BML.

2. Graham EA to H Ickes [letter], 1939 Jan 25. St. Louis: Washington University School of Medicine—BML.

3. Graham EA to H Ickes [letter], 1939 Feb 1. St. Louis: Washington University School of Medicine—BML.

4. Physicians named to get supplies for Britain. St. Louis Globe Democrat 1940 Oct 25.

5. Coates JB, Wiltes CM, editors. Medical department United States Army in World War II. Personnel. Washington (DC): Office of the Surgeon General, Department of the Army; 1963. p. 160–205.

6. American Medical Association. Committee on Post-War Medical Services. Chicago: AMA; 1943, Jun 5. St. Louis: Washington University School of Medicine—BML.

7. Graham EA to EP Lehman [letter], 1943 Dec 8. St. Louis: Washington University School of Medicine—BML.

8. Graham EA to H Stone [letter], 1944 Dec 13. St. Louis: Washington University School of Medicine—BML.

9. Graham EA to C Mixter [letter], 1944 Mar 16. St. Louis: Washington University School of Medicine—BML.

10. Dr. Evarts Graham opposes drafting medical students. St. Louis Post-Dispatch 1941 Mar 12.

11. Graham EA. What kind of medical officers do the Armed Services want? Surg Gynecol Obstet 1944;79:217–219.

12. Graham EA to A Gregg [letter], 1944 Oct 19. St. Louis: Washington University School of Medicine—BML.

13. Kirk NT to EA Graham [letter], 1944 Aug 16. St. Louis: Washington University School of Medicine—BML.

14. Graham EA to NT Kirk [letter], 1944 Aug 22. St. Louis: Washington University School of Medicine—BML.

15. Kirk NT to EA Graham [letter], 1944 Aug 25. St. Louis: Washington University School of Medicine—BML.

16. Graham EA to F Rankin [letter], 1945 Jan 8. St. Louis: Washington University School of Medicine—BML.

17. Graham EA. Have the Armed Services crippled medical education? Saturday Evening Post 1945 Jan 27;34–42.

18. Graham EA to K Menninger [letter], 1945 Feb 7. St. Louis: Washington University School of Medicine—BML.

19. Graham EA to A Ochsner [letter], 1945 Mar 15. St. Louis: Washington University School of Medicine—BML.

20. Graham EA to RH Major [letter], 1945 Mar 27. St. Louis: Washington University School of Medicine—BML.

21. Dodds H to EA Graham [letter], 1945 Jan 29. St. Louis: Washington University School of Medicine—BML.

22. Graham EA to H Dodds [letter], 1945 Feb 1. St. Louis: Washington University School of Medicine—BML.

23. Dock W to EA Graham [letter], 1945 Feb 2. St. Louis: Washington University School of Medicine—BML.

24. Graham EA to W Dock [letter], 1945 Feb 6. St. Louis: Washington University School of Medicine—BML.

25. Graham EA to AO Whipple [letter], 1945 Jan 26. St. Louis: Washington University School of Medicine—BML.

26. Graham EA to F Rankin [letter], 1945 Mar 26. St. Louis: Washington University School of Medicine—BML.

27. Graham EA. Welcoming address to freshman class, September 21, 1938. Washington University. Medical Alumni Quarterly 1938;2:25–36.

28. Graham EA. Medical education: a war casualty. Washington University. Medical Alumni Quarterly 1945; Aug:147–153.

29. Frank RB. Downfall: the end of the Imperial Japanese Empire. New York: Random House; 1989. p. 131–148.

30. Lee RI to members of the Committee on Post-War Medical Services [letter], 1943 Apr 27. St. Louis: Washington University School of Medicine—BML.

31. Lee RI to members of the Committee on Post-War Medical Services [letter], 1943 Apr 27. St. Louis: Washington University School of Medicine—BML.

32. Lee R to the Committee on Post-War Medical Services [memorandum], 1944 Aug 4. St. Louis: Washington University School of Medicine—BML.

33. Graham EA to RI Lee [letter], 1944 Aug 9. St. Louis: Washington University School of Medicine—BML.

34. Johnson V to W Judd [letter], 1945 May 22. St. Louis: Washington University School of Medicine—BML.

35. Minutes of meeting of Committee on Post-War Medical Services 1945 May 12. St. Louis: Washington University School of Medicine—BML.

36. Graham EA to V Johnson [letter], 1945 May 22. St. Louis: Washington University School of Medicine—BML.

37. Memorandum for President Harry S. Truman regarding the supply of medical students and physicians 1945 Jun. St. Louis: Washington University School of Medicine—BML.

38. Johnson V to EA Graham [letter], 1945 Jun 1. St. Louis: Washington University School of Medicine—BML.

39. Johnson V to EA Graham [letter], 1945 Jul 29. St. Louis: Washington University School of Medicine—BML.

40. Statement by the American College of Surgeons concerning the drafting of doctors [editorial]. Bull Am Coll Surg 1950;Oct:14–16.

41. Stinson HS. Confidential memorandum establishing a committee to study the medical department of the army. 1942 Sep 10. St. Louis: Washington University School of Medicine—BML.

42. Gill C. Confidential report of Committee to Study the Medical Department of the Army. 1943 Jan 2. St. Louis: Washington University School of Medicine—BML.

43. Graham EA to LI Dublin [letter], 1943 Aug 28. St. Louis: Washington University School of Medicine—BML.

44. Coates JB, Wiltes CM, editors. Medical department United States Army in World War II. Organization and administration in World War II. Washington (DC): Office of the Surgeon General, Department of the Army; 1963. p. 145–185.

45. Graham EA to CH Goddard [letter], 1951 Nov 7. St. Louis: Washington University School of Medicine—BML.

46. Goddard CH to EA Graham [letter], 1951 Dec 11. St. Louis: Washington University School of Medicine—BML.

47. Pugh HL to EA Graham [letter], 1947 Dec 12. St. Louis: Washington University School of Medicine—BML.

48. Lahey F to EA Graham [letter], 1950 May 11. St. Louis: Washington University School of Medicine—BML.

49. Graham EA to F Lahey [letter], 1950 May 18. St. Louis: Washington University School of Medicine—BML.

50. Bortz E to JE Paullin [letter], 1950 May 13. St. Louis: Washington University School of Medicine—BML.

51. Kimball DA to EA Graham [letter], 1950 Dec 4. St. Louis: Washington University School of Medicine—BML.

CHAPTER 17

1. Health plan trial urged. St. Louis Post-Dispatch 1946 Feb 11.

2. Graham EA to R Duncan [letter], 1949 Mar 18. St. Louis: Washington University School of Medicine—BML.

3. Starr P. The social transformation of American medicine. New York: Basic Books; 1982.

4. Executive order no. 10317 establishing the President's Commission on the Health Needs of the Nation, 1951 Dec 29. St. Louis: Washington University School of Medicine—BML.

5. President's Commission (PCHNN-PR-9), 1952 Jun 3. St. Louis: Washington University School of Medicine—BML.

6. Doctor declines place on Truman health survey, calls it political. St. Louis Post-Dispatch 1951 Dec 31.

7. Rusk H. Fight on Truman health unit as political held unjustified. New York Times 1952 Jan 5. p. 78.

8. President's Commission (PCHNN-PR-13), 1952 July 16. St. Louis: Washington University School of Medicine—BML.

9. President's Commission (PCHNN-PR-21), 1952 Aug 28. St. Louis: Washington University School of Medicine—BML.

10. Graham EA to L Breslow [letter], 1952 Dec 4. St. Louis: Washington University School of Medicine—BML.

11. Building America's health. Report of the President's Commission on the Health Needs of the Nation. Washington (DC): Government Printing Office; 1953 Apr 15.

12. Magnuson P to EA Graham. Western Union telegram [letter], 1952 Dec 4. St. Louis: Washington University School of Medicine—BML.

13. Dr. Graham calls article on AMA attack "wrong". St. Louis Post-Dispatch 1952 Sep 15. p. 1.

14. Dr. Graham hopes new plan will spread medical costs more fairly. St. Louis Post-Dispatch 1952 Dec 18. p. 1.

15. American Medical Association. Creeping socialism by commission [editorial]. JAMA 1953;151:1003.

16. EA Graham to R Lee [letter], 1953 Jan 9. St. Louis: Washington University School of Medicine—BML.

17. EA Graham to P Magnuson [letter], 1953 Jan 12. St. Louis: Washington University School of Medicine—BML.

18. Graham E. The right to health; a new concept. St. Louis Post-Dispatch 1953 Dec 13. p. 30.

19. Sherman T to EA Graham [letter], 1953 Feb 20. St. Louis: Washington University School of Medicine—BML.

20. Graham EA to T Sherman [letter], 1953 Jul 29. St. Louis: Washington University School of Medicine—BML.

21. Graham EA to T Sherman [letter], 1953 Aug 17. St. Louis: Washington University School of Medicine—BML.

22. Sherman T to EA Graham [letter], 1953 Aug 19. St. Louis: Washington University School of Medicine—BML.

23. Dr. Graham praises health program offered by president. St Louis Post-Dispatch 1954 Jan 20.

24. Hoover H to EA Graham [letter], 1953 Oct 11. St. Louis: Washington University School of Medicine—BML.

25. Agenda, first meeting of Task Force on Federal Medical Services, 1953 Nov. 11. St. Louis: Washington University School of Medicine—BML.

26. Minutes, first Meeting of Special Committee on Planning, Task Force on Federal Medical Services 1953 Dec 3. St. Louis: Washington University School of Medicine—BML.

27. Klumpp TG to H Hoover [letter], 1954 Nov 10. St. Louis: Washington University School of Medicine—BML.

28. Report of the medical task force of the Commission on Organization of the Executive Branch of the Government, 1954 Nov. St. Louis: Washington University School of Medicine—BML.

29. Klumpp TC to members of the medical services task force [letter], 1955 Feb 2. St. Louis: Washington University School of Medicine—BML.

30. Donovan RJ. Report on the Hoover commission. Colliers 1955; Jul 8:23–27.

31. Graham EA to TG Klumpp [letter], 1955 Feb 11. St. Louis: Washington University School of Medicine—BML.

32. Churchill EB. Evarts Graham, early years and the hegira. Ann Surg 1952;136:16.

33. Blake RE to EA Graham [letter], 1955 Nov 5. St. Louis: Washington University School of Medicine—BML.

34. Graham EA to RE Blake [letter], 1955 Nov 30. St. Louis: Washington University School of Medicine—BML.

35. Graham EA to WG Reidy [letter], 1956 Jan 19. St. Louis: Washington University School of Medicine—BML.

36. Graham EA to L Hill [letter], 1956 Mar 22. St. Louis: Washington University School of Medicine—BML.

37. Report on National Committee of Physicians and Surgeons for Stevenson, undated. St. Louis: Washington University School of Medicine—BML.

38. Graham helping lead volunteers for Stevenson-Kefauver. St. Louis Post-Dispatch 1956 Oct 4.

39. Statement prepared by Stevenson/Kefauver headquarters, Washington, DC, undated. St. Louis: Washington University School of Medicine—BML.

40. Graham EA to H Milbank [letter], 1956 Oct 16. St. Louis: Washington University School of Medicine—BML.

41. Report of talks on H-bomb denied. New York Times 1956 Nov 2.

42. Stevenson sees cover up on bomb. New York Times 1956 Nov 3.

43. Graham EA to AE Stevenson [letter], 1956 Nov 1. St. Louis: Washington University School of Medicine—BML.

44. Graham EA. Preliminary statement. 1956 Oct 23. St. Louis: Washington University School of Medicine—BML.

45. Dick E, Bingham B, Alexander AS to EA Graham [letter], 1956 Nov 5. St. Louis: Washington University School of Medicine—BML.

46. Twenty-four Washington University scientists issue statement. St. Louis Post-Dispatch 1956 Oct 24.

47. Our scientists declare themselves [editorial]. St. Louis Post-Dispatch 1956 Oct 28.

48. Pond TA. Petition to Joint Committee of Atomic Energy, 1956 Nov 12. St. Louis: Washington University School of Medicine—BML.

49. Graham EA to E Cheit [letter], 1956 Nov 15. St. Louis: Washington University School of Medicine—BML.

50. Graham EA. Material to be presented at hearing of Sub-committee on Disarmament of U.S. Senate on December 12 [abstract], undated. St. Louis: Washington University School of Medicine—BML.

51. Report on hearing of Senate Foreign Relations Committee on Disarmament, 1956 Dec 12. St. Louis: Washington University School of Medicine—BML.

52. Graham EA to S Symington [letter], 1956 Dec 14. St. Louis: Washington University School of Medicine—BML.

53. Dr. Walker widely known surgeon dies. Baltimore Sun 1936 Jun 7.

54. Announcement of Finney-Howell Research Foundation Inc., 1937 Oct 15. St. Louis: Washington University School of Medicine—BML.

55. Finney JMT to EA Graham [letter], 1937 Jun 2. St. Louis: Washington University School of Medicine—BML.

56. Graham EA to JMT Finney [letter], 1937 Jun 9. St. Louis: Washington University School of Medicine—BML.

57. Fischer WA to EA Graham [letter], 1941 Mar 4. St. Louis: Washington University School of Medicine—BML.

58. Doctors for Britain [editorial]. JAMA 1941; Apr: 1910–1911.

59. Ryan PE to EA Graham [letter], 1942 Mar 17. St. Louis: Washington University School of Medicine—BML.

60. Rhoads CP to EA Graham [letter], 1941 Apr 22. St. Louis: Washington University School of Medicine—BML.

61. Graham EA to CP Rhoads [letter], 1941 May 5. St. Louis: Washington University School of Medicine—BML.

62. Rhoads CP to EA Graham [letter], 1941 May 9. St. Louis: Washington University School of Medicine—BML.

63. O'Connor B to EA Graham [letter], 1945 Aug 13. St. Louis: Washington University School of Medicine—BML.

64. Graham EA to B O'Connor [letter], 1945 Sep 12. St. Louis: Washington University School of Medicine—BML.

65. Potthoff CJ to EA Graham [letter], 1946 Apr 30. St. Louis: Washington University School of Medicine—BML.

66. Graham EA to the members of the Committee on Surgery of the American Red Cross [letter], 1947 Feb 17. St. Louis: Washington University School of Medicine—BML.

67. Graham EA to CJ Potthoff [letter], 1947 Mar 18. St. Louis: Washington University School of Medicine—BML.

68. Graham EA to LH Weed [letter], 1949 Jun 27. St. Louis: Washington University School of Medicine—BML.

69. Gates TS to EA Graham [letter], 1944 Jun 23. St. Louis: Washington University School of Medicine—BML.

70. Hospital group plans study of post-war needs. St. Louis Post-Dispatch 1944 Jul 2.

71. Gates TS to EA Graham [letter], 1944 Jul 18. St. Louis: Washington University School of Medicine—BML.

72. Gates TS to EA Graham [letter], 1945 Apr 24. St. Louis: Washington University School of Medicine—BML.

73. Graham EA to TS Gates [letter], 1945 May 4. St. Louis: Washington University School of Medicine—BML.

74. Graham EA to C Poe [letter], 1944 Nov 22. St. Louis: Washington University School of Medicine—BML.

75. Graham EA to MR Reid [letter], 1941 Oct 14. St. Louis: Washington University School of Medicine—BML.

76. Patterson JT. The dread disease: cancer and modern American culture. Cambridge: Harvard University Press; 1987.

77. Wright FE to EA Graham [letter], 1941 Apr 30. St. Louis: Washington University School of Medicine—BML.

78. Coomb RG to FB Jewett [letter], 1946 Aug 2. St. Louis: Washington University School of Medicine—BML.

79. Jewett FB to EA Graham [letter], 1946 Oct 7. St. Louis: Washington University School of Medicine—BML.

80. Graham EA, Churchill ED. Subcommittee report to be placed within the total report, undated. St. Louis: Washington University School of Medicine—BML.

81. Andrus F to EA Graham [letter], 1947 Mar 20. St. Louis: Washington University School of Medicine—BML.

82. Graham EA to EC Andrus [letter], 1947 Mar 20. St. Louis: Washington University School of Medicine—BML.

83. Graham EA to EC Andrus [letter], 1948 Jan 14. St. Louis: Washington University School of Medicine—BML.

84. Place WF to EA Graham [letter], 1948 Mar 22. St. Louis: Washington University School of Medicine—BML.

85. Hess HL to EA Graham [letter], 1955 Mar 31. St. Louis: Washington University School of Medicine—BML.

CHAPTER 18

1. Wynder EL, Graham EA. Tobacco smoking as a possible etiologic factor in bronchiogenic carcinoma. A study of six hundred and eighty-four proved cases. JAMA 1950;143:329–336.

2. Doll R, Hill AB. Smoking and carcinoma of the lung. Br Med J 1950;2:739–748.

3. Adler I. Primary malignant growths of the lungs and bronchi. New York: Longman Greens and Co.; 1912.

4. Proctor RN. The Nazi war on cancer. Princeton: Princeton University Press; 1999. p. 191–198.

5. Müller FH. Tabakmissbrauch und Lungen carzinom. Krebsforsuching 1939;49:57–85.

6. Müller FH. Abuse of tobacco and carcinoma of the lungs [abstract]. JAMA 1939;113:1372.

7. Proctor RN. The Nazi war on tobacco: ideology, evidence and possible cancer consequences. Bull Hist Med 1997;71:435–488.

8. Ochsner A, DeBakey M. Primary pulmonary malignancy. Treatment by total pneumonectomy; analysis of 79 collected cases and presentation of 7 personal cases. Surg Gynecol Obstet 1939;68:435–451.

9. DeBakey M, Ochsner A. Carcinoma of the lung. Tristate Med J 1940;12:2524-2527.

10. Ochsner A, DeBakey M. Primary carcinoma of the lung. New Orleans Med Surg J 1941;93:387–394.

11. Ochsner A, DeBakey M. Carcinoma of the lung. Arch Surg 1941;42:209–258.

12. Wilds J, Harkey I. Alton Ochsner, surgeon of the south. Baton Rouge: Louisiana State University Press; 1990.

13. Graham EA to A Ochsner [letter],1940 Oct 28. St Louis: Washington University School of Medicine—BML.

14. Wynder E in conversation with CB Mueller, 1992 Mar 11. St Louis: Washington University School of Medicine—BML.

15. Graham EA to A Ochsner [letter], 1949 Feb 18. St Louis: Washington University School of Medicine—BML.

16. Lowry O in conversation with CB Mueller, 1992 May 12. St Louis: Washington University School of Medicine—BML.

17. Wynder EL, Graham EA, Croninger AB. Experimental production of carcinoma with cigarette tar. Cancer Res 1953;13:855–864.

18. Graham EA, Wynder EL, Croninger AB. Cigarette smoking and cancer of the lung [abstract]. Science 1952;116:521–522.

19. Wynder EL, Graham EA, Croninger AB. Experimental production of carcinoma with cigarette tar, II. Tests with different mouse strains. Cancer Res 1955;15:445–448.

20. Graham EA, Croninger AB, Wynder EL. Experimental production of carcinoma with cigarette tar, III. Occurrence of cancer after prolonged latent period following application of tar. Cancer 1957;10:431-435.

21. Graham EA, Croninger AB, Wynder EL. Experimental production of carcinoma with cigarette tar, IV. Successful experiments with rabbits. Cancer Res 1957;17: 1058–1066.

22. Croninger AB, Graham EA, Wynder EL. Experimental production of carcinoma with tobacco products, V. Carcinoma induction in mice with cigar, pipe and all-tobacco cigarette tar. Cancer Res 1958;18:1263–1271.

23. Suntzeff V, Croninger AB, Wynder EL, Cowdry EV, Graham EA. Use of sebaceous-gland test of primary cigarette-tar fractions and of certain noncarcinogenic poly-cyclic hydrocarbons. Cancer 1957;10:250–254.

24. Wynder EL, Graham EA. Etiologic factors in bronchiogenic carcinoma with special reference to industrial exposures. Report of eight hundred and fifty-seven proved cases. Arch Industrial Hygiene 1951;4:221–235.

25. Graham EA. Etiologic factors of bronchiogenic carcinoma. Proceedings of the second National Cancer Conference. American Cancer Society; 1954. p. 859–866.

26. Ochsner A to EA Graham [letter], 1954 Dec 27. St Louis: Washington University School of Medicine—BML.

27. Graham EA to W Reinhoff [letter], 1950 Aug 11. St Louis: Washington University School of Medicine—BML.

28. Wynder E to CB Mueller [letter], 1996 May 30. St Louis: Washington University School of Medicine—BML.

29. Hammond EC, Horn D. Relationship of human smoking habits and death rates. JAMA 1954;155:1316–1328.

30. Ochsner A. Smoking and lung cancer. A doctor's report. New York: Julian Messner, Inc.; 1954.

31. Graham EA to A Ochsner [letter], 1954 Sep 15. St Louis: Washington University School of Medicine—BML.

32. Graham EA to A Ochsner [letter], 1950 Nov 29. St Louis: Washington University School of Medicine—BML.

33. Graham EA to A Ochsner [letter], 1950 Dec 21. St Louis: Washington University School of Medicine—BML.

34. Graham EA to C Cameron [letter], 1954 Jan 7. St Louis: Washington University School of Medicine—BML.

35. Cameron C to EA Graham [letter], 1954 Jan 29. St Louis: Washington University School of Medicine—BML.

36. Graham EA to C Cameron [letter], 1954 Feb 24. St Louis: Washington University School of Medicine—BML.

37. Little CC. Smoking and lung cancer [editorial]. Cancer Res 1956;16:183–184.

38. Graham EA to HP Rusch [letter], 1956 Mar 30. St Louis: Washington University School of Medicine—BML.

39. Graham EA. Letter to the editor. Cancer Res 1956;16:816–817.

40. Little CC. Letter to the editor. Cancer Res 1956;16:817–818.

41. Graham EA to AB Hill [letter], 1956 Aug 9. St Louis: Washington University School of Medicine—BML.

42. Graham EA. Radio talk at University of Chicago Round Table. 1954 Mar 30. St Louis: Washington University School of Medicine—BML.

43. Graham EA. Foreword. In: Ochsner A. Smoking and cancer: a doctor's report. New York: Julian Messner, Inc.; 1954.

44. Wynder EL, Wright G. A study of tobacco carcinogenesis. I. The primary fractions. Cancer 1957;10:255–271.

45. Wynder EL. Some reflections on smoking and lung cancer. J Thorac Cardiovasc Surg 1984;88:854–857.

CHAPTER 19

1. Womack NA in an interview with PD Olch, 1971 Dec 9. St. Louis: Washington University School of Medicine—BML.

2. Six report cards from this period are available in the Helen Tredway Graham collection. St. Louis: Washington University School of Medicine—BML.

3. Comments made on evening of retirement dinner held in honor of Dr. Helen Graham, 1959 Oct 27. St. Louis: Washington University School of Medicine—BML.

4. Graham EA, Graham HT. Retardation by sugars of diffusion of acids in gels. J Am Chem Soc 1918;40:1900–1917.

5. Steiglitz J, Graham HT. The thermal decomposition of symmetrical diarylhydrazines. J Am Chem Soc 1916;38:1736–1760.

6. Eiseman B. Evarts A. Graham—surgeon, scientist, statesman and teacher. Ann Surg 1993; 217 (Suppl): 1–8.

7. Hornback J. Notes from an interview with PD Olch, undated. St. Louis: Washington University School of Medicine—BML.

8. Graham HT in conversation with CB Mueller, 1996 Nov 2. St. Louis: Washington University School of Medicine—BML.

9. Lamson PD. John Jacob Abel M.D. investigator, teacher, prophet 1857–1938. Baltimore: Williams and Wilkins; 1957.

10. Landau W in conversation with CB Mueller, 1997 May 10. St. Louis: Washington University School of Medicine—BML.

11. Graham EA to S Moore [letter], 1925 Jun 20. St. Louis: Washington University School of Medicine—BML.

12. Eiseman B to CB Mueller [letter], 1993 Jun 25. St. Louis: Washington University School of Medicine—BML.

13. Graham DT in conversation with CB Mueller, 1992 Feb 8. St. Louis: Washington University School of Medicine—BML.

14. Graham E Jr in conversation with CB Mueller, 1994 Feb 10. St. Louis: Washington University School of Medicine—BML.

15. Graham EA Jr to PD Olch [letter], 1983 Nov 7. St. Louis: Washington University School of Medicine—BML.

16. Smyth HD. Atomic energy for military purposes: the official report on the development of the atomic bomb. Washington (DC): United States Government Printing Office; 1945.

17. Marshall LH. The fecundity of aggregates: the axonologists at Washington University. Perspect Biol Med 1983;26:613–636.

18. Gasser HS, Erlanger J. The cathode ray oscillograph as a means of recording nerve action currents and induction shocks. Am J Physiol 1922;62:496–524.

19. Landau WO. George Holman Bishop 1889–1973. Biographical Memoirs 1965; 55:45–66.

20. Graham HT, Lowry OH, and Harris FB. Microchemical determination of histamine in biological fluids. J Pharmacol Exp Ther 1951;101:15.

21. Lowry O in conversation with CB Mueller, 1991 Dec 7. St. Louis: Washington University School of Medicine—BML.

22. Graham HT, Scarpellini JD, Hubke BP, Lowry OH. Measurement and normal range of free histamine in blood plasma. Biochem Pharmacol 1968;17:2271–2280.

23. Hunter FE in conversation with CB Mueller, 1992 May 7. St. Louis: Washington University School of Medicine—BML.

24. van Surdam Graham N to CB Mueller [letter], 1997 Jul 14. St. Louis: Washington University School of Medicine—BML.

25. Card file is in Helen Tredway Graham collection. St. Louis: Washington University School of Medicine—BML.

26. Gas storage petition. St. Louis Post-Dispatch 1953 Mar 2.

27. Residents form own underground storage firm to block Laclede. St. Louis Post-Dispatch 1953 Apr 2.

28. Two ransack home. Take housekeeper's $2150 savings. St. Louis Post-Dispatch 1955 Jan 28.

29. Few clues found to 2 who held up women in home. St. Louis Post-Dispatch 1955 Jan 29.

30. Notes, letters, and other memorabilia concerning civic involvements are available in the Helen Tredway Graham collection. St. Louis: Washington University School of Medicine—BML.

31. Parry MI. A way of life, the story of John Burroughs School 1923–1973. St. Louis: John Burroughs School; 1973.

32. Peterson R to CB Mueller [letter], 1996 Dec 4. St. Louis: Washington University School of Medicine—BML.

33. Lowry O. Helen Tredway Graham, July 21, 1890–April 4, 1971. Pharmacologist 1971;13:110–111.

34. Mrs. Evarts A. Graham dies: surgeon's widow. St. Louis Post-Dispatch 1971 Apr 5.

35. Fisher T. Helen Tredway Graham. Comments made at memorial service for Dr. Helen Graham, 1971 Apr 26. St. Louis: Washington University School of Medicine—BML.

36. Lowry O. In Memoriam: Helen Tredway Graham. Comments made at memorial service for Dr. Helen Graham, 1971 Apr 26. St. Louis: Washington University School of Medicine—BML.

CHAPTER 20

1. Glaser RJ to CB Mueller [letter], 1991 May 1. St. Louis: Washington University School of Medicine—BML.

2. Moore RA to CB Mueller, circa 1961. St. Louis: Washington University School of Medicine—BML.

3. Evarts A. Graham. St. Louis: Barnes Hospital Records and Archives.

4. Graham EA to F Lahey [letter], 1949 Feb 11. St. Louis: Washington University School of Medicine—BML.

5. Stone LD to EA Graham [letter], 1949 Feb 1. St. Louis: Washington University School of Medicine—BML.

6. Graham EA to LD Stone [letter], 1949 Feb 4. St. Louis: Washington University School of Medicine—BML.

7. Olch IY in an interview with JF Newsome, undated, circa 1977. St. Louis: Washington University School of Medicine—BML.

8. Hanvey A in an interview with PD Olch, 1971 Jun 18. Bethesda (MD): National Library of Medicine, Oral History Section 67; St. Louis: Washington University School of Medicine—BML.

9. Ackerman LV in conversation with CB Mueller, 1993 Jan 22. St. Louis: Washington University School of Medicine—BML.

10. Ackerman LV. Dr. Evarts Graham and surgical pathology. J Thorac Cardiovasc Surg 1984;88 (Suppl):851–853.

11. Graham EA to E Wynder [letter], 1957 Feb 6. St. Louis: Washington University School of Medicine—BML.

12. Graham EA to C Eckert [letter], 1957 Feb 10. St. Louis: Washington University School of Medicine—BML.

13. Graham EA to A Ochsner [letter], 1957 Feb 14. St. Louis: Washington University School of Medicine—BML.

14. Ochsner A to EA Graham [letter], 1957 Feb 19. St. Louis: Washington University School of Medicine—BML.

15. Graham EA to O Wangensteen [letter], 1957 Feb 18. St. Louis: Washington University School of Medicine—BML.

16. Farmer L to EA Graham [letter], 1957 Feb 15. St. Louis: Washington University School of Medicine—BML.

17. Graham EA to L Farmer [letter], 1957 Feb 22. St. Louis: Washington University School of Medicine—BML.

18. Underwood CR to CB Mueller [letter], 1993 Oct 14. St. Louis: Washington University School of Medicine—BML.

19. Dunihoo D to CB Mueller [letter], 1996 Jul 4. St. Louis: Washington University School of Medicine—BML.

20. Ferguson TB to CB Mueller [letter], 1994 Oct 17. St. Louis: Washington University School of Medicine—BML.

21. Spratt JS, Spjut HS, Roper CL. The frequency distribution of the rates of growth and estimated duration of primary pulmonary carcinomas. Cancer 1963;16:687–693.

22. Leaves bulk of estate to his wife. Rewarded faithful secretary with $5,000. St. Louis Post-Dispatch 1957 Mar 8.

23. Peterson RR to CB Mueller [letter], 1996 Oct 29. St. Louis: Washington University School of Medicine—BML.

24. Nissen S to CB Mueller [letter], 1998 Oct 29. St. Louis: Washington University School of Medicine—BML.

CHAPTER 21

1. Krackov A. The historic hilltop Graham Chapel, Washington University Magazine and Alumni News 1994;64:23–24.

2. Evarts Ambrose Graham. March 19 1883 Chicago, IL,–March 4 1957 St. Louis, MO. Memorial Service, Graham Chapel; 1957 Mar 31; St. Louis: Washington University School of Medicine—BML.

3. Illingworth CFW. Evarts Ambrose Graham. Lancet 1957;March 16:590–591.

4. Burford TH. Evarts Ambrose Graham (1883–1957) Eulogy. J Thorac Surg 1958;36:281–284.

5. Whipple AO. Doctor Graham and American surgery. Comments at 20 year celebration, 1939 Oct 12. [Unpublished.] St. Louis: Washington University School of Medicine—BML.

6. Womack NA, Blades BB. Evarts Ambrose Graham 1883–1957. Trans Am Surg Assoc 1957;LXXV:419–422.

7. Burford TH. Evarts Graham—the surgeon. Bull St. Louis Med Soc 1965;July 28:537–539.

8. Blades BB. Evarts Ambrose Graham, a benign paradox. Bull Am Coll Surg 1973;58:13–14.

9. Wynder EL. Evarts A. Graham, M.D. (1883–1957). Cancer 1957;10:430.

10. Dragstedt LR. Evarts Ambrose Graham Mar 19, 1883–Mar 4, 1957. N Y Acad Sci Biographical Memoirs 1976;XLVII:221–231.

11. Evarts Graham Jr in conversation with CB Mueller, 1994 Feb 16. St. Louis: Washington University School of Medicine—BML.

12. Hanlon CR to CB Mueller [letter], 1992 Dec 16. St. Louis: Washington University School of Medicine—BML.

INDEX OF THE LIVES

In this index, page numbers followed by the letter "n" designate biographical or informational footnotes.